HEATH

PASSPORT

TO MATHEMATICS

BOOK 1

AN INTEGRATED APPROACH

Roland E. Larson

Laurie Boswell

Lee Stiff

McDougal Littell
Evanston, Illinois ◆ Boston ◆ Dallas

About the Cover

The cover photographs show one real-life context where people use mathematics—in amusement parks. To see how mathematics is used there, see pages 35, 39, 82, 353, and 481. The math statements and diagrams on the cover show some of the topics that are presented in this book—algebra, geometry, data analysis, percents, and fractions. Look for other exciting applications of these topics as you study mathematics this year!

Acknowledgements

Editorial Development Jane Bordzol, Rita Campanella, Anne M. Collier, Peter R. Devine, Tamara Trombetta Gorman, Susan E. Kipp Handler, Marlys Mahajan, George J. Summers

Marketing Jo DiGiustini

Advertising Phyllis Lindsay, Jane H. Murphy, Hope Tompkins

Design Robert Botsford, Pamela Daly, Carmen Johnson

Production Patrick Connolly

D. C. Heath is committed to publishing educational materials that accurately and fairly reflect the diversity of all peoples; that promote a better understanding of one another; that acknowledge the contributions of all groups; and that avoid stereotypes, ridicule, and bias. Our instructional materials foster an appreciation of differences in culture, religion, age, gender, ability, and socio-economic background. Our products promote respect for the intrinsic worth of all individuals and prepare people to live and work together in a diverse world. D. C. Heath believes that in order to flourish in a changing world, we must value diversity.

Roland E. Larson is professor of mathematics at the Behrend College of Pennsylvania State University at Erie. He is a member of NCTM and the author of many well known middle school, high school and college mathematics textbooks, including D.C. Heath's *Passport to Algebra and Geometry*, *Algebra 1*, *Geometry*, *Algebra 2*, *Precalculus*, and *Calculus*. He is a pioneer in the development of interactive textbooks, and his calculus textbook is published on CD-ROM.

Laurie Boswell is a mathematics teacher at Profile Junior-Senior High School in Bethlehem, New Hampshire. She is active in NCTM and local mathematics organizations and is a frequent convention speaker. A 1986 recipient of the Presidential Award for Excellence in Mathematics Teaching, she is also the 1992 Tandy Technology Scholar and the 1991 recipient of the Richard Balomenos Mathematics Education Service Award presented by the New Hampshire Association of Teachers of Mathematics. She is also an author of D.C. Heath's *Passport to Algebra and Geometry* and *Geometry*.

Lee Stiff is an associate professor of mathematics education in the College of Education and Psychology of North Carolina State University at Raleigh and has taught mathematics at the middle school and high school levels. He was a member of the NCTM Board of Directors and the writing team for NCTM's Professional Standards for Teaching Mathematics. He is the 1992 recipient of the W.W. Rankin Award for Excellence in Mathematics Education presented by the North Carolina Council of Teachers of Mathematics. He is an author of D.C. Heath's *Passport to Algebra and Geometry*, *Algebra 1*, *Geometry*, *Algebra 2*, and a contributing author of the elementary series, *Heath Mathematics CONNECTIONS*.

REVIEWERS AND CONTRIBUTORS

Renee Arrington
Mathematics Specialist
Alief Middle School
Houston, TX

Lyn Baier
Mathematics Teacher
Hopkins West Middle School
Hopkins, MN

Deborah J. Barrett
Curriculum Coordinator, K-12
Wapato School District
Wapato, WA

Jeff Beatty
Mathematics Teacher
Thomas Harrison Middle School
Harrisonburg, VA

Nancy Belsky
Mathematics Teacher
Westmoreland School
Westmoreland, NH

Rochelle Brown
Mathematics Teacher
Burnside Scholastic Academy
Chicago, IL

Marianne Cavanaugh
Head Mathematics Teacher
Gideon Welles Middle School
Glastonbury, CT

Linda Cooke
Mathematics Teacher
Lincoln Middle School
Pullman, WA

Charleen DeRidder
Supervisor of Mathematics, K-12
Knox County School District
Knoxville, TX

Betty Erickson
Mathematics Coordinator and Teacher
Kearsarge Regional School District
Bradford, NH

Madelaine Gallin
Mathematics Coordinator
Consolidated District #5
Brooklyn, NY

Linda Gojak
Mathematics Teacher/Department Chairperson
Hawken School
Lyndhurst, OH

Thomas Keating
Mathematics Teacher
Chase Middle School
Spokane, WA

Nancy W. Lewis
Mathematics Teacher
Thurmont Middle School
Thurmont, MD

Richard D. Lodholz
Mathematics Coordinator
Parkway School District
St. Louis, MO

Donna Long
Mathematics Consultant
Indiana Department of Education
Indianapolis, IN

Carol Mellett
Mathematics Teacher
Lincoln School
Brookline, MA

Janice Mosley
Mathematics Teacher
Bellevue Middle School
Nashville, TN

John Peter Penick
District Mathematics Coordinator
Marcus Whitman Junior High School
Port Orchard, WA

Susan Powell
Mathematics Teacher
Brentwood Middle School
Pensacola, FL

Marsha A. Rosenwasser
Mathematics Teacher/Department Head
J.Q. Adams Middle School
Metairie, LA

Frank C. Santoro
Mathematics Teacher
Lincoln School
Brookline, MA

Donna Schneller
Mathematics Teacher
Lake Riviera Middle School
Brick, NJ

Dee Ann Shook
Mathematics Teacher
Putnam City Central Middle School
Oklahoma City, OK

Cynthia G. Siebert
Mathematics Teacher/Department Chair
Ballenger Creek Middle School
Fredrick, MD

Robin Silbey
Mathematics Specialist
Montgomery County Public Schools
Baltimore, MD

Diana G. Sullivan
Mathematics Teacher
Murray Avenue School
Huntington Valley, PA

William F. Tate
Professor of Mathematics Education
University of Wisconsin
Madison, WI

Vicky Vaughn
Mathematics Teacher
Putnam City Central Middle School
Oklahoma City, OK

Beverly Weldon
Regional Mathematics Consultant
Region 10 Educational Service Center
Richardson, TX

Norma Wilson
Mathematics Department Chairperson
Weston Middle School
Weston, CT

Stacey E. Wood
Mathematics Department Chairperson
O'Donnell Middle School
Alief, TX

Brenda Wright
Mathematics Specialist
Dozier Middle School
Newport News, VA

To the Students

Mathematics evolved over thousands of years in many stages. The early stages were concerned with using mathematics to answer questions about real life. We wrote this book in much the same way. We centered the concepts around the real-life use of mathematics.

As more and more mathematics was discovered, people began to collect and categorize the different rules, formulas, and properties. However, mathematics is more than a set of rules and skills—it is a process. Doing mathematics is the process of investigating, testing, reasoning, and communicating what we understand.

As you study our book, you will be expected to do mathematics as you work with a group or independently. You will use manipulatives, visual models, and graphs to aid the investigative process. You should not try to memorize rules. Instead, try to understand how and why a concept is used. We begin each lesson by explaining what you should learn and why you should learn it, which we hope will help you master each concept.

Remember, math is not a spectator sport. It is a valuable tool you can use in everyday life, and the more you use it, the more useful it becomes.

Roland E. Larson

Laurie Boswell

Lee Stiff

Chapter Themes relate mathematics to fun activities and ideas, such as origami and computers.

Chapter Projects let you use your math skills in new ways.

Look through the list of themes and projects below to find the ones that interest you most.

Look through this list for things that interest you. Then find out how they are linked to mathematics. You may be surprised at all the ways mathematics is connected to your favorite topics!

Amusement Parks 35, 39, 82, 353, 481

Animals/Pets 30, 43, 87, 117, 138, 142, 169, 184, 194, 205, 225, 229, 239, 257, 297, 337, 341, 439, 571, 587, 589

Architecture/Construction 22, 23, 24, 69, 84, 95, 113, 180, 248, 249, 250, 263, 266, 268, 269, 287, 373, 410, 413, 431, 473

Art/Design 14, 25, 31, 48, 169, 246, 266, 275, 294, 321, 369, 378, 401, 403, 415, 420, 426, 442, 447, 475, 485, 561, 578

Astronomy 59, 136, 182, 185, 460

Banking 329, 517

Books/Literature 180, 193, 199, 205, 221, 243, 309, 337, 491

Braille 209

Business and Industry 12, 14, 19, 52, 63, 67, 78, 87, 112, 340, 419, 531, 571

Clothing/Shoes 11, 117, 166, 226, 234, 258, 293, 574, 585

Community Service 337, 391, 578

Computers 50, 52, 53, 63, 66, 71, 73, 77, 83, 87, 91, 93, 96, 97, 529

Consumer Spending 17, 29, 32, 33, 35, 37, 47, 105, 107, 146, 149, 157, 161, 163, 165, 175, 180, 192, 194, 197, 223, 231, 234, 245, 279, 291, 293, 375, 559, 563, 573, 589

Cooking 75, 97, 285, 323, 355, 359, 360, 376, 422, 472, 578, 589

Earning Money 87, 167, 169, 235, 273, 381, 533

Education 31, 45, 72, 87, 96, 124, 128, 143, 150, 195, 207, 216, 226, 232, 238, 246, 255, 281, 380, 487, 536, 571, 578

Energy 12, 30, 197

Food and Nutrition 11, 12, 14, 20, 25, 45, 47, 107, 123, 140, 142, 145, 163, 166, 181, 184, 191, 198, 199, 204, 228, 236, 240, 295, 581, 491, 574, 575

Friendship 25, 260, 337

Games 37, 40, 44, 63, 71, 76, 101, 139, 147, 243, 263, 361, 459, 492, 494, 495, 499, 546, 556, 561, 565, 579, 583, 586, 587

Geography/Maps 17, 41, 44, 59, 164, 185, 195, 230, 232, 294, 336, 344, 393, 394, 401, 431, 455, 473, 479, 487, 501, 508, 517, 524, 532, 537, 543, 544, 570

Health and Fitness 7, 11, 44, 76, 77, 228, 231, 245, 287, 305, 309, 330, 385, 395, 439

History/Social Studies 52, 54, 55, 58, 66, 83, 91, 108, 111, 141, 146, 164, 210, 213, 264, 266, 291, 325, 339, 346, 362, 460, 476, 542, 557

Hobbies and Collections 1, 2, 3, 11, 20, 24, 26, 32, 37, 45, 48, 231, 258, 261, 263, 331, 491, 564, 578

International 98, 99, 100, 101, 107, 119, 123, 133, 139, 143, 185, 210, 232, 398, 431, 561, 565, 583

Jobs 16, 97, 112, 136, 139, 167, 175, 189, 211, 223, 224, 273, 310, 384, 410, 422, 426, 447, 511, 529

Money 89, 95, 107, 119, 123, 133, 139, 143, 146, 147, 262

Movies/TV/Entertainment 19, 49, 71, 78, 35, 39, 82, 85, 149, 180, 184, 192, 195, 209, 233, 242, 266, 268, 283, 297, 345

Music 26, 66, 122, 141, 225, 242, 310, 317, 331, 395, 486, 575, 585

Neighborhoods 4, 24, 533

Newspapers/Journalism 180, 205, 446, 447, 448, 459, 467, 474, 491, 498

Professional Sports 82, 119, 126, 131, 149, 206, 207, 226, 228, 238, 242, 340, 379

Puzzles 1, 43

Recycling and the Environment 30, 343

Restaurants 44, 49, 133, 150, 151, 157, 159, 163, 165, 175, 181, 191, 195, 198, 237

Science and Medicine 14, 16, 26, 30, 59, 131, 136, 182, 184, 185, 190, 195, 200, 210, 225, 226, 291, 325, 361, 393, 421, 422, 441, 502, 508, 510, 523, 524, 537, 545, 561

Sewing 330, 331, 379

Sports and Athletics 7, 9, 11, 19, 31, 37, 40, 44, 49, 76, 77, 82, 95, 124, 126, 131, 145, 159, 193, 194, 214, 221, 226, 233, 245, 259, 323, 343, 367, 369, 445, 471, 481, 487, 495, 515, 517, 556, 563, 573, 582, 585

Surveys 11, 117, 119, 124, 142, 174, 193, 204, 226, 227, 233, 237, 238, 242, 245, 281, 283, 291, 295, 297, 355, 376, 439, 489, 491

Taxes 128, 173

Telephones 15, 139, 174, 297

Transportation 17, 18, 239, 269

Travel and Vacations 19, 44, 82, 119, 143, 239, 242, 340, 346, 353, 375, 491, 579

Washington, D.C. 298, 300, 301, 305, 309, 317, 324, 331, 344

Weather 215, 232, 243, 245, 341, 505, 510, 517, 521, 544, 554, 560, 561, 570

Wildlife 43, 184, 208, 229, 355, 361, 380, 383, 409, 420, 500, 588

People . . . Places . . . Facts

EXPLORING AND INVESTIGATING MATHEMATICS

Mathematics is more fun and more understandable when you can play around with mathematical ideas and discover how they work. In this text, you will be introduced to new concepts and skills by exploring them through hands-on Labs and by using technology. These Labs and technology activities are listed below.

CHAPTER 1

Problem Solving Together

Technology in Chapters 1 and 2

Interactive Real-Life Investigations
— CD-ROM projects
Interactions: Real Math
— *Real Careers* videodisc
Using a Calculator *9, 33, 41, 64, 65, 67, 77, 80, 81*

Integrated Throughout
A Algebra
G Geometry and Measurement
D Data and Graphs
PS Problem Solving

CHAPTER
2

Place-Value Systems and Operations

Real-Life Applications
Measuring Systems *59*
Resizing Recipes *75*
Radio Stations *78*
Baseball Runs *82*
Walk-Through Computer *96*
. . . <u>and more</u>

Look for....
Connections within mathematics among
• data analysis
• probability
• patterns
• algebra
• geometry
—and connections to other disciplines, such as
• social studies
• the sciences
• music
• and many more.

CHAPTER 3

Exploring Decimals and Percent

Real-Life Applications
Money *105*
Nutrition *107*
Interpreting a Survey *117*
Using Video Cameras *122*
Decision Making *131*
. . . and more

Technology in Chapters 3 and 4
Interactive Real-Life Investigations
—CD-ROM projects
Interactions: Real Math
—Real Careers videodisc
Using a Calculator *113, 138, 139, 163, 165, 173, 175, 183, 184, 188, 190, 191*

Integrated Throughout
A Algebra
G Geometry and Measurement
D Data and Graphs
PS Problem Solving

Applications of Decimals and Percents

Real-Life Applications
Restaurant Bills *157*
Olympic Ski-Jumping *159*
Snack Foods *163*
Truck Driving *167*
Sales Tax *173*
Astronomy *185*
. . . and more

Look for....
Opportunties for active learning — you will use a hands-on approach that makes learning fun through
• labs
• manipulatives
• technology
• thematic projects.

Statistics and Graphs

Real-Life Applications

Fish Ladders *208*
World Flags *210*
First Ladies *213*
English Tests *219*
Weather Patterns *232*
Caves *247*
. . . <u>and more</u>

Technology in Chapters 5 and 6

Interactive Real-Life
  Investigations
  —CD-ROM projects
Interactions: Real Math
  —*Real Careers* videodisc
Using a Calculator *220, 221, 225, 226, 245, 277, 283, 291*
Using a Computer
  Spreadsheet *227*

Opportunities for Continual Review

Integrated Throughout

A Algebra
G Geometry and Measurement
D Data and Graphs
PS Problem Solving

CHAPTER 6

Exploring Fractions, Ratios, and Proportions

Real-Life Applications
Pet Guinea Pigs *257*
Kites *261*
Reading Blueprints *266*
Checking Prices *279*
Baking *285*
Genetics *291*
. . . <u>and more</u>

Look for....
Critical thinking and reasoning in every lesson.

Adding and Subtracting Fractions

Technology in Chapters 7 and 8
Interactive Real-Life Investigations
—CD-ROM projects
Interactions: Real Math
—*Real Careers* videodisc
Using a Calculator *310, 311, 324, 363 , 369*

Integrated Throughout
A Algebra
G Geometry and Measurement
D Data and Graphs
PS Problem Solving

CHAPTER 8

Multiplying and Dividing Fractions

Opportunities for Continual Review

Real-Life Applications

Look for....
Opportunities for continual review and practice of skills in every lesson.

Geometry and Patterns

Technology in Chapters 9 and 10

Interactive Real-Life Investigations
— CD-ROM projects
Interactions: Real Math
— *Real Careers* videodisc
Using a Calculator *410, 411, 422, 460, 461, 477, 479, 483, 487, 498*

Integrated Throughout

A Algebra
G Geometry and Measurement
D Data and Graphs
PS Problem Solving

CHAPTER 10

Geometry and Measurement

Real-Life Applications
Road Construction *455*
Sailing *471*
Geography *473*
Architecture *479*
At the Beach *491*
... <u>and more</u>

Look for....
The Communicating about Mathematics feature appears in every lesson. It encourages you to share your ideas about the lesson and to justify your reasoning.

CHAPTER

11

Algebra: Integers and the Coordinate Plane

Real-Life Applications
Temperature *505*
Miniature Golf *515*
Geography *524*
Computer Graphics *529*
Health *541*
. . . and more

Technology in Chapters 11 and 12
Interactive Real-Life Investigations
— CD-ROM projects
Interactions: Real Math
— *Real Careers* videodisc
Using a Calculator *504, 505, 525, 566*

Integrated Throughout
A Algebra
G Geometry and Measurement
D Data and Graphs
PS Problem Solving

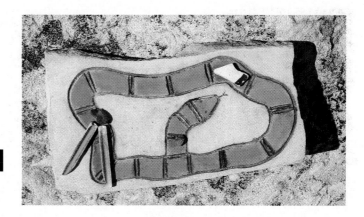

CHAPTER
12

Algebra: Equations and Probability

Real-Life Applications
Bowling *556*
Shopping *559*
Science *561*
Savings Plan *563*
Inventions *571*
. . . and more

Look for....
Clear, step-by-step instructions and a readable writing style throughout the program.

Student Handbook

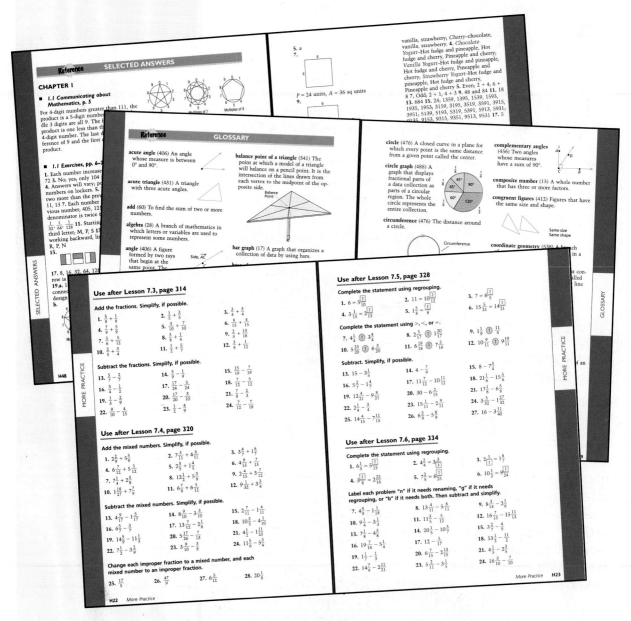

You can use the reference tools in
the Student Handbook to help you
find answers to your math questions.

Have you ever wondered ...

What will your life be like in the next decade?
How will you interact with people?
How will you get information—and how fast?
What career will you choose?

You can be sure that technology will play a leading role in your day-to-day life, in making your future a productive future.

That's why *Passport to Mathematics* integrates two new multimedia components—*Interactions: Real Math—Real Careers*™ and *Interactive Real-Life Investigations*. Both magnify the real-world applications of mathematics, showing you where math fits into your daily life.

Find out about technology. It's just one more way to put the math you're learning to work.

Interactions: Real Math—Real Careers™, a videodisc multimedia resource, connects math to actual careers and on-the-job problem solving through a wide range of interactive projects.

Interactive Real-Life Investigations are interactive projects for solving real-world problems in a variety of career-related situations—civil engineering, museum curatorship, conservation—using mathematics and real-world data sets. The investigations are available on CD-ROM and diskette.

Problem Solving Together

This photo shows a few of the 18,000 puzzles that Jerry Slocum, an aerospace engineer, has collected. They were all made by the British company Journet during World War I.

Real Life
Collections

People of all ages like to collect things. The table shows the number of items in some of the largest known collections. *(Source: Guinness Book of World Records)*

Item	Number	Collector
Puzzles	18,000	J. Slocum
Beverage coasters	140,100	L. Pisker
Bottle caps	73,823	H. Friholm
Earrings	14,850	C. McFadden

Think and Discuss

1. How might you count a collection that contained thousands of items?
2. Do you think the numbers in the table are exact?
3. What would be a good way to display the data in the table? Why?

You be the Teacher

Theme: Collections and Hobbies What mathematics do you remember from last year? If you were a teacher, how would you find out what your students remembered? One way would be to give your students a quiz.

In this project, you will write a quiz about the mathematics you remember from last year. The questions will use data about collections and hobbies and include the following.

▷ **In Lesson 1.2:** Write questions using the data from a survey of your class. (page 11)

▷ **In Lesson 1.4:** Write questions that use data from a bar graph. (page 20)

▷ **In Lesson 1.5:** Make a diagram and use it to write questions. (page 24)

▷ **In Lesson 1.6:** Write equations about a frog collection for students to solve. (page 32)

▷ **In Lesson 1.7:** Use the amount of money spent on comic books to find out how much money you started with. (page 37)

▷ **In Lesson 1.9:** Make up a logic puzzle. (page 45)

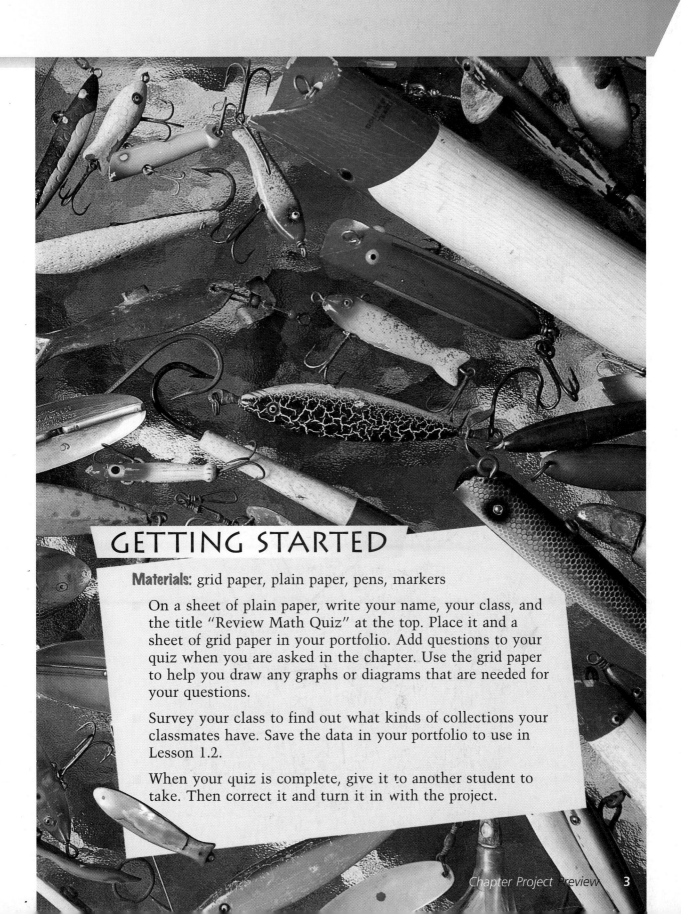

GETTING STARTED

Materials: grid paper, plain paper, pens, markers

On a sheet of plain paper, write your name, your class, and the title "Review Math Quiz" at the top. Place it and a sheet of grid paper in your portfolio. Add questions to your quiz when you are asked in the chapter. Use the grid paper to help you draw any graphs or diagrams that are needed for your questions.

Survey your class to find out what kinds of collections your classmates have. Save the data in your portfolio to use in Lesson 1.2.

When your quiz is complete, give it to another student to take. Then correct it and turn it in with the project.

1.1

Problem-Solving Strategy: Looking for a Pattern

What you should learn:

Goal 1 How to use a problem-solving plan

Goal 2 How to look for a pattern in data

Why you should learn it:

Finding a pattern in a set of numbers can help you organize data. For example, this strategy can help you find how many metal digits you need to buy to number houses.

Goal 1 A Problem-Solving Plan

Problem solving is a big part of mathematics. Many strategies, such as **Looking for a Pattern,** can be used to solve problems.

Lesson Investigation

■ Investigating Number Patterns

Group Activity A new housing development has 50 houses. Your job is to purchase metal digits to create the house number for each house. The houses will be numbered by fours, beginning with 4. How many of each digit do you need to buy?

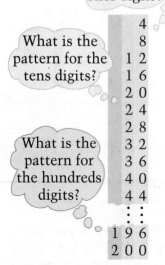

What is the pattern for the ones digits?

What is the pattern for the tens digits?

What is the pattern for the hundreds digits?

```
  4
  8
 12
 16
 20
 24
 28
 32
 36
 40
 44
  ⋮ ⋮
196
200
```

The following four steps can help you when looking for a pattern or using other problem-solving strategies.

1. **Understand the Problem** The houses will be numbered
   4, 8, 12, 16, 20, 24, 28, 32, . . . 196, 200.

   You need to decide how many 0's, 1's, 2's, 3's, 4's, 5's, 6's, 7's, 8's, and 9's to buy.

2. **Collect and Organize the Data** Make a list of the house numbers as shown at the left. What patterns in the digits can you find? For instance, the pattern for the ones digits is

   4, 8, 2, 6, 0.

   How many times does this pattern repeat? How do you know?

3. **Solve the Problem** Use the patterns you found to decide how many of each digit you need. For instance, in the ones digits, each of the digits 0, 2, 4, 6, and 8 are used 10 times.

4. **Look Back at Your Solution** Is your solution reasonable? Can you think of a way to check your answer?

Goal 2 | Looking for a Pattern

A collection of numbers is called **data.** Organizing data can help you find patterns.

| Example | *Collecting and Organizing Data* |

Find a pattern for multiplying the following numbers by 9.

111, 222, 333, 444, 555, 666, 777, 888, 999

1. Understand Problem

Solution This problem asks you to find a pattern when certain numbers are multiplied by 9.

2. Collect Data

You can collect the data by making a list of the products.

$9 \times 111 = \ 999$ *Multiply 9 times 111.*

$9 \times 222 = 1998$ *Multiply 9 times 222.*

$9 \times 333 = 2997$ *Multiply 9 times 333.*

$9 \times 444 = 3996$ *Multiply 9 times 444.*

$9 \times 555 = 4995$ *Multiply 9 times 555.*

$9 \times 666 = 5994$ *Multiply 9 times 666.*

$\vdots$

$9 \times 999 = 8991$ *Multiply 9 times 999.*

3. Solve the Problem

A pattern for the products can be seen from the following.

1 less than 5   Two 9's   **First and last digits total 9.**

$9 \times 555 = 4995$

4. Look Back

You can check this pattern by applying it to other products in the list. You can also test the pattern in similar problems. ∎

Communicating about MATHEMATICS

Cooperative Learning

▶ **Sharing Ideas about the Lesson**

Extending the Example Predict a pattern for the product of 9 and a 4-digit number whose digits are all the same. Use the pattern to find the product of 9 and 8888. Check your result by multiplying and revise if necessary.

EXERCISES

▶ CHECK for Understanding

In Exercises 1–3, use the following list.

8, 16, 24, 32, 40, 48, . . .

1. Describe any patterns that you see.
2. Write the next 3 numbers in the list.
3. If the list were continued, would 108 be in the list? Would 104 be in the list? Explain your reasoning.

4. Give an example of a pattern of numbers that occurs in your school.

Independent Practice

Finding a Pattern In Exercises 5–10, describe the pattern. Then write the next 3 numbers.

5. 1, 3, 5, 7, ?, ?, ?,...

6. 50, 45, 40, 35, ?, ?, ?,...

7. 5, 15, 45, 135, ?, ?, ?,...

8. 3, 6, 9, 12, ?, ?, ?,...

9. $\frac{1}{2}, \frac{1}{4}, \frac{1}{8}, \frac{1}{16},$?, ?, ?,...

10. $1, \frac{1}{2}, \frac{1}{3}, \frac{1}{4},$?, ?, ?,...

Finding a Pattern In Exercises 11–14, describe the pattern. Then write the next three letters.

11. A, D, G, J, ?, ?, ?,...

12. A, Z, B, Y, ?, ?, ?,...

13. Z, X, V, T, ?, ?, ?,...

14. A, N, B, O, ?, ?, ?,...

Geometry In Exercises 15 and 16, sketch the next 3 figures.

15. ▭ ▯ ▭ . . .

16. ⊖ ⊖ ⊖ . . .

17. *Number Theory* The pattern of numbers at the right is called Pascal's Triangle, named after the French mathematician Blaise Pascal. Find the sum of the numbers in each row of the triangle. Complete the table. Describe the pattern for the sums.

```
                        1
Row 1 ──────→    1    1
Row 2 ──────→  1    2    1
Row 3 ───→  1    3    3    1
Row 4 →  1    4    6    4    1
        1    5   10   10    5    1
      1    6   15   20   15    6    1
    1    7   21   35   35   21    7    1
```

Row	1	2	3	4	5	6	7
Sum	2	4	?	?	?	?	?

18. Find a pattern for multiplying the following numbers by themselves.

1; 11; 111; 1111; 11,111; 111,111

19. *Circle Designs* The first four multiples of 3 are shown below.

3, 6, 9, 12, . . .

Each number in the ones digit can be connected as shown at the right.

a. Find the next seven multiples of 3 to finish the design. What happens if you find even more multiples?

b. Create circle designs for the multiples of 4, 5, 6, 7, and 8.

c. Are any of the circle designs the same? If so, which ones?

d. What do you think the circle designs for the multiples of 43 and 65 look like? Explain.

20. You begin a weight-training program. The first week you lift 12 pounds. The following three weeks you lift 13, 14.5, and 16.5 pounds. If the pattern continues, during which week will you first lift over 50 pounds?

Cassie Clark, 16, placed first in the U.S. National Junior Weight-Lifting Championships. She lifted 297.5 pounds—more than twice her weight—above her head.

Integrated Review

Making Connections within Mathematics

Computation Sense Solve. Which exercises did you solve using mental math?

21. $185 + 99$
22. $168 - 103$
23. $6040 - 26$
24. $430 + 28 + 96$
25. 839×10
26. $826 \div 7$
27. 795×100
28. 262×45
29. $7258 \div 19$

Exploration and Extension

30. *Group Activity: Name That Pattern* Write down three numbers that follow a pattern that you have made up. (For instance, if your pattern is "all numbers that are multiples of 3," then you write down 3, 6, 9.) Have the members of your group guess three other numbers that they think follow the pattern. Answer yes or no to each guess. The group continues guessing until one person can describe the pattern. Repeat until each person in your group has had a turn.

1.2

Problem-Solving Strategy: Making and Reading a Table

What you should learn:

Goal 1 How to solve problems by making a table

Goal 2 How to solve problems by reading a table

Why you should learn it:

Making a Table is a strategy for organizing data for a problem. One problem it can help solve is comparing the popularity of sports by age groups.

Goal 1 **Making a Table**

The **perimeter** of a rectangle is the distance around it. The **area** of a rectangle is the number of unit squares within it.

Example 1 *Comparing Perimeter and Area*

Use dot paper to draw a 5-by-5 rectangle and a 3-by-7 rectangle. Find the perimeter and area of each.

Solution The rectangles are shown below. To find the perimeter of a rectangle, add the side lengths. To find the area of a rectangle, multiply the length and the width.

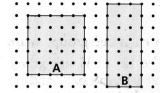

You can find the area of each rectangle by counting the number of unit squares in the rectangle.

Unit Square

Perimeter of Rectangle A	Perimeter of Rectangle B
$5 + 5 + 5 + 5 = 20$ units	$3 + 7 + 3 + 7 = 20$ units
Area of Rectangle A	Area of Rectangle B
$5 \times 5 = 25$ square units	$3 \times 7 = 21$ square units

The rectangles have the same perimeter, different areas.

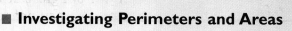

Lesson Investigation

■ **Investigating Perimeters and Areas**

Partner Activity On dot paper, how many rectangles with different measurements can be drawn with a perimeter of 6? Of 12? Of 18? Of 24? Make a table like the one at the left and record the perimeter, area, and dimensions of each rectangle that you find. What patterns do you see?

Perimeter	Area	Dimensions
6	2	1-by-2
12	?	?
12	?	?
24	?	?
24	?	?

Real Life Sports

Soccer is the most popular field sport in Europe and South America. It is becoming more and more popular in the United States.

Example 2 *Reading a Table*

The table below shows the numbers (in thousands) of people in the United States who participated in basketball, football, soccer, softball, and swimming at least once a year. (*Source: National Sporting Goods Association*)

a. In each age group, which sport is most popular?

b. Which sports have more participants in the 12- to 17-age group than in the 7- to 11-age group?

Sport	Age Group					
	7–11	**12–17**	**18–24**	**25–34**	**35–44**	**45–54**
Basketball	4970	7990	4440	4837	3000	777
Football	2806	4463	2767	2258	763	194
Soccer	3741	3581	1167	843	386	260
Softball	2358	4286	3671	5326	2932	859
Swimming	10,244	9959	9152	12,747	11,561	5745

Solution

a. In each age group, swimming is the most popular.

b. The 12- to 17-age group has *more* participants in basketball, football, and softball. The 12- to 17-age group has *fewer* participants in soccer and swimming. ■

Communicating about MATHEMATICS

Cooperative Learning

▶ **Sharing Ideas about the Lesson**

Geometry: Perimeter and Area Find the perimeter and area of each court, field, or pool. List the playing regions from greatest to least by perimeter, then by area. Are the orders the same?

Basketball Court
50 ft by 94 ft

Football Field
195 ft by 300 ft

Soccer Field
150 ft by 300 ft

Softball Field
120 ft by 120 ft

Olympic Pool
80 ft by 164 ft

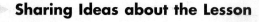

EXERCISES

Think and Discuss

▶ CHECK for Understanding

1. Give the measurements of two rectangles with a perimeter of 10.

2. Give the measurements of two rectangles that have an area of 12.

3. Describe two ways to find the area of a rectangle drawn on dot paper.

4. Complete the statement with the word *perimeter* or *area*.

   a. A rectangle has a(an) ⟨?⟩ of 14 square centimeters.

   b. A rectangle has a(an) ⟨?⟩ of 14 centimeters.

5. Which of the following statements is true?

   a. Every square is a rectangle.

   b. Every rectangle is a square.

Independent Practice

Geometry   In Exercises 6–9, sketch a rectangle with the given dimensions. Then find its perimeter and area.

6. 3-by-8   7. 6-by-6   8. 4-by-5   9. 7-by-9

Looking for a Pattern   In Exercises 10 and 11, the first 3 figures of a pattern are shown. Make a table of their perimeters and areas. Describe any patterns that you see. Find the perimeter and area of the next three figures. Check your answers with sketches.

10.   . . .   11.   . . .

12. On dot paper, how many rectangles with different measurements can be drawn with a perimeter of 8? Of 10? Of 12? Of 14?

    a. Organize your results in a table. Describe any patterns you see.

    b. Use the pattern to predict the number of rectangles with different measurements that can be drawn with a perimeter of 22.

Logical Reasoning   In Exercises 13 and 14, complete the statement with the word *sometimes, always,* or *never*.

13. Two rectangles with different side lengths and the same perimeter ⟨?⟩ have the same area.

14. A rectangle with a perimeter of 24 is ⟨?⟩ a square.

15. *Data Analysis* The table at the right shows the percent of 3 types of shoes sold in 1991 for different age groups. *(Source: National Sporting Goods Association)*

   a. What is the most popular shoe for people who are 17 and under?

   b. Which age group buys more walking shoes than aerobic shoes or sneakers?

	Aerobic Shoes	Sneakers	Walking Shoes
Under 14	6.6	39.3	3.3
14–17	3.5	10.7	1.9
18–24	11.7	8.5	2.7
25–34	30.9	13.2	12.2
35–44	21.0	11.4	16.2
45–64	19.5	11.6	36.6

16. The table below shows the amounts of fruits and nuts (in thousands of tons) produced in 1989, 1990, and 1991. *(Source: U.S. Dept. of Agriculture)*

	Avocados	Grapes	Hazelnuts	Pineapples	Walnuts
1989	139	5930	13	580	229
1990	156	5660	22	575	227
1991	179	5555	26	555	259

   a. Which fruits and nuts increased in production from 1989 to 1991?

   b. In what year was the production of grapes about 10 times the production of pineapples?

Integrated Review

Making Connections within Mathematics

Vocabulary Building Match the figure with its name.

a. hexagon   b. sphere   c. pentagon   d. pyramid

17. 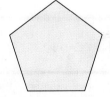   18. 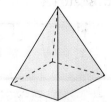   19. 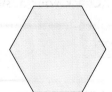   20.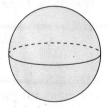

Exploration and Extension

21. *Group Activity: Making a Prediction* What total occurs most often when two 6-sided number cubes are tossed? Confirm your prediction by tossing two number cubes 25 times. Record the totals of the number cubes in a table. Collect data from 4 other groups. Discuss your findings.

22. *Building Your Chapter Project* Survey your class to find out what collections each person has. Organize your data in a table. Write a problem for the Review Math Quiz that uses your data.

1.3 Problem-Solving Strategy: Making a List

Goal 1 Making a List

Example 1 *Making a List of Fractions*

A digital clock uses 15 squares to create the digits from 0 through 9. For each digit, write a fraction that represents the portion of the region that is lit. Which digit uses the least electricity? Which uses the most?

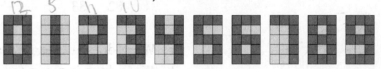

Solution For each fraction, the denominator is 15 and the numerator is the number of lighted squares.

Clock Digit	0	1	2	3	4	5	6	7	8	9
Fraction	$\frac{12}{15}$	$\frac{5}{15}$	$\frac{11}{15}$	$\frac{10}{15}$	$\frac{9}{15}$	$\frac{11}{15}$	$\frac{12}{15}$	$\frac{7}{15}$	$\frac{13}{15}$	$\frac{12}{15}$

From this list, you can see that the digit 1 uses the least electricity and the digit 8 uses the most. ■

Helen Giddings started a snack shop that sells food to travelers at the Love Field Airport in Dallas, Texas.

Lesson Investigation

■ Investigating Combinations

Group Activity Your snack shop has a special for a 1-pound mix of 3 different snacks for $4.95. The snacks are pineapple rings (P), apricots (A), banana slices (B), cashews (C), and raisins (R). A customer asks you to prepare one of each possible combination. How many mixtures do you have to make? To answer this, copy and complete the following list.

1st Snack	P	P	P	P	. . .
2nd Snack	A	A	A	B	. . .
3rd Snack	B	C	R	?	. . .

Example 2 *Using a List of Numbers*

The following list shows the whole numbers from 2 through 100. The red numbers are **prime** and the blue are **composite**.

	2	3	4	5	6	7	8	9	10
11	12	13	14	15	16	17	18	19	20
21	22	23	24	25	26	27	28	29	30
31	32	33	34	35	36	37	38	39	40
41	42	43	44	45	46	47	48	49	50
51	52	53	54	55	56	57	58	59	60
61	62	63	64	65	66	67	68	69	70
71	72	73	74	75	76	77	78	79	80
81	82	83	84	85	86	87	88	89	90
91	92	93	94	95	96	97	98	99	100

a. What does it mean for a number to be composite?

b. What does it mean for a number to be prime?

Solution

a. Every composite number can be written as the product of other whole numbers (other than 1). For instance, $4 = 2 \times 2$ and $28 = 4 \times 7$.

b. Every prime number cannot be written as the product of other whole numbers greater than 1. ∎

> **Study Tip**
>
> In mathematics you need to understand the meaning of special words. For instance, the words "prime" and "composite" are important. Note that the number 1 is neither prime nor composite.

Communicating about MATHEMATICS

Cooperative Learning

▶ **Sharing Ideas about the Lesson**

Writing Composite Numbers as Products Write each composite number from 51 through 70 as the product of as many smaller whole numbers as possible. Here is a sample.

$54 = 6 \times 9$	*Product of 2 numbers*
$54 = 2 \times 3 \times 9$	*Product of 3 numbers*
$54 = 2 \times 3 \times 3 \times 3$	*Product of 4 numbers*

Of the composite numbers between 51 and 70, which can be written as the product of the most whole numbers?

EXERCISES

▶CHECK for Understanding

1. Name the only number that is prime *and* even.

2. Explain the difference between a prime number and a composite number. Give several examples of each.

Yogurt Shop Your yogurt shop has a special on yogurt sundaes. Customers have a choice of chocolate, vanilla, or strawberry yogurt, and hot fudge, pineapple, and cherry toppings.

3. Make a list of the different sundaes you could sell using one topping.

4. Make a list of the different sundaes you could sell using two toppings.

Independent Practice

Even or Odd? In Exercises 5–7, make a list with several examples of the indicated types of numbers. Is the sum even or odd?

5. even + even = ?   6. odd + odd = ?   7. even + odd = ?

Number Theory In Exercises 8 and 9, use the list of whole numbers from 2 to 100 on page 13.

8. Twin primes are prime numbers that are two units apart, such as 3 and 5 or 5 and 7. Find all the twin primes.

9. Find all the numbers that are divisible by 12 and whose digits add up to 12.

10. *Probability* A bag contains 5 marbles numbered 1 to 5. You choose three marbles and add up the numbers on the marbles. List the possible sums.

11. You are making a display of your shell collection. You have 3 scallop, 2 olive, and 3 conch shells. If you choose one of each type, how many different displays could you make?

12. *Vocabulary Building* List the different ways you can rearrange the letters in the word at the right. Which arrangements are English words?

Because the common names of shells vary, collectors identify shells by their scientific names. For instance, the scientific name for a spider conch is Lambis chiragra.

STAR

In Exercises 13 and 14, name the number described by the clues. The number is in the list below.

6248 7232 8426 374 6482 6314
2648 338 1661 4640 8642 518
5135 6062 684 4514 1822 1580

13. No two digits are alike. None of the digits are odd. The number is a multiple of 6.

14. The sum of the digits is 14. The number is divisible by 2. The number has more than three digits. The number is less than 5000. The number is a multiple of 8.

15. *Reasoning* You want to call your friend on the telephone, but you have forgotten her phone number. You do remember that the first three digits are 621 and the last four digits contain the numbers 1, 3, 5, and 9. List the possible phone numbers. How many did you find?

16. *Making Change* You are selling baked goods at a bake sale. A customer buys a cookie for $0.35 and gives you $1.00.

    a. List the different ways that you can give the customer change if you have quarters, dimes, and nickels.

    b. Which way uses the least coins? Which uses the most?

In the United States, over 1 billion phone calls are made each day.

Integrated Review

Making Connections within Mathematics

Consider the number 7,913.586. Name the digit in the indicated place-value position.

17. tenths
18. thousands
19. hundredths
20. ones
21. thousandths
22. hundreds

Exploration and Extension

23. *Group Activity: Number Puzzle* Use each of the digits from 1 through 9 once to make a true addition problem.

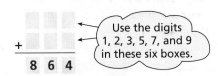

Use the digits 1, 2, 3, 5, 7, and 9 in these six boxes.

One solution is 739 + 125 = 864. How many other solutions can you find? (Note: 125 + 739 = 864 is not considered to be another solution.)

Write the first number as a product of the second number and another number.

1. 63, 9   2. 16, 2   3. 36, 4   4. 51, 3
5. 56, 8   6. 81, 27   7. 75, 5   8. 63, 21

State whether the first number is a multiple of the second.

9. 18, 3   10. 28, 3   11. 54, 6   12. 40, 6

Measurement   Find the number of quarts.

13. 2 gallons   14. 12 cups   15. 2 pints   16. 2 cups

Reasoning   Is the statement reasonable? Explain.

17. A book is 5 meters long.   18. A nickel weighs 5 grams.
19. The race is 5 kilometers long.   20. A can holds 5 milliliters.

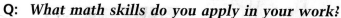

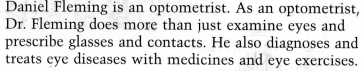

Career Interview

Optometrist   Daniel Fleming is an optometrist. As an optometrist, Dr. Fleming does more than just examine eyes and prescribe glasses and contacts. He also diagnoses and treats eye diseases with medicines and eye exercises.

Q: *What math skills do you apply in your work?*
A: About half of my job is related to medical science—biology and chemistry. The other half deals with optics—using measurements, mathematical formulas, and tables to determine a person's prescription.

Q: *How often do you use mental math?*
A: Everyday. When I calculate prescriptions, I perform most of the math mentally. The handier you are with your math skills, the less time it takes to figure out the prescriptions.

Q: *What is your favorite part of your job?*
A: When I can teach kids how to use their eyes better so they can learn how to read and succeed in school.

Problem-Solving Strategy: Using a Graph

What you should learn:

Goal 1 How to solve problems using a graph

Goal 2 How to color code a map

Why you should learn it:

Using a Graph is a strategy for comparing data. It can be used, for example, to compare the average gasoline expenses in different parts of the country.

In 1993, retail gasoline sales in the United States were more than $130,000 million.

Goal 1 Using a Graph

Graphs, pictures, and diagrams can help you interpret data. For instance, the **bar graph** below shows the average amount per year spent on gasoline in different regions in the United States. *(Source: U.S. Bureau of Census)*

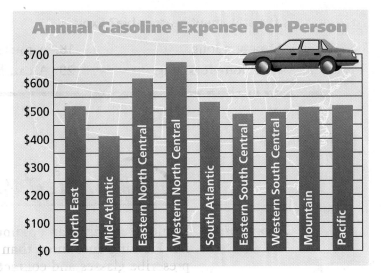

Annual Gasoline Expense Per Person

Example 1 *Using a Graph*

Use the bar graph to estimate each region's average gasoline expense. Order the averages from least to greatest.

Solution

Mid-Atlantic	A little more than $400
Eastern South Central	A little less than $500
Western South Central	A little less than $500
Mountain	A little more than $500
North East	A little more than $500
Pacific	A little more than $500
South Atlantic	About halfway between $500 and $550
Eastern North Central	A little more than $600
Western North Central	A little more than $650

Real Life
Transportation

North East
ME, NH, VT, MA, RI, CT

Mid-Atlantic
NY, NJ, PA

Eastern North Central
OH, IN, IL, MI, WI

Western North Central
MN, IA, MO, ND, SD,
NE, KS

South Atlantic
DE, MD, DC, VA, WV,
NC, SC, GA, FL

Eastern South Central
KY, TN, AL, MS

Western South Central
AR, LA, OK, TX

Mountain
MT, ID, WY, CO,
NM, AZ, UT, NV

Pacific
WA, OR, CA, AK, HI

Example 2 *Color Coding a Map*

Use the list on page 17 to make a color-coded map.
Show the average amount people spend on gasoline in
different regions of the United States.

Solution Begin by deciding which colors to use for
each range of averages. Use one color for 400 to 449,
another color for 450 to 499, and so on. Next, color each
region with the color that matches its average.

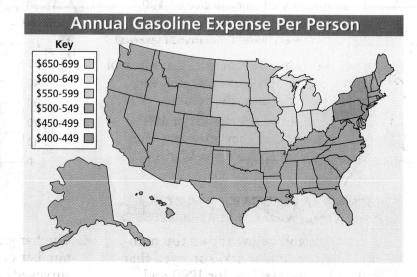

Annual Gasoline Expense Per Person

Key
- $650-699
- $600-649
- $550-599
- $500-549
- $450-499
- $400-449

Communicating about **MATHEMATICS**

Cooperative Learning

▶ **Sharing Ideas about the Lesson**

Extending the Examples With a partner, use the
graph, list, or map to answer the questions.

A. Why do you think the Mid-Atlantic region has the
smallest average? Why do you think the Western
North Central region has the largest average?

B. Estimate how much a four-person family in Oregon
spends a year on gasoline.

C. Which regions have averages in the same range?

EXERCISES

Think and Discuss

▶**CHECK for Understanding**

1. Give an example of data that you could represent using a bar graph.
2. Give an example of data that you could represent by color coding a map of your state.

Data Analysis The graph at the right shows the number of people out of 100 surveyed who misplace their television's remote control each week. *(Source: Magnavox)*

3. From the graph, estimate the number of people out of 100 surveyed who say they never misplace the remote.

4. What number of people out of 100 surveyed say that they misplace the remote at least once a week?

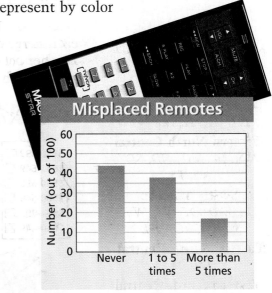

Independent Practice

5. The bar graph below shows the number of stores out of 100 surveyed that offered these services for 1990 and 1993. Which service increased the most during this time? Which service increased the least? *(Source: Maclean Hunter Media, Inc.)*

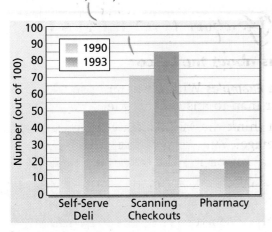

6. The bar graph below shows the number of vacationers out of 100 surveyed who participated in five outdoor sports. What sport was about 3 times more popular than sailing? List the sports from most popular to least popular. *(Source: Travel Industry Association of America)*

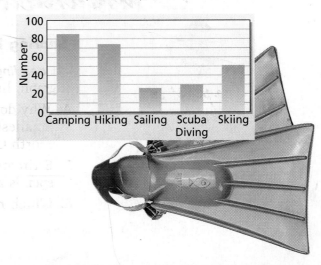

7. The average amount of soft drinks (in gallons per year) that people drink is listed below. Use the list to color code a map. Use the ranges 35–39.9, 40–44.9, 45–49.9, and 50–54.9. *(Source: Beverage World)*

North East	43.3
Mid-Atlantic	46.2
Eastern North Central	48.3
Western North Central	48.8
South Atlantic	50.2
Eastern South Central	54.9
Western South Central	48.1
Mountain	37.1
Pacific	40.9

Many soft drinks, especially colas, had their start in the late 1800's in the southern United States.

8. *It's Up to You* The bar graph at the right shows some data. Estimate the height of each bar. Then make up a story about what the numbers might mean.

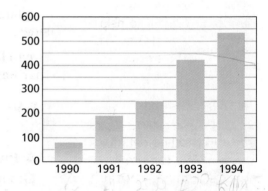

Integrated Review   Making Connections within Mathematics

Round the number to the nearest hundred.

9. 82   10. 517   11. 125   12. 351

Round the number to the nearest thousand.

13. 2004   14. 1875   15. 949   16. 343

Exploration and Extension

17. *Building Your Chapter Project* The bar graph at the right shows the number of items in the largest collections in the world in 1990. Write a problem for the Review Math Quiz that uses the bar graph. *(Source: Guinness Book of World Records)*

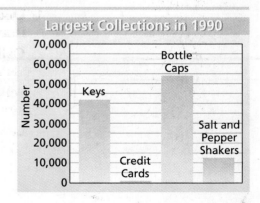

Largest Collections in 1990

1.5 Connections to Geometry: Drawing a Diagram

What you should learn:

Goal 1 How to solve problems by drawing a diagram

Goal 2 How to use a diagram to help you solve real-life problems

Why you should learn it:

Drawing a Diagram is a strategy for collecting data for a problem. You can use it, for example, to find how much wood you need to build a storage box for CD's.

Study Tip

Many mathematical words come from other languages. For instance, the word "quadrilateral" comes from the Latin words quattuor (four) and lateralis (side). The Spanish word for "four," quatro, also comes from Latin.

Goal 1 **Drawing a Diagram**

In Lesson 1.4, you used graphs to help you solve problems. Now you will use diagrams or pictures to help you solve problems.

A **quadrilateral** is a figure with four sides.

A **parallelogram** is a quadrilateral that has two pairs of parallel sides.

Quadrilateral

Parallelogram

Lesson Investigation

■ Investigating Quadrilaterals

Group Activity How many different quadrilaterals can be drawn in a 3-by-3 grid of dot paper? Two examples are shown below. How many of the quadrilaterals are parallelograms?

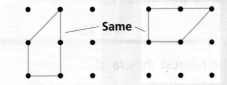

Same

Parallelogram

In your investigation, remember the problem-solving plan.

1. **Understand the Problem** Discuss in your group what it means for two quadrilaterals to be different.

2. **Collect the Data** Draw as many different quadrilaterals as you can. Label the parallelograms.

3. **Solve the Problem** Count the number of different quadrilaterals. Then count the parallelograms.

4. **Look Back at Your Solution** Compare your answers with other groups in your class.

Real Life
Woodworking

Example   *Drawing a Diagram*

You are planning to build a storage box for your CD collection, as shown at the left. You plan to cut the pieces from a board that is 12 inches wide. How long should the board be?

Solution   The storage box has 6 pieces. One way to arrange the pieces on a board that is 12 inches wide is shown below. To find how long the board should be, add the lengths.

$$
\begin{array}{r}
10.0 \text{ in.}\\
5.5 \text{ in.}\\
13.0 \text{ in.}\\
+13.0 \text{ in.}\\
\hline
41.5 \text{ in.}
\end{array}
$$

To allow for cutting, the board should be at least 42 inches long.

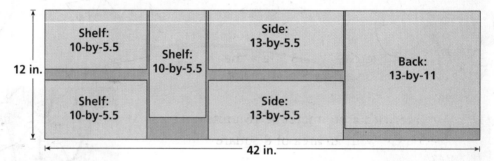

11 in.

13 in.

5.5 in.

10 in.

Shelf:
10-by-5.5

Shelf:
10-by-5.5

Side:
13-by-5.5

Back:
13-by-11

12 in.

Shelf:
10-by-5.5

Side:
13-by-5.5

42 in.

Communicating about MATHEMATICS

Sharing Ideas about the Lesson

Extending the Example The areas of the six pieces are as follows. How much of the 12 by 42 inch board is not used for the storage box? Explain your reasoning.

Area of Each Shelf: $5.5 \times 10 = 55.0$ sq in.
Area of Each Side: $5.5 \times 13 = 71.5$ sq in.
Area of Back: $11 \times 13 = 143$ sq in.

EXERCISES

Think and Discuss

> CHECK for Understanding

Geometry In Exercises 1–4, sketch a rectangle with the given dimensions. Then find the perimeter of the rectangle.

1. 1-by-2
2. 2-by-3
3. 3-by-4
4. 4-by-5

5. *Looking for a Pattern* Describe the pattern for the perimeters in Exercises 1–4. Then predict the perimeter of a 5-by-6 rectangle. Check your prediction by drawing a diagram and finding the perimeter.

Independent Practice

Geometry In Exercises 6–9, find the area of the figure. Each small triangle has an area of 2 square units.

6.
7.
8.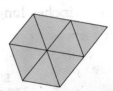
9.

Geometry In Exercises 10–13, draw the figure or figures on a 5-by-5 grid of dot paper.

10. A square with a perimeter of 16 units
11. A rectangle with an area of 8 square units
12. A rectangle with an area of 4 square units and a perimeter of 8 units
13. Two different rectangles with a perimeter of 10 units

14. *Reasoning* How many different sizes of rectangles can be drawn on a 3-by-4 grid of dot paper? Illustrate your answer by drawing one rectangle of each size.

15. *Drawing a Diagram* You are building the planter shown at the right. You plan to cut the pieces from a 4-foot by 4-foot piece of plywood. Is this possible? Illustrate your answer with a diagram.

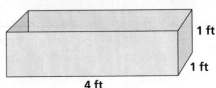

1 ft

1 ft

4 ft

Reasoning You and 6 friends live in the same city within several blocks of one another. The table shows the number of blocks to your friends' homes from your home. (You live on the corner of a block.)

16. Use grid paper to draw a diagram that shows the locations of all the homes.

17. Which friend lives closest to you? How many blocks away does he or she live?

18. Which two friends live closest to each other? How many blocks apart do they live?

19. Describe the path from Carmen's home to Yoko's home.

20. How many blocks do Luis and Steve live from one another?

Friend	Distance (in blocks)
Luis	2 West, 3 North
Carmen	4 East, 3 North
Yoko	3 North
Steve	2 West, 5 South
Sue Ellen	2 East, 3 South
Jesse	6 East, 1 South

Integrated Review

Making Connections within Mathematics

Complete the tree diagram.

21.

22.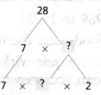

23.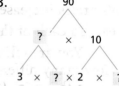

Exploration and Extension

Vocabulary Building In Exercises 24–26, copy the grid of letters at the right. Use the clues to discover each word.

24. Start at M.
Left 2, up 2.
Right 4, down 3.
Left 2, up 2.

25. Start at I.
Down 2.

26. Start at F.
Down 3.
Right 3, up 2.

A	B	C	D	E
F	G	H	I	J
K	L	M	N	O
P	Q	R	S	T
U	V	W	X	Y

27. What sentence is formed by Exercises 24–26?

28. *Building Your Chapter Project*
The diagram at the right shows an open box. Copy the diagram and add dimensions that you think are reasonable for a box to store a rock collection. Then write a problem that uses the diagram for the Review Math Quiz.

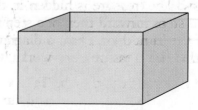

Take this test as you would take a test in class. The answers to the exercises are given in the back of the book.

Looking for a Pattern   In Exercises 1–3, match the description with the pattern. **(1.1)**

a. Each number is 5 times the number before it.

b. Each number is 5 more than the number before it.

c. Each number is the sum of the two numbers before it.

1. 3, 8, 13, 18   2. 3, 15, 75, 375   3. 3, 8, 11, 19

Reading a Table   In Exercises 4 and 5, use the table at the right. It lists the prices of 4 foods from 1989 to 1993. (Bread: 1 pound; Eggs: 1 dozen; Ice cream: half gallon; Oranges: 1 pound) **(1.2)**
(Source: U.S. Bureau of Labor Statistics)

	1989	1990	1991	1992	1993
Bread	$0.69	$0.70	$0.72	$0.74	$0.76
Eggs	$1.14	$1.00	$1.01	$0.93	$0.87
Ice Cream	$2.67	$2.54	$2.63	$2.49	$2.59
Oranges	$0.53	$0.56	$0.65	$0.52	$0.56

4. Which food's prices increased from 1989 to 1993?

5. In which year did each of these four foods cost the most?

6. *Making a List*   You are taking a true-false quiz with 5 questions. How many different ways can you answer all the questions on the quiz? **(1.3)**

Using a Graph   The bar graph at the right shows the number of people out of 100 surveyed who think the factor is important to friendship. **(1.4)** *(Source: MCI Communications)*

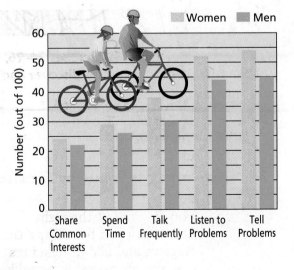

7. What factor is considered most important by both men and women?

8. Do men and women have the same views about friendship? Explain.

9. *Drawing a Diagram*   You are baby-sitting and create a "treasure hunt." The clues are listed below. The treasure is hidden in the closet, two steps forward then one step to the left of the front door. Draw a diagram to check that the treasure hunt works. **(1.5)**

a. Start at the front door.

b. Take 6 steps forward and turn right.

c. Take 4 steps forward and turn left.

d. Take 2 steps forward and turn left.

e. Take 5 steps forward and turn left.

f. Take 6 steps forward.

Materials Needed: paper, pencils

Part A *Classifying and Grouping* In your group, solve each problem on a separate sheet of paper. Then sort the papers into two piles that you have labeled *Addition Problems* and *Subtraction Problems*. Be prepared to explain how your group decided to classify each problem.

A. You have 13 baseball cards. You sell 4 cards to a friend. How many do you have left?

B. You have 11 necklaces. Four are gold and the rest are silver. How many are silver?

C. On Monday, you have 26 stickers. During the week you get 7 more. How many do you have on Saturday?

D. You give your cousin 12 seashells from your collection. You now have 43 seashells. How many did you start with?

E. You have 33 stuffed animals. How many more do you need to have a total of 50 stuffed animals?

F. You have 126 comics in your collection. Six of the comics are duplicates. How many different comics do you have?

G. You have 17 model planes and 12 model rockets in your collection. How many models do you have altogether?

H. Your music collection has 43 cassettes and CD's. Twenty-five of the recordings are CD's. How many are cassettes?

I. You have 145 butterflies and your friend has 178. How many more does your friend have than you?

Part B *Comparing Results* Compare the way your group classified the nine problems with the way other groups classified them.

1. Are there some problems that you classified as addition but other groups classified as subtraction? Discuss your reasoning.

Part C *Writing Number Sentences* Here are two number sentences that you could have used to solve Problem A.

Addition Number Sentence   *Subtraction Number Sentence*

$4 + \boxed{?} = 13$ $13 - 4 = \boxed{?}$

In each number sentence, $\boxed{?}$ represents the number of cards you have left.

2. Make a table that shows how each of the other 8 problems can be represented as an addition number sentence *and* a subtraction number sentence.

On Your Own   Critical Thinking

3. *Algebra* Solve each problem. After you solve the problem, decide whether you would classify it as a *Multiplication Problem* or a *Division Problem*. Explain your reasoning.

A. You have four boxes of football cards. Each box has 85 cards. How many cards do you have?

B. Your collection of 39 model cars is displayed on three shelves. Each shelf has the same number of cars. How many are on each shelf?

4. *Writing Number Sentences* Copy and complete the table. Write each of the problems in Exercise 3 as a multiplication number sentence and as a division number sentence.

	Multiplication Sentence	Division Sentence
Problem A	?	?
Problem B	?	?

1.6 Algebra and Equations

What you should learn:

Goal 1 How to use mental math to solve addition and subtraction equations

Goal 2 How to use mental math to solve multiplication and division equations

Why you should learn it:

Algebra uses symbols to solve problems. Learning to write equations for real-life problems can help you solve them. Learning to solve equations is an important part of algebra.

Goal 1 Addition and Subtraction Equations

To begin this lesson, let's take another look at the baseball card problem on page 26.

You have 13 baseball cards. You sell 4 cards to a friend. How many do you have left?

This problem can be solved using a verbal sentence that can be rewritten as an **equation.** An equation is a mathematical sentence with an equal sign " = " in it.

Verbal Sentence	Number of cards left	=	Number of cards you started with	−	Number of cards sold

Equation   ? = 13 − 4

In this equation, ? stands for the number of cards left. The word **algebra** comes from the Arabian word *al-jabr.* In algebra, the number of cards left is represented by a letter, such as *c*.

Algebraic Equation $c = 13 - 4$

The value of *c* that makes the equation true is the **solution** of the equation. What is the solution of this equation?

One way to solve an equation is to use mental math.

Study Tip

Any letter of the alphabet can be used in an equation. To help remember what the letter represents, you can use letters such as c for cards, t for time, and p for price.

Example 1 Solving Equations with Mental Math

Solve the equation.

a. $n + 4 = 19$ b. $20 - y = 12$

Solution

a. The solution is $n = 15$ because $15 + 4 = 19$.

b. The solution is $y = 8$ because $20 - 8 = 12$. ∎

Multiplication and Division Equations

Mental math can also be used to solve multiplication and division equations.

Example 2 *Solving Equations with Mental Math*

Solve the equation.

a. $8 \cdot x = 56$ b. $m \div 5 = 10$ c. $72 \div p = 8$

Solution

a. The solution is $x = 7$ because $8 \cdot 7 = 56$.
b. The solution is $m = 50$ because $50 \div 5 = 10$.
c. The solution is $p = 9$ because $72 \div 9 = 8$.   ■

Need to Know

Mutiplication can be written with the symbol "•" or "×."

Example 3 *Writing an Equation*

Real Life
Shopping

You are shopping for earrings and decide to buy 5 pairs. Each pair costs $1.65. Write an equation that can be used to find the total cost of 5 pairs.

Solution

Verbal Sentence	Total cost	=	Number of pairs	×	Price per pair

Equation $T = 5 \times 1.65$

Because $5 \times 1.65 = 8.25$, the total cost is $8.25.   ■

Communicating about MATHEMATICS

▶ **Sharing Ideas about the Lesson**

Using Different Symbols Which equation uses a better multiplication symbol? Why?

$12 \cdot x = 60$ or $12 \times x = 60$

EXERCISES

Guided Practice

Think and Discuss

▶ CHECK for Understanding

For Exercises 1 and 2, use the problem below. Complete the statement with the word *equation* or *solution*.

> You are bowling and knock down 8 of the 10 pins. To get a spare, you must knock down the remaining pins. How many pins must you knock down?

1. The ? that shows this problem is $p = 10 - 8$.
2. The ? of the equation is $p = 2$.
3. Your cat eats 2 cans of cat food every day. What letter would you use to stand for the number of cans of cat food you must buy every week? Why did you select that letter?

Recycling One recycled aluminum can saves enough energy to keep a 100-watt light bulb burning for $3\frac{1}{2}$ hours. You recycle 336 aluminum cans. The amount of energy saved is enough to keep a 100-watt light bulb burning for how many hours?

4. Complete the verbal sentence for the problem.

   Total hours = ? × ?

5. Write an equation that can be used to find the total number of hours the bulb will burn. Solve it.

6. *Mental Math* Solve the equation $140 \div m = 14$ using mental math.

Cats rank second only to dogs in popularity as pets. About 40 million cats are kept as pets in the United States.

Independent Practice

Algebra and Mental Math Use mental math to solve.

7. $18 + m = 25$
8. $x + 36 = 42$
9. $18 - s = 11$
10. $122 + 33 = t$
11. $p - 11 = 12$
12. $50 - 15 = d$
13. $9 \cdot y = 54$
14. $40 \div b = 10$
15. $n \times 15 = 45$
16. $x \div 5 = 7$
17. $r \div 4 = 8$
18. $m \cdot m = 16$

Equations   **Write an equation for the problem. Then solve.**

19. What number can you add to 6 to get 21?
20. What number can you subtract from 17 to get 5?
21. What number can you multiply by 5 to get 40?
22. What number can you divide by 2 to get 18?

Looking for a Pattern   **Solve the equations. Then describe the pattern for d.**

23. $2 + d = 10$
    $4 + d = 10$
    $6 + d = 10$
    $8 + d = 10$

24. $d - 5 = 10$
    $d - 5 = 15$
    $d - 5 = 20$
    $d - 5 = 25$

25. $d \cdot 5 = 25$
    $d \cdot 5 = 30$
    $d \cdot 5 = 35$
    $d \cdot 5 = 40$

26. $d \div 2 = 7$
    $d \div 2 = 8$
    $d \div 2 = 9$
    $d \div 2 = 10$

27. *Geometry*   The area of the rectangle at the right is 288 square meters. The width is 12 meters. Write an equation that you can use to find the length of the rectangle. Then solve the equation.

12 m

28. *Art*   You sign up for a pottery class that costs $3 for each lesson. How many lessons can you take if you have $36? Use the following verbal sentence to write an equation for the problem. Then solve.

| Number of lessons | = | Money you have | ÷ | Cost per lesson |

Write an equation for the problem. Then solve.

29. At the end of fifth grade, you were 59 inches tall. At the beginning of sixth grade, you were 61.5 inches tall. How many inches did you grow?

30. In table tennis, the first player to get 21 points wins the game. Your score is 14. How many more points do you need to win?

31. Each day at swim team practice you must swim 1 mile. If one half mile is 36 lengths of the pool, how many lengths must you swim each day?

32. You are taking a standardized test. The test is in 6 equal parts, and the total time for the test is 180 minutes. How long is each part of the test?

Players from more than 100 countries belong to the International Table Tennis Federation.

Units of Measure   **Complete the statement.**

33. 5 years = [?] months

34. [?] hours = 480 minutes

35. 102 inches = [?] feet

36. 10.5 dollars = [?] cents

37. [?] pounds = 56 ounces

38. 15 inches = [?] centimeters

Exploration and Extension

39. *Building Your Chapter Project*
Use the information in the table to write a problem with an equation for the Review Math Quiz. The table lists some items in a museum gift shop. The student should be able to solve the equation using mental math.

Item	Price
Frog pins	$6.95
Stuffed frog	$0.75
Frog T-shirt	$5.25
Wind-up frog	$1.35

Louise Mesa collects toy frogs and has more than 6000 in her museum in Eureka Springs, Arkansas.

Mixed REVIEW

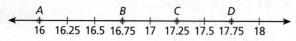

Add, subtract, multiply, or divide.

1. 40.1 + 13.7
2. 12.22 − 10.01
3. 1.8 × 12
4. 4.5 ÷ 9
5. 33.18 + 21.55
6. 120.21 − 50.34
7. 1.67 × 15
8. 78.15 ÷ 15

Measurement   **Measure the length of each item to the nearest inch.**

9. Unsharpened pencil
10. Quarter
11. Math book
12. Chalkboard

Use the number line below to find the distance between the points.

```
      A           B       C       D
  ←───┼───┼───┼───┼───┼───┼───┼───┼───→
     16  16.25 16.5 16.75  17  17.25 17.5 17.75  18
```

13. A and B
14. B and C
15. B and D
16. A and D

Many real-life problems contain decimal numbers. You can solve these problems in three ways: by hand, with a calculator, and by estimating using mental math.

Real Life
Buying Gasoline

Example	Three Ways to Solve a Problem

You buy 12 gallons of gasoline that cost $1.249 per gallon. You have $16. Is that enough to pay for the gas?

a. How would you answer the question if you don't have a pencil, paper, or a caculator?

b. How would you answer the question if you have paper and a pencil, but you don't have a calculator?

c. How would you answer the question with a calculator?

Solution

a. Without pencil, paper, or a calculator, use mental math to estimate the cost of the gasoline. Because $1.249 is about $1.25, you could reason that the cost is as follows.

$$12 \times \$1.00 = \$12$$
$$\underline{12 \times \$0.25 = \$\ 3}$$
$$\$15$$

Study Tip

You should be able to add, subtract, multiply, and divide decimal numbers by hand. Here is an example.

$$
\begin{array}{r}
1.249 \\
\times\ \ \ 12 \\
\hline
2\ 498 \\
\underline{12\ 49} \\
14.988
\end{array}
$$

b. With paper and pencil, multiply 1.249 by 12 as shown at the left. The result is about $15.

c. With a calculator, enter the following keystrokes.

12 $\boxed{\times}$ 1.249 $\boxed{=}$

The calculator should display 14.988, which is about $15. ∎

Exercises

Use a calculator. Add, subtract, multiply, or divide.

1. $1.248 + 1.456$ 2. $4.509 + 6.826$ 3. $8.408 - 6.507$ 4. $7.532 - 5.002$

5. 1.23×3.2 6. 4.25×8.12 7. $5.36 - 1.2$ 8. $6.58 \div 2.3$

9. You buy 15 gallons of gasoline that cost $1.199 per gallon. You have $18. Is that enough to pay for the gas? Answer the question three ways: (a) by estimating, (b) by hand, and (c) with a calculator. Which way do you like best? Why?

1.7 Connections to Algebra: Working Backward

What you should learn:

Goal 1 How to work backward to solve an equation

Goal 2 How to work backward to solve a real-life problem

Why you should learn it:

You can work backward to solve real-life problems when you want to know the original amount of something. An example is finding the amount of money you started with at a water park.

Goal 1 Working Backward

What reasoning can you use to solve this equation?

$n \div 2 = 7$ *Original equation*

One way is to rewrite it as "What number can be divided by 2 to get 7?" To find the answer, you can **Work Backward.** Start with 7. Then multiply by 2 to get 14.

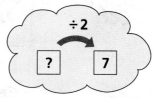

You can **check** to see if 14 is the solution by **replacing** 14 for n in the original equation.

$n \div 2 = 7$ *Original equation*

$14 \div 2 \stackrel{?}{=} 7$ *Replace n with 14.*

$7 = 7$ *Solution checks.* ✓

Example 1   *Solving Equations*

Write each equation as a question. Then solve the equation by answering the question.

a. $x + 83 = 94$ b. $11 \cdot p = 99$

Solution

a. This equation can be rewritten as the following question.

   What number can be added to 83 to get 94?

   The answer is 11 because $11 + 83 = 94$.

b. This equation can be rewritten as the following question.

   What number can be multiplied by 11 to get 99?

   The answer is 9 because $11 \cdot 9 = 99$. ∎

Example 2	*Working Backward*

You went to a water park with a friend. You spent half of your money on general admission, which let you ride on all the slides. You forgot to bring a towel, so you spent half the money that was left on a new one. Then you had $4 left, which you spent on lunch. How much money did you take to the water park?

Solution You can solve the problem by working backward.

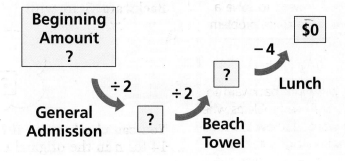

In 1994, there were 550 water parks in the United States.

Because you spent $4 on lunch, you must have spent $4 on the towel. Because lunch and the towel cost $8, you must have spent $8 on the admission. The amount you took to the park was $16. You can check this as follows.

$4 for lunch	+	$4 for towel	+	$8 for admission	=	Total of $16

Communicating about MATHEMATICS

Sharing Ideas about the Lesson

Solving a Puzzle Work backward to find the original number. Explain your steps.

$$-5 \quad \times 2 \quad +7 \quad \div 3$$

?	?	?	?	5

EXERCISES

▶CHECK for Understanding

1. Copy and complete the diagram below. Work backward to solve. Explain your steps.

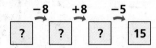

In Exercises 2–5, rewrite the equation as a question. Then solve the equation and check your answer.

2. $78 + n = 93$ 3. $54 - p = 48$ 4. $3 \cdot y = 39$ 5. $42 \div b = 6$

6. *Checking a Solution*   Explain how to check a solution. Show how to check the solution to Exercise 1.

Independent Practice

Working Backward   In Exercises 7–10, copy and complete the diagram.

7.
	÷8		−4		×6		+7	
?		?		?		?		7

8.
	×3		÷2		−2		+7	
?		?		?		?		11

9.
	+8		÷5		×3		−3	
?		?		?		?		18

10.
	+1		÷6		−9		×5	
?		?		?		?		20

In Exercises 11–22, rewrite the equation as a question. Then solve the equation and check your answer.

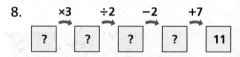

11. $x + 5 = 24$ 12. $18 - y = 6$ 13. $a - 32 = 51$ 14. $6 + n = 45$

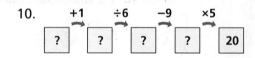

15. $t + 55 = 66$ 16. $68 - d = 52$ 17. $8 \cdot b = 48$ 18. $p \div 7 = 10$

19. $c \div 8 = 14$ 20. $m \times 4 = 112$ 21. $63 \cdot x = 189$ 22. $156 \div y = 12$

Writing Equations   In Exercises 23–26, write an equation that represents the question. Then solve the equation and check your answer.

23. What number can be added to 18 to get 27?

24. What number can be subtracted from 95 to get 23?

25. What number can be multiplied by 7 to get 105?

26. What number can be divided by 4 to get 17?

Geometry   Find the length of the side or sides labeled *x*.

27. Area: 48 square meters

8 m

x   *x*

8 m

28. Perimeter: 44 feet

15 ft   12 ft

x

29. *Golf Galore*   You play in a 9-hole miniature golf tournament. Your scores for the last 7 holes are shown at the right. You forgot your scores for the first two holes. You do remember that the score of the 1st hole was 1 stroke less than the score for the 2nd hole. Your total score is 22. What were the scores for the 1st and 2nd holes?

30. *Video Arcade*   You and a friend go to the arcade. You exchange half of your money for tokens. For each dollar, you get 4 tokens. You use half of the tokens playing video games. You use half of the remaining tokens to play air hockey, which leaves you with 4 tokens.

a. How many tokens did you begin with?

b. How much money did you begin with?

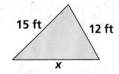

Hole	Strokes
1	?
2	?
3	2
4	3
5	4
6	2
7	3
8	1
9	2

Integrated Review   ***Making Connections within Mathematics***

Number Sense   Complete the statement using $>$, $<$, or $=$.

31. $\frac{1}{6}$? $\frac{1}{3}$

32. $\frac{1}{8}$? $\frac{1}{12}$

33. $\frac{2}{7}$? $\frac{4}{7}$

34. 1 ? $\frac{4}{4}$

35. $\frac{5}{6}$? $\frac{6}{6}$

36. $\frac{1}{2}$? $\frac{1}{4}$

Exploration and Extension

37. *Building Your Chapter Project*   Write a problem for the Review Math Quiz about collecting comic books. Include information about the amount of money spent on comic books at 3 stores. Try to write a problem that asks the question, "How much money did you start with?"

38. *Number Puzzle*   Use the following clues to find the *two* numbers.

- Each number is less than 14.
- The product of the two numbers is greater than 30.
- The difference of the two numbers is 8.
- Each number is even.

1.8 Problem-Solving Strategy: Solving a Simpler Problem

What you should learn:

Goal 1 How to use the strategy of Solving a Simpler Problem

Goal 2 How to solve real-life problems by solving a simpler problem

Why you should learn it:

You can often solve a simpler problem when a real-life problem is complex and confusing. An example is finding the number of pairs in a group of eight people.

Goal 1 Solving a Simpler Problem

Lesson Investigation

■ **Counting Moves**

Group Activity The game below has 5 blue markers on the left and 5 red markers on the right. Your goal is to reverse the positions of the colors with as few moves as possible. The rules are:

1. A marker can be moved to an adjoining open space or can jump over another marker to an open space.

2. Blue markers can only move right and red markers can only move left.

How many moves does it take to reverse the colors?

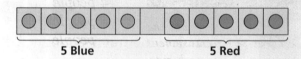

5 Blue   5 Red

To solve the problem in the investigation, try using the strategy of **Solving a Simpler Problem.** Instead of working with 5 markers of each color, try 1 of each color.

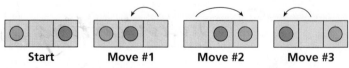

Start   Move #1   Move #2   Move #3

With 1 blue and 1 red marker, you need at least 3 moves to reverse the colors. Record this result in a table like that shown at the left.

Increase the number of markers to 2, 3, and 4, and record the results. Then find a pattern for the number of moves. Use the pattern to predict the number of moves for 5 markers of each color. Then check your solution by actually moving the markers.

Markers	Moves
1 blue, 1 red	3
2 blue, 2 red	?
3 blue, 3 red	?
4 blue, 4 red	?
5 blue, 5 red	?

Solving Real-Life Problems

Real Life
Roller Coaster

Roller coasters are the
most popular amusement
park ride.

Example   *Counting Combinations*

You and seven friends go to an amusement park.
Suppose you decide that each person in the group wants
to ride in the same car of the roller coaster with each
other person in the group. The roller coaster costs $2.25
for two people. How much will your group spend on the
roller coaster?

Solution   One way to solve this problem is to use the
strategy of Solving a Simpler Problem. You can draw a
diagram to count the number of rides with different
numbers of people.

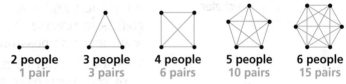

| **2 people** | **3 people** | **4 people** | **5 people** | **6 people** |
| 1 pair | 3 pairs | 6 pairs | 10 pairs | 15 pairs |

It appears that the pattern is as follows.

2 *people*	1 pair
3 *people*	$1 + 2 = 3$ pairs
4 *people*	$1 + 2 + 3 = 6$ pairs
5 *people*	$1 + 2 + 3 + 4 = 10$ pairs
6 *people*	$1 + 2 + 3 + 4 + 5 = 15$ pairs

With this pattern, you can predict the number of pairs
with 8 people to be

8 *people* $1 + 2 + 3 + 4 + 5 + 6 + 7 = 28$ pairs.

It will cost your group $28 \times \$2.25$ or $63. ∎

Communicating about MATHEMATICS

Cooperative
Learning

▶ **Sharing Ideas about the Lesson**

Group Activity: Extending the Example In the example,
suppose that you double the number of people who
go to the amusement park. If every person still
wanted to ride with every other person, would it
cost twice as much money? Explain your reasoning.
Share your results with another group.

EXERCISES

Think and Discuss

▶ **CHECK for Understanding**

Choosing a Strategy Which strategy would best solve the problem? Choose from: Make a List, Solve a Simpler Problem, and Draw a Diagram.

1. *A stack of quarters is worth $1000. How high is the stack?*

2. *How many squares can be drawn on a 3-by-3 grid of dot paper?*

3. *In how many different orders can 5 people stand in a line?*

In Exercises 4 and 5, describe a simpler problem that you could solve.

4. An exercise program requires you do 1 sit-up the first day and double the number you do each day. How many sit-ups will you do on the 8th day?

5. You form a club with 6 people. Each member is to exchange a friendship ring with each other member. How many rings will be exchanged?

Independent Practice

In Exercises 6–8, begin by solving a simpler problem.

6. You are scheduling the chess club tournament. There are 7 members and they play each other once. How many games must you schedule?

7. Triangular numbers are represented by dots arranged in a triangle, as shown at the right. Find the number of dots in the 8th triangular number.

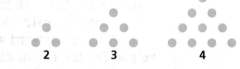

1 **2** **3** **4**

8. Look at the checkerboard at the right. To find the total number of squares of different sizes on the board, begin by solving simpler problems. The table shows the number of squares of different sizes on smaller checkerboards.

Size of board	2×2	3×3	4×4	5×5
Number of squares	5	14	30	55

a. What is the difference in the number of squares on a 4×4 and on a 3×3 checkerboard? A 5×5 and a 4×4 checkerboard?

b. Find the number of all possible squares on a 6×6 checkerboard.

9. Copy the diagram at the right. Then put the numbers 1 through 19 in the circles so that each row of 3 numbers has the same sum. (One number is already used.)

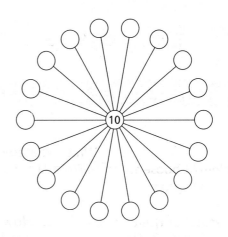

10. *Geometry* The first 4 figures of a pattern are shown below. Describe the pattern for the perimeters. Find the perimeter of the 15th figure.

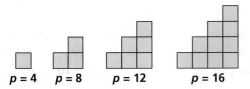

p = 4   p = 8   p = 12   p = 16

Integrated Review

Estimation Use the map of Florida at the right. Estimate the distance between the two cities.

11. St. Petersburg and Ft. Lauderdale
12. Tallahassee and Pensacola
13. Tallahassee and Ft. Lauderdale

Making Connections within Mathematics

Pensacola • Tallahassee

St. Petersburg

Ft. Lauderdale

1 inch
320 miles

Exploration and Extension

14. *Calculator Crossword* Many digits of a calculator display look like letters when turned upside down. The clues for the crossword are given below. Do the calculation, and then turn the calculator upside down to find the word.

0 - O	5 - S
1 - I	6 - g
2 - Z	7 - L
3 - E	8 - B
4 - h	9 - G

ACROSS

1. 1000 − 396   A farm animal
2. 2161 + 1412   Do it or [?]!
3. 4910 − 1205   Bottom of a shoe
5. 26487 + 12589   Model of the world
6. 30900 ÷ 10   Musical instrument
8. 384.5 • 12   Opposite of low
10. 8305.5 ÷ 1.5   More or [?]
11. 83.8 + 251.2   Homonym of sea
12. 1110 − 377   Can be electric

DOWN

1. 25669 ÷ 3.5   Part of a foot
3. 3691 • 125   Has jingle bells
4. 7 • 501   Misplace
5. 228609 + 151297   A barnyard noise
7. 2020 ÷ 4   A distress signal
9. 2624 + 5090   Opposite of valley

1.9 A Summary of Problem-Solving Strategies

What you should learn:

Goal 1 How to decide which problem-solving strategies to use

Goal 2 How to use problem-solving strategies to solve puzzles

Why you should learn it:

Problem solving is important in all parts of life. Learning to solve problems in mathematics can help you solve many problems in everyday living.

Goal 1 Problem-Solving Strategies

In this chapter, you studied many problem-solving strategies.

Looking for a Pattern	*Lesson 1.1*
Making a Table	*Lesson 1.2*
Making a List	*Lesson 1.3*
Using a Graph	*Lesson 1.4*
Drawing a Diagram	*Lesson 1.5*
Classifying and Grouping Data	*Lab 1.6*
Working Backward	*Lesson 1.7*
Solving a Simpler Problem	*Lesson 1.8*

Example 1 shows another useful strategy: **Guess, Check, and Revise.**

Example 1 *Using Guess, Check, and Revise*

A square room has an area of 156.25 square feet. What is the length of each side of the room?

Solution   One way to solve this problem is to *guess* the length of each side, *check* to see if the area is correct, and *revise* the length if necessary.

You know that a 12-foot by 12-foot room has an area of 144 square feet.

   Area = 12 × 12 = 144 sq ft.   *12 by 12 room*

So, you can start by guessing lengths that are larger than 12 feet. The area of a 13-foot by 13-foot room is

   Area = 13 × 13 = 169 sq ft.   *13 by 13 room*

Because this is too large, revise your guess by choosing a smaller length, such as 12.5 feet. The area of a 12.5-foot by 12.5-foot room is

   Area = 12.5 × 12.5 = 156.25 sq ft.   *12.5 by 12.5 room*

Each side of the room is 12.5 feet long.   ∎

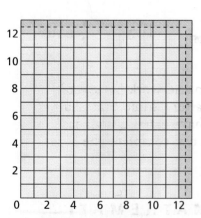

☐ 12-by-12 is too small.
■ 13-by-13 is too big.
☐ 12.5-by-12.5 is just right.

Problem Solving
Puzzles

Example 2 *Choosing a Strategy*

One by one, six chimpanzees walk by a bowl of bananas.

- Chimp 1 eats $\frac{1}{6}$ of the bananas.

- Chimp 2 eats $\frac{1}{5}$ of what Chimp 1 left.

- Chimp 3 eats $\frac{1}{4}$ of what Chimp 2 left.

- Chimp 4 eats $\frac{1}{3}$ of what Chimp 3 left.

- Chimp 5 eats $\frac{1}{2}$ of what Chimp 4 left.

- Chimp 6 eats the remaining 2 bananas.

How many bananas were originally in the bowl?

Solution There are many ways to solve this problem.

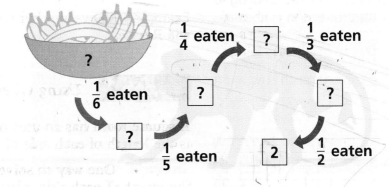

Chimpanzees are one of five types of apes. The others are gorillas, baboons, gibbons, and orangutans.

One way is to draw a diagram and work backward. Because 2 bananas were left after Chimp 5 ate half of the bananas, Chimp 5 must have eaten 2 bananas. Using similar reasoning, you can complete the solution.

Communicating about MATHEMATICS

Cooperative Learning

▶ **Sharing Ideas about the Lesson**

Completing the Example Copy the diagram in Example 2. Find the number of bananas represented by each question mark. What steps did you use?

EXERCISES

Think and Discuss

▶ CHECK for Understanding

Choosing Strategies   In Exercises 1 and 2, name two strategies that you could use to solve the problem. Tell why you chose them.

1. In Minnesota, to get from Meadowlands to Zim, you must go through either Tiovola or Kelsey. A road connects Tiovola and Kelsey. Describe the routes you could take.

2. At an Italian restaurant, you have a choice of lasagna, ravioli or spaghetti for a main course and a choice of cannoli or spumoni for dessert. How many different meals can you have?

3. Give an example of a problem that you could solve using the strategy of Guess, Check, and Revise.

4. Which problem-solving strategy do you like best? Why?

Independent Practice

Guess, Check, and Revise   In Exercises 5 and 6, solve the problem using the strategy of Guess, Check, and Revise.

5. *Reasoning*   Copy and complete the magic square. Use the digits 1–9. The sum in each row and column is 15.

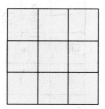

6. *Two Wrongs Make a Right*   Replace the letters in the sum below with the digits 2, 3, 4, 5, 6, 7, 8, and 0. Each digit should be used for only one letter. (Hint: R is 5.)

$$
\begin{array}{r}
\text{W R O N G} \\
+\text{W R O N G} \\
\hline
\text{R I G H T}
\end{array}
$$

In Exercises 7 and 8, solve the problem using any strategy. State the strategy or strategies you used and why.

7. *Fitness*   You are helping the coach tape lines on the gym floor to divide the length of the gym into 8 regions of the same size. If it takes 1 minute to tape 1 line, how long will it take to do the job?

8. *Reasoning*   You are playing the card game Crazy Eights. During the game, you pick up twice as many cards as you lay down, and you lay down 7 cards. If you now have 15 cards in your hand, how many cards did you start with?

Playing cards probably started in China or in Hindustan about A.D. 800.

Estimating Use the graph at the right about 5–17 year old students. It shows the average number of days of school missed per student for seven years. *(Source: U.S. Center for Health Statistics)*

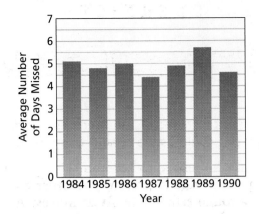

9. Estimate the number of days missed in each year, to the nearest half day.

10. In 1990, about 46,000,000 students in the United States were 5- to 17- years old. Use this number to estimate the *total* number of days missed by students in 1990. Explain.

11. With 1 straight cut, you can cut a pizza into 2 pieces. With 2 straight cuts, you can cut it into 4 pieces. With 3 straight cuts, the most pieces you can make is 7. What is the most pieces 5 straight cuts can make?

Integrated Review   *Making Connections within Mathematics*

12. *Logic Puzzle* Copy and complete the table at the right. Use the clues below to determine the favorite activity of each student. Mark an X in the table when it cannot be true, and an O in the table when it must be true.

a. Pam doesn't like to read.

b. Jill likes fishing better than hiking.

c. Sam's favorite activity is dancing.

d. Jill likes reading better than fishing.

e. Bill prefers hiking to fishing.

	Read	Fish	Dance	Hike
Bill				
Jill				
Sam				
Pam				

Exploration and Extension

13. *Building Your Chapter Project* Make up a logic puzzle for the Review Math Quiz that has clues about collections. The puzzle should ask the students to figure out the collections that 4 people have. Students could complete a table to solve the problem.

Chapter Summary

What did you learn?

Skills

1. Find the perimeter and area of a rectangle. **(1.2)**
2. Recognize composite and prime numbers. **(1.3)**
3. Use mental math to solve an equation. **(1.6)**

Strategies

4. Use different problem-solving strategies.
   - Look for a Pattern. **(1.1)**
   - Make a Table. **(1.2)**
   - Make a List. **(1.3)**
   - Use a Graph. **(1.4)**
   - Draw a Diagram. **(1.5)**
   - Classify and Group Data. **(Lab 1.6)**
   - Work Backward. **(1.7)**
   - Solve a Simpler Problem. **(1.8)**
   - Guess, Check, and Revise. **(1.9)**

Exploring Data

5. Organize and display data
   - with a table. **(1.2)**
   - with a graph. **(1.4)**

Why did you learn it?

Mathematics can help you solve problems that occur in real life. Here are some examples you studied in this chapter.

- Compare participation in sports by age groups. **(1.2)**
- Compare gasoline expenses in different regions of the country. **(1.4)**
- Draw plans for making a CD storage box. **(1.5)**
- Find the cost of riding a roller coaster. **(1.8)**

In the remaining chapters of this book, you will study many other real-life problems that can be solved with mathematics.

How does it fit into the bigger picture of mathematics?

Mathematics was developed to help people solve problems. When you are solving problems, remember that there are many strategies that can be used. With every strategy, you should consider the following steps.

1. Understand the problem.
2. Collect and organize the data.
3. Solve the problem.
4. Look back at your solution.

Looking for a Pattern In Exercises 1–4, describe the pattern.
Then write the next 3 numbers or letters. **(1.1)**

1. $1, \frac{7}{8}, \frac{6}{8}, \frac{5}{8}$, ?, ?, ?, . . .

2. 35, 40, 46, 53, ?, ?, ?, . . .

3. A, B, D, G, ?, ?, ?, . . .

4. $\frac{1}{21}, \frac{1}{18}, \frac{1}{15}, \frac{1}{12}$, ?, ?, ?, . . .

Making a Table In Exercises 5 and 6, the first 3 figures of a
pattern are shown. Make a table of their perimeters and areas.
Describe any patterns that you see. Predict the perimeter and area
of the next three figures. Check with sketches. **(1.1, 1.2)**

5.   . . .

6.   . . .

Algebra In Exercises 7 and 8, write an equation you can
use to solve the problem. Then solve. Check your result. **(1.6)**

7. You take $25 to a hockey game. You
leave the game with $9. How much
did you spend?

8. Together, you and a friend caught 26
fish. You caught 15. How many did
your friend catch?

Drawing a Diagram In Exercises 9 and 10, draw the figure
or figures on a 6-by-6 grid of dot paper. **(1.5)**

9. A rectangle with an area of 16 square units

10. Three different rectangles with a perimeter of 12 units

Using a Graph In Exercises 11–13, use
the bar graph. It shows the consumption
(in pounds) of whole and lowfat milk in
the United States for several years. **(1.2,
1.4)** *(Source: U.S. Department of Agriculture)*

11. What year did lowfat milk become
more popular than whole milk?

12. Between which 2 years did lowfat
milk consumption increase the most?

13. During which year did whole milk
consumption increase? Explain.

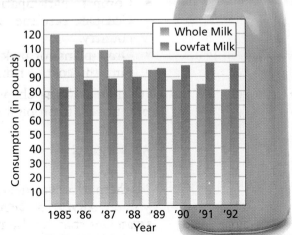

14. *Geometry* Use the Guess, Check, and Revise strategy to
find the length of each side of a square that has an area of
94.09 square units. **(1.9)**

15. *Making a List*   You are making a collage of leaves for an art project. You can choose maple, oak, beech, hickory, birch, poplar, or aspen leaves. Make a list of the different combinations of the 3 types of leaves your collage can contain. How many different combinations are possible? **(1.3)**

Working Backward   You have a collection of 21 yo-yos. Each costs $1.50. When you began your collection, you bought 1 yo-yo. Each week you bought 1 more than the preceding week. **(1.7)**

16. In how many more weeks will your collection have 36 yo-yos?

17. How much did you spend the 3rd week?

18. How much did you spend during the first 5 weeks?

19. During the first 4 weeks, you spent one fourth of your money. How much money did you start with?

Jim Marvy of Minneapolis, Minnesota, collects yo-yos. He has several hundred in his collection.

20. *Draw a Diagram*   You are organizing your football card collection in an $8\frac{1}{2}$-inch by 11-inch album. Each card is $2\frac{1}{2}$ inches by $3\frac{1}{2}$ inches. Draw a diagram showing the number of cards you can fit on each page. If the album has 30 pages, how many cards can it hold? **(1.5)**

21. *Language Building*   Copy the puzzle on a piece of grid paper. Then find each word and circle it.

buttons	frogs	shells
cards	key chains	stamps
CD's	leaves	stickers
coins	marbles	tapes
comics	pins	trains
dolls	pop cans	trolls
earrings	rings	yo-yos
fish	rocks	

```
T P R S O B U T T O N S B L
R S E T M S S O C D H C L V
O O I A N N G T O S I I S T
L Y E M I H E L I K E M Y S
L O A P T O L F N C L O E D
S Y R S O S A R S S K C O R
L N R N I P M A R B L E S A
L N I K E Y C H A I N S R C
E G N A M A T A L E A V E S
H S G O R F R I N G S H E D
S M S A T T A P E S I C S C
```

22. In Exercise 21, the letters that were *not* circled form a phrase. Find the phrase. Then write a paragraph about what you have learned in this chapter about the phrase.

Looking for a Pattern Describe the pattern. Then write the next 3 numbers or letters.

1. 60, 59, 56, 51, ?, ?, ?, . . .

2. 1, 2, 4, 7, ?, ?, ?, . . .

3. $\frac{1}{10}, \frac{2}{10}, \frac{4}{10}, \frac{8}{10}$, ?, ?, ?, . . .

4. A, D, G, J, ?, ?, ?, . . .

Mental Math Use mental math to solve.

5. $4 + b = 22$

6. $x - 15 = 34$

7. $78 \div y = 13$

8. $14 \cdot n = 70$

Algebra Write the equation as a question. Solve the equation by answering the question. Check your result.

9. $p - 45 = 110$

10. $\frac{a}{3} = 14$

11. *Reasoning* At a restaurant, you have a choice of 6 cheeseburger toppings. The toppings are lettuce (L), tomato (T), ketchup (K), mustard (M), pickle (P), and mayonnaise (Y). Make a list to find the number of combinations of two different toppings you can have on your cheeseburger.

12. How many triangles with different measurements can be drawn on a 3-by-3 grid of dot paper? Sketch your answer.

13. *Geometry* The rectangle at the right has an area of 97.5 square units. Write an equation that can be used to find the width of the rectangle. Then use Guess, Check, and Revise to find the width of the rectangle.

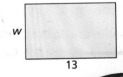

w

13

14. *Choosing a Strategy* At 7:45 A.M., you begin a 12-mile hike. At 8:20 A.M., you have walked 1 mile. If you hike at the same speed the entire day, how many hours will it take you to finish your hike?

The bar graph shows the average number of hours per year people watch movies at home and in theaters. (*Source: Veronis, Suhler, and Associates*)

15. What year did home videos become more popular than movies at the theater?

16. Estimate the average number of hours people watched movies in the theater and at home in 1991.

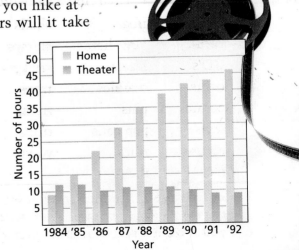

Place-Value Systems and Operations

This beautiful shape is a fractal. Benoit Mandelbrot is credited with discovering these complex, self-repeating, computer-generated patterns.

An algorithm is a description of a process that continually repeats. For example, there is an algorithm for addition or multiplication of whole numbers. Computers have made it possible to apply algorithms to any kind of repeating process like fractals. A Polish mathematician named Waclaw Sierpinski (1882-1969) gave the world its first fractal.

Sierpinski Gasket

Think and Discuss

1. Look at the series of figures. Describe an algorithm for creating a Sierpinski gasket.
2. What number patterns do you notice in the series of figures?

CHAPTER THEME:

Computers

Managing a Software Company

Theme: Computers Can you imagine starting a company that makes computer games? To run the company successfully, you must know how to design good games. But you must also know how to find people to buy your product, how to find good people to work for you, and how to keep track of the money you make and spend.

In this project, you will make a booklet that tells some things your computer software company does. It will include the following:

➡ **In Lesson 2.2:** Design a game that uses subtraction and addition. (page 63)

➡ **In Lesson 2.3:** Make a form for a bill and fill it out. (page 71)

➡ **In Lesson 2.4:** Design a computer screen for a game. (page 77)

➡ **In Lesson 2.5:** Design a poster showing a time line of the history of computers. (page 83)

➡ **In Lesson 2.6:** Calculate the sum of several orders. (page 87)

➡ **In Lesson 2.7:** Crack a code used in a computer game. (page 93)

This early calculating machine, known as the UNIVAC, only had about 10 times the memory capacity of a hand-held graphing calculator.

This data glove is linked to a computer at the Massachusetts Institute of Technology in Boston, Massachusetts.

GETTING STARTED

Materials: paper, pencils, colored pens or markers

- Make a booklet using several sheets of paper folded in half.

- Think of a name for your company and design a company logo, or emblem.

- Put the name of your company, its logo, and your name on the cover of the booklet.

- Place the booklet in your portfolio and add information to it as you do this chapter.

Materials Needed: paper, colored pencils

The oldest way that people wrote numbers is with tally marks. For instance, the cave drawing at the right probably meant that 7 deer had been killed in a hunt.

Writing larger numbers such as 34 with tally marks is difficult. So people began to group tally marks. Because people have 5 fingers on each hand, the groups usually had 5 or 10 tally marks.

34 marks

Grouped by 5's

Grouped by 10's

The ancient Egyptian number system grouped by 10's. The system included symbols for 1, 10, 100, 1000, and so on.

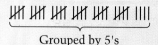

Staff	Heelbone	Scroll	Lotus Flower	Pointing Finger	Fish	Astonished Man
1	10	100	1000	10,000	100,000	1,000,000

Here are three examples of numbers that are written with the ancient Egyptian system.

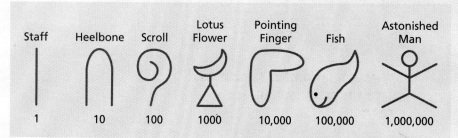

354   12,042   1,312,270

Part A *The Tally System*

1. In your group, show the number 28 in three different tally systems. Which of the three ways do you think is best? Explain.

2. Suppose you found some ancient writing that uses two number systems. You believe that both numbers are the same. Describe the second system.

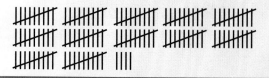

3. Three ancient Egyptian numbers are shown below. Write the numbers using our number system.

   a.  𓏼𓏼𓏼𓏼𓏼𓏼𓏼𓏼𓏼∩∩||||

   b.  𓆼𓏤𓏤𓏤∩∩∩∩∩∩∩||

   c.  𓂀𓂀𓂀𓂀𓏤𓏤𓏤𓏤𓏤𓏤||||||||

4. Write the numbers 304 and 2,210,008 in the Egyptian number system.

5. How do you think the Egyptians might have written the following sum?

   453 + 734 = 1187

6. Discuss some problems of the ancient Egyptian system.

7. With your partner or group, design a number system that does not have the problems of the tally system or the ancient Egyptian number system.

On Your Own   *Critical Thinking*

8. Do you think the ancient Egyptians would have written the number 122 as follows? Explain your reasoning.

   ∩∩∩∩∩∩∩∩∩∩∩∩||

9. Do you think the ancient Egyptians would have written the number 134 using either of the ways below? Explain.

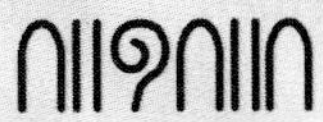

   𓏼||||∩∩∩   ∩||𓏼∩||∩

10. How would the ancient Egyptians have written the number 999?

11. Using the ancient Egyptian symbols, make up a way to write numbers less than 1.

2.1 The Base-Ten Place-Value System

What you should learn:

Goal 1 How to write place-value numbers in expanded notation

Goal 2 How to use base-ten place-value numbers to solve real-life problems

Why you should learn it:

An understanding of base-ten place-value systems will help you understand the operations that are used in our number system.

Study Tip

Because the ancient Egyptian number system was not a place-value system, it didn't need a symbol for zero. In a place-value system, a symbol for zero is a place-holder that allows you to tell the difference between numbers such as 38, 380, and 308.

Goal 1 Place-Value Systems

Our modern number system is *similar* to the ancient Egyptian number system. Both are **base-ten** systems that use symbols that group by ten.

Our modern number system is *different* from the ancient Egyptian number system because our system is a **place-value** system. For instance, you know that the symbol 734 represents seven hundred thirty-four because of the positions of the digits 7, 3, and 4.

Notice that the place-value position of 7 tells you it is 7 "hundreds," or 700.

Our place-value system has an addition property, which allows numbers to be written in **expanded notation**.

$$734 = 700 + 30 + 4 \qquad \textit{Addition property}$$
$$= 7 \times 100 + 3 \times 10 + 4 \times 1 \qquad \textit{Expanded notation}$$

Example 1 *Writing Expanded Notation*

Write the numbers in expanded notation.
a. 83 b. 5042

Solution

a. $\quad 83 = 80 + 3 \qquad \textit{Addition property}$

$\qquad = 8 \times 10 + 3 \times 1 \qquad \textit{Expanded notation}$

b. $5042 = 5000 + 40 + 2 \qquad \textit{Addition property}$

$\qquad = 5 \times 1000 + 4 \times 10 + 2 \times 1 \qquad \textit{Expanded notation}$

Goal 2 — Solving Real-Life Problems

You use many different systems of measure for length, time, and volume. Some of these are base-ten systems and some are not.

Real Life
Measuring Systems

Example 2 — Classifying Measuring Systems

Use only the units given. Which form base-ten systems? Explain your reasoning.

a. Time
1 hour = 60 minutes
1 minute = 60 seconds

b. Volume
1 gallon = 4 quarts
1 quart = 4 cups

c. English Length
1 yard = 3 feet
1 foot = 12 inches

d. Metric Length
1 meter = 100 centimeters
1 centimeter = 10 millimeters

Solution

a. The second-minute-hour system for time *is not* a base-ten system. It is a base-sixty system.

b. The cup-quart-gallon system for volume *is not* a base-ten system. It is a base-four system.

c. The inch-foot-yard system for length *is not* a base-ten system. It does not have a base.

d. The metric system for length *is* a base-ten system. The *decimeter* makes it easier to see the base ten.

1 meter	= 10 decimeters	*Multiply by 10.*
1 decimeter	= 10 centimeters	*Multiply by 10.*
1 centimeter	= 10 millimeters	*Multiply by 10.* ∎

Communicating about MATHEMATICS

▶ **Sharing Ideas about the Lesson**

Writing Numbers Write each number in words.
A. 157   **B.** 2048   **C.** 10,904   **D.** 1,240,052

EXERCISES

Think and Discuss

▶ CHECK for Understanding

History In Exercises 1–3, use the Roman numeral system shown at the right.

I	V	X	L	C	D	M
1	5	10	50	100	500	1000

Sample: 276 = CCLXXVI

1. Is the Roman system a base-ten system? Explain.
2. Is the Roman system a place-value system? Explain.
3. Write the number 362 in Roman numerals.

4. Write the number 102,681 in words.

Communicating Is the statement true or false? Explain.

5. In a base-ten system, you must have a symbol for zero.
6. In the metric system for length, 1 meter = 1000 millimeters.

Independent Practice

In Exercises 7–10, write the number given by the expanded notation.

7. $6 \times 100 + 4 \times 10$

8. $5 \times 10,000 + 3 \times 100 + 7 \times 1$

9. $4 \times 10,000 + 4 \times 1000 + 4 \times 10$

10. $2 \times 1,000,000 + 3 \times 10,000 + 1 \times 100$

In Exercises 11–14, complete the statement.

Sample: 2800 = 28 hundreds

11. 5200 = ? hundreds

12. 1010 = ? tens

13. 325,000 = ? thousands

14. 2,400,000 = ? ten thousands

In Exercises 15–18, match the number with the words.

a. Two million, sixteen thousand, five hundred
b. Two hundred ten thousand, six hundred fifty
c. Twenty thousand, one hundred sixty
d. Two hundred one thousand, six hundred fifty

15. 201,650   16. 2,016,500   17. 20,160   18. 210,650

Reasoning In Exercises 19–22, consider all 3-digit numbers that use the digits 3, 5, 6, and 8 no more than once in each number.

19. Which number is largest?

20. Which number is smallest?

21. Which number is closest to 400?

22. Which numbers are between 400 and 700?

23. *Geography* The areas (in square miles) of some provinces in Canada are listed below. Write the provinces in order from smallest to largest area. For each province's area, write the place-value position for the digit 5.

British Columbia	366,158
Manitoba	251,000
New Brunswick	28,354
Nova Scotia	21,425
Quebec	594,860
Saskatchewan	251,700

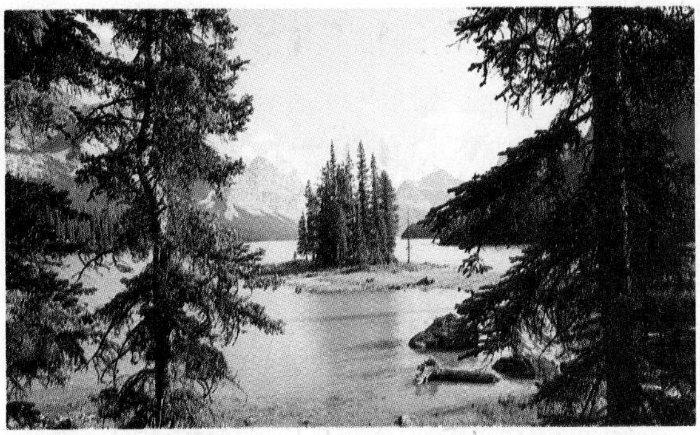

Canada is the second largest country in the world but ranks 32nd in population.

Measuring Systems In Exercises 24 and 25, do the given units form a base-ten system? Explain your reasoning.

24. 1 chain = 22 yards
    1 furlong = 10 chains
    1 mile = 8 furlongs

25. 1 decade = 10 years
    1 century = 10 decades
    1 millenium = 10 centuries

Science In Exercises 26–28, write the number.

26. Neptune has a diameter of thirty thousand, eight hundred miles.
27. Saturn's year has ten thousand, seven hundred fifty-nine days.
28. The distance from Venus to the sun is sixty-seven million, two hundred thirty thousand miles.

Integrated Review

Making Connections within Mathematics

Complete the statement using >, <, or =.

29. 120 hundreds (?) 12,000
30. 500,000 (?) 51 hundred thousands
31. 2,000,000 (?) 199 hundred thousands
32. 2500 tens (?) 25,000

Exploration and Extension

Use the graph at the right to decide whether the statement is reasonable. Explain.

33. The weight of $0.45 in quarters and dimes is 10 grams.
34. A package of 500 paper clips weighs 50 grams.
35. A fruit cup of 15 strawberries and 15 grapes weighs 100 grams.

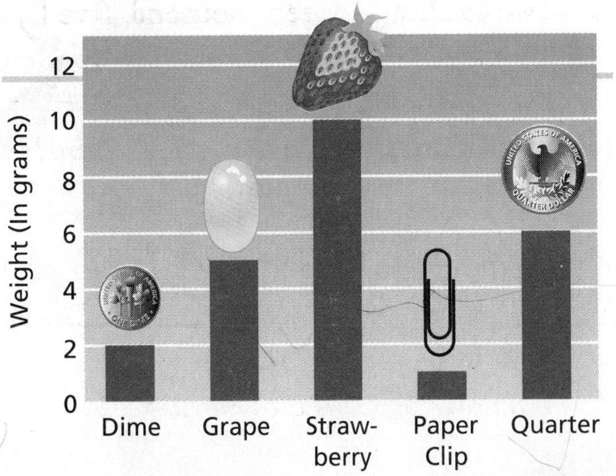

Exploring Whole-Number Addition and Subtraction

What you should learn:

Goal 1 How to use base-ten pieces to add and subtract whole numbers

Goal 2 How to add and subtract whole numbers by regrouping

Why you should learn it:

Using base-ten pieces to add and subtract numbers helps you understand the idea of regrouping.

Base-Ten Pieces

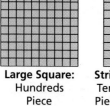

Large Square:	Strip:	Small Square:
Hundreds Piece	Tens Piece	Ones Piece
100	10	1

10 ones = 1 ten
10 tens = 1 hundred
100 ones = 1 hundred

Goal 1 **Using Base-Ten Pieces**

In a base-ten system, addition and subtraction can be modeled with **base-ten pieces.**

Example 1 *Using Base-Ten Pieces*

Use base-ten pieces to add or subtract.

a. $27 + 14$ b. $53 - 28$

Solution

a.

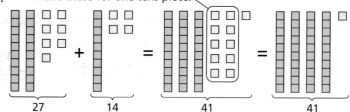

Trade these for one tens piece.

27 14 41 41

b.

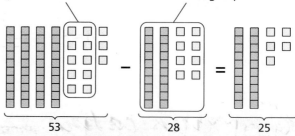

Trade one tens piece for these. Remove these pieces from the first group.

53 28 25

Lesson Investigation

■ **Investigating Addition and Subtraction**

Partner Activity Use base-ten pieces to add or subtract the following. In which cases do you need to trade base-ten pieces? Explain why.

1. $135 + 263$ 2. $255 + 148$
3. $386 - 143$ 4. $324 - 258$

In Example 1, you sometimes needed to trade base-ten pieces to add or subtract.

When you add or subtract by hand, you sometimes use a similar method. This is called **regrouping.**

Example 2	*Regrouping*

Add or subtract. Use regrouping, if necessary.

a. $128 + 241$ **b.** $458 + 154$ **c.** $423 - 36$

Solution

a. For this problem, regrouping is not necessary.

$$\begin{array}{r} 128 \\ +241 \\ \hline 369 \end{array}$$

b. For this problem, regrouping is necessary.

$$\boxed{1 + 5 + 5 = 11} \quad \begin{array}{r} \overset{1\,1}{458} \\ +154 \\ \hline 612 \end{array} \quad \boxed{8 + 4 = 12}$$

c. For this problem, regrouping is necessary.

$$\boxed{11 - 3 = 8} \quad \begin{array}{r} \overset{3\,11\,1}{4\,2\,3} \\ -\ 36 \\ \hline 387 \end{array} \quad \boxed{13 - 6 = 7}$$

Communicating about MATHEMATICS

Cooperative Learning

▶ **Sharing Ideas about the Lesson**

Mental Math Use mental math to add or subtract the numbers. Then compare the mental steps you used with the mental steps others in your group used.

A. $432 - 203$ **B.** $125 + 376$ **C.** $524 - 99$

Which of these is easiest to do with mental math? Why?

EXERCISES

Think and Discuss

▶ CHECK for Understanding

In Exercises 1–3, write the problem that is shown or represented by the base-ten pieces. Then solve.

1. + = ? 2. − = ? 3. − = ?

4. Give examples of two addition problems: one that must be regrouped and one that must not.

5. Give examples of two subtraction problems: one that must be regrouped and one that must not.

Independent Practice

In Exercises 6–8, write the problem that is shown by the base-ten pieces. Then solve.

6. − = ? 7. + = ? 8. − = ?

In Exercises 9–16, solve the problem without using a calculator. Show your work.

9. $135 + 62$ 10. $387 - 123$ 11. $243 + 68$ 12. $125 - 87$

13. $980 - 198$ 14. $764 + 397$ 15. $4324 + 2999$ 16. $8001 - 5667$

Number Sense In Exercises 17–20, find the missing digits.

17.
$$\begin{array}{r} \blacksquare\;4 \\ +\;3\;3\;\blacksquare \\ \hline 5\;3\;3 \end{array}$$

18.
$$\begin{array}{r} 5\;\blacksquare\;\blacksquare \\ -\;2\;4\;6 \\ \hline \blacksquare\;2\;4 \end{array}$$

19.
$$\begin{array}{r} 5\;\blacksquare\;5 \\ +\;\blacksquare\;7\;\blacksquare\;2 \\ \hline 7\;0\;1\;6 \end{array}$$

20.
$$\begin{array}{r} \blacksquare\;2\;\blacksquare\;8 \\ -\;\blacksquare\;8\;\blacksquare \\ \hline 4\;5\;8\;7 \end{array}$$

Algebra and Mental Math In Exercises 21–26, use mental math to solve.

21. $m + 25 = 65$ 22. $80 - s = 29$ 23. $c + 146 = 245$

24. $325 + p = 500$ 25. $1000 - b = 202$ 26. $w - 998 = 4002$

Reasoning In Exercises 27–29, choose two numbers from among 16, 25, 35, 38, 43, and 49 to make the statement true.

27. $\boxed{?} + \boxed{?} = 84$ 28. $\boxed{?} - \boxed{?} > 30$ 29. $\boxed{?} - \boxed{?} = 9$

Data Analysis In Exercises 30–32, use the bar graph at the right. It shows the sales of software (in millions of dollars) for 1993. Decide whether the statement is true or false. Explain. *(Source: Software Publishers Association)*

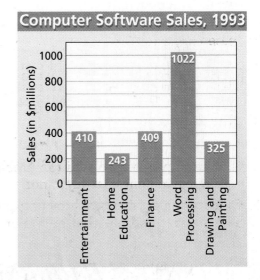

Computer Software Sales, 1993

30. The total software sales is over 2400 million dollars.

31. More is spent on word processing software than on home education, entertainment, and drawing and painting software combined.

32. The difference between the amount spent on finance software and on home education software is 166 million dollars.

Integrated Review

Making Connections within Mathematics

Tell how many digits the answer has. Use estimation.

33. $54 + 39$
34. $127 - 19$
35. $223 + 367$
36. $898 + 236$
37. $1040 - 50$
38. $4456 + 6331$

Exploration and Extension

39. *Probability* Consider the following game.

    Toss a number cube 4 times. Record the results in the boxes marked 1 through 4. You win the game if your total is 60 or more.

    If you played this game many times, do you think you would win more often than you lose or lose more often than you win? Explain.

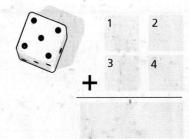

40. *Building Your Chapter Project* Your computer company designs and sells educational computer games. Design a game that uses addition and subtraction. Draw a computer screen of what your game will look like, and write a description of how it works. Think of a name for your game.

Lab 2.2

Mental Math Activities

Materials Needed: calculator, worksheet, pencils

Part A *The Game of Nim*   Play the game of Nim with a partner. Use only one calculator and start with "0" in the display. Take turns adding either 1, 2, or 3 to the number showing in the display. The first player with a sum of 21 or more loses. For instance, in the game shown below, Player 2 loses the game. Play the game several times. Then answer the questions.

1. Does the person who begins always win?

2. Is there a winning strategy? If so, describe it.

Move	1	2	3	4	5	6	7	8
Player 1	3		+2=		+3=		+3=	
Player 2		+3=		+3=		+3=		+1=

| 3 | 6 | 8 | 11 | 14 | 17 | 20 | 21 |

Part B *Addition and Subtraction Game*   You and your partner each need a calculator. Your teacher will give you a copy of the game board shown below. Each player tries to connect his or her sides of the game board with X's or O's. To mark a number on the game board (with an X or an O), players take turns choosing and adding or subtracting the circled numbers. For instance, Player X could win by marking X's on the numbers 77, 84, 64, 162, and 98.

3. Can every number on the board be marked? Use mental math to make your decisions.

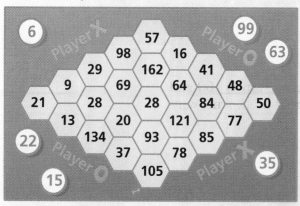

- Players can start on either of their sides.

- X and O cannot be on the same number.

- Numbers can be used more than once. For example, 77 = 6 + 6 + 15 + 15 + 35.

Part C *Addition and Subtraction Game*   Two people have each taken two turns in the game.

4. Which circled numbers did Player X use?

5. Which circled numbers did Player O use?

6. If Player X started first, who will win the game? If Player O started first, who will win the game? Explain.

7. Play the game with your partner at least twice. Take turns starting first. Does the person who starts first always win? Explain.

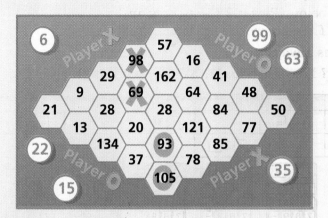

On Your Own

Critical Thinking

8. A friend uses a calculator to add 83 and 36 and gets 146. How do you know that the answer is wrong? What do you think your friend did wrong?

9. Explain how you can use the sums 30 + 80 = 110 and 40 + 90 = 130 to estimate the sum of 34 and 83 mentally.

10. Find five different numbers whose sum is 100 and have the given property. If it is not possible, explain why.

    a. All five numbers are even.

    b. All five numbers are odd.

    c. All five numbers have two digits.

    d. One of the numbers is 90.

11. Find five different 2-digit numbers whose sum is 100 and have the given property. If it is not possible, explain why.

    a. Each number is less than 20.

    b. Four of the five numbers are odd.

    c. One of the numbers is greater than 80.

Mixed REVIEW

Use mental math to solve.

1. 42×100 2. 500×10 3. 5×100 4. 25×1000

5. $660 \div 10$ 6. $7200 \div 100$ 7. $800 \div 100$ 8. $7500 \div 10$

Find all the numbers from 1 to 50 that have the given property.

9. Multiples of 4   10. 7 is a factor.   11. Prime   12. Odd *and* composite

Which unit would you use to measure the object: milligrams, grams, or kilograms?

13. Apple   14. Person   15. Sheet of paper

16. Car   17. Feather   18. Pencil

19. Sketch two lines that are parallel.   20. Sketch two lines that are not parallel.

Milestones   EARLY COMPUTERS

1750   1800   1850   1900   1950   2000

Babbage born, 1792   Ada Byron born, 1815   William Burroughs' adding machine, 1890's   BASIC programming language, 1960's   Atari launches video game *Pong*, 1972

In 1822, an English mathematician, Charles Babbage recognized that many mathematical computations were algorithmic; that is, repetitious. So he proposed to invent a machine that would perform repeating tasks.

One of the few people who understood and helped Babbage was Augusta Ada Byron, the Countess of Lovelace, daughter of the poet Lord Byron. In describing the steps the machine would take, she wrote that the machine "can do whatever we know how to order it to perform." She is credited with being the first computer programmer and has the computer language ADA named after her.

- *Try to write a program that would instruct a computer to subtract any three-digit number from 1000.*

Ada Lovelace predicted computer music a whole century before it was actually produced.

Using a Calculator

When you add long lists of numbers, it is easy to make a mistake. Most people who add long lists of numbers in their job use a calculator.

Try It Yourself

Try adding this list by hand. Do you get the result shown in the Example?

40
32
40
44
42
24
20
48
40
32
44
42
36
+ 40

Example   *Adding a Long List of Numbers*

You do the accounting for a small business that has 14 employees. The following list shows the number of hours that the employees worked during the week. Find the total number of hours.

40, 32, 40, 44, 42, 24, 20, 48, 40, 32, 44, 42, 36, 40

Solution   One way to find the total is to use a calculator.

40 ⊞ 32 ⊞ 40 ⊞ 44 ⊞ 42 ⊞ 24 ⊞ 20 ⊞
48 ⊞ 40 ⊞ 32 ⊞ 44 ⊞ 42 ⊞ 36 ⊞ 40 🟰

After entering these keystrokes, your calculator should display 524. The total number of hours worked by the 14 employees is 524. ■

You can check the reasonableness of this answer by *estimating* the total. Because each of the 14 employees worked about 40 hours, the total would be about 14×40 or 560 hours. So, a total of 524 hours is reasonable.

Exercises

In Exercises 1–6, use a calculator to add the numbers.

1. $32 + 56 + 48 + 78 + 26 + 68$
2. $124 + 145 + 150 + 136 + 243 + 208$
3. $37 + 35 + 69 + 89 + 14 + 72$
4. $346 + 298 + 435 + 789 + 356 + 456$
5. $256 + 146 + 128 + 340 + 204 + 206$
6. $1567 + 1341 + 2078 + 1450 + 1254$

7. *Number Sense*   Without adding the numbers, how do you know that each total in Exercises 1–6 must be an even number?

8. *Estimation*   Without adding the numbers, how do you know that the totals in Exercises 1 and 3 are less than 600?

9. *Business and Industry*   Your company ships 18 boxes whose weights (in pounds) are shown below. What is their total weight?

13, 18, 24, 19, 32, 25, 26, 31, 45, 14, 18, 25, 36, 26, 27, 40, 25, 30

2.3

Connections to Geometry: Exploring Whole-Number Multiplication

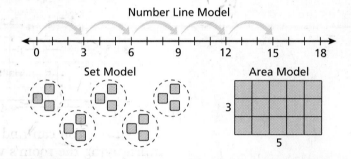

What you should learn:

Goal 1 How to use diagrams to represent whole-number multiplication

Goal 2 How to use multiplication to solve real-life problems

Why you should learn it:

Multiplication can help you find the amount of materials you need for a project. An example is finding the number of tiles needed to cover a floor.

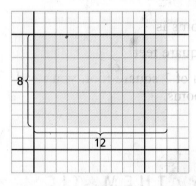

Goal 1 Using Multiplication Models

Diagrams can help you "see" the **product** of two whole numbers. Here are three ways to show $5 \times 3 = 15$.

Number Line Model

Set Model   **Area Model**

Example 1 *Drawing an Area Model*

Use base-ten grid paper to create an area model for 8×12.

Solution Draw a rectangle that is 8 units wide and 12 units long. To find the area, think of the rectangle as having two parts. One part is 8-by-10 and has an area of 80. The other part is 8-by-2 and has an area of 16.

$8 \times 10 = 80$ *Mental math*

$8 \times 2 = 16$ *Mental math*

The total area of the two parts is 96.

$80 + 16 = 96$ *Add 80 and 16.*

Lesson Investigation

■ **Investigating Area Models**

Group Activity Use base-ten grid paper to draw area models for the multiplication problems. Find the area of each model and use the result to find the product. Explain your models to another group.

a. 7×14 **b.** 6×28 **c.** 13×24

Connections
Geometry

Thin sheets of clay are baked in kilns to make tiles. To give the tiles a smooth surface, salt is added to the kiln or they are washed with chemicals.

Example 2 *Finding Areas*

You work in a store that sells floor tiles. You are asked to find the number of 1-foot by 1-foot tiles that are needed to cover the rooms shown below. In the diagram, each square is 1 foot by 1 foot. Explain how you would solve this problem.

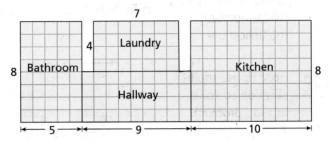

Solution You can find the area of each room by multiplying the room's width by its length.

$5 \times 8 = 40$ *Area of bathroom*

$4 \times 7 = 28$ *Area of laundry room*

$4 \times 9 = 36$ *Area of hallway*

$8 \times 10 = 80$ *Area of kitchen*

The total area of the four rooms is

$40 + 28 + 36 + 80 = 184$ square feet.

Because each tile has an area of 1 square foot, you need 184 tiles to cover the four rooms. ■

Communicating about MATHEMATICS

Cooperative Learning

Sharing Ideas about the Lesson

Extending the Example In Example 2, instead of using 1-foot by 1-foot tiles, suppose you are using smaller tiles. How many of each size tile do you need?

A. 6-inch by 6-inch tiles   **B.** 3-inch by 3-inch tiles

Do you need twice as many 3-inch by 3-inch tiles as 6-inch by 6-inch tiles? Explain your reasoning.

EXERCISES

Think and Discuss

▶ CHECK for Understanding

In Exercises 1 and 2, write the multiplication problem that is shown by the area model.

1.
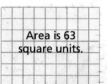
Area is 63
square units.

2.
Area is 44
square units.

3. Use base-ten grid paper to draw a model for 7×11. Find the area.

4. *Geography* Use the scale drawing at the right to approximate the area of Wyoming.

5. Cut a square piece of paper. Fold it in half to make a rectangle. Then fold the rectangle in half to make a square. Unfold the paper. Write a multiplication problem that can be modeled by the paper.

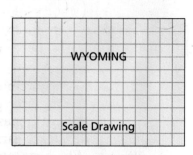
WYOMING

Scale Drawing

The side of each small square is 25 miles.

Independent Practice

In Exercises 6–10, write the problem and its answer that is shown or represented by the model.

6.
Area is 50
square units.

7.
Area is 48
square units.

8.
Area is 21
square units.

9.

10.
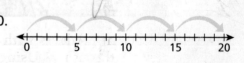

Geometry In Exercises 11–14, use grid paper to sketch the area model for the problem. What is the area?

11. 4×12 12. 11×11 13. 4×13 14. 15×3

In Exercises 15–18, draw the indicated model for the problem.

15. Set Model; 3×9

16. Set Model; 9×3

17. Number Line Model; 7×2

18. Number Line Model; 2×7

Algebra   In Exercises 19–22, use mental math to solve.

19. $3 \cdot s = 33$
20. $5 \cdot d = 25$
21. $4 \cdot n = 16$
22. $100 \cdot m = 3500$

Number Sense   In Exercises 23–26, is the product even or odd?
Give examples to support your answer.

23. even × even
24. even × odd
25. odd × even
26. odd × odd

In Exercises 27 and 28, solve the equations. Describe a pattern for *n*.

27. $2 \times 22 = n$, $4 \times 22 = n$, $8 \times 22 = n$

28. $n \times 6 = 12$, $n \times 6 = 24$, $n \times 6 = 48$

29. *Drawing a Diagram*   You are raking
leaves that cover a rectangular part of
your yard that is 8 feet by 9 feet. Can
you complete the job in an hour if it
takes you 10 minutes to rake an area
that is 12 sq ft? Draw a diagram.

30. *Video Games*   A Super Nintendo
Entertainment System costs $200, and
you want to buy three games that cost
$50 each. A Sega Genesis costs $150,
and you want three games that cost
$60 each. Which system with 3 games
costs less? *(Source: Zillions: Consumer
Reports for Kids)*

The job of leaves is to make food for trees.

Integrated Review

Making Connections within Mathematics

Complete the statement.

31. 3 quarters = ⒯ nickels
32. 15 dimes = ⒯ quarters
33. 32 dimes = ⒯ nickels
34. 30 nickels = ⒯ quarters
35. $1.70 = ⒯ dimes
36. $0.65 = ⒯ nickels

Exploration and Extension

37. How many different products with 2 factors can be made
using the digits 1 through 7? Using the digits 1 through 9?
(Hint: 2×3 is the same as 3×2.)

38. *Building Your Chapter Project*   A computer store
wants to buy the following software from your
company.

| 12 games at $45 each | 6 games at $55 each |
| 8 games at $50 each | 10 games at $60 each |

Design a company bill that you can use to charge the store.
Then write the order and its total on the bill.

Lab 2.4
Using Division Models

Materials Needed: paper, pencils, counters

Part A *A Set Model for Division* Consider the following question.

> *A class of 24 students is divided into groups of 4 to work on a project. Each group needs a computer. How many computers does the class need?*

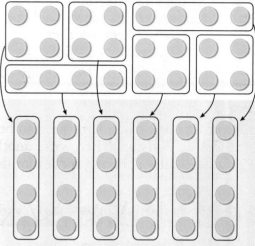

Start with 24 counters.

Put the counters into groups of 4.

One way to answer this question is to use a set model. Start with 24 counters. Then take out sets of 4 counters until all 24 counters have been used. You get 6 sets of 4 counters, so there are 6 groups. Therefore, the class needs 6 computers.

The question can also be answered with division.

$$24 \div 4 = 6$$

A Sharing Model for Division Consider the following question.

> *A class of 30 students is divided into 6 teams. Each team has the same number of students. How many students are on each team?*

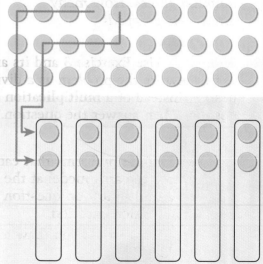

Start with 30 counters.

Deal the counters, one at a time, into 6 groups.

One way to answer this question is to use a sharing model. Start with 30 counters. Then deal the counters, one at a time, into 6 groups. Each of the 6 groups will end up with 5 counters, so there are 5 students on each team.

The question can also be answered with division.

$$30 \div 6 = 5$$

Part B *Drawing Models*

1. Draw a model that answers each question. Did you use a set model or a sharing model? Explain your choice. Write a division sentence for the question.

   a. *A computer game has 28 movable square pieces. The pieces are grouped inside circles that contain 4 pieces each. How many groups are there?*

   b. *Your class receives several boxes that contain a total of 42 computer programs. Each box contains 6 programs. How many boxes are there?*

   c. *Your class receives a shipment of 36 calculators that are packed in 9 boxes. How many calculators are in each box?*

Part C *Writing in Real Life*

2. Write a real-life problem that can be modeled with a set model for division. Then write another problem that can be modeled with a sharing model for division.

On Your Own

Critical Thinking

3. *Multiplication Model* Draw an area model to help you answer the question.

   A software company ships 8 boxes of computer games to your store. Each box contains 12 computer games. How many games were shipped?

4. *Reasoning* Use Exercise 3 and its answer to rewrite the problem as a division question instead of a multiplication question. Then answer the question.

5. Write two real-life problems that can be modeled with the area model at the right. Make one a multiplication question and the other a division question.

6. *Reasoning* How would you draw a model for 32 ÷ 5?

2.4 Exploring Whole-Number Division

What you should learn:

Goal 1
How to write answers to division problems that have remainders

Goal 2
How to use division to solve real-life problems

Why you should learn it:

Division can help you when cooking. An example is dividing the amounts to make one fourth of a recipe.

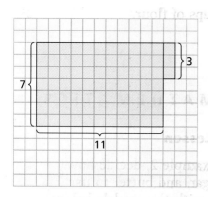

In this area model, 80 can be modeled as a 7-by-11 rectangle with a 1-by-3 rectangle. The 1-by-3 rectangle represents the remainder.

Goal 1 Quotients with Remainders

Each of the numbers in a division problem has a name.

Dividend
Quotient
$$24 \div 3 = 8$$
Divisor

3 | Area is 24 square units. | 8

Here, 3 **divides evenly** into 24 because the quotient is a whole number. Quotients that are not whole numbers can be written in two ways:

With a Remainder   *With a Fraction*
$$26 \div 3 = 8 \text{ R2}$$ $$26 \div 3 = 8\frac{2}{3}$$

Example 1 *Dividing Whole Numbers*

Solve $80 \div 7$ and write the quotient in two ways.

Solution Divide 7 into 80:

$$\begin{array}{r} 11 \\ 7\overline{)80} \\ 7 \\ \hline 10 \\ 7 \\ \hline 3 \end{array}$$

Remainder

The result can be written in two ways:

$$80 \div 7 = 11 \text{ R3} \quad \textit{With a remainder}$$

$$80 \div 7 = 11\frac{3}{7} \quad \textit{With a fraction}$$

■

Lesson Investigation

■ Investigating Area Models for Division
Use grid paper to draw an area model for each problem. Then write each quotient in two ways.

a. $96 \div 5$ **b.** $144 \div 7$ **c.** $82 \div 4$ **d.** $38 \div 5$

| Example **2** | *Writing Quotients with Fractions* |

You get a recipe for peanut cookies from a restaurant. The recipe makes 16 dozen cookies. To make 4 dozen cookies, you want to divide each measure by 4. How much flour should you use?

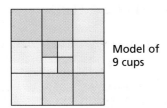

Model of
9 cups

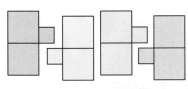

Models of $2\frac{1}{4}$ cups each

This model shows that when 9 is divided into 4 equal parts, each part is $2\frac{1}{4}$.

3 cups butter	1 tablespoon baking soda	1 teaspoon salt
5 cups sugar	1 tablespoon baking powder	3 cups rolled oats
7 eggs	7 cups crushed peanuts	
9 cups flour	1 tablespoon vanilla	

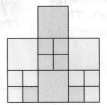

Solution   Divide 9 by 4, as follows.

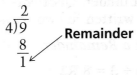

Remainder

Writing the quotient as 2 R1 doesn't tell you how much flour to use. But writing the quotient with a fraction

$2\frac{1}{4}$ *Quotient written with a fraction*

tells you that you need $2\frac{1}{4}$ cups of flour.   ■

Communicating about MATHEMATICS

▶ **Sharing Ideas about the Lesson**

Extending the Example In Example 2, decide how much crushed peanuts, sugar, and butter to use. Then match your answers with the models below.

A.   **B.**   **C.**

EXERCISES

Think and Discuss

▶ CHECK for Understanding

In Exercises 1–3, use the division problem 27 ÷ 4.

1. Name the dividend and the divisor in the problem.
2. Sketch an area model to represent the problem.
3. Find the quotient. Write your answer in two ways.

In Exercises 4–6, match the division problem with its area model.
Then write the quotient in two ways.

a.   b.   c.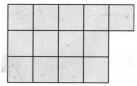

4. 13 ÷ 3   5. 13 ÷ 6   6. 19 ÷ 6

Independent Practice

In Exercises 7 and 8, write a division problem that represents the
statements. Then divide to solve the problem.

7. You have 52 playing cards. You separate them into 4 piles. Each pile has
the same number of cards. How
many cards are in each pile?

8. You and some friends have a bag of
60 golf tees. Each person in the group
takes 15 golf tees. How many people
are in the group?

In Exercises 9–16, divide. Then write the quotient in two ways.

9. 39 ÷ 4   10. 77 ÷ 9   11. 43 ÷ 3   12. 76 ÷ 6
13. 119 ÷ 5   14. 128 ÷ 3   15. 245 ÷ 4   16. 385 ÷ 14

In Exercises 17 and 18, write the division problem shown
by the model.

17. 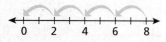   18.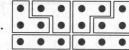

In Exercises 19–21, sketch an area model for the problem.
Then find the quotient.

19. 14 ÷ 5   20. 21 ÷ 4   21. 30 ÷ 8

22. *Number Sense* Solve $140 \div 10$. Then solve $280 \div 10$. What happens to the quotient if you double the dividend? Explain.

23. *Error Analysis* Your friend is using a calculator to solve $720 \div 45$. The result on the display is 0.0625. What did your friend do wrong? What should the display be?

24. *Calculator Patterns* Find the quotients and describe any patterns that you see. Write the next 2 problems.

$9 \div 9 = \boxed{?}$, $\qquad 108 \div 9 = \boxed{?}$,

$1107 \div 9 = \boxed{?}$, $\qquad 11{,}106 \div 9 = \boxed{?}$ . . .

25. *In-Line Skating* You are skating on a path. In two hours, you travel a total distance of 5 miles. Find your average speed by solving the following division problem.

$(5 \text{ miles}) \div (2 \text{ hours}) = \boxed{?}$ miles per hour

There are over 12.6 million in-line skaters in the United States.

Integrated Review $\qquad$ *Making Connections within Mathematics*

Geometry **Find the length of the side labeled *x*.**

26. The area is 78 square units.

13

x

27. The area is 81 square units.

x

x

28. The perimeter is 36 units.

x

x

Exploration and Extension

Riddles **Solve the riddle.**

29. I am a 2-digit number. When I am divided by 3, the quotient is 22 more than the quotient when I am divided by 9.

30. I am a 3-digit number. When I am divided by 24, the quotient is 9 more than the quotient when I am divided by 36.

31. *Building Your Chapter Project* Your company is developing a program that helps teach division to elementary students. One of the screens of the program is shown. It shows how 16 can be divided into 4 groups of 4. Design 2 other screens that you can include in the program.

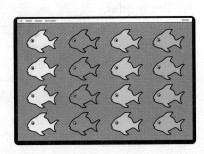

Take this test as you would take a test in class. The answers to the exercises are given in the back of the book.

In Exercises 1–4, write the number given by the expanded notation. **(2.1)**

1. $7 \times 100 + 8 \times 10$

2. $4 \times 10,000 + 1 \times 1000 + 3 \times 10 + 5 \times 1$

3. $6 \times 1000 + 2 \times 100 + 9 \times 1$

4. $2 \times 1,000,000 + 8 \times 10,000 + 6 \times 10$

In Exercises 5–7, write the number in words. **(2.1)**

5. 4054   6. 30,870   7. 652,001

In Exercises 8 and 9, write the problem that is shown by the model. Then solve. **(2.2)**

8.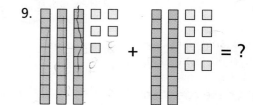

9.

In Exercises 10–12, make a sketch of the problem. **(2.3, 2.4)**

10. Area Model
9×7

11. Number Line Model
3×6

12. Set Model
$40 \div 5$

Algebra In Exercises 13–18, use mental math to solve. **(2.2, 2.3, 2.4)**

13. $x + 42 = 62$

14. $50 - y = 14$

15. $p - 47 = 38$

16. $5 \cdot a = 35$

17. $b \cdot 25 = 100$

18. $q \div 5 = 10$

Estimation The bar graph at the right compares the numbers of different types of radio stations in the United States in 1991 and 1992. *(Source: Radio Information Center)* **(2.2)**

19. About how many more country radio stations were there in 1992 than in 1991?

20. About how many more golden oldies stations were there in 1992 than in 1991?

21. About how many fewer contemporary stations were there in 1992 than in 1991?

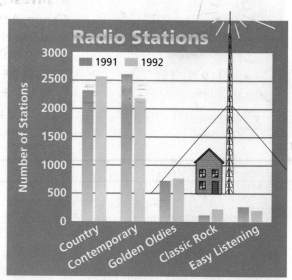

Radio Stations

2.5

Order of Operations

What you should learn:

Goal 1 How to evaluate an expression

Goal 2 How to use order of operations

Why you should learn it:

When more than one operation is used in an expression, it is important to know the order in which the operations must be performed.

Study Tip

One of your goals as you study this book is to learn to read and write about numbers. You can avoid confusion when communicating mathematical ideas by using an established **order of operations.**

Goal 1 Evaluating an Expression

A **numerical expression** is a collection of numbers that can be linked by addition, subtraction, multiplication, and division. Finding the value of the expression is **evaluating** the expression.

Example 1 *Evaluating Expressions*

a. $13 - 8$ *The value of $13 - 8$ is 5.*
b. 4×12 *The value of 4×12 is 48.*
c. $9 \div 2$ *The value of $9 \div 2$ is $4\frac{1}{2}$.*   ■

Each expression in Example 1 has only one operation. When an expression has two or more operations, its value can depend on the order in which you do the operations.

Lesson Investigation

■ **Investigating Order of Operations**

Group Activity Evaluate each expression. Does the value of the expression depend on the order in which you do the operations? Discuss which order you think gives the correct value.

1. $2 \times 4 + 5$ 2. $3 + 4 \times 6$
3. $16 \div 4 \times 2$ 4. $4 \times 12 \div 3$
5. $12 + 8 - 5$ 6. $23 - 5 + 8$
7. $2 \times 6 - 2 \times 2$ 8. $20 - (4 \times 3) + 2$

Grouping symbols, such as parentheses, help you decide in which order to do the operations. Here is an example.

$$3 \times (2 + 4) = 3 \times 6 = 18$$

Using Order of Operations

Order of Operations

1. First do operations within grouping symbols.
2. Then multiply and divide from left to right.
3. Finally add and subtract from left to right.

Example 2 *Using Order of Operations*

a. $20 - 4 \times 3 = 20 - 12$ *Multiply:* 4×3

$\qquad\qquad\quad = 8$ *Subtract:* $20 - 12$

b. $48 \div (6 \div 2) = 48 \div 3$ *Divide:* $6 \div 2$

$\qquad\qquad\qquad = 16$ *Divide:* $48 \div 3$

c. $48 \div 6 \div 2 = 8 \div 2$ *Divide:* $48 \div 6$

$\qquad\qquad\quad = 4$ *Divide:* $8 \div 2$ ■

Study Tip

In Example 3, if your calculator displays 14 when you enter

6 ⊞ 24 ⊡ 3 ⊟ ,

then it uses the established order of operations. If it displays the incorrect answer of 10, then it uses a simple left-to-right order.

Example 3 *Using a Calculator*

Use a calculator to evaluate $6 + 24 \div 3$.

Solution   The value of this expression is $6 + 8$ or 14. Entering the keystrokes

6 ⊞ 24 ⊡ 3 ⊟

on a calculator may or may not give the correct value. What value does your calculator display?   ■

Communicating about MATHEMATICS

▷ **Sharing Ideas about the Lesson**

Grouping Symbols Evaluate the expression. Then rewrite the expression with parentheses in two ways: (1) one way that does not change the value, and (2) one way that does change the value.

A. $32 - 5 + 6$ **B.** $32 - 5 \times 6$

EXERCISES

Think and Discuss

▶ CHECK for Understanding

In Exercises 1–4, match the expression with its value.

a. 53   b. 23   c. 16   d. 25

1. $6 \times 3 + 10 - 5$ 2. $6 \div 3 \times 10 + 5$ 3. $6 - 3 + 10 \times 5$ 4. $6 \times 3 - 10 \div 5$

5. Add parentheses to the statement to make it true.

   $5 \times 9 - 3 + 12 \div 6 = 32$

6. Put an operation and a number in each empty box to make the next number correct. There is more than one correct answer.

12								2	d.	5	e.	45	f.
÷3	4	×6	24	a.	3	b.	14	c.					15

Independent Practice

In Exercises 7–15, evaluate the expression.

7. $11 + 5 \times 2$ 8. $26 - 8 \times 3$ 9. $20 - (4 + 8)$

10. $4 \times 7 \times 2$ 11. $32 \div (4 \times 2)$ 12. $54 \div 9 \div 2$

13. $8 + 5 \times (4 \div 2)$ 14. $12 \times 3 - 6 \times 3$ 15. $72 \div 9 + 56 \div 7$

In Exercises 16–21, use a calculator to evaluate the expression.

16. $44 + 66 \div 11$ 17. $12 \times 13 - 12$ 18. $75 \div 5 \div 5$

19. $128 \div 8 \times 5 + 20$ 20. $23 \times 5 - 20 \times 5$ 21. $144 \div 16 - 54 \div 6$

Writing Expressions   In Exercises 22–24, write the expression that is described. Use parentheses if necessary. Then evaluate.

22. Subtract 8 from 17, then multiply the difference by 5.

23. Add 4 to the product of 8 and 4.

24. Subtract the product of 4 and 5 from 25.

In Exercises 25–28, use the numbers 2, 4, 5, 7, and 9 to make the statement true.

25. $\boxed{?} \times \boxed{?} - \boxed{?} = 26$ 26. $\boxed{?} + \boxed{?} \times \boxed{?} = 25$

27. $\boxed{?} \times \boxed{?} \div \boxed{?} = 18$ 28. $\boxed{?} + \boxed{?} \div \boxed{?} = 11$

In Exercises 29–31, complete the statement. Use $+$, $-$, $\times$, or $\div$.

29. $9\ \boxed{?}\ 7\ \boxed{?}\ 2\ \boxed{?}\ 6 = 17$ 30. $6\ \boxed{?}\ 2\ \boxed{?}\ 6\ \boxed{?}\ 4 = 14$ 31. $5\ \boxed{?}\ 3\ \boxed{?}\ 8\ \boxed{?}\ 2 = 19$

Theme Parks At Busch Gardens in Williamsburg, Virginia, a 3-day pass costs $43. The hotel costs $40 per person per night. You and a friend are going to Busch Gardens for 3 days and 2 nights.

32. Write an expression that represents how much you and your friend will pay for 3-day passes and the hotel.

33. You and your friend take $400 on your trip. Write an expression that represents the amount you have left after paying for the 3-day passes and the hotel.

34. *Math Maze* Find the correct path through the maze.

Busch Gardens theme park has sections that show the cultures of England, France, Germany, and Italy.

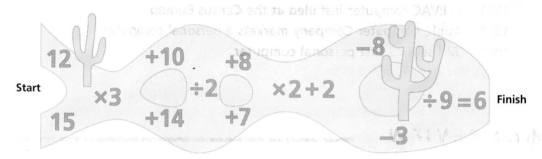

Integrated Review

Making Connections within Mathematics

Reading a Table The table at the right shows the number of runs scored by the top 7 Major League Baseball players as of 1994. *(Source: Major League Baseball)*

35. Find the difference between the runs scored by Ty Cobb and Stan Musial.

36. Find the sum of the runs scored by Babe Ruth and Hank Aaron.

37. Which two players had a difference in runs of about 100?

38. Which two players had a difference in runs of about 300?

Player	Career Runs
Ty Cobb	2245
Babe Ruth	2174
Hank Aaron	2174
Pete Rose	2165
Willie Mays	2062
Stan Musial	1949
Lou Gehrig	1888

39. *Group Activity*   Write the numbers 2 through 10 using exactly four 4's, any of the symbols $+$, $-$, $\times$, and $\div$, and parentheses. The number 1 is done for you. Compare your results with other groups.

   Sample: $4 - 4 + 4 \div 4 = 1$

40. *Building Your Chapter Project*   Your company is designing a poster that shows part of the history of computers. Use the list below to make a time line for the poster. Illustrate the time line with appropriate drawings or photographs. Then use an encyclopedia, a book, or a magazine to add two events to the time line.

1642   Pascal invents the first mechanical calculator.

1801   Jacquard uses punched cards to automate a weaving loom.

1842   Lovelace writes first computer program.

1888   Hollerith uses punched card system for adding U.S. Census results.

1944   Aiken builds the first digital computer, Mark I.

1951   UNIVAC computer installed at the Census Bureau.

1977   Apple Computer Company markets a personal computer.

1981   IBM sells its first personal computer.

Mixed REVIEW

You are given the dimensions of a rectangle. Find its perimeter and area. **(1.2)**

   1. 6 in. by 11 in.   **2.** 11 cm by 4 cm   **3.** 7 ft by 7 ft   **4.** 4 m by 10 m

Use mental math to solve the equation. Explain your mental steps. **(2.2, 2.3, 2.4)**

   5. $s + 119 = 229$ **6.** $m + 189 = 500$ **7.** $110 - d = 40$ **8.** $t - 71 = 69$
   9. $5 \cdot s = 125$ **10.** $116 \times p = 232$ **11.** $500 \div k = 10$ **12.** $121 \div a = 11$

Round the number to the nearest indicated place.

13. 74 (tens)   **14.** 129 (hundreds)   **15.** 1107 (tens)
16. 1877 (hundreds)   **17.** 2499 (thousands)   **18.** 2990 (thousands)

Describe the pattern. Then write the next three numbers. **(1.1)**

19. 3, 11, 19, [?], [?], [?]   **20.** 1, 4, 9, 16, [?], [?], [?]

2.6 Connections to Algebra: The Distributive Property

What you should learn:

Goal 1 How to use the Distributive Property

Goal 2 How to evaluate variable expressions

Why you should learn it:

The Distributive Property can help you use mental math to evaluate expressions.

Goal 1 ## The Distributive Property

You already know two symbols for multiplication, "**·**" and "**×**." Multiplication can also be symbolized by parentheses. Here are some examples.

$$5(8) = 40 \qquad (5)8 = 40 \qquad (5)(8) = 40$$

Example 1 *Finding the Area of a Room*

The hallway below is 8 feet wide and 37 feet long. Explain how to use mental math to find the area of the hallway.

8 ft

37 ft

Study Tip

In English, the word "distribute" means to give something to everyone in a group. In mathematics, its meaning is similar. For instance, in the equation

$$8(30 + 7) = 8 \times 30 + 8 \times 7$$

the 8 is "given" to the 30 and to the 7.

Solution One way is to think of the length as $30 + 7$. Then, instead of multiplying 8 by 37, you can multiply 8 by 30 and 8 by 7 and add the results.

$$8 \times 37 = 8(30 + 7) \qquad \textit{Rewrite 37 as 30 + 7.}$$
$$= 8 \times 30 + 8 \times 7 \qquad \textit{See area model below.}$$
$$= 240 + 56 \qquad \textit{Use mental math.}$$
$$= 296 \qquad \textit{Use mental math.}$$

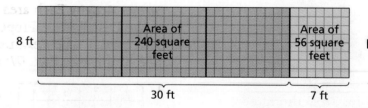

8 ft | Area of 240 square feet | Area of 56 square feet

30 ft   7 ft

The Distributive Property

Let a, b and c be numbers. $a(b + c) = a \times b + a \times c$
Example: $8(30 + 7) = 8 \times 30 + 8 \times 7$

In algebra, a letter that can be replaced by any number is a **variable**. A **variable expression** is an expression that has one or more letters. Replacing or substituting numbers for the variables is **evaluating** the expression.

Example 2 *Evaluating an Expression*

Find the value of each expression when $n = 3$.

a. $7(2 + n)$ b. $7 \times 2 + 7 \times n$

What can you conclude?

Solution

a. $7(2 + n) = 7(2 + 3)$ *Substitute 3 for n.*

         $= 7(5)$ *Add 2 and 3.*

         $= 35$ *Multiply 7 and 5.*

b. $7 \times 2 + 7 \times n = 7 \times 2 + 7 \times 3$ *Substitute 3 for n.*

              $= 14 + 21$ *Multiply.*

              $= 35$ *Add 14 and 21.*

Each expression has the same value. This is an example of the Distributive Property: $7(2 + n) = 7 \times 2 + 7 \times n$. ∎

In each expression, n can be replaced by any number. What is its value when $n = 8$? When $n = 0$?

Your class of 30 students is being treated to a movie. How much will it cost to buy a ticket ($5.00), popcorn ($2.00), and a drink ($1.50) for each person? Does your solution use the Distributive Property?

Communicating about MATHEMATICS

Cooperative Learning

▷ **Sharing Ideas about the Lesson**

Partner Activity Each area model shows an example of the Distributive Property. Write an equation for each model. Then evaluate the expression on each side of the equation. What can you conclude?

A.

B.

EXERCISES

Guided Practice

Think and Discuss

▶ **CHECK for Understanding**

1. *Communicating* Why is the Order of Operations important when using the Distributive Property? Give examples.

2. *Error Analysis* Find and correct the error.
   $$5(6 + 5) = 30 + 5$$
   $$= 35$$
   (crossed out)

3. Evaluate $7(10 + 8)$ in two ways. Which way do you prefer?

4. *Area Model* Write an equation for the area model at the right. Then evaluate the numerical expression on each side of the equation. Explain how the results are related to the Distributive Property.

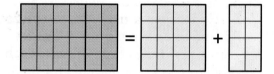

Independent Practice

In Exercises 5–12, evaluate the expression in two ways.

5. $3(4 + 7)$ 6. $2(5 + 9)$ 7. $6(8 + 1)$ 8. $9(6 + 3)$

9. $4(25 + 5)$ 10. $7(10 + 11)$ 11. $2(15 + 50)$ 12. $8(40 + 1)$

In Exercises 13–16, match the expression with an equivalent expression. Then evaluate both expressions when $n = 4$. What can you conclude?

a. $6 \times 5 + 6 \times n$ b. $5 \times n + 5 \times 6$ c. $3 \times 8 + 3 \times n$ d. $8 \times n + 8 \times 3$

13. $3(8 + n)$ 14. $5(n + 6)$ 15. $8(n + 3)$ 16. $6(5 + n)$

In Exercises 17 and 18, write an equation for the area model.

17.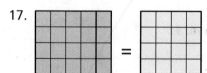

18.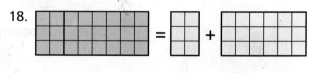

Mental Math In Exercises 19–22, use mental math to evaluate.

19. 4×36 20. 3×95 21. 7×53 22. 9×28

Mental Math In Exercises 23–26, solve. Explain the strategy you used.

23. $3(n + 6) = 30$ 24. $7(5 + x) = 63$ 25. $8(7 + y) = 88$ 26. $4(a + 4) = 28$

27. For your computer company, you rent an office that is 60 feet by 72 feet. Explain how you can use mental math with the Distributive Property to find the area of the office.

28. Your class is selling "made to order" computer-generated cards and posters. You need to raise at least $700 for a class picnic. It costs $115 for materials. Your class sells 112 posters and 220 cards, each for $2.25. How much money was raised? Did your class raise the $700?

29. Your class of 75 students and 5 teachers takes a field trip to the zoo. The admission costs are $7.00 for adults and $5.50 for students. Each student feeds the animals for $0.50. For lunch, each person gets a sandwich for $1.50 and a juice for $0.50. How much money did it cost for the entire group to go to the zoo?

The Lincoln Park Zoo in Chicago has the most visitors of any in the United States—over 4 million a year.

Integrated Review
Making Connections within Mathematics

Reasoning Describe the pattern. Write the next 3 numbers.

30. 1, 5, 25, ?, ?, ?

31. 1, 2, 4, 8, ?, ?, ?

Algebra Find the value of the expression when $y = 5$.

32. $y \times 27$ 33. $124 \times y$ 34. $525 \div y$ 35. $86 \div y$

Exploration and Extension

Properties of Algebra Describe the property in your own words.

36. $1 + 2 = 2 + 1$ *Commutative Property of Addition*
37. $1 \cdot 2 = 2 \cdot 1$ *Commutative Property of Multiplication*
38. $(1 + 2) + 3 = 1 + (2 + 3)$ *Associative Property of Addition*
39. $(1 \cdot 2) \cdot 3 = 1 \cdot (2 \cdot 3)$ *Associative Property of Multiplication*

40. *Building Your Chapter Project* Your company has received orders from 3 stores for a new game. Make up numbers for the price of the game and how many each store ordered. Show how the Distributive Property can be used to find the total amount you will receive from the 3 stores.

Lab 2.7

Investigating Different Bases

Materials Needed: paper, pencils, base-five pieces

Part A *Describing Base-Five Pieces* Look at the 3 pieces shown below. With others in your group, answer the questions.

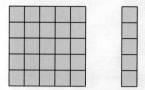

1. Describe the shape of each piece.
2. How many "small" squares are in each piece?
3. What would be good names for these pieces? Why do you think so?

Part B *Using Base-Five Pieces* Form a collection of base-five pieces like that shown below. This collection has 12 pieces. The total number of ones pieces, or small squares, is

$$(3 \times 25) + (2 \times 5) + (7 \times 1) = 75 + 10 + 7$$
$$= 92.$$

Number of 25's Pieces	Number of Fives Pieces	Number of Ones Pieces	Total Number of Pieces
3	2	7	12
?	?	?	?
?	?	?	?
?	?	?	?

4. Use at least one large square. Find other collections of base-five pieces that have a total of 92 ones pieces. Record your results in a table like that shown above.

5. How many different collections can you find that have a total of 73 ones pieces? Record your results in a new table.

6. Look back at your two tables. In each table, circle the collection that contains the fewest pieces.

Part C *Writing Numbers in Base Five* Here are four examples of base-five notations.

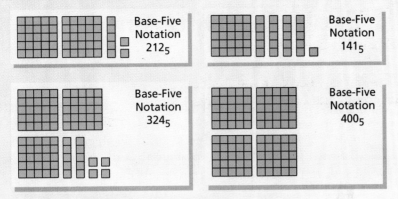

Base-Five Notation 212_5

Base-Five Notation 141_5

Base-Five Notation 324_5

Base-Five Notation 400_5

7. What digits are used in base-five notation?

8. In base-five notation, does the number 274_5 make sense? Explain.

9. Write the base-five notation for 121 ones pieces, 89 ones pieces, and 42 ones pieces.

On Your Own   *Critical Thinking*

10. *Base-Five Digits* Explain why 0, 1, 2, 3, and 4 are the only digits that occur in base-five notation.

11. In base ten, 999 is the largest 3-digit number. What is the largest 3-digit number in base five? How many ones pieces does it represent?

12. You are visiting a planet that has a base-five number system. You are asked to multiply four by four, and you write

    $4 \times 4 = 16.$

    Your guide corrects you and writes

    $4_5 \times 4_5 = 31_5.$

    Why was your answer wrong?

13. Using only pennies, nickels, and quarters, can you show the same amount of money with fewer coins? Explain.

    a.

    b.

2.7

Exploring Different Bases

What you should learn:

Goal 1 How to read and write numbers in base five

Goal 2 How to read and write numbers in other bases

Why you should learn it:

Understanding the way numbers are written in different bases helps you get a better understanding of the base-ten system.

Goal 1 Reading and Writing in Base Five

In the base-ten place-value system, each place value is 10 times larger than the place value to its right. In the base-five place-value system, each place is 5 times larger.

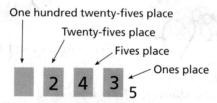

One hundred twenty-fives place

Twenty-fives place

Fives place

Ones place

$$2 \quad 4 \quad 3_5$$

Notice that base-five numbers, such as 243_5, are written with a 5 at the lower right.

Example 1 *Reading Numbers in Base Five*

How many ones pieces are represented by 243_5?

Solution

$$243_5 = (2 \times 25) + (4 \times 5) + (3 \times 1)$$
$$= 50 + 20 + 3$$
$$= 73$$

The base-five number 243_5 has 73 ones pieces. Therefore, 243_5 is 73 in base ten. ∎

Example 2 *Writing Numbers in Base Five*

Write the base-five number for 208 ones pieces.

Solution Begin by showing 208 using the fewest base-five pieces. This is shown at the left. It has

1 125's piece, 3 25's pieces, 1 5's piece, and 3 1's pieces.

It follows that the base-five notation is 1313_5. ∎

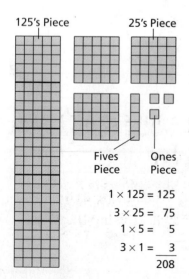

125's Piece   25's Piece

Fives   Ones
Piece   Piece

$$1 \times 125 = 125$$
$$3 \times 25 = 75$$
$$1 \times 5 = 5$$
$$3 \times 1 = \underline{3}$$
$$208$$

Goal 2 | Reading and Writing in Other Bases

Throughout history, most number systems have been base ten. Some systems, however, had other bases. For instance, the ancient Babylonian system had base 60.

Today the most commonly used "different base" is base two. It is the base that is used by computers to store numbers. Computer memories have millions of tiny switches that can be *on* (1) or *off* (0).

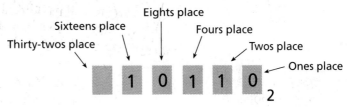

What would base two pieces look like?

Ancient Babylonians were one of the earliest cultures to keep written records. They inscribed their writings on clay tablets such as the one shown above.

Example 3 | Reading Numbers in Base Two

In a computer memory, what number does the following show?

Solution   The figure shows the base-two number 10110_2.

$$10110_2 = (1 \times 16) + (1 \times 4) + (1 \times 2)$$
$$= 16 + 4 + 2$$
$$= 22$$

In base ten, the number is 22. ∎

Communicating about MATHEMATICS

▶ **Sharing Ideas about the Lesson**

Partner Activity: Writing Base-Ten Numbers in Base Two
Write the following numbers in base two. Begin by sketching the number on grid paper using the few base-two pieces.

A. 7   **B.** 31   **C.** 17

EXERCISES

Think and Discuss

▶ **CHECK for Understanding**

1. Which of the models below better shows 176 ones pieces in base five?

   a.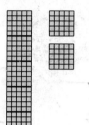

   b.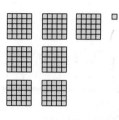

2. Write the base-five number that has 77 ones pieces.
3. Write the number 38 in base five.
4. What base-ten number is represented by 10011_2?
5. In the base-six system, what digits can you use?
6. Sketch a picture of what you think base-four pieces look like.
7. *Error Analysis* Explain why 16123_5 is not a base-five number.

Independent Practice

In Exercises 8–11, make a sketch that shows how to use 25's pieces, fives pieces, and ones pieces to represent the number in base five.

8. 15	9. 43	10. 111	11. 124

Reading Base-Five Numbers In Exercises 12–17, write the number in base ten. (Hint: How many ones pieces would the number be?)

12. 122_5	13. 303_5	14. 444_5
15. 1412_5	16. 2003_5	17. 4444_5

Writing Base-Five Numbers In Exercises 18–23, write the number in base five.

18. 27	19. 75	20. 89
1. 144	22. 525	23. 310

xercises 24–27, match the base-five or base-two number with
se-ten number.

b. 21	c. 24	d. 29
25. 42_5	26. 11101_2	27. 11000_2

Reading Base-Two Numbers In Exercises 28–33, write the number in base ten.

28. 1001_2
29. 1010_2
30. 1111_2
31. 11010_2
32. 10001_2
33. 11111_2

Writing Base-Two Numbers In Exercises 34–39, write the number in base two.

34. 11
35. 23
36. 31
37. 59
38. 44
39. 62

In Exercises 40–42, use the base-eight number system described below. Write the number in base ten.

Five hundred twelves place

Sixty-fours place

Eights place

Ones place

$$1 \times 64 = 64$$
$$7 \times 8 = 56$$
$$2 \times 1 = \underline{2}$$
$$122$$

1 7 2 $_8$

40. 33_8
41. 65_8
42. 76_8

Integrated Review
Making Connections within Mathematics

Science Match the temperature with the description.

a. 350°F
b. 32°F
c. 85°F
d. 212°F
e. 98°F
f. 22°F

43. Water boils.
44. A summer day
45. A winter day
46. A healthy person
47. Water freezes.
48. An oven

Exploration and Extension

49. *Building Your Chapter Project* Your company is trying out a new computer game. It shows you how to crack a computer code by telling you that computers use 8 "bits" in base two to represent letters. The letter A is sixty-five. The letter B is sixty-six, and so on. A space is thirty-two. The game asks you to crack the code to find different messages. A sample message in base two is shown. Can you crack the code? The first letter is done for you.

0	1	0	1	1	0	0	1	← Y
0	1	0	0	1	1	1	1	
0	1	0	1	0	1	0	1	
0	0	1	0	0	0	0	0	
0	1	0	0	0	0	0	1	
0	1	0	1	0	0	1	0	
0	1	0	0	0	1	0	1	
0	0	1	0	0	0	0	0	
0	1	0	1	0	0	1	1	
0	1	0	0	1	1	0	1	
0	1	0	0	0	0	0	1	
0	1	0	1	0	0	1	0	
0	1	0	1	0	1	0	0	

Chapter Summary

What did you learn?

1. Write place-value numbers in expanded notation. **(2.1)**
2. Add and subtract whole numbers. **(2.2)**
3. Multiply whole numbers. **(2.3)**
4. Divide whole numbers. **(2.4)**
   - Write quotients with a remainder. **(2.4)**
   - Write quotients with a fraction. **(2.4)**
5. Evaluate an expression. **(2.5)**
   - Evaluate a variable expression. **(2.6)**
6. Use order of operations. **(2.5)**
7. Use the Distributive Property. **(2.6)**
8. Read and write numbers in different bases. **(2.7)**

9. Use problem-solving strategies to solve problems. **(2.1–2.7)**

10. Use tables and graphs to solve problems. **(2.1–2.7)**

Why did you learn it?

Four operations are used to combine numbers: addition, subtraction, multiplication, and division. These operations can be used to model and solve real-life problems. Here are some of the examples you studied in this chapter.

- Find the total computer software sales. **(2.2)**
- Find the number of tiles needed to tile a floor. **(2.3)**
- Rewrite a recipe to serve fewer people. **(2.4)**
- Find the amount of money needed to visit a theme park. **(2.5)**
- Read and write base-two computer codes. **(2.7)**

How does it fit into the bigger picture of mathematics?

Before you began this chapter, you already knew how to add, subtract, multiply, and divide whole numbers. In mathematics, however, knowing *how* to do something is only half the story. It is also important to know *why* the procedure works. In this chapter, you learned that the techniques for adding, subtracting, multiplying, and dividing succeed because our number system is a place-value, base-ten system.

In this chapter, you also learned that number operations can be modeled with diagrams that help you understand the operations.

In Exercises 1–4, write the number in words and in expanded notation. **(2.1)**

1. 97   2. 436   3. 35,790   4. 680,201

In Exercises 5–13, evaluate the expression. **(2.2, 2.4, 2.5, 2.6)**

5. $384 + 21$ 6. $1576 + 449$ 7. $803 - 267$

8. $298 \div 4$ 9. $404 \div 18$ 10. 6×39

11. $15 + (3 \times 4)$ 12. $50 - (6 \times 8) \div 3$ 13. $19 \times 4 + 45 \div 9$

In Exercises 14–17, write the multiplication problem shown. **(2.3)**

14.    15.
27 square units

16. 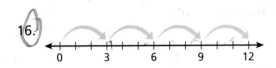   17.
22 square units

In Exercises 18–21, complete each equation and describe the pattern. Then write the next 2 numbers. **(2.2, 2.3, 2.4, 2.6)**

18. $2 \times 14 = \boxed{?}$ 19. $125 \div 5 = \boxed{?}$ 20. $1(1 + 1) = \boxed{?}$ 21. $111 + 9 = \boxed{?}$

$3 \times 14 = \boxed{?}$ $100 \div 5 = \boxed{?}$ $2(2 + 2) = \boxed{?}$ $222 + 9 = \boxed{?}$

$4 \times 14 = \boxed{?}$ $75 \div 5 = \boxed{?}$ $3(3 + 3) = \boxed{?}$ $333 + 9 = \boxed{?}$

In Exercises 22–25, rewrite the number in base ten. **(2.7)**

22. 423_5 23. 440_5 24. 11110_2 25. 101101_2

26. *Earning Money* You work washing cars for your neighbors. Today you earned $5.00 per car for 7 cars and received $4 in tips. Write a numerical expression to represent the total amount you earned. **(2.5)**

27. *Architecture* You are designing an ice rink. Its floor plan is drawn on a grid like that shown at the right. Each square in the grid represents 10 feet by 10 feet. Explain why the total area of the rink can be written in any of the following ways. **(2.3, 2.6)**

a. $15 \times 8 \times 100$

b. 80×150

c. $80 \times (100 + 50)$

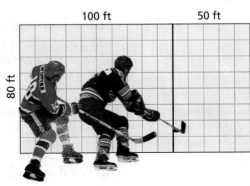
100 ft   50 ft
80 ft

Computers in School   The table below shows the number of computers used in public schools for 1984–85 and 1992–93. *(Source: Market Data Retrieved)*

	1984–85	1992–93
Elementary	215,500	1,605,000
Middle/Junior High	100,000	640,000
Senior High	230,000	1,125,000

28. Which school level increased computer use the most?

29. What was the total number of computers used in 1984–85? In 1992–93?

Walk-Through Computer   At the Computer Museum in Boston, Massachusetts, visitors can learn how a computer works by walking through it. The Walk-Through Computer is exactly like a desktop one, but 20 times bigger.

30. On the keypad of a desktop computer, a key is about 12 millimeters wide. Estimate the width of a key on the Walk-Through Computer.

31. On a desktop computer, the monitor is about 50 centimeters wide. Estimate the width of the monitor on the Walk-Through Computer.

32. For a desktop computer, a disk is about 91 millimeters wide. Estimate the width of a disk for the Walk-Through Computer.

Emily Knight is shown pressing a key on the Walk-Through Computer at the Computer Museum in Boston.

Computer Talk   In Exercises 33–35, evaluate the expression. Then look up the number at the right to figure out the word in "computer talk."

33. Hand-held box to control a computer

$$\overline{22 \times 33} \quad \overline{1422 + 598} \quad \overline{451 - 123} \quad \overline{2193 \div 51} \quad \overline{181 \times 12}$$

34. Allows computers to make phone calls

$$\overline{4356 \div 6} \quad \overline{35 \times 52} \quad \overline{215 - 66} \quad \overline{1617 + 555} \quad \overline{275 + 451}$$

35. Small region on a computer screen

$$\overline{595 \div 119} \quad \overline{751 - 512} \quad \overline{55 \times 61} \quad \overline{6516 \div 3} \quad \overline{143 + 658}$$

A	B	C	D
212	517	39	149
E	**F**	**G**	**H**
2172	33	1214	93
I	**J**	**K**	**L**
239	8	167	801
M	**N**	**O**	**P**
726	818	1820	5
Q	**R**	**S**	**T**
73	2001	43	1976
U	**V**	**W**	**X**
328	92	413	3355
Y	**Z**		
21	100		

In Exercises 1 and 2, write the number in words and in expanded notation.

1. 5110

2. 19,003

In Exercises 3–6, add or subtract. State whether you used regrouping.

3. $124 + 711$ 4. $1310 - 219$ 5. $556 + 968$ 6. $3124 + 1901$

In Exercises 7 and 8, write the multiplication problem shown.

7.
Area is 60 square units.

8.
Area is 60 square units.

In Exercises 9–12, divide. Write the quotient in two ways.

9. $37 \div 5$ 10. $88 \div 3$ 11. $255 \div 4$ 12. $451 \div 6$

In Exercises 13 and 14, simplify the expression.

13. $(10 + 5) \times 4$ 14. $57 - 45 \div 3$

In Exercises 15 and 16, rewrite the number in base ten.

15. 4431_5 16. 10011_2

17. You are baking 8 pies. It takes 6 minutes to make each crust and 8 minutes to make each filling. Use the Distributive Property to write an expression that represents the total time it takes to get the pies ready to bake. Then evaluate the expression.

In Exercises 18 and 19, use the table below. It shows the number of people employed in computer-related jobs in 1992 and the number expected to be employed in 2005. *(Source: U.S. Bureau of Labor Statistics)*

18. How many fewer computer operators are expected in 2005 than in 1992?

19. How many more computer programmers are expected in 2005 than in 1992?

It's Dave Ferina's job to check out new computer games and programs and advise customers whether to invest in the companies that create them.

Job	Computer Scientist	Computer Operator	Systems Analyst	Computer Programmer
1992	211,000	266,000	455,000	555,000
2005	447,000	161,000	956,000	723,000

Exploring Decimals and Percent

People throughout the world flavor food with spices. Common spices include pepper, nutmeg, cloves, ginger, allspice, mace, mustard, and cinnamon.

Real Life
Foreign Money

When visiting a foreign country, you need to have foreign money. The table below shows about how much 1 unit of foreign currency is worth in U.S. dollars and how much 1 U.S. dollar is worth in each country. *(Source: Wall Street Journal, 1995)*

	In U.S. $	Currency per U.S. $
Japan (Yen)	0.011	88.400
Britain (Pound)	1.612	0.621
Germany (Mark)	0.723	1.383
South Africa (Rand)	0.279	3.587
Greece (Drachma)	0.004	226.560

Think and Discuss

1. Which is worth more: a mark or a rand? Explain your reasoning.
2. How many pounds do you get for 100 U.S. dollars? Explain.

CHAPTER THEME:
Money around the World

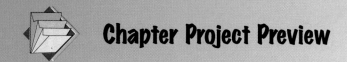
Making a Travel Trivia Game

Theme: Money around the World Have you ever played board games such as Trivial Pursuit®? In games like these, answering questions correctly helps you get closer to winning the game.

In this project, you will make a Travel Trivia Game and write the questions for it. The questions may be about the following.

➡ **In Lesson 3.1:** Candy in Swedish money (page 107)

➡ **In Lesson 3.3:** A hotel room in Japan (page 119)

➡ **In Lesson 3.4:** A flag in South Africa (page 123)

➡ **In Lesson 3.6:** Food at an Indian restaurant (page 133)

➡ **In Lesson 3.7:** Chilean money conversions (page 139)

➡ **In Lesson 3.8:** A souvenir in Greece (page 143)

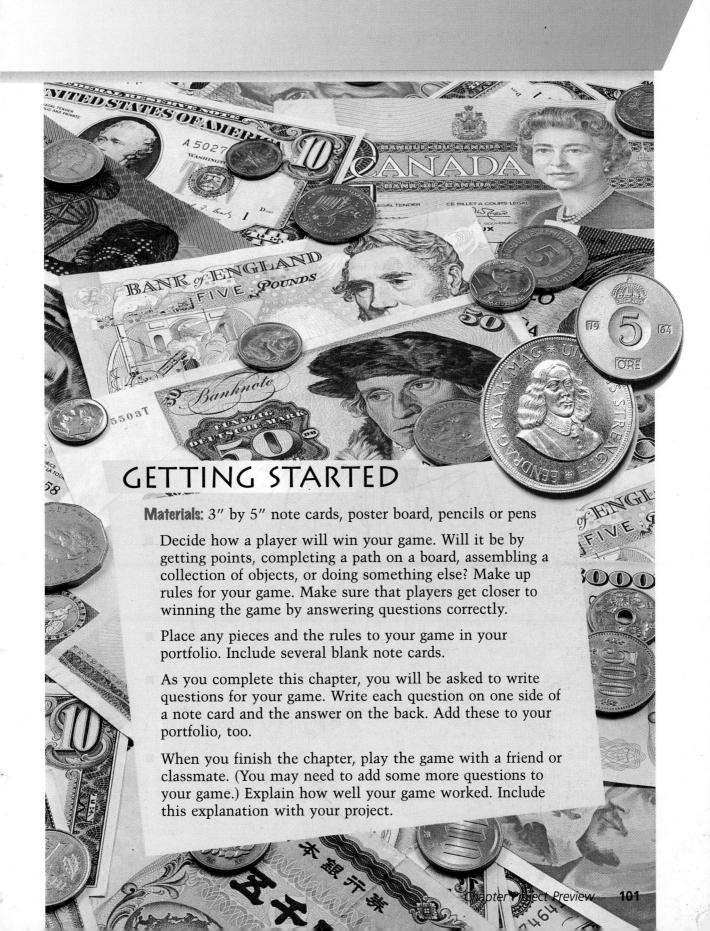

GETTING STARTED

Materials: 3" by 5" note cards, poster board, pencils or pens

Decide how a player will win your game. Will it be by getting points, completing a path on a board, assembling a collection of objects, or doing something else? Make up rules for your game. Make sure that players get closer to winning the game by answering questions correctly.

Place any pieces and the rules to your game in your portfolio. Include several blank note cards.

As you complete this chapter, you will be asked to write questions for your game. Write each question on one side of a note card and the answer on the back. Add these to your portfolio, too.

When you finish the chapter, play the game with a friend or classmate. (You may need to add some more questions to your game.) Explain how well your game worked. Include this explanation with your project.

Materials Needed: base-ten pieces, paper, pencils

In Chapter 2, you learned how to use base-ten pieces to represent whole numbers. For instance, the number 328 can be modeled with 3 large squares, 2 strips, and 8 small squares.

Base-ten pieces for 328

In this investigation, you will learn how to use base-ten pieces to model decimals.

Part A Let the large square below represent the number 1. Divide the square into 10 equal strips. What number (or fraction of the square) does each strip represent? Say the number *in words.* Then discuss how to write the number as a decimal.

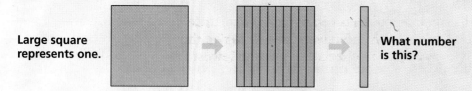

Large square represents one.

What number is this?

Now divide the strip into 10 small squares. What number does each small square represent? Say the number *in words.* Then discuss how to write the number as a decimal.

Begin with strip.

What number does each small square represent?

1. How many small squares does it take to make one large square?

2. If a small square were divided into ten small strips, what number would each small strip represent?

3. Use the base-ten pieces to model these numbers: 3.2, 3.02, and 0.32. Draw a sketch of each number.

Part B The base-ten pieces below represent 7 tenths and 13 hundredths.

4. Find other ways that you can use base-ten pieces to represent the same number. Organize your results in a table like that shown below.

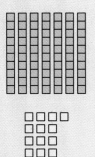

7 tenths
13 hundredths

Tenths	Hundredths	Total Number of Pieces
7	13	20
8	3	?
?	?	?
?	?	?
?	?	?
?	?	?
?	?	?
?	?	?
?	?	?

5. What patterns do you see in the table?

6. Which collection has the fewest pieces? How is this collection related to the decimal form of the number?

Part C Form each collection of base-ten pieces. Then trade pieces to form a collection with the fewest pieces. Write the decimal number shown by your collection with the fewest pieces.

7. 1 ones, 12 tenths, 16 hundredths

8. 15 tenths

9. 347 hundredths

10. 2 ones, 48 hundredths

On Your Own   *Critical Thinking*

11. Draw a picture to explain the difference between 3 tens and 3 tenths.

12. Draw a picture to explain the difference between 2 hundreds and 2 hundredths.

13. What is eleven tens equal to? What is eleven tenths equal to?

14. Draw a base-ten model for 0.24.

3.1

Exploring Decimal Representation

What you should learn:

Goal 1
How to write decimals in expanded notation

Goal 2
How the choice of a unit changes the decimal representation of a number

Why you should learn it:

An understanding of the base-ten place-value system will help you understand the decimal form of numbers. For instance, $0.75 and 75¢ use decimals in different ways to represent the same amount of money.

Goal 1 **Expanded Notation of Decimals**

In Chapter 2, you wrote whole numbers in the base-ten place-value system. In this chapter, you will study decimal numbers such as the one shown below. It is read as "two and fifty-eight hundredths."

Example 1 *Using Base-Ten Pieces*

Use base-ten pieces to write 2.58 in expanded notation.

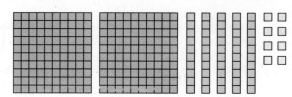

Solution

$$2.58 = 2 + 0.5 + 0.08$$
$$= (2 \times 1) + (5 \times 0.1) + (8 \times 0.01)$$

■

Study Tip

The way you write a number depends on the **units** that you select. For example, the number in Example 1 can be written in the following ways.

258 small squares or
258 hundredths

25.8 strips or
25.8 tenths

2.58 large squares or
2.58 ones

Lesson Investigation

■ **Investigating Representations of Decimals**
Draw each base-ten model using the fewest pieces. Write 3 names for the number that is represented.

a. 134 small squares **b.** 1.02 large squares **c.** 23.1 strips

How does the position of the decimal point depend on the units that are selected?

Goal 2 Selecting Units for Numbers

In Lab 3.1, you needed to know the unit before you could write the decimal. To write a price, you need to know which unit to use.

Real Life
Money

Cat Collar $1.45 a.

Fishbowl $2.25 b.

Aquarium Plant 89¢ c.

Gravel 94¢ d.

Example 2 *Name Amounts of Money*

Write each price in a different way.

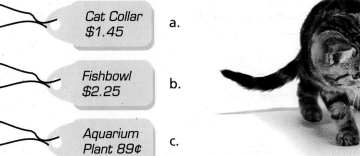

Solution

a. This dollar price can be written as 145 cents or 145¢.
b. This dollar price can be written as 225 cents or 225¢.
c. This cents price can be written as 0.89 dollars or $0.89.
d. This cents price can be written as 0.94 dollars or $0.94.

You can state the results of Example 2 as follows.

1. *Dollars to Cents:* Move the decimal point 2 places to the right.
2. *Cents to Dollars:* Move the decimal point 2 places to the left. ∎

Communicating about MATHEMATICS

▶ **Sharing Ideas about the Lesson**

Units for Money Write each amount in dollar units. In each case, explain your reasoning.

A. 2.0 hundred-dollar bills **B.** 4.0 dimes
C. 3.0 ten-dollar bills **D.** 6.0 one-dollar bills

EXERCISES

Guided Practice

Think and Discuss

▶ **CHECK for Understanding**

Match the name with the model.

a. strips   1. ones
b. small squares   2. hundredths
c. large squares   3. tenths

4. Write a number that has a 7 in the thousands place *and* a 7 in the thousandths place.
5. Write 678 cents in dollar units.
6. Write 79 cents using both ¢ and $.

In this exercise set, use the following values for base-ten pieces.

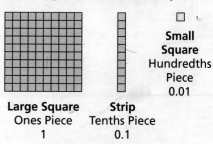

Large Square
Ones Piece
1

Strip
Tenths Piece
0.1

Small Square
Hundredths Piece
0.01

Independent Practice

In Exercises 7–9, sketch the base-ten model using the fewest pieces. Then write 3 names for the number that is represented.

7. 1.12 large squares   8. 15.6 strips   9. 121 small squares

In Exercises 10–12, use the base-ten pieces to name the number. Then name the number another way.

10. 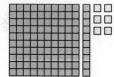   11.   12.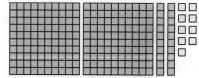

In Exercises 13–15, use the model at the right. Complete the statement with the words *ones, tenths,* or *hundredths*.

13. 3.22 [?]   14. 322 [?]   15. 32.2 [?]

Communicating   In Exercises 16–19, write the number.

16. Three and four tenths
17. Twelve and fifty-two hundredths
18. Two hundred twenty thousandths
19. Five hundred and three hundredths

In Exercises 20–22, write the number in expanded notation.

20. 5.48   21. 23.936   22. 101.021

True or False? In Exercises 23–26, write whether the statement is true or false. Explain your reasoning.

23. 100 tenths = 10 ones

24. 10 hundredths = 100 tenths

25. 10 hundredths = 1 tenth

26. 1000 thousandths = 1 one

Cost of Driving In Exercises 27–29, use the graph at the right. It shows the approximate cost of driving a car 1 mile for different years. Write the amounts in dollars. *(Source: American Petroleum Institute)*

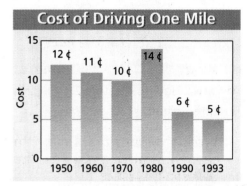

Cost of Driving One Mile

27. The cost of driving 1 mile in 1950

28. The cost of driving 10 miles in 1970

29. The cost of driving 100 miles in 1993

Nutrition The table at the right shows the amount in grams of protein, carbohydrates, and fat in some food from Arby's. In the metric system, 1000 milligrams = 1 gram. Write the amounts in milligrams. *(Source: Arby's, Inc.)*

	Protein	Carbo-hydrates	Fat
Roast beef sandwich	22.0 g	35.4 g	18.2 g
French fries	2.1 g	29.8 g	13.2 g
Vanilla shake	10.5 g	46.2 g	11.5 g

30. Protein in a vanilla shake

31. Carbohydrates in a roast beef sandwich

32. Fat in french fries

Integrated Review

Making Connections within Mathematics

Complete the statement using >, <, or = .

33. 41 42

34. 209 208

35. 101 110

36. 1150 1105

Exploration and Extension

37. *Building Your Chapter Project* A question you can use for the Travel Trivia Game is:

Suppose you own a store that accepts money from any country. At your store, which two of the following could be the cost of a candy bar?

a. *4.3 krona*   b. *43 ore*

c. *430 ore*   d. *43 krona*

Answer this question. Then write another multiple-choice question about Swedish money for your Travel Trivia Game.

Swedish Money

5 Ore   1 Krona
100 ore = 1 krona

1994 Rate:
1 krona = $0.14

3.2

Measuring Length: The Metric System

What you should learn:

Goal 1 How to measure length in the metric system

Goal 2 How to change units of length in the metric system

Why you should learn it:

The metric system is used in most countries of the world. It is also used in the United States—especially in science.

Goal 1 Using the Metric System

The metric system is about 200 years old. Before that, many measuring systems were used in the world. In the United States, *two* measuring systems are used—the metric system and the customary system (inches, feet, miles).

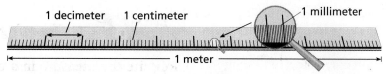

1 decimeter   1 centimeter   1 millimeter

1 meter

The metric system is a *base-ten* system. The customary system is *not* a base-ten system.

The Metric System of Length

Unit	Symbol	Prefix Meaning	Notation
Millimeter	mm	Thousandth	0.001 m
Centimeter	cm	Hundredth	0.01 m
Decimeter	dm	Tenth	0.1 m
Meter	m	—	1.0 m
Dekameter	dkm	Ten	10.0 m
Hectometer	hm	Hundred	100.0 m
Kilometer	km	Thousand	1000.0 m

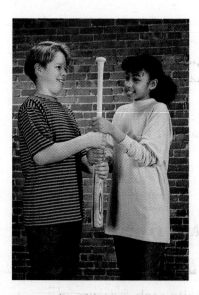

To comfortably use the metric system, it helps to relate the lengths to real-life objects. For instance, the width of a hand is about 1 decimeter.

Example 1 *Estimating Lengths*

	Unit	Real-Life Object
a.	Millimeter	About the thickness of a dime
b.	Centimeter	About the width of a fingernail
c.	Decimeter	About the width of your hand
d.	Meter	About the height of a kitchen counter
e.	Dekameter	About the width of a classroom
f.	Hectometer	About the width of 2 football fields
g.	Kilometer	About the length of 5 city blocks ∎

| **Changing Metric Units**

To change units in the metric system, remember that it is a base-ten system.

Changing Metric Units
10 millimeters = 1 centimeter
10 centimeters = 1 decimeter
10 decimeters = 1 meter
10 meters = 1 dekameter
10 dekameters = 1 hectometer
10 hectometers = 1 kilometer

Study Tip

The most common units in the metric system are millimeters, centimeters, meters, and kilometers. To use these measures, the following relationships help.

1000 millimeters = 1 meter
100 centimeters = 1 meter
1000 meters = 1 kilometer

Example 2 *Changing Metric Units*

Rewrite the measure in a more reasonable metric unit.

a. Elaine is 150 centimeters tall.

b. A pencil is 0.006 meters wide.

c. You went on a 3000 meter subway ride.

Solution

a. Because 100 centimeters is equal to 1 meter, it is more reasonable to say that *Elaine is 1.5 meters tall.*

b. Because 0.001 meter is equal to 1 millimeter, it is more reasonable to say that *a pencil is 6 millimeters wide.*

c. Because 1000 meters is equal to 1 kilometer, it is more reasonable to say that *you went on a 3 kilometer subway ride.*

Communicating about MATHEMATICS

▶ **Sharing Ideas about the Lesson**

Extending the Example Rewrite each measure in a more reasonable unit. Then write a sentence that uses that measure.

A. 250 centimeters   **B.** 250 millimeters

C. 4000 meters   **D.** 0.02 meters

EXERCISES

▶ **CHECK for Understanding**

1. Is the customary system of length (inches, feet, yards, miles) a base-ten system? Explain.

Fill in the missing unit for the length of the object.

2. 13.2 ?

3. 50 ?

4. 25 ?

5. 15 ?

6. *Communicating*   Name an object in your classroom that can be measured reasonably in each of these: millimeters, centimeters, and decimeters. Give each measurement.

In Exercises 7 and 8, complete the statement.

7. 1 meter = ? decimeters

8. ? millimeters = 1 centimeter

Independent Practice

Match the real-life object with its measure.

    a. 1.8 m   b. 4.75 dm   c. 91 m   d. 12.5 cm

9. Length of a computer keyboard

10. Average height of a human being

11. Height of a soda can

12. Length of a soccer field

Complete the statement.

13. 1 km = ? m

14. 780 ? = 78 m

15. 250 m = ? km

16. 3.45 m = 345 ?

17. 100 ? = 0.1 m

18. ? cm = 1 km

19. 0.90 m = 900 ?

20. ? mm = 0.602 cm

21. 13,000 ? = 13 km

Geometry   Use a metric ruler to measure the sides of the rectangle in the given units. Then find its perimeter.

22. Millimeters

23. Centimeters

24. Measure the four sides of this book's cover. Use a reasonable metric unit. Then find the perimeter of the cover.

Writing In Exercises 25–30, rewrite the measure in a more reasonable metric unit. Then write a sentence that uses the rewritten measure and describes a real-life object.

25. 57 centimeters **26.** 6500 millimeters **27.** 0.28 kilometer

28. 3600 meters **29.** 0.004 meter **30.** 1000 centimeters

Number Sense Complete the statement using >, <, or = .

31. 1 mm ⟨?⟩ 1000 m **32.** 0.1 km ⟨?⟩ 1000 cm **33.** 35 cm ⟨?⟩ 3.5 mm

34. 0.68 km ⟨?⟩ 68 cm **35.** 4 m ⟨?⟩ 40 cm **36.** 2 km ⟨?⟩ 2000 mm

Dinosaurs In Exercises 37 and 38, use the following dinosaur lengths.

Ankylosaurus	4800 mm
Brontosaurus	2400 cm
Ornitholestes	1.8 m
Stegosaurus	0.006 km
Torosaurus	9000 mm
Tyrannosaurus Rex	0.012 km

This cement Brontosaurus near Cabazon, California is a replica of one from the Jurassic Period.

37. Rewrite the table giving the lengths in meters. List the dinosaurs from shortest to longest.

38. Which dinosaurs are 5 times as long as another?

Integrated Review

Making Connections within Mathematics

Algebra Use mental math to solve the equation.

39. $15 + p = 21$ **40.** $60 \div s = 15$ **41.** $5 \cdot t = 75$ **42.** $t - 16 = 14$

43. $m + 25 = 37$ **44.** $4 \cdot n = 48$ **45.** $19 - p = 8$ **46.** $m \div 27 = 3$

Exploration and Extension

47. *History of Meter* When the metric system was first developed in the late 1700s, a meter was defined to be $\frac{1}{10,000,000}$ of the distance between the equator and the North Pole. What is the distance between the equator and the North Pole in kilometers?

48. A myriameter is equal to 10 kilometers. What is the distance between the equator and the North Pole in myriameters?

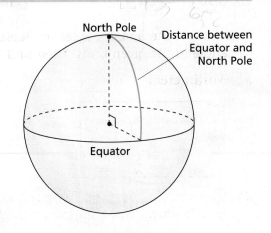

North Pole

Distance between Equator and North Pole

Equator

Mixed REVIEW

Write the number in words. **(2.1, 3.1)**

1. 1432
2. 18,067
3. 9.55
4. 16.043

Write the number in expanded notation. **(2.1)**

5. 2167
6. 8098
7. 20,450
8. 97,902
9. 306,520
10. 1,001,010

Algebra   Use mental math to solve the equation. **(1.6, 1.7)**

11. $x + 13 = 27$
12. $36 - y = 25$
13. $16 \cdot p = 48$
14. $q \div 10 = 12$
15. $95 \div n = 9.5$
16. $2.2 \cdot m = 220$

Geometry   Sketch an area model for the problem. **(2.3, 2.4)**

17. 4×6
18. 9×8
19. $40 \div 3$
20. $9 \div 3$

Career Interview

Consultant

Stephanie Fan works for PEACH Corporation in Boston, Massachusetts. She is hired by organizations to help them for a short time when they have a problem.

Q: *What types of things are you hired to do?*
A: I might do accounting work, hire new employees, or give workshops about the diversity in the community.

Q: *What math skills do you use in your job?*
A: I use all the basic math skills and estimation, especially when I work with an organization's finances.

Q: *Do you use mathematical reasoning?*
A: My job is really problem solving. Organizations hire me when they have a problem. I go in, study it, and help them find a solution. The problems are always different.

Q: *What would you like to tell kids about math?*
A: There is so much to learn. Schooling doesn't end at twelfth grade. It is a life long experience. Learning keeps you energized and young forever.

Real Life
Drafting

Example   *Changing Metric Measures*

Part of a blueprint is shown below. Use a metric ruler to find the perimeter of the room shown. Then use the scale to help you find the perimeter of the actual room.

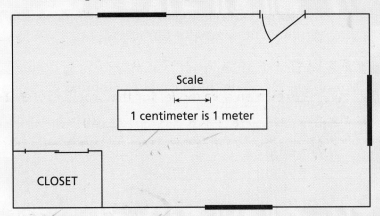

Scale

1 centimeter is 1 meter

CLOSET

Solution   The width is 51 millimeters and the length is 98 millimeters. The perimeter is

51 $+$ 51 $+$ 98 $+$ 98 $=$

or 298 millimeters. To find the perimeter in centimeters, divide this number by 10.

298 $\div$ 10 $=$

The display is 29.8, which means the perimeter is 29.8 centimeters. Because each centimeter on the blueprint represents 1 meter in the actual room, the actual room must have a perimeter of 29.8 meters. ∎

Exercises

In Exercises 1–4, rewrite each measure in millimeters and in meters.

1. 7.31 cm   2. 125.8 cm   3. 924.1 cm   4. 18.4 cm

In Exercises 5–8, rewrite each measure in centimeters and in meters.

5. 775.3 mm   6. 89.5 mm   7. 1139.2 mm   8. 19.235 mm

In Exercises 9–12, rewrite each measure in millimeters and in centimeters.

9. 2.45 m   10. 0.56 m   11. 2.69 m   12. 3.4 m

Materials Needed: base-ten grid paper, plain paper, pencils

In this chapter, you have seen that numbers can have different names. The name depends on the unit you select. For instance, you might read the number 2500 as 2.5 thousand or 25 hundred.

In this investigation, you will learn how area models can help you discover different names for numbers.

Part A Because the blue region in each square is the same size, you can reason that 3 tenths is equal to 30 hundredths. In decimal notation, you can write $0.3 = 0.30$.

Unit square is divided
into 10 strips.
Each strip has an
area of 1 tenth.

Unit square is divided
into 100 small squares.
Each small square has
an area of 1 hundredth.

1. How many tenths are shown by the shaded region? How many hundredths? Redraw the model on base-ten grid paper. Sketch the number as hundredths.

   a. 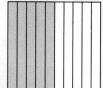   b. 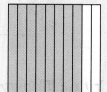   c.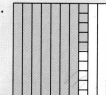

2. How many hundredths are shown by the shaded region? How many tenths? Redraw the model on base-ten grid paper. Sketch the number as tenths.

   a. 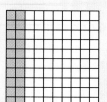   b. 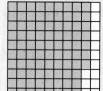   c.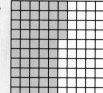

Part B The following area model represents 3.14 ones.

3. Name the number as tenths and as hundredths.

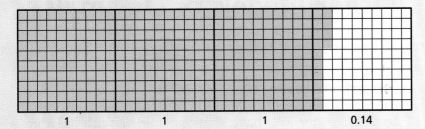

| 1 | 1 | 1 | 0.14 |

4. Draw a model for 2.32 ones. Name the number as tenths and as hundredths.

Part C In each case, a unit square has been divided into regions that have the same area.

5. Redraw the model on base-ten grid paper. All sides should be 10 units long. Then name the number shown by the blue region as tenths and hundredths.

a.

b.

c.

d.

e.

f.

On Your Own   *Critical Thinking*

---

6. Complete each statement.
   a. 4.67 tenths = $\boxed{?}$ hundredths   b. 4.67 hundredths = $\boxed{?}$ tenths
   c. 4.67 ones = $\boxed{?}$ tenths

7. Write a description of how you can change a number's name from tenths to hundredths. Give some examples.

8. Write a description of how you can change a number's name from hundredths to tenths. Give some examples.

3.3

Other Models of Decimals

What you should learn:

Goal 1 How to represent decimals with number-line models and set models

Goal 2 How to use decimals to solve real-life problems

Why you should learn it:

Decimals can be used to represent data from a survey. An example is the portion of families who own a dog.

Goal 1 **Modeling Decimals**

In this chapter, you have shown decimals with base-ten pieces and area models. You can also show decimals with number-line models and set models.

Each of the following models shows 0.3 or 3 tenths. In the models, you can think of 0.3 as a portion of the whole (which is 1).

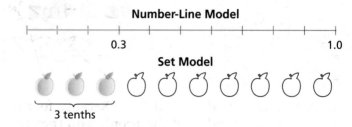

Number-Line Model

0.3   1.0

Set Model

3 tenths

Example 1 **Drawing Models**

You are shown a model for a portion of a whole. Draw the model for the whole.

a.   b.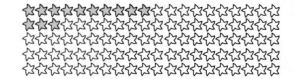

0.4

0.13

Solution

a. Because the line shows 4 tenths and has 4 parts, the whole must have 10 parts.

0.4   1.0

b. Because the set model has 13 stars and shows 13 hundredths, the whole must have 100 stars.

Study Tip

One of the problem-solving strategies that you studied in Chapter 1 was Draw a Diagram. Number-line models and set models are two types of diagrams that are used to help solve problems.

In the United States, 35% of all families own a dog and 30% own a cat. Many of these own two or more pets.

Example 2 *Interpreting a Survey*

Two hundred people were asked which types of pets they have. The results are shown in the graph. Estimate the portion that said they had each type of pet. List your answers as decimals.

Portion of People who Own Pets

Each symbol is 0.1 of the 200 people surveyed.

Dog	🐕🐕🐕🐕🐕🐕🐕🐕🐕🐕
Cat	🐈🐈🐈🐈🐈🐈🐈🐈🐈🐈
Bird	🕊🕊🕊🕊🕊🕊🕊🕊🕊🕊

Solution Because four dogs are shaded, 4 tenths or 0.4 of the people said they have a dog.

Because about three and a half cats are shaded, 3.5 tenths or about 0.35 of the people said they have a cat.

Because about one and a half birds are shaded, 1.5 tenths or about 0.15 of the people said they have a bird. ∎

Communicating about MATHEMATICS

Problem Solving
Draw a Diagram

▶ **Sharing Ideas about the Lesson**

Drawing Models You are shown a model for a portion of a whole. Draw the model for the whole.

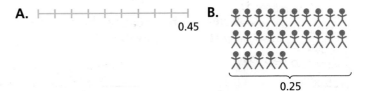

A. ├──┼──┼──┼──┼──┼──┼──┼──┼──┤
                              0.45

B. 👤👤👤👤👤👤👤👤👤👤👤
   👤👤👤👤👤👤👤👤👤👤👤
   👤👤👤👤👤
   0.25

EXERCISES

Guided Practice

Think and Discuss

▶ **CHECK for Understanding**

In Exercises 1–3, the "whole" part represents 1. What portion does the blue part represent?

1. 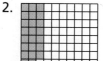   2. 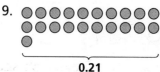   3.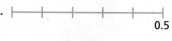

4. Draw a number-line model, a set model, and an area model to show 0.6.

Independent Practice

5. *Number Sense*   Sketch a number-line model to show 0.2.
6. *Number Sense*   Sketch a set model to show 0.9.
7. *Geometry*   Sketch an area model to show 0.45.

In Exercises 8–10, you are shown a model for a portion of a whole. Describe a model of the whole.

8.

0.35

9.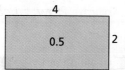

0.21

10.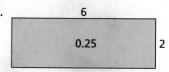

0.5

Geometry   The model shows a portion of a whole. Draw two rectangles that could represent the whole.

11.   12. 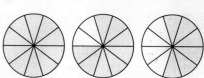   13.

Look for a Pattern   In Exercises 14 and 15, write the decimals shown by the models. Describe the pattern. Then write the next two decimals and draw their models.

14. 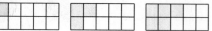   15.

16. *Interpreting a Graph* A survey of a group of women was taken. They were asked whether they were interested in some professional sports. The results are shown in the graph below. Estimate the portion that said they had an interest in each sport. List your answers as decimals.

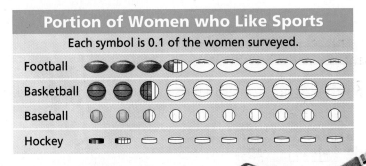

Portion of Women who Like Sports

Each symbol is 0.1 of the women surveyed.

| Football |
| Basketball |
| Baseball |
| Hockey |

Integrated Review
Making Connections within Mathematics

17. *Language Building* Copy the metric ruler on a piece of paper, then locate each letter on the ruler. What words are spelled out?

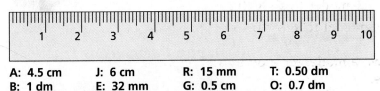

| A: 4.5 cm | J: 6 cm | R: 15 mm | T: 0.50 dm |
| B: 1 dm | E: 32 mm | G: 0.5 cm | O: 0.7 dm |

Exploration and Extension

18. *Building Your Chapter Project* The graph shows the approximate 1994 dollar value of 3 Japanese coins. A question you can use for your Travel Trivia Game is as follows.

You visit your pen pal from Japan. You stay in a hotel that costs 30,000 yen a night. How much would this be in dollars?

Japanese Money

| (100 yen) |
| (500 yen) |
| (1000 yen) |

Key $ = $1

Answer this question. Then write another question using the graph for your Travel Trivia Game.

3.4 Rewriting Decimals: Fractions and Percents

What you should learn:

Goal 1 How to rewrite decimals as fractions

Goal 2 How to rewrite decimals as percents

Why you should learn it:

Decimals can be rewritten as fractions and percents. To become a better problem solver, you need to be able to use all three ways.

Goal 1 Rewriting Decimals as Fractions

In this lesson, you will learn how to rewrite decimals: (1) as fractions and (2) as percents. Here are some examples of decimals that are rewritten as fractions.

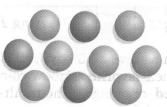

0.7 or $\frac{7}{10}$ of the balls are red.

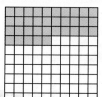

$0.35 = \frac{35}{100}$

$\frac{35}{100}$ **of the squares are green.**

Example 1 *Rewriting Decimals as Fractions*

Rewrite each decimal in words and then as a fraction.
a. 0.31   b. 0.027

Solution

a. Thirty-one hundredths can be rewritten as $\frac{31}{100}$.

b. Twenty-seven thousandths can be rewritten as $\frac{27}{1000}$. ■

> **Study Tip**
> The fraction $\frac{7}{10}$ and the decimal 0.7 are both read as "seven tenths."

Example 2 *Rewriting Fractions as Decimals*

Rewrite each fraction in words and then as a decimal.
a. $\frac{8}{10}$ b. $\frac{53}{100}$ c. $\frac{739}{1000}$

Solution

a. Eight tenths can be rewritten as 0.8.

b. Fifty-three hundredths can be rewritten as 0.53.

c. Seven hundred thirty-nine thousandths can be rewritten as 0.739. ■

Rewriting Decimals as Percents

In real-life problems, decimals are often rewritten as **percents.** Here are three examples.

$$0.62 = 62\%, \qquad 0.4 = 0.40 = 40\%, \qquad 0.24 = 24\%$$

The *cent* in percent means hundred. So, you can think of *percent* as "per hundred."

To rewrite a decimal as a percent, first name the decimal as *hundredths.* For instance, 0.4 can be named as 40 hundredths, or 40%.

Real Life
Survey

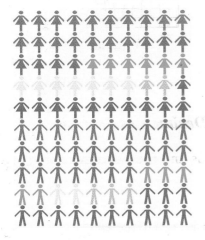

Example 3 *Writing Percents*

In a survey, 50 boys and 50 girls were asked to name their favorite rainbow color (purple, blue, green, yellow, red, or orange). The results are shown in the diagram at the left.

a. What percent named red?

b. What percent are boys who named red?

c. What percent are girls who named yellow?

Solution

a. Because 24 of the 100 figures are red, 24% named red.

b. Because 13 of the 100 figures are red and boys, 13% are boys who named red.

c. Because 7 of the 100 figures are yellow and girls, 7% are girls who named yellow. ■

Communicating about MATHEMATICS

Cooperative Learning

Sharing Ideas about the Lesson

Partner Activity Use the diagram above to answer each question. Then write another question that can be answered using the graph.

A. What percent of the people named orange?

B. What percent of the people are boys?

C. What percent of the people did not name blue?

EXERCISES

Think and Discuss

▶**CHECK for Understanding**

In Exercises 1–3, write the number of blue dots in the model at the right in each of the following forms.

1. A decimal portion of the total

2. A fractional portion of the total

3. A percent of the total

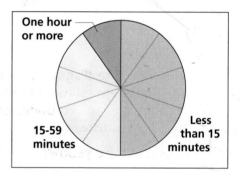

In Exercises 4–6, write each number in words.

4. 67%   5. $\frac{15}{100}$ 6. 0.45

Reading a Graph The circle graph shows the monthly recording times for people who own video cameras. *(Source: NFO Research, Inc.)*

7. What portion records less than 15 minutes per month? Write this result as a decimal, a percent, and a fraction.

8. What portion records 1 hour or more per month? Write this result as a decimal, a percent, and a fraction.

One hour or more

15-59 minutes

Less than 15 minutes

Independent Practice

In Exercises 9 and 10, write the decimal, fraction, and percent shown by the blue portion of the model.

9.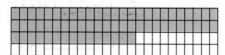

10.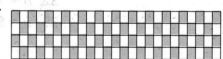

In Exercises 11–14, rewrite the number as a fraction.

11. 0.55   12. 12%   13. 45%   14. 0.129

Language Skills In Exercises 15 and 16, use the first 100 letters of *The Star-Spangled Banner,* by Francis Scott Key, below.

Oh! say, can you see, by the dawn's early light,
What so proudly we hailed at the twilight's last gleaming?
Whose broad stripes an . . .

15. What fraction are vowels (a, e, i, o, u)?   16. What percent are t's?

True or False? In Exercises 17–20, is the statement true or false? If false, correct it.

17. $\frac{53}{100} = 53\%$ **18.** $\frac{2}{100} = 20\%$ **19.** $9\% = \frac{9}{100}$ **20.** $42\% = \frac{421}{1000}$

In Exercises 21–24, rewrite the number as a percent.

21. 0.24 **22.** $\frac{33}{100}$ **23.** $\frac{85}{100}$ **24.** 0.12

In Exercises 25–28, use the model. Express the blue portion of the circle as a fraction and a percent.

25. 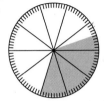 **26.** 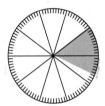 **27.** 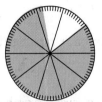 **28.**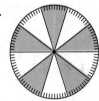

M&M® Candies The diagram at the right shows the number (in millions) of M&M candies that are sold in the United States per day. *(Source: M&M/Mars)*

29. What percent are yellow?

30. What percent are not green?

Integrated Review

Making Connections within Mathematics

Algebra Use mental math to solve.

31. $\$1.00 = 10 \times m$ **32.** $b \div 10 = \$6.00$ **33.** $s \times \$5.00 = \$500.00$
34. $\$43.00 \div 10 = c$ **35.** $n = \$7.49 \times 100$ **36.** $10 \times t = \$300.00$

Exploration and Extension

37. *Building Your Chapter Project* A question you can use for your Travel Trivia Game is:

You send your pen pal in South Africa $40 to buy a South African flag that costs 140 rand. Is it true that $40 is more than 140 rand? Explain your reasoning.

Answer this question. Then write another true or false question about South African money for your Travel Trivia Game.

South African Money

1 Dollar 0.5 Rand
1994 Rate:
1 rand = 28% of $1.00

Take this test as you would take a test in class. The answers to the exercises are given in the back of the book.

In Exercises 1–3, sketch a model of the number using the fewest base-ten pieces. **(3.1)**

1. 1.43

2. 1.89

3. 2.65

In Exercises 4–9, complete the statement. **(3.1, 3.2)**

4. 1 one = 100 ?

5. 100 ? = 1 tenth

6. ? tenths = 100 ones

7. 56 cm = ? mm

8. 1.78 ? = 178 m

9. ? km = 12.3 m

In Exercises 10–12, you are shown a model for a portion of a whole. Draw a model of the whole. **(3.3)**

10.

0.7

11.

♥ ♥ ♥ ♥ ♥ ♥ ♥ ♥ ♥ ♥
♥ ♥ ♥ ♥ ♥ ♥ ♥ ♥

0.18

12.

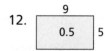

9

0.5 5

In Exercises 13–15, write the portion that is blue as a decimal, a fraction, and a percent of the whole. **(3.4)**

13.

14.

15.

World Records The table shows three of the men's and women's international track-and-field records. (*Source: International Amateur Athletic Federation*) **(3.4)**

Event	Men's	Women's
High jump	245 cm	2090 mm
Long jump	8950 mm	752 cm
Discus	0.0741 km	7680 cm

16. Rewrite the table using meters.

17. In which event did a woman have a better world record than a man?

18. *Education* A survey was taken in which people were asked whether they have taken lessons in the arts. The results are shown in the graph below. About what percent said they had taken each type of lesson? (*Source: National Endowment for the Arts*)

Portion of People Who Have Taken Lessons in the Arts

Music

Dance

Creative Writing

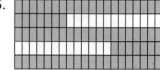

3.5 Comparing and Ordering Decimals

What you should learn:

Goal 1 How to order decimals

Goal 2 How to use ordering of decimals to solve real-life problems

Why you should learn it:

Decimals can be used to compare quantities, such as the winning times in an Olympic race.

Goal 1 Ordering Decimals

You already know how to locate whole numbers on a number line. For instance, the number line below shows the locations of 2, 7, and 9. Notice that the numbers get larger as you move from left to right.

Number Line

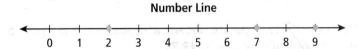

Lesson Investigation

■ Locating Decimals on a Number Line

Group Activity Use a centimeter ruler to draw a number line that is over 20 centimeters long. Draw 11 tick marks on the line, two centimeters apart. Then label the marks from 0 through 10. Locate the following decimals on the line. Explain how you found each location. Explain how to use the result to order the numbers from least to greatest.

a. 3.2   b. 9.9   c. 0.5   d. 9.3   e. 5.75

Example 1 *Ordering Decimals*

Order the numbers from least to greatest.

2.3, 2.09, 2.32, 2.29, 2.37

Solution One way to order the numbers is to locate them on a number line. To order the numbers from least to greatest, read them from left to right.

2.09, 2.29, 2.3, 2.32, 2.37   *Written in order*

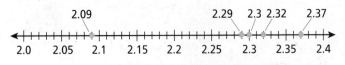

Study Tip

On a number line, the number to the right of another number is greater. For example, 6.7 is greater than 6.4, which is written as

6.7 > 6.4 or 6.4 < 6.7.

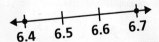

Goal **2**   **Solving Real-Life Problems**

Real Life
Olympics

Example 2   *Comparing Times*

The winning times for the Women's 100-Meter Freestyle swimming race in the Olympics from 1972–1992 are given in the bar graph. Order the times from least to greatest.

Study Tip

You can compare two decimals by comparing their place values from left to right. For instance, you can compare 54.79 and 54.65 as follows.

Compare tens digits.

54.79 Tens digit is 5.
54.65 Tens digit is 5.

Compare ones digits.

54.79 Ones digit is 4.
54.65 Ones digit is 4.

Compare tenths digits.

54.79 Tenths digit is 7.
54.65 Tenths digit is 6.

From left to right, the first digits that differ are in the tenths place. Because 7 is greater than 6, it follows that 54.79 is greater than 54.65.

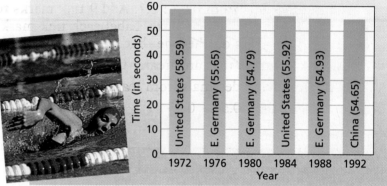

Winning Times in Women's 100-Meter Freestyle

Solution   From the graph, you can see the times are

58.59,   55.65,   54.79   55.92,   54.93,   54.65.

Written from least to greatest, the winning times are

54.65,   54.79,   54.93,   55.65,   55.92,   58.59.

In the bar graph, notice that the shortest time has the shortest bar and the longest time has the tallest bar. ∎

Communicating about MATHEMATICS

Cooperative Learning

▸ **Sharing Ideas about the Lesson**

Partner Activity Six circles are numbered at the top of this page. Use a ruler with centimeters. Measure the distance from the center of point A to the centers of each of the six circles to the nearest tenth of a centimeter. Then order the lengths from shortest to longest.

A ⊙

EXERCISES

Think and Discuss

▶ **CHECK for Understanding**

1. Name the numbers represented by the letters on the number line.

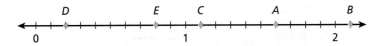

2. Draw a number line from 0.6 to 0.7. Add 9 tick marks to divide the line into 10 equal parts. Label each tick mark. Name three numbers on the line that are larger than 0.67.

3. Write three numbers that are greater than 6.5 and less than 6.6.

4. Order the following decimals from least to greatest.

   0.5,   0.4,   0.04,   0.54,   0.45

Independent Practice

Number Sense   Order the numbers from least to greatest.

5. 0.25,   0.5,   2.5,   0.2,   0.02
6. 0.10,   0.07,   0.17,   1.7,   0.7
7. 6.82,   6.08,   6.8,   6.18,   6.12
8. 4.1,   4.39,   4.03,   4.4,   4.13

Reasoning   Decide whether the numbers are ordered correctly from least to greatest. If not, write the correct ordering.

9. 0.026,   0.26,   0.126,   0.06,   0.2
10. 5.143,   5.14,   5.13,   5.104,   5.1
11. 1.69,   1.107,   1.9,   1.709,   1.76
12. 4.281,   4.18,   4.118,   4.218,   4.081

Number Sense   In Exercises 13–20, complete each statement using >, <, or =.

13. 0.5 (?) 0.3
14. 0.18 (?) 0.2
15. 6.7 (?) 6.72
16. 3.109 (?) 3.011
17. 1.5 (?) 1.50
18. 0.06 (?) 0.6
19. 0.40 (?) 0.4
20. 2.35 (?) 2.305

Reading a Graph   In Exercises 21–25, each bar of the bar graph represents a decimal between 0 and 1.

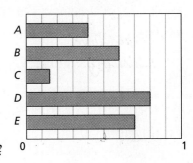

21. Order the bars from shortest to longest.
22. Which bar represents 0.7?
23. Which bar represents 0.15?
24. Which bar appears about twice as long as another?
25. Which bar appears about four times as long as another?

In Exercises 26–28, write the decimal shown by the model.

26.

27.

28.

29. Order the decimals found in Exercises 26–28 from least to greatest.

30. Draw a number line from 3.2 to 3.3. Divide the line into 10 equal parts and label each tick mark. In what place value is each tick mark?

31. *Tax Rates*   The 1992 sales tax rates for five states are given in the bar graph at the right. Order the states by ordering their tax rates from least to greatest.

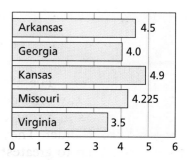

32. *Library Science*   Most libraries use the Dewey Decimal System to classify books. The system gives a decimal to a book according to the subject of the book. Suppose you are helping in the school library. Put the following books in order by ordering their numbers from least to greatest.

Integrated Review   *Making Connections within Mathematics*

Language Building   Write the decimal in words.

33. 0.1   **34.** 0.37   **35.** 4.26   **36.** 82.5

37. 0.061   **38.** 0.929   **39.** 13.022   **40.** 0.045

Look for a Pattern   Describe the pattern. Then list the next 3 numbers.

41. 1.8, 1.5, 1.2, ?, ?, ?   **42.** 1.1, 1.2, 1.4, 1.7, ?, ?, ?

43. 0.12, 0.10, 0.08, ?, ?, ?   **44.** 10.00, 10.25, 10.50, ?, ?, ?

Exploration and Extension

Guess, Check, and Revise Write numbers of the form ? 1 . ? 9
by placing one of the digits 0, 2, 3, 4, 5, 6, 7, or 8 in each box. A
number cannot be used more than once.

45. What is the smallest number you can write?

46. What is the greatest number you can write?

47. Name the number that is about $1\frac{1}{2}$.

48. Name the number that is between 60 and 61.1.

49. *Decimal Tic-Tac-Toe* The Tic-Tac-Toe game at the right can only be won if the three numbers in a row, column, or diagonal are in order. They can be in order from least to greatest or from greatest to least. Copy the game and draw lines through the possible ways to win.

0.9	0.71	0.6
0.04	0.5	0.65
0.05	0.34	0.45

Mixed REVIEW

State whether the number is prime or composite. **(1.3)**

1. 33 **2.** 23 **3.** 27 **4.** 48

Divide. **(2.4)**

5. $45 \div 6$ **6.** $33 \div 4$ **7.** $121 \div 5$ **8.** $220 \div 9$

Evaluate the expression. **(2.5)**

9. $10 + 16 \div 8$ **10.** $24 - 8 \times 2$ **11.** $(14 + 13) \div 9$ **12.** $54 \div 9 \times 2$

Write the number in base 10. **(2.7)**

13. 13_5 **14.** 414_5 **15.** 1101_2 **16.** 11011_2

Write the number. **(3.1)**

17. One and five tenths

18. Four and fifty-seven hundredths

19. One hundred and one hundredth

20. Ten and fifty thousandths

3.6

Rounding Decimals

What you should learn:

Goal 1 How to round decimals

Goal 2 How to use rounding of decimals to solve real-life problems

Why you should learn it:

Many times in real life, you need to round decimals. Examples include buying gasoline or finding baseball averages.

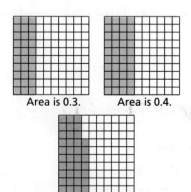

Area is 0.3.   Area is 0.4.

Area is 0.37.

Which of the blue models is more like the red model? The answer tells you whether 0.37 should round to 0.3 or 0.4.

Goal 1 **Rounding Decimals**

In many real-life situations, decimals may have more digits than are appropriate. For instance, if you buy 6 gallons of gasoline at $1.139 per gallon, then the *exact* total would be 6 × 1.139 or $6.834. You can't really pay this amount, so you round to the nearest cent.

Round down or round up?

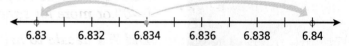

6.83   6.832   6.834   6.836   6.838   6.84

Because $6.834 is closer to $6.83 than to $6.84, you should *round down* to $6.83.

Rounding Numbers

To round to a given place, look at the digit to its right.
1. If the digit is 4 or less, round down.
2. If the digit is 5 or more, round up.

Example 1 *Rounding Whole Numbers*

Original Number	Given Place Value	Round Up or Down?	Rounded Number
a. 3146	Tens	Up	3150
b. 71,479	Thousands	Down	71,000 ∎

Example 2 *Rounding Decimals*

Original Decimal	Given Place Value	Round Up or Down?	Rounded Decimal
a. 3.157	Hundredths	Up	3.16
b. 12.449	Tenths	Down	12.4
c. 1359.5	Ones	Up	1360 ∎

Example 3 | *Making a Decision*

Ted Williams was a famous baseball player who played for the Boston Red Sox for 19 seasons (1939–1960). Here is a story about Ted Williams and rounding numbers.

It was the night before the last game of the season in 1941. Ted, who was 23 years old, had a batting average of 0.39955. If Ted decided not to play the game, his batting average would round up to 0.400. If Ted decided to play the game, his average could drop below 0.400.

No major league player had finished a season with 0.400 or more for several years.

Did Ted decide to help his team and play the game? Or did he decide to "play it safe" and keep his 0.400 season batting average?

Solution In real life, Ted Williams decided to play. The Boston Red Sox played a double header that day. Ted had 6 hits, raising his season average to 0.4057. This rounded to 0.406.

By taking a chance and playing for his team, Ted ended up a hero for the day. ∎

Real Life
Baseball

As of 1994, Ted Williams was the last Major League player to have ended the season with a batting average of 0.400 or more.

Communicating about MATHEMATICS

Problem Solving
Reading a Graph

Sharing Ideas about the Lesson

Rounding Numbers in a Graph Round the number represented by each bar to the nearest tenth.

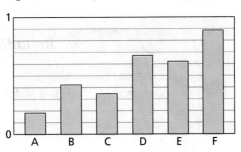

EXERCISES

Think and Discuss

▷ **CHECK for Understanding**

1. *Communicating* Give examples of real-life situations in which you would round a decimal.

2. Draw a model that helps show how to round 0.24 to the nearest tenth.

In Exercises 3–6, round 4.5239 to the given place value.

3. Thousandths   4. Hundredths   5. Tenths   6. Ones

7. *Error Analysis* A friend of yours is asked to round 6.3487 to the nearest tenth. Your friend first rounded to the nearest hundredth to get 6.35, and then rounded to the nearest tenth to get 6.4. Was your friend correct? Explain your reasoning.

Independent Practice

In Exercises 8–10, draw a number line. Show how to round 6.263 to the given place value.

8. Hundredths   9. Tenths   10. Ones

Number Sense Round each whole number to the given place value.

11. 269 (tens)   12. 34,575 (thousands)   13. 411,990 (hundreds)

Number Sense Round each decimal to the given place value.

14. 5.41 (tenths)   15. 20.7 (ones)   16. 8.5165 (thousandths)

True or False? Decide whether the statement is true or false. If false, correct the blue number.

17. 2.15 rounded to the nearest one is 2.

18. 13,099 rounded to the nearest thousand is 13,000.

19. 5.445 rounded to the nearest tenth is 5.5.

20. 4.999 rounded to the nearest hundredth is 5.00.

Round the instrument reading to the given place value.

21. Odometer (hundreds)   22. Thermometer (ones)   23. Digital Scale (tens)

In Exercises 24–27, round to the nearest dollar.

24. $32.25 **25.** $25.49 **26.** $611.50 **27.** $1209.89

28. *Coins* The bar graph at the right shows the cost of making different coins. Round the number shown by each bar to the nearest tenth. *(Source: United States Treasury Department)*

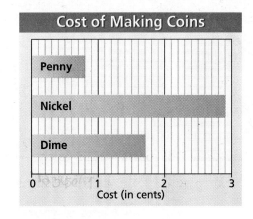

Cost of Making Coins

Science To tell whether a solution is an acid or a base, scientists use a number from 0 to 14 called pH. A pH below 7 means that the solution is an acid. A pH above 7 means that the solution is a base. Round the pH number to the nearest tenth. Is the substance an acid or a base?

29. Milk 6.52 **30.** Blood 7.44 **31.** Rainwater 6.22 **32.** Eggs 7.75

Integrated Review

Order the decimals from least to greatest.

33. 13.89, 14.27, 14.02, 13.09
35. 0.012, 0.002, 0.2, 0.02

Making Connections within Mathematics

34. 9.11, 9.01, 9.101, 9.1
36. 4.751, 4.57, 4.705, 4.75

Exploration and Extension

37. *Building Your Chapter Project* A question that you can use for your Travel Trivia Game is as follows:

> *Since 1988, you have owned a restaurant that serves Indian food and accepts money from India. During which years could a customer have ordered a dish that costs $3 and paid you 53 rupees? Use the table, which shows the number of rupees that you could exchange for one dollar for the years 1987 to 1994. Would you round the numbers in the table to answer the question? Explain why or why not.*

Answer this question. Then write another question using the table about Indian money for your Travel Trivia Game.

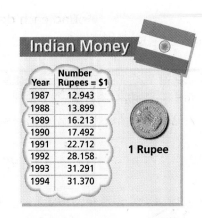

Indian Money

Year	Number Rupees = $1
1987	12.943
1988	13.899
1989	16.213
1990	17.492
1991	22.712
1992	28.158
1993	31.291
1994	31.370

1 Rupee

Materials Needed: paper, pencil

Part A There are five sizes of base-ten pieces on this page.

1. Which pieces are 10 times larger than another piece?
2. Describe any other patterns that you see among the pieces.
3. Describe the next larger piece.
4. Describe the next smaller piece.

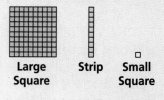

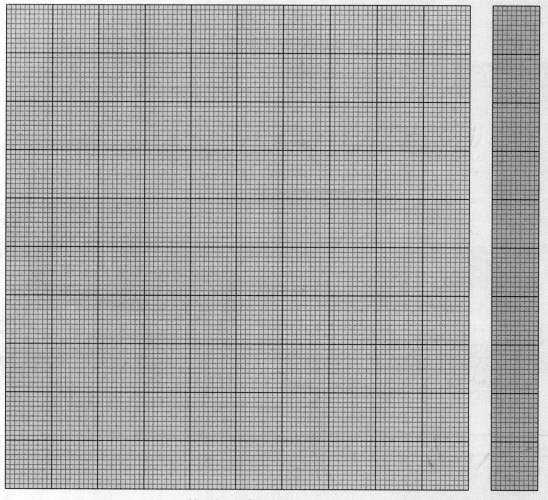

Very Large Square

Large Strip

Part B Consider the five base-ten pieces on page 134.

5. Which pieces are 100 times larger than another piece?
6. Which pieces are 1000 times larger than another piece?
7. Which piece is 10,000 times larger than another piece?
8. Suppose you drew the next two larger pieces. You can call them a very large strip and a very, very large square. How many small squares would these two pieces each contain?

Part C Complete the following statements.

1st Number: 10 = 10

9. *2nd Number:* $10 \times 10 = \boxed{?}$
10. *3rd Number:* $10 \times 10 \times 10 = \boxed{?}$
11. *4th Number:* $10 \times 10 \times 10 \times 10 = \boxed{?}$
12. *5th Number:* $10 \times 10 \times 10 \times 10 \times 10 = \boxed{?}$
13. *6th Number:* $10 \times 10 \times 10 \times 10 \times 10 \times 10 = \boxed{?}$
14. Describe the pattern for the results. What would the 10th number be?

On Your Own   *Critical Thinking*

15. If a small square represents 0.01, what will a very large square represent?
16. If a small square represents 0.1, what will a very large square represent?
17. If a small square represents 0.001, which piece will represent 1?
18. If a strip represents 1, what will a large strip represent?
19. If a very large square represents 1, what will a strip represent?
20. How many small cubes are in the large cube at the right? Explain your reasoning.

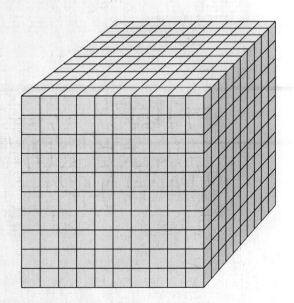

Connections to Algebra: Powers of Ten and Exponents

What you should learn:

Goal 1
How to use exponents to write powers

Goal 2
How to evaluate expressions that have exponents

Why you should learn it:

Exponents allow you to write mathematical expressions in simpler ways. For instance, $10 \times 10 \times 10$ can be written as 10^3.

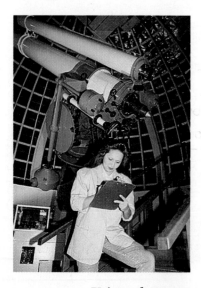

Using telescopes, astronomers were able to prove that the earth rotates around the sun at an average distance of 1.488 × 10⁹ km.

Goal 1 — **Using Exponents to Write Powers**

In Lab 3.7 you worked with expressions such as $10 \times 10 \times 10$. You can write this expression in a simpler way by using an **exponent**.

$$\underbrace{10 \times 10 \times 10}_{\text{Factors}} = \underbrace{10^3}_{\text{Power}}$$

Base — Exponent

The number 10 is the **base**. The number 3 is the **exponent**. The entire expression is a **power**.

Example 1 — *Writing Powers*

Number	Product	Power	Name
a. 16	4×4	4^2	4 to the 2nd power or 4 squared
b. 125	$5 \times 5 \times 5$	5^3	5 to the 3rd power or 5 cubed
c. 10,000	$10 \times 10 \times 10 \times 10$	10^4	10 to the 4th power

The numbers 10^2, 10^3, 10^4, and so on are called **powers of 10.** Powers of 10 can be used to help you write numbers in expanded notation.

Example 2 — *Numbers in Expanded Notation*

a. $1453 = (1 \times 1000) + (4 \times 100) + (5 \times 10) + (3 \times 1)$
$= (1 \times 10^3) + (4 \times 10^2) + (5 \times 10) + (3 \times 1)$

b. $3.92 = (3 \times 1) + (9 \times 0.1) + (2 \times 0.01)$

$= (3 \times 1) + \left(9 \times \frac{1}{10}\right) + \left(2 \times \frac{1}{100}\right)$

$= (3 \times 1) + \left(9 \times \frac{1}{10}\right) + \left(2 \times \frac{1}{10^2}\right)$

Evaluating Expressions

Connections
Geometry

Example 3 *Evaluating an Expression*

The area of a square whose sides have a length of x cm is given by x^2. Evaluate this expression when x is equal to 1, 2, 3, and 4. Then illustrate your results with a diagram.

Solution

Value of x	Expression	Substitute	Value
$x = 1$	x^2	1^2	1 square centimeter
$x = 2$	x^2	2^2	4 square centimeters
$x = 3$	x^2	3^2	9 square centimeters
$x = 4$	x^2	4^2	16 square centimeters

A diagram of the four squares is shown below.

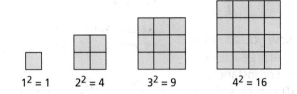

$1^2 = 1$ $2^2 = 4$ $3^2 = 9$ $4^2 = 16$

Powers need to be added to the list of order of operations on page 80.

Study Tip

Notice that in the order of operations, powers are evaluated after grouping symbols but before multiplication, division, addition, and subtraction. For example:

$$(3 + 2)^2 \times 2 = 5^2 \times 2$$
$$= 25 \times 2$$
$$= 50.$$

Order of Operations
1. First do operations within grouping symbols.
2. Then evaluate powers.
3. Then multiply and divide from left to right.
4. Finally add and subtract from left to right.

Communicating about **MATHEMATICS**

▶ **Sharing Ideas about the Lesson**

Algebra Evaluate each expression when $n = 3$. Explain your steps.
A. $(2 + n)^3$ **B.** $2 + n^3$ **C.** $2 + 3 \times n^3$

EXERCISES

Think and Discuss

▶ CHECK for Understanding

In Exercises 1–3, name each of the following in the expression 22^6.

1. Base
2. Exponent
3. Power
4. Write the values of 10^2, 10^3, 10^4, 10^5, and 10^6.
5. Write the number 29.23 in expanded notation using powers of ten.
6. *True or False?* The value of the expression $4^3 - 6 \times 10 + 5$ is 585. If false, what is the value?

Independent Practice

In Exercises 7–10, find the value of the exponent.

7. $36 = 6^{\boxed{?}}$
8. $16 = 2^{\boxed{?}}$
9. $27 = 3^{\boxed{?}}$
10. $\dfrac{1}{1000} = \dfrac{1}{10^{\boxed{?}}}$

In Exercises 11–14, find the value of the base.

11. $81 = \boxed{?}^2$
12. $64 = \boxed{?}^3$
13. $32 = \boxed{?}^5$
14. $\dfrac{1}{10,000} = \dfrac{1}{\boxed{?}^4}$

In Exercises 15–20, evaluate the power.

15. 5^4
16. 3^6
17. 9^3
18. $\dfrac{1}{10^4}$
19. $\dfrac{1}{100^3}$
20. 7^3

In Exercises 21–24, use a calculator to evaluate the power.

Sample: $8^3 = 8 \;\boxed{\times}\; 8 \;\boxed{\times}\; 8 \;\boxed{=}\;$ or $\; 8^3 = 8 \;\boxed{y^x}\; 3 \;\boxed{=}$

21. 23^3
22. 125^2
23. 11^4
24. 50^3

Science In Exercises 25–28, the swimming speed (in cm per second) of four animals is given. Write the number in expanded notation using powers of ten.

25. Goldfish: 75
26. Penguin: 380
27. Dolphin: 1030
28. Water mite: 0.4

Penguins are unusual birds because they stand upright on very short legs.

Evaluate the power. Then round the number to the nearest ten.

29. 7^2 **30.** 5^3 **31.** 13^3 **32.** 24^2

Geometry You are given the area of a square. Find the lengths of the sides.

33. 64 square cm   **34.** 49 square in.   **35.** 100 square mm   **36.** 121 square ft

Complete the statement.

37. $10^4 = \boxed{?} \times 10^2$ **38.** $10^5 = \boxed{?} \times 10^2$

Algebra Evaluate the expression when $t = 4$.

39. $(t - 2)^5 - 5$ **40.** $8 + 2 \times t^2$ **41.** $6 + t^3 \div 8$ **42.** $30 - (t + 1)^2$

43. *Reasoning* The ski club sets up a telephone tree. The first person in the tree calls 4 people. Each of the 4 people call 4 other people. They each call 4 other people. How many people have been called?

44. You are working in a warehouse. You can stack boxes in a room so that they are 12 high, 12 wide, and 12 long. How many boxes can you fit in the room?

Integrated Review   *Making Connections within Mathematics*

Number Theory Complete the statement and evaluate. Then use a calculator to check your answer.

Example: $37 \times (3 + 7) = 3^3 + 7^3 = 370$

45. $48 \times (4 + 8) = 4^3 + \boxed{?}^3$ **46.** $111 \times (11 + 1) = 11^3 + \boxed{?}^3$

47. $147 \times (14 + 7) = \boxed{?}^3 + 7^3$ **48.** $148 \times (14 + 8) = \boxed{?}^3 + 8^3$

Exploration and Extension

49. *Building Your Chapter Project* A question that you can use for your Travel Trivia Game is as follows.

> *You are studying the Chilean money system. You tell a friend that 10×10^2 centavos is equal to 2 cents. Your friend says that it is about 10,000 centavos. Which of you is correct? Why?*

Answer this question. Then write a question about Chilean money for your Travel Trivia Game.

Chilean Money

1 Peso

100 centavos = 1 peso

1994 Rate:

10 pesos = \$0.02

More Problem Solving Using Decimals, Fractions, and Percents

What you should learn:

Goal 1 How to use fractions to solve real-life problems

Goal 2 How to use percents to solve real-life problems

Why you should learn it:

Decimals can be written as fractions or percents. You need to use all three forms to be an effective problem solver.

Real Life
Advertising

The average person in the United States consumes about 14 pounds of oranges per year.

Goal 1 **Using Fractions in Real Life**

Remember that decimals can be written as fractions or percents. Here is an example.

Decimal Form	Fraction Form	Percent Form
0.2	$\frac{2}{10}$	20%

Many real-life problems have questions of the form, "What is $\frac{2}{10}$ of 30 cars?" or "What is 20% of 30 cars?"

One way to answer this question is to use a **set model**, like that shown below. In the model, each group represents one tenth, so two tenths contain 6 cars.

Example 1 *Using Fractions in Real Life*

An advertisement states that $\frac{4}{10}$ of all middle school students drink orange juice at least once a week. There are twenty students in your class. According to the ad, how many drink orange juice at least once a week?

Solution One way to solve this problem is to use a set model and divide the 20 students into 10 groups.

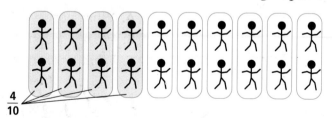

Because each group represents 1 tenth of the class, 4 tenths must contain 8 students.

Example 2   *Using Percents in Real Life*

In a survey, 200 people were asked whether they played a musical instrument. Thirty-five percent said they did. How many said they played a musical instrument?

Solution   Remember that 35% can be written as 0.35 or $\frac{35}{100}$. To find 35% of 200, divide a collection of 200 objects into 100 groups. Count the number of objects in 35 of the groups. From the model, you can see that 35% of 200 is 70. Thus, 70 people said they played a musical instrument.

The 200 dots are divided into 100 groups.

Each group has 2 dots.

35 of the groups have 70 dots.

Real Life
Music

The saxophone, invented in 1840 by Adolphe Sax, is a popular instrument in concert, dance, and jazz bands.

Communicating about MATHEMATICS

▶ **Sharing Ideas about the Lesson**

Decimals, Fractions, and Percents Use the numbers at the left to write three answers for each question. What model did you use to solve these? Why?

A. What portion of the instruments are trumpets?
B. What portion of the instruments are guitars?
C. What portion of the instruments are saxophones?

Cooperative Learning

30%   0.50 $\frac{5}{10}$

$\frac{20}{100}$ 0.2

20%   0.3 $\frac{3}{10}$

50%

EXERCISES

Think and Discuss

▶ **CHECK for Understanding**

1. Use a set model to find 60% of 40 strawberries.
2. The area model at the right shows 50% of 1000 students who do an after-school activity. How many students does this represent?

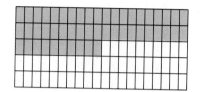

Statistics In Exercises 3–5, choose three correct answers for each exercise from the numbers at the right. A survey was taken of 20 students who were asked to name their favorite Popsicle® flavor: cherry, orange, or grape. The results are shown in the figure at the right.

$$25\% \qquad \frac{35}{100} \qquad \frac{7}{20} \qquad 35\% \qquad \frac{4}{10}$$
$$0.40 \qquad \frac{1}{4} \qquad 0.25 \qquad 40\%$$

3. What portion of the Popsicles are cherry?
4. What portion of the Popsicles are orange?
5. What portion of the Popsicles are grape?

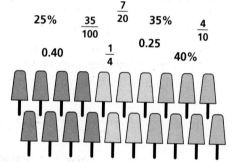

Independent Practice

In Exercises 6 and 7, write the decimal, fraction, and percent that represent the blue portion of the figure.

6.

7.

Use a set model to help you answer the question.

8. What is 70% of 20 baseballs?

9. What is 30% of 30 dollars?

Use the area model to help you find the number.

10. 15% of 300

11. 40% of 500

12. *Animals and Pets* On an average day, $\frac{7}{100}$ of all new dogs registered are Labrador retrievers. If 200 dogs are registered, how many are Labrador retrievers? *(Source: American Kennel Club)*

13. *Education* A class of 50 students took a test. The portions of students who received each letter grade are shown in the table. Use a set model to find the number of students that received each letter grade.

A	$\frac{4}{10}$
B	30%
C	0.20
D	10%

14. *Reading a Graph* On each work day, over 35 million United States coins are minted. The portions of these that are pennies, nickels, dimes, and quarters are shown in the graph below. Write each portion as a decimal, fraction, and percent. *(Source: U.S. Mint)*

Pennies	● ● ● ● ● ● ● ● ○ ○
Nickels	◐ ○ ○ ○ ○ ○ ○ ○ ○ ○
Dimes	● ○ ○ ○ ○ ○ ○ ○ ○ ○
Quarters	● ○ ○ ○ ○ ○ ○ ○ ○ ○

15. *Football* A survey of 200 people asked if they would rather watch a professional football game at home or at a stadium. Fifty-five percent said they would rather watch the game at home. Was this more than 100 people? Explain.

Integrated Review   Making Connections within Mathematics

Look for a Pattern Look for patterns to help you find the missing number. Explain your reasoning.

16.

1.3	0.1	1.4
1.2	?	2.2
2.5	1.1	3.6

17.

90.9	40.3	50.6
20.5	11.4	9.1
70.4	28.9	?

Exploration and Extension

18. *Building Your Chapter Project* A question that you can use for your Travel Trivia Game is as follows.

You have won a trip to Greece. While in Greece, you buy a souvenir for your friend. You spend 20% of 5830 drachmas. Use a model to find how many drachmas you spent. How much money is this in dollars?

Answer this question. Then write a similar question about Greek money for your Travel Trivia Game.

Greek Money

20 Drachma
1994 Rate:
5830 Drachmas = $25

3

Chapter Summary

What did you learn?

Skills

1. Write decimals in expanded notation. **(3.1)**
2. Measure lengths in the metric system. **(3.2)**
3. Change units of length in the metric system. **(3.2)**
4. Show decimals with models:
   - Area models **(Lab 3.3)**
   - Number-line models and set models **(3.3)**
5. Rewrite decimals as fractions or percents. **(3.4)**
6. Compare and order decimals. **(3.5)**
7. Round decimals. **(3.6)**
8. Use exponents to write powers. **(3.7)**
9. Evaluate expressions that have exponents. **(3.7)**

Strategies

10. Use problem-solving strategies to solve problems. **(3.1–3.8)**

Exploring Data

11. Use tables and graphs to organize data and solve problems. **(3.1–3.8)**

Why did you learn it?

Many real-life problems cannot be easily solved using whole numbers. Instead, you need to use decimals, fractions, or percents. Here are some examples you studied in this chapter.

- Interpret a graph for a survey about owning pets. **(3.3)**
- Interpret a diagram for a survey about favorite colors. **(3.4)**
- Compare winning times for a women's freestyle race. **(3.5)**
- Make a decision about batting averages in baseball. **(3.6)**
- Interpret an advertising claim about orange-juice drinkers. **(3.8)**

How does it fit into the bigger picture of mathematics?

Throughout your school life, you will take many classes in mathematics. You will find that the different parts of mathematics have many connections. For instance, in this chapter, you found connections among decimals, fractions, and percents.

Understanding the connections among the parts of mathematics makes you a better problem solver, because it gives you more choices. For instance, in this chapter, you learned to use a set model to find the percent of a number. In the next chapter, you will learn how to use decimal multiplication to solve similar problems.

Complete the statement. **(3.1)**

1. 100 tenths = $\boxed{?}$ hundredths
2. 100 thousandths = $\boxed{?}$ tenths
3. 10 ones = $\boxed{?}$ hundreds
4. 1000 hundredths = $\boxed{?}$ thousandths

Write the number in expanded notation using decimals. **(3.1)**

5. 75.24
6. 100.72
7. 541.99
8. 1004.701

Write which metric unit (millimeter, centimeter, meter, or kilometer) would be reasonable to measure the object. **(3.2)**

9. Width of a pencil lead
10. Distance between two cities
11. Width of a calculator
12. Height of a room

13. *Making Connections* Rewrite the decimals 0.25, 0.50, and 0.75 as fractions and as percents. Which of the three forms do you prefer? Why do you prefer it? **(3.4)**

Write the number as a fraction. **(3.4)**

14. 0.54
15. 67%
16. 33%
17. 0.897

Sports and Athletics In Exercises 18 and 19, use the table at the right. It shows the winning times (in seconds) for women running the 100-meter dash in the Olympics. **(3.5, 3.6)**

Year	1976	1980	1984	1988	1992
Time	11.01	11.06	10.97	10.54	10.82

18. Order the times from least to greatest.
19. Round the times to the nearest tenth.

Reading a Graph The graph at the right shows the portion of teachers who prefer red and golden delicious apples. *(Source: U.S. Bureau of Labor Statistics)* **(3.8)**

20. What fraction prefer red delicious?
21. What fraction prefer golden delicious?

Apples Teachers Prefer

Red Delicious   Golden Delicious

In Exercises 22–25, evaluate the power. **(3.7)**

22. 12^2
23. 2^6
24. 6^3
25. 10^3

Use a set model to answer the question. **(3.8)**

26. What is 30% of 60 books?
27. What is 25% of 200 pages?

The table at the right shows the prices of two items in 1967 and 1990. *(Sources: Hershey's USA, Motion Picture Association)*

Year	Candy Bar	Movie Ticket
1967	$0.10	$1.25
1990	$0.50	$4.50

28. The price of a candy bar in 1967 is 20% of the 1990 price. Write this percent as a fraction.

29. The price of a movie in 1967 is 28% of the 1990 price. Write this percent as a decimal.

30. *"Who's on the Dollar?" Puzzle* The names of the people shown on the $1, $5, $10, $20, $50, and $100 bills are listed below. To find who is on each bill, order the names according to the numbers next to the names, from least to greatest. The first person in the list is on the $1 bill, the second person is on the $5 bill, and so on.

George Washington

Abraham Lincoln   Andrew Jackson

a. Abraham Lincoln $\frac{205}{1000}$

b. Ulysses S. Grant 0.222

c. Benjamin Franklin 22%

d. Alexander Hamilton 0.21

e. George Washington 20%

f. Andrew Jackson $\frac{215}{1000}$

31. *Printing Money* The United States Bureau of Engraving and Printing produces all new paper money. The bar graph below shows the number (in millions) of bills that are printed per day. Round the number shown by each bar to the nearest tenth of a million. *(U.S. Bureau of Engraving and Printing)*

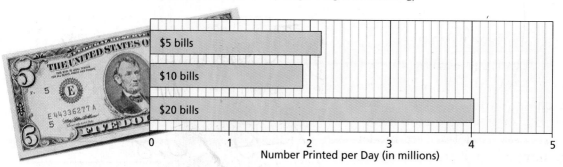

Foreign Coins Evaluate the expressions. Unscramble the word by ordering the values of the expressions from least to greatest.

32. Coin from Peru

$$\frac{N}{160 \div 2^2} \quad \frac{T}{4^2 \times 3} \quad \frac{I}{4 \times 3^2} \quad \frac{I}{(5+1) \times 3^3}$$

33. Coin from Bangladesh

$$\frac{A}{6^2 - 2} \quad \frac{A}{3^2 \times 2^2} \quad \frac{T}{5^2 + 1} \quad \frac{K}{(7-4)^3 + 8}$$

In Exercises 1–4, write the number.

1. Six and nine tenths

2. Fourteen and five hundredths

3. Six hundred twelve thousandths

4. Three hundred and three hundredths

In Exercises 5–9, complete the statement.

5. 1.45 ones = [?] tenths

6. [?] hundredths = 30 thousandths

7. 205 m = [?] km

8. 0.71 = [?] %

9. $\dfrac{[?]}{100} = 0.06$

In Exercises 10 and 11, you are given a model for a portion of a whole. Draw the model for the whole.

10.

0.7

11.

0.29

In Exercises 12 and 13, order the numbers from least to greatest.

12. 6.109, 6.2, 6.019, 6.19, 6.129

13. 32.89, 33.09, 32.94, 33.90, 32.08

Statistics The bar graph at the right shows the portion of income that people in each country save. *(Source: Organization for Economic Cooperation and Development)*

14. Round each number to the nearest hundredth.

15. Rewrite each rounded number as a percent.

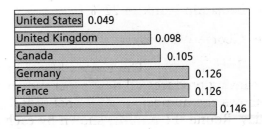

United States	0.049
United Kingdom	0.098
Canada	0.105
Germany	0.126
France	0.126
Japan	0.146

Evaluate the expression when $n = 5$.

16. $1 + n^2$

17. $(1 + n)^2 \div 4$

18. *Drawing a Diagram* In order to be in the chess tournament, you must attend 90% of the chess club meetings. Use a set model or area model to find how many of the 40 meetings you must attend.

19. *Checkers* Each player in checkers has 12 checkers. You have captured $\frac{5}{6}$ of your opponent's checkers. How many of your opponent's checkers do you have?

In 1991, Judit Polgar (far right) of Hungary, age 15, became the youngest chess grandmaster in the world.

Finding a Pattern In Exercises 1 and 2, the first three figures of a pattern are shown. Make a table of their perimeters and areas. Describe the pattern. Find the perimeter and area of the next three figures. Check your answer with sketches. **(1.1, 1.2)**

1.

2.
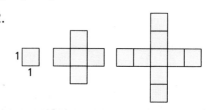

Drawing a Diagram In Exercises 3 and 4, draw the figure on a 6-by-6 grid of dot paper. **(1.5)**

3. A square with an area of 9 square units

4. Two rectangles with perimeters of 12 units

Algebra and Mental Math Use mental math to solve. **(1.6, 2.3, 2.4, 2.6)**

5. $x - 14 = 12$

6. $58 - y = 17$

7. $675 + a = 1000$

8. $b \cdot 12 = 48$

9. $s \cdot s = 121$

10. $27 \div t = 1$

11. $d \div 4 = 60$

12. $2(x + 1) = 14$

13. $5(3 + y) = 30$

Working Backward Copy and complete the model. **(1.7)**

14.
$$\times 7 \quad \div 5 \quad -6 \quad +8$$
| ? | ? | ? | ? | 16 |

15.
$$-7 \quad \div 3 \quad +4 \quad \times 2$$
| ? | ? | ? | ? | 38 |

In Exercises 16–19, complete the statement. **(2.1, 3.2)**

16. $\boxed{?}$ hundreds = 6400

17. $8150 = \boxed{?}$ tens

18. 0.392 km = $\boxed{?}$ m

19. $\boxed{?}$ mm = 5.75 cm

In Exercises 20–22, look at the base-ten pieces at the right. Complete the statement with the words *large squares*, *strips*, or *small squares*. **(3.1)**

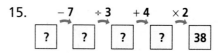

20. 31.5 $\boxed{?}$

21. 315 $\boxed{?}$

22. 3.15 $\boxed{?}$

Algebra Evaluate the expression. **(2.5, 3.7)**

23. $2^3 + (3 \times 4) - 5$

24. $33 \div 3 + 2 \times 7$

25. $37 - 3^4 \div 9 \times 4$

Evaluate the expression in two ways. **(2.6)**

26. $4(9 + 6)$

27. $3(12 + 10)$

28. $7(8 + 12)$

29. $3(13 + 2)$

In Exercises 30 and 31, you are shown a model for a portion of a whole. Draw a model of the whole. **(3.3)**

30.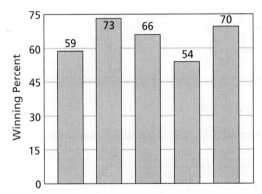

0.24

31.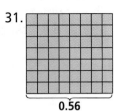

0.56

True or False? In Exercises 32–35, decide whether the statement is true or false. Explain your reasoning. **(3.4)**

32. $\frac{9}{10} = 90\%$

33. $30\% = \frac{3}{100}$

34. $\frac{8}{10} = 0.08$

35. $70\% = 0.7$

Round each number to the given place value. **(3.6)**

36. 6.93 (tenths)

37. 24.8 (ones)

38. 7511 (thousands)

39. *Probability* You flip a coin three times. List the different outcomes of heads (h) and tails (t) you could get. **(1.3)**

Reading Graphs The bar graphs below show the winning percents of the top five teams in the NBA Eastern Conference for the 1992–93 season. *(Source: National Basketball Association)* **(1.4, 3.4–3.6)**

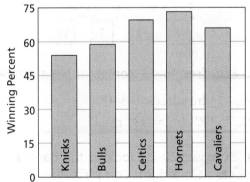

40. Match the teams with their winning percents.
41. Change each percent to a decimal.
42. Order the decimals from greatest to least.
43. Round each decimal to the nearest tenth.
44. *Buying a Radio* You are saving money to buy a radio that costs $50. Each week you earn $20. The first week you save 40% of your earnings. Each week you save 10% more of your earnings than the week before. How many weeks will it take you to save enough money to buy your radio? **(1.8, 1.9, 3.8)**

Applications of Decimals and Percents

These students at a Culinary Institute are studying the art of cooking. After culinary training, they could become restaurant owners, chefs, or one of many restaurant-related professionals.

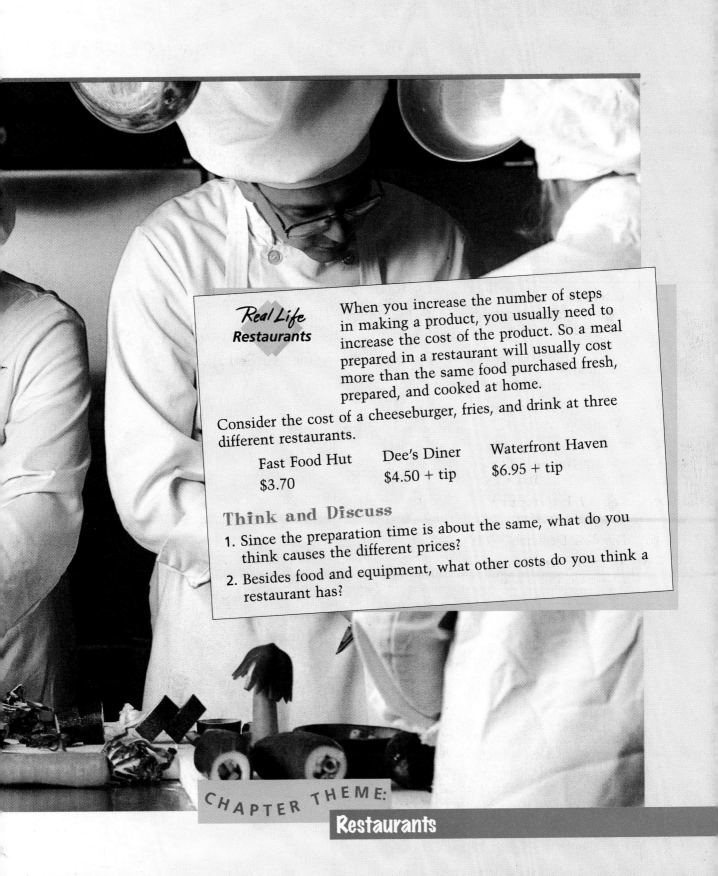

Real Life
Restaurants

When you increase the number of steps in making a product, you usually need to increase the cost of the product. So a meal prepared in a restaurant will usually cost more than the same food purchased fresh, prepared, and cooked at home.

Consider the cost of a cheeseburger, fries, and drink at three different restaurants.

Fast Food Hut	Dee's Diner	Waterfront Haven
$3.70	$4.50 + tip	$6.95 + tip

Think and Discuss

1. Since the preparation time is about the same, what do you think causes the different prices?

2. Besides food and equipment, what other costs do you think a restaurant has?

Making an

Employee Training Manual

Theme: Restaurants Has anyone in your family started a new job recently? If so, you may have seen their employee training manual.

An employee training manual shows employees how to do some of the basic tasks of their job, such as writing up an order or computing their wages.

In this project, imagine that you own a restaurant. You will make an employee training manual for the restaurant. The manual will explain the following things.

⇨ **In Lesson 4.1:** How to write up a sample bill with its total (page 159)

⇨ **In Lesson 4.2:** How to make change for a customer (page 163)

⇨ **In Lesson 4.4:** How to find a 15% tip for a bill (page 175)

⇨ **In Lesson 4.5:** How to find the amount of uncooked hamburger needed for a quarter-pound of cooked hamburger (page 181)

⇨ **In Lesson 4.7:** How to purchase the best food buys (page 191)

⇨ **In Lesson 4.8:** How to calculate an employee's wages (page 195)

GETTING STARTED

Materials: Plain paper, colored pencils or markers, pens

Decide what type of food your restaurant will serve. Will it be pizza, hamburgers, Chinese, seafood, or something else? Choose a name for your restaurant.

Fold several sheets of plain paper in half. This will create a booklet with a front and back cover. On the front cover, write your name, your restaurant's name, and *Employee Training Manual*.

Place the booklet in your portfolio. Write new pages for your training manual when you are asked throughout the chapter.

Materials Needed: base-ten pieces or grid paper, paper, pencils

In Chapter 3, you learned how to use base-ten pieces to show decimal numbers. For instance, you can let a large square be one, a strip be 1 tenth, and a small square be 1 hundredth.

Base-ten pieces can be used to show addition and subtraction of decimals. Two examples are shown below.

Base-Ten Pieces

Large Square
Ones
piece
1

Strip
Tenths
piece
0.1

Small Square
Hundredths
piece
0.01

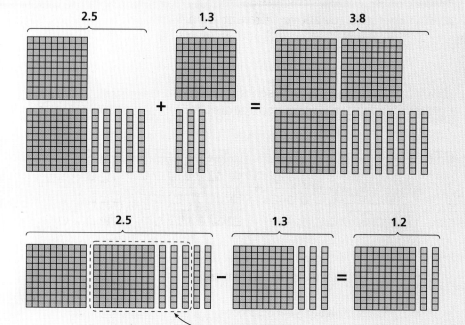

Remove these.

Part A *Modeling Addition with Base-Ten Pieces*

1. Use base-ten pieces to show each addition problem. Draw a sketch to help you add.

   a. 3.2 + 1.4   b. 0.62 + 0.37   c. 3 + 0.33   d. 1.36 + 2.47

2. In (b) above, suppose you added 1 hundredth piece to the answer. What would you get? Explain.

3. In (c) above, write the problem in vertical form.

4. How is the addition problem in (d) above different from the other three addition problems? How did you solve it?

5. Use base-ten pieces to show each subtraction problem. Draw a sketch to help you subtract.

    a. $3.4 - 1.2$ b. $0.67 - 0.36$ c. $3.2 - 0.2$ d. $3.36 - 2.27$

6. In (b) above, suppose you subtracted 1 hundredth piece from the answer. What would you get?

7. In (c) above, write the problem in vertical form.

8. How is the subtraction problem in (d) above different from the other three subtraction problems? How did you solve it?

Part C *Making Connections*

9. Use the diagram below. If a large square represents one, what addition problem is shown? If a large square represents 1 hundred, what addition problem is shown?

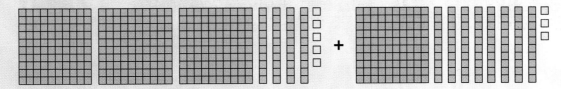

On Your Own   *Critical Thinking*

10. Draw a sketch of base-ten pieces to help you add or subtract.

    a. $2.75 + 1.34$ b. $2 + 1.04$ c. $4.04 - 0.4$ d. $4 - 1.6$

11. Which do you think is the best vertical form of $1.46 + 3$? Explain your reasoning.

    a. $\begin{array}{r} 1.46 \\ + 3 \\ \hline \end{array}$ b. $\begin{array}{r} 1.46 \\ + 3 \\ \hline \end{array}$ c. $\begin{array}{r} 1.46 \\ +3 \\ \hline \end{array}$

12. Which do you think is the best vertical form of $13.2 - 0.28$? Explain your reasoning.

    a. $\begin{array}{r} 13.2 \\ - .28 \\ \hline \end{array}$ b. $\begin{array}{r} 13.2 \\ - .28 \\ \hline \end{array}$ c. $\begin{array}{r} 13.2 \\ -.28 \\ \hline \end{array}$

4.1

Adding Decimals

What you should learn:

Goal 1 How to add decimals

Goal 2 How to use decimal addition to solve real-life problems

Why you should learn it:

Decimal addition can be used to help you find the total cost of things. An example is finding the total of a restaurant bill.

Goal 1 Adding Decimals

Example 1 *Vertical Form to Add Decimals*

Use base-ten pieces to show or model $2.2 + 0.87$. Then write the problem in vertical form.

Solution

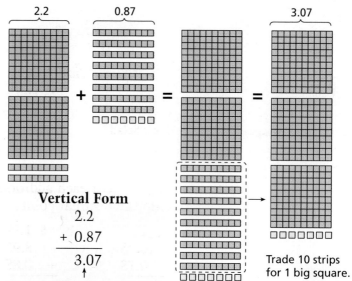

2.2   0.87   3.07

Vertical Form

$$
\begin{array}{r}
2.2 \\
+\ 0.87 \\
\hline
3.07
\end{array}
$$

Line up decimal points so that the same units are added.

Trade 10 strips for 1 big square.

Notice that the steps for adding decimals are similar to the steps for adding whole numbers.

Study Tip

Remember that whole numbers have an **"unwritten" decimal point.** For instance, 5 is the same as 5.0.

Lesson Investigation

■ Investigating Decimal Addition

Group Activity Use a vertical form to add each problem. Do your answers seem reasonable? Compare your answers with others in your group.

a. $4.72 + 2.5$ **b.** $5.32 + 7$ **c.** $0.247 + 1.9$

d. $1.09 + 2.91$ **e.** $42 + 0.38$ **f.** $0.01 + 5$

Solving Real-Life Problems

Example 2 *Adding Decimals*

Part of a menu is shown below. Find the cost of each order.

a. 1 green salad, 1 chicken dinner, 1 milk
b. 1 fruit salad, 1 pasta dinner, 1 iced tea
c. 1 onion soup, 1 steak dinner, 1 sparkling water

Real Life
Restaurant

Of all the pastas, spaghetti is the most popular in Italy and the best known around the world.

Menu

Dinners

Pasta Dinner	$8.95
Chicken Dinner	$10.25
Steak Dinner	$13.75

Soup & Salad

Onion Soup	$1.59
Green Salad	$1.19
Fruit Salad	$1.39

Beverages

Milk	$0.78
Iced Tea	$0.88
Sparkling Water	$1.28

Solution For each addition, use a vertical form and line up the decimal points.

a.
$$\begin{array}{r} \$\ 1.19 \\ 10.25 \\ +\ \ 0.78 \\ \hline \$12.22 \end{array}$$

b.
$$\begin{array}{r} \$\ 1.39 \\ 8.95 \\ +\ \ 0.88 \\ \hline \$11.22 \end{array}$$

c.
$$\begin{array}{r} \$\ 1.59 \\ 13.75 \\ +\ \ 1.28 \\ \hline \$16.62 \end{array}$$ ∎

Communicating about MATHEMATICS

Cooperative Learning

▶ **Sharing Ideas about the Lesson**

Group Activity Here are three totals for food ordered from the menu shown above. What could have been ordered? How can you tell?

A. $10.14   **B.** $11.32   **C.** $16.02

EXERCISES

Think and Discuss

▶ **CHECK for Understanding**

1. Copy and complete the base-ten model. Write the problem in vertical form and solve. (Large square = 1 unit)

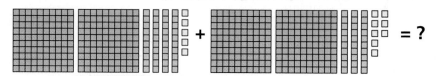

2. *Error Analysis* Describe the error at the right. Then write a similar problem that *does* have 2 as its sum.

3. Write three different addition problems whose sum is 10.45.

Independent Practice

In Exercises 4 and 5, copy and complete the model.
Write and solve in vertical form. (Large square = 1 unit)

4.

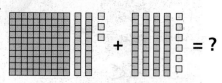

5.

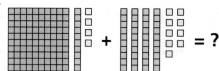

In Exercises 6–9, use a vertical form to add.

6. $6.87 + 7.24$ 7. $0.3 + 9.06$ 8. $0.08 + 8$ 9. $13.6 + 0.95 + 2.2$

In Exercises 10–13, find the missing digits.

10.
$$\begin{array}{r} 3.8\boxed{?} \\ +\ 0.\boxed{?}5 \\ \hline \boxed{?}.95 \end{array}$$

11.
$$\begin{array}{r} \boxed{?}.07 \\ +\ 3.\boxed{?}\boxed{?} \\ \hline 9.91 \end{array}$$

12.
$$\begin{array}{r} 4.\boxed{?}\boxed{?} \\ +\ 0.5 \\ \hline \boxed{?}.37 \end{array}$$

13.
$$\begin{array}{r} \boxed{?}2.0 \\ +\ \boxed{?}.\boxed{?} \\ \hline 36.3 \end{array}$$

Algebra In Exercises 14–16, use mental math to solve.

14. $0.01 + x = 48.01$ 15. $y + 0.36 = 31.36$ 16. $26.2 + z = 35.2$

Geometry In Exercises 17 and 18, find the perimeter of the figure.

17.
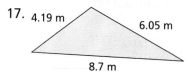

18.
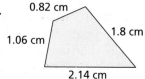

In Exercises 19 and 20, use a calculator to add. Describe any patterns that you see. Write the next 2 problems in the pattern.

19. $28.012 + 94.3 = \boxed{?}$

    $29.123 + 94.3 = \boxed{?}$

    $30.234 + 94.3 = \boxed{?}$

20. $545.45 + 565.55 = \boxed{?}$

    $656.56 + 1565.44 = \boxed{?}$

    $767.67 + 2565.33 = \boxed{?}$

Number Puzzle In Exercises 21 and 22, copy and complete the pyramid. Each number is the sum of the two numbers below it.

21.

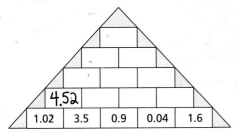

| 4.52 | | | | |
| 1.02 | 3.5 | 0.9 | 0.04 | 1.6 |

22.

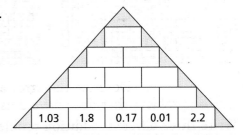

| 1.03 | 1.8 | 0.17 | 0.01 | 2.2 |

Ski Jumping You are an Olympic ski-jumper. You participate in three different jumps. Your points for the three jumps are 85.39, 92.6, and 89.07. To win a medal, your total points must be at least the following: Gold—270.08, Silver—265.54, and Bronze—263.1.

23. What is your total score? What medal did you win?

24. Use mental math to find the number of points your score was from the gold medal position.

Kip Lutu, 13, from Steamboat Springs, Colorado, has been ski jumping since age 6. He can fly off a 90-meter jump like those used in the Olympics.

Integrated Review   *Making Connections within Mathematics*

Round the number to the given place value.

25. 3.062 (tenths)

26. 6.49 (ones)

27. 8.013 (hundredths)

28. 15.096 (hundredths)

29. 16.5 (ones)

30. 20.746 (tenths)

Exploration and Extension

31. *Building Your Chapter Project* For your restaurant's *Employee Training Manual,* write a menu that shows some or all of the items you will serve. Include the price of each item. Then write a sample bill that shows how your employees should total a bill. Include at least 3 menu items on the bill.

4.2

Subtracting Decimals

What you should learn:

Goal 1 How to subtract decimals

Goal 2 How to use decimal subtraction to solve real-life problems

Why you should learn it:

Decimal subtraction can be used to help you make change with money. An example is finding your change when you pay for a purchase.

Goal 1 **Subtracting Decimals**

Example 1 *Using a Vertical Form to Subtract*

Use base-ten pieces to show or model $2.6 - 0.43$. Then write and solve the problem in vertical form.

Solution

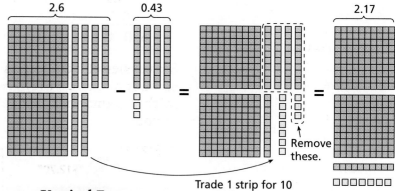

Trade 1 strip for 10 small squares.

Vertical Form

$$
\begin{array}{r}
2.60 \\
-\ 0.43 \\
\hline
2.17
\end{array}
$$

Line up decimal points so that the same units are subtracted.

Notice that the steps for subtracting decimals are similar to the steps for subtracting whole numbers.

Study Tip

Error Analysis Here are two common subtraction errors when writing $3.2 - 1.78$. What is wrong with each subtraction?

a. $\begin{array}{r} 3.2 \\ -1.78 \\ \hline 1.54 \end{array}$

b. $\begin{array}{r} 1.78 \\ -3.2 \\ \hline 1.46 \end{array}$

Lesson Investigation

■ **Investigating Decimal Subtraction**

Group Activity Use a vertical form to subtract each problem. Compare your answers with others in your group.

a. $3.42 - 2.4$ **b.** $4.63 - 3$ **c.** $4.247 - 1.9$
d. $8 - 0.38$ **e.** $0.14 - 0.13$ **f.** $6.69 - 4.2$

Example 2 *Making Change*

You buy a T-shirt for $12.69. You give the sales clerk $20. How much change do you get back?

Solution You can subtract to solve this problem.

$$\begin{array}{r} \$20.00 \\ -\ 12.69 \\ \hline \$\ 7.31 \end{array}$$

$20.00 *Amount you give clerk*
$12.69 *Cost of T-shirt*
$ 7.31 *Change*   ∎

You can check the result of a subtraction problem by adding.

$$\begin{array}{r} \$12.69 \\ +\ 7.31 \\ \hline \$20.00 \end{array}$$

$12.69 *Cost of T-shirt*
$ 7.31 *Change*
$20.00 *Amount you give clerk*

Some sales clerks use this technique to check the amount of change they give. Here is how a sales clerk might "count your change" when he or she hands it to you.

> **Study Tip**
>
> When you subtract a decimal from a whole number, it helps to write a decimal point and 1 or more zeros with the whole number. For example, here is how you can find 3 − 1.56.
>
> $$\begin{array}{r} 3.00 \quad \text{(Write 2 zeros.)} \\ -\ 1.56 \\ \hline 1.44 \end{array}$$

"$12.69" "$12.70"

"$12.80"

"$12.90" "$13.00" "$14.00" "$15.00" "$20.00"

Communicating about MATHEMATICS

Cooperative Learning

▶ Sharing Ideas about the Lesson

Making Change With your partner, take turns being the customer and the sales clerk. The sales clerk should first subtract to find the change, then "count the change" as it is handed back to the customer.

A. Customer hands clerk $20 for a bill of $13.53.

B. Customer hands clerk $30 for a bill of $21.18.

EXERCISES

Guided Practice

Think and Discuss

▶ **CHECK for Understanding**

1. What subtraction problem is modeled by the base-ten pieces below? Solve the problem. (Large square = 1 unit)

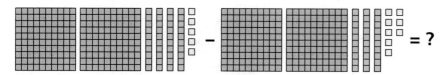

Error Analysis In Exercises 2–4, decide whether the vertical form is correct. If not, correct the form.

2. 0.76−0.2

$$\begin{array}{r} 0.76 \\ -\ 0.2 \\ \hline \end{array}$$

Correct vertical form?

3. 3−2.75

$$\begin{array}{r} 3.00 \\ -2.75 \\ \hline \end{array}$$

Correct vertical form?

4. 7.2−1.05

$$\begin{array}{r} 1.05 \\ -7.2 \\ \hline \end{array}$$

Correct vertical form?

Independent Practice

In Exercises 5 and 6, write the decimal problem shown by the model. Use a vertical form. Then solve. (Large square = 1 unit)

5.

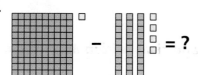

6.

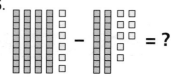

7. Choose the correct vertical form for 2 − 0.81. Then solve.

a.
$$\begin{array}{r} 2 \\ -\ 0.81 \\ \hline \end{array}$$

b.
$$\begin{array}{r} 2.00 \\ -\ 0.81 \\ \hline \end{array}$$

Data Analysis The table at the right shows the percents of people 18–24 years old who are different heights. *(Source: United States Center for Health Statistics)*

8. Find the difference in percents of men who are 5-foot 9-inches and 5-foot 8-inches.

9. Find the difference in percents of women who are 5-foot 3-inches and 5-foot 2-inches.

Height	Percent of Men	Percent of Women
5′ 2″	0.16	8.62
5′ 3″	0.27	11.31
5′ 4″	1.76	12.75
5′ 5″	1.48	16.28
5′ 6″	4.39	16.67
5′ 7″	7.94	10.61
5′ 8″	10.50	6.93
5′ 9″	12.21	3.93
5′ 10″	14.77	2.11
5′ 11″	14.59	1.04
6′ 0″	11.89	0.62

In Exercises 10–17, use a vertical form to subtract.

10. $6.75 - 2.3$ **11.** $4.33 - 3.9$ **12.** $7.619 - 3.8$ **13.** $5.452 - 2.91$

14. $5 - 2.89$ **15.** $12 - 7.652$ **16.** $0.88 - 0.39$ **17.** $1.25 - 0.056$

In Exercises 18–21, use a calculator to evaluate the expression.

18. $3.421 - 1.42 + 1.301$ **19.** $7.56 - 2.019 + 5.451$

20. $2.25 + 7.789 - 4.342$ **21.** $11.010 + 5.672 - 8.999$

Nutrition The map at the right shows the average pounds of snack foods such as pretzels and popcorn that people eat in a year. *(Source: Snack Food Association)*

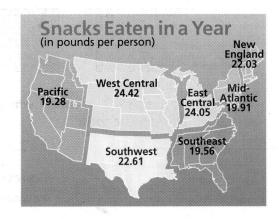

22. Where are the most snacks eaten? Where are the fewest? What is the difference between the amounts eaten in these two regions?

23. How many more pounds of snacks do people in the Southwest eat than people in the Mid-Atlantic?

Consumer Spending   Was the correct change given? Explain.

24. You give the clerk a $20 bill and receive a $10 bill and 2 dimes in change for a purchase of $10.80.

25. You use $20 to buy a concert ticket for $18.74. The clerk counts your $1.26 change as "$18.75, $19.00, $20.00."

Integrated Review   *Making Connections within Mathematics*

Use the Distributive Property to complete the statement.

26. $3(4.5 + 3.35) = 3 \times (4.5) + 3 \times (\boxed{?})$

27. $5 \times (5.01) + 5 \times (4.23) = 5(\boxed{?} + 4.23)$

28. *Number Sense*   I am a 3-digit number divisible by 2. My last 2 digits are the same. The sum of my digits is 25. What number am I?

Exploration and Extension

29. *Building Your Chapter Project*   For your restaurant's *Employee Training Manual*, write 2 samples that show how to find the amount of change a customer should get. The samples should include items from your menu.

Describe the pattern. Then write the next 3 numbers. **(1.1)**

1. $\frac{1}{3}, \frac{1}{6}, \frac{1}{9},$?, ?, ?

2. 9.25, 9.5, 9.75, ?, ?, ?

Find the missing digits. Use a calculator to check. **(2.2–2.4)**

3.
$$\begin{array}{r} ?6? \\ +\ 1?5 \\ \hline 604 \end{array}$$

4.
$$\begin{array}{r} 65? \\ -\ 3?7 \\ \hline ?78 \end{array}$$

5.
$$\begin{array}{r} ?9 \\ \times\ ? \\ \hline ?78 \end{array}$$

6.
$$1?\overline{)456}\ \ \ 3?$$

7. The height of Angel Falls, in Venezuela, is 3212 feet. Write this number in words. **(2.1)**

Round to the given place value. **(3.6)**

8. 7.094 (tenths)

9. 169.5 (ones)

10. 23.1845 (hundredths)

Milestones   THE ABACUS

Magic Squares, China
1100–1200 B.C.

1000 B.C.

Coins, Turkey
650 B.C.

600 B.C.

200 B.C.

A.D. 200

A.D. 600

Paper Money,
China
900

A.D. 1000

Hindu-Arabic
Numerals,
1000

Fibonacci
born,
1170

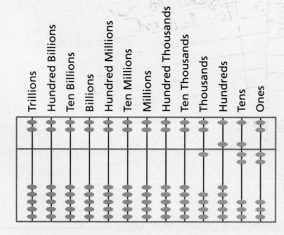

Each bead above the crossbar represents 5 units, and each below it represents 1 unit. Numbers are shown by moving beads to the crossbar. This suan-pan shows the number 1572.

In China today, some native clerks working in foreign banks prefer to use one of the oldest computing devices (except for finger arithmetic) still in operation today, the Chinese *suan-pan*.

The Babylonians, more than 5000 years ago, were among the first to record arithmetic calculations symbolically on a dust-covered board. The Babylonian term *ebeq* for "dust" and the Greek word *abak* for "slab" became translated into Latin as *abacus* and into Chinese as *suan-pan*. The abacus is the most well-known descendent of the dust-covered board.

• *How would you use an abacus to show the number 563? The number that is 238 more than 563?*

Real Life
Price Checking

Example *Checking a Bill*

You are checking the bills that were written at your restaurant during the day. Two are shown below. Are the bills correct?

Solution The last item on the second bill is not correct. Using a calculator, you can determine that 3 orders of tea should cost $3.30.

1.10 [+] 1.10 [+] 1.10 [=]   ■

Early Bird Restaurant

Number	Description	Amount
1	Grilled cheese	$ 2.19
1	Cole slaw	$ 1.19
1	French fries	$ 1.29
2	Fish & chips $4.69 each	$ 9.38
2	Milk $0.89 each	$ 2.89
1	Chicken salad	$ 4.39
3	Green salad with French dressing $0.95 each	$ 2.85
2	Iced tea $1.45 each	$ 1.45

Total **$25.63**

Early Bird Restaurant

Number	Description	Amount
3	Egg roll $1.49 each	$ 4.47
3	Tomato soup $1.29 each	$ 2.58
1	Mashed potatoes	$ 1.29
2	White rice $0.89 each	$ 0.89
1	Pork chop dinner	$ 6.89
1	Beef with broccoli	$ 6.89
1	Vegetables with cheese	$ 4.69
3	Tea $1.10 each	$ 3.10

Total **$30.80**

Exercises

1. Each description and price on the first bill is correct. Are the amounts correct? If not, copy the bill and write the correct amounts and total.

2. Each description and price on the second bill is correct. Are the amounts correct? If not, copy the bill and write the correct amounts and total.

4.3

Estimating Sums and Differences

What you should learn:

Goal 1 How to use rounding to estimate sums and differences

Goal 2 How to use front-end estimation

Why you should learn it:

Estimating sums and differences can be used to help you make decisions quickly using mental math. An example is deciding if you have enough money to pay for your groceries.

In 1993, Americans spent over $100,000 million in apparel and accessory stores.

Goal 1 Using Rounding to Estimate

In this lesson, you will study two strategies for estimating sums and differences. The first is **rounding.**

Example 1 Buying Groceries

You take $5 to a convenience store. You need to buy bread, eggs, and milk. If you have enough money, you also want to buy a package of frozen waffles. Use the prices below to decide whether you can buy the waffles.

Loaf of bread	$1.39	*Dozen eggs*	$0.89
Half gallon of milk	$1.79	*Package of waffles*	$1.65

Solution One way to make your decision is to round each of the prices to the nearest half-dollar.

	Exact Amount	Rounded Estimate
Bread	$1.39	$1.50
Eggs	$0.89	1.00
Milk	$1.79	2.00
Waffles	$1.65	+1.50
		$6.00

You don't have enough money to buy the waffles. ■

Example 2 Estimating a Difference

You give a clerk $30 to pay for $23.16 worth of clothes. Estimate your change.

Solution By rounding to the nearest dollar, you can estimate your change to be

$30 − $23 = $7.

Is your estimate for the change too low or too high? How can you tell? ■

Goal 2 Using Front-End Estimation

The second strategy for estimating a sum or a difference is **front-end estimation.**

Real Life
Truck Driving

Example 3 *Front-End Estimation*

You are driving a truck that weighs 12,450 pounds. You are carrying two loads. One weighs 5,750 pounds and the other weighs 3,490 pounds. You see the sign shown at the left. Should you cross the bridge?

Solution You can estimate the total using only the "front digits" of each weight.

	Exact Weight	*Front-End Estimate*
Truck	12,450	12,???
Weight 1	5,750	5,???
Weight 2	3,490	3,???
		20,???

From your estimate, your truck and cargo weigh more than 20,000 pounds. So you shouldn't cross the bridge. ■

Communicating about MATHEMATICS

Problem Solving
Estimation

▶ Sharing Ideas about the Lesson

Estimation and Bar Graphs Your club has a fund-raiser. The amounts you received and spent for 4 weeks are shown in the bar graph. Estimate the amount you made each week by estimating the differences between what you received and spent.

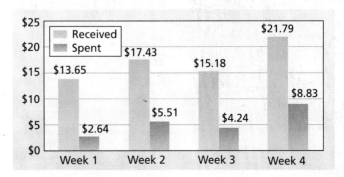

EXERCISES

Guided Practice

Think and Discuss

▶ CHECK for Understanding

1. Name 2 strategies for estimating sums and differences. Give a real-life situation where you could use each type.

Reasoning In Exercises 2 and 3, use the sample at the right. It shows front-end estimation with 3 steps.

2. Describe the 3 steps of front-end estimation.

3. Use front-end estimation to estimate the sum or difference.
   a. $9.75 + 12.54$ b. $8.62 - 2.18$

1.	5.73	2.	5.73
	+ 3.45		+ 3.45
	about 8.00		about 1.00

3. $8.00 + 1.00 = 9.00$

4. You and a friend go bowling. You have to be home in $2\frac{1}{2}$ hours. It takes about 13 minutes each way to ride your bike to and from the bowling lanes. It takes about 25 minutes to bowl a game. About how many games can you plan to bowl?

Independent Practice

In Exercises 5–10, round each number to the given place value.

5. 8.547 (ones)

6. 13.015 (hundredths)

7. 19,620 (thousands)

8. 58.34 (tens)

9. 2.645 (tenths)

10. 675.082 (hundreds)

Number Sense In Exercises 11–16, estimate each answer by rounding *and* by front-end estimation.

11. $675 + 589$

12. $4580 - 310$

13. $\$14.79 - \$2.65$

14. $\$3.28 + \$11.85 + \$5.70$

15. $12,580 + 6790 + 4260$

16. $\$258.74 - \$63.29$

Geometry In Exercises 17–19, you are given the perimeter of the figure. By rounding, estimate the length of the side labeled *x*.

17. Perimeter = 28 units

18. Perimeter = 46.5 units

19. Perimeter = 24.5 units

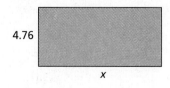

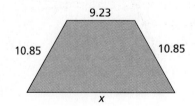

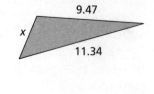

20. *Pets*   You go to the pet store with $25. You decide to buy 2 goldfish for $3.69 each and fish food for $4.19. Bowl-shaped tanks are $11.48. Square-shaped tanks are $14.89. Estimate your total cost to find which tank you can buy. About how much money will you have left?

21. *Art Supplies*   You go to the art supply store to buy paint and brushes. You need one brush for each container of paint. Each brush is $1.27 and each container of paint is $2.85. About how many sets can you buy if you have $15?

22. You have a summer job mowing lawns. The amount of money you earned and spent for 4 weeks is shown at the right. Estimate the amount you saved each week. Then estimate your total savings.

Lawn Mowing Record

Integrated Review

Making Connections within Mathematics

Geometry   Find the length of the side labeled *x*.

23. Perimeter = 25.2 units

24. Perimeter = 25.6 units

x

8.55

Exploration and Extension

25. *Group Activity: Estimating Game*   Copy the 20 numbers at the right. Take turns choosing 2 numbers and writing an addition *or* subtraction problem. Estimate the answer. Write the estimate and the number of points by the problem. After using the numbers, cross them off the list. Continue the game until all 20 numbers are used. Total your group's points. Compare them with the totals of other groups. Play again to see if you can improve your score.

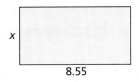

1.86	24.6	7.35	6.28	31.01
16.9	3.42	9.89	0.63	4.14
58.16	15.19	0.88	41.8	13.53
5.77	38.2	25.07	19.11	7.9

Estimated Range	Points
1 - 20	2 points
20.1 - 40	4 points
40.1 - 60	5 points
60.1 - 80	4 points
80.1 - 100	2 points

Lab 4.4 Connections to Geometry:
Investigating Decimal Multiplication

Materials Needed: base-ten grid paper, paper, pencils

In Chapter 2, you learned how to use base-ten grid paper to model multiplication of whole numbers. For instance, the product of 6 and 7 can be modeled as shown below at the left. The same diagram can be used to model the product of 0.6 and 0.7.

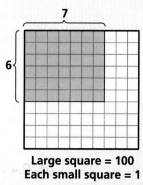

Large square = 100
Each small square = 1

Area of 6-by-7 rectangle
is 42 square units.

Large square = 1
Each small square = $\frac{1}{100}$ or 0.01

Area of 0.6-by-0.7 rectangle
is $\frac{42}{100}$ or 0.42 square units.

Part A *Making Connections*

1. Write *two* products that could be modeled by each base-ten sketch: one with two whole numbers and one with two decimals. For each of your two products, tell what a small square represents. Then count the number of small squares and write the answer.

a. 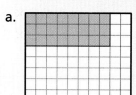 b. 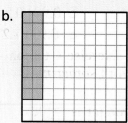 c.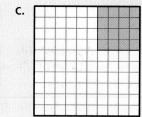

d. 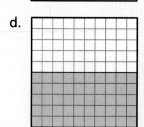 e. 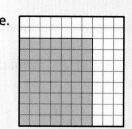 f.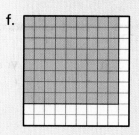

Part B *Using Area Models* The base-ten grid shows a model of the multiplication problem 1.6×2.7. Use the model to find the product.

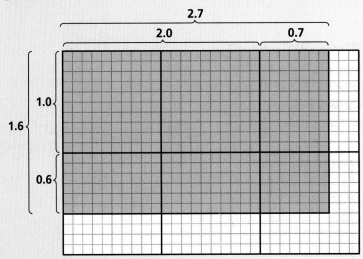

2. On base-ten grid paper, sketch a model to find the product.

   a. 0.3×0.6 b. 1.4×3.0 c. 1.8×1.4 d. 0.4×3.8

Part C *Making Connections*

3. On base-ten grid paper, sketch a model to find the product. Tell what each small square represents.

   a. 12×3 b. 1.2×3 c. 1.2×0.3

On Your Own   *Critical Thinking*

4. Find each product.

   a. 0.1×0.7 b. 0.3×0.8 c. 0.9×0.2 d. 0.9×0.9

   e. 1.2×0.7 f. 1.3×0.8 g. 0.9×1.2 h. 2.2×0.1

5. *Reasoning* Use the products you found in Exercise 4 to complete the following statements with the word *sometimes*, *always*, or *never*. Give 2 examples.

   a. If two numbers are less than 1, their product is ? less than 1.

   b. If one number is less than 1 and another is greater than 1, their product is ? less than 1.

6. Two numbers are greater than 1. Do you think their product will *sometimes*, *always*, or *never* be less than 1?

4.4

Decimal Multiplication and Percent

What you should learn:

Goal 1 How to multiply decimals

Goal 2 How to use decimal multiplication to find a percent of a number

Why you should learn it:

Decimal multiplication can be used to help you when buying something. An example is finding the sales tax on the items you buy.

Goal 1 Multiplying Decimals

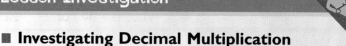

Lesson Investigation

■ **Investigating Decimal Multiplication**

Group Activity In the lab on page 171, you used base-ten grid paper to sketch the following products.

a. 12×3 **b.** 1.2×3 **c.** 1.2×0.3

Use a calculator to find each product again. Then use the calculator to find the following products.

d. 0.12×3 **e.** 0.12×0.3 **f.** 0.12×0.03

With others in your group, discuss how the number of decimal places in the factors is related to the number of decimal places in the product. Test your conclusion with the product 0.012×0.003.

In this investigation, you may have discovered that the number of decimal places in the product is equal to the sum of the number of decimal places in the factors.

Example 1 *Multiplying Decimals*

a.

$$\begin{array}{r} 3.06 \\ \times \quad 1.4 \\ \hline 1\,224 \\ 3\,06 \\ \hline 4.284 \end{array}$$

    3.06 *2 decimal places*
    1.4 *1 decimal place*
    4.284 *3 decimal places*

b.

$$\begin{array}{r} 1.46 \\ \times \quad 0.02 \\ \hline 0.0292 \end{array}$$

    1.46 *2 decimal places*
    0.02 *2 decimal places*
    0.0292 *4 decimal places*

└── Write 0 to make 4 decimal places in the product. ■

Study Tip

When you multiply two decimals, you can use estimation to check whether your answer is reasonable. For instance, in part (a) of Example 1, the answer seems reasonable because it is greater than 1×3 or 3 and less than 2×3 or 6.

The word *of* often means to multiply. For instance, to find 0.4 *of* 2, you multiply to get $0.4 \times 2 = 0.8$.

In real-life problems, decimal multiplication can often be used with percents or fractions.

Question	*Plan*	*Answer*
What is 0.4 of 2?	Multiply 0.4 and 2.	$0.4 \times 2 = 0.8$
What is $\frac{4}{10}$ of 2?	Rewrite $\frac{4}{10}$ as 0.4.	$0.4 \times 2 = 0.8$
What is 40% of 2?	Rewrite 40% as 0.4.	$0.4 \times 2 = 0.8$

Tax

Real Life
Sales Tax

Example **2** *Finding a Percent of a Number*

Your food bill at a restaurant is $15.69, plus 6% sales tax. How much is your sales tax?

Solution   To find 6% of $15.69, rewrite 6% as a decimal and multiply.

$15.69	*2 decimal places*
0.06	*2 decimal places*
$0.9414	*4 decimal places*

By rounding to the nearest hundredth, your sales tax is $0.94. ■

A 6% sales tax means that for each dollar you pay, you must pay 6 cents extra in tax.

Communicating about MATHEMATICS

▶ **Sharing Ideas about the Lesson**

Extending the Example Most states have a sales tax. (As of 1994, Alaska, Delaware, Montana, Nebraska, New Hampshire, and Oregon didn't.) Use a calculator to find the sales tax and total cost for each item.

State	*Item*	*Amount*	*Sales Tax*
A. Colorado	Pair of jeans	$24.95	3%
B. Michigan	Comic book	$1.50	4%
C. Vermont	Bicycle	$139.90	5%
D. Pennsylvania	Computer	$1590	6%

EXERCISES

Guided Practice

Think and Discuss

▶ **CHECK for Understanding**

In Exercises 1–3, without multiplying, state how many decimal places are in the product.

1. 0.08×5.2
2. 12.23×4.563
3. 44.358×3.001

In Exercises 4 and 5, use the graph at the right. Two hundred people were asked how many phones they have. The survey results are shown as percents in the circle graph. *(Source: NFO Research, Inc.)*

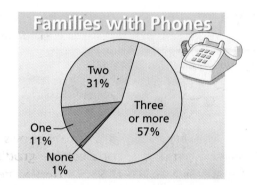

Families with Phones

Two 31%
Three or more 57%
One 11%
None 1%

4. How many people have only 1 phone?
5. How many people have more than one phone?

Independent Practice

In Exercises 6–9, without multiplying, match the multiplication problem with its answer. Explain your reasoning.

a. 12.22
b. 1.222
c. 122.2
d. 0.1222

6. 52×2.35
7. 0.52×0.235
8. 5.2×0.235
9. 5.2×2.35

In Exercises 10–13, place the decimal point in the product.

10. $4.1 \times 2.5 = 1025$
11. $6.113 \times 31 = 189503$
12. $2.01 \times 8.01 = 161001$
13. $5.6 \times 2.115 = 118440$
14. Multiply 2000 by 0.2, 0.5, 0.8, 0.9, 0.95, and 0.99. What happens to the product as the second factor gets closer and closer to 1?

Algebra In Exercises 15–17, use mental math to solve.

15. $0.15 \times m = 0.45$
16. $n \times 2.01 = 6.03$
17. $2 \times 2.2 = t$

Geometry In Exercises 18–20, find the area of the figure.

18.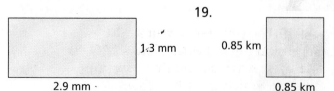

1.3 mm

2.9 mm

19. 0.85 km

0.85 km

20. 0.72 cm

1.112 cm

In Exercises 21–26, find the product. Use estimation to check that your answer is reasonable.

21. 2.25×5.61

22. 0.41×3.507

23. 5.89×1.125

24. 7.72×0.08

25. 6.643×1.495

26. 0.034×8.802

Measurement In Exercises 27–30, use a calculator to help you rewrite the length in centimeters. Use 1 inch = 2.54 cm.

Sample: 2 inches = 2×2.54 cm = 5.08 cm

27. 4 inches

28. 6.9 inches

29. 0.4 inch

30. 0.561 inch

In Exercises 31–34, write a multiplication problem that you could use to answer the question. Then answer the question.

31. What is $\frac{3}{10}$ of 6?

32. What is 12% of 80?

33. What is 48% of 6.75?

34. What is $\frac{43}{100}$ of 9.5?

Careers The table at the right shows the average hourly pay for a college graduate just starting a career. *(Source: Northwestern University Placement Center, 1993)*

35. Find the weekly pay for a chemist who works 40 hours per week.

36. Find the amount of money saved every hour by a business manager who saves 20% of his or her pay.

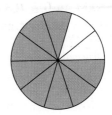

Career	Hourly Pay
Accountant	$13.47
Business Manager	$13.25
Chemist	$14.64
Computer Scientist	$14.98

Integrated Review

Making Connections within Mathematics

Name the percent of the diagram that is shaded.

37.
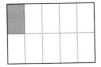

38.

39.

Exploration and Extension

40. *Building Your Chapter Project* For your restaurant's *Employee Training Manual*, explain how to calculate a 15% tip for a bill. Show a sample bill for which the tip is about $2. Show another sample bill for which the tip is about $5.

Take this test as you would take a test in class. The answers to the exercises are given in the back of the book.

In Exercises 1–6, use a vertical form to add or subtract. **(4.1, 4.2)**

1. $3.09 + 6.14$

2. $\$7.59 - \$3.16$

3. $3.1 + 0.85$

4. $14 - 4.82$

5. $27.96 - 16.34$

6. $\$4.75 + \$19.30 + \$0.22$

In Exercises 7–9, estimate the amount. Describe the estimation procedure you used. **(4.3)**

7. $\$6.43 + \$5.29$

8. $33,840 - 7800$

9. $\$9.17 + \$8.05 + \$12.36$

Algebra   In Exercises 10–15, use mental math or paper and pencil to solve. **(4.1–4.4)**

10. $4.75 + x = 8.25$

11. $5.79 - y = 1.23$

12. $m - 25.05 = 10.85$

13. $n + 0.58 = 3.64$

14. $z \times 0.1 = 0.054$

15. $2.4 \times p = 0.12$

Geometry   In Exercises 16–18, find the value of x. **(4.1–4.4)**

16.

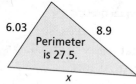

17.

18.

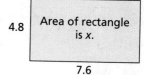

In Exercises 19–21, write the multiplication problem that you could use to answer the question. Then answer the question. **(4.4)**

19. What is 0.8 of 75?

20. What is $\frac{5}{10}$ of 37?

21. What is 35% of 46?

Consumer Spending   In Exercises 22–24, use the menu at the right. **(4.1–4.4)**

22. Estimate the cost of a garden salad, a ravioli dinner, and a glass of iced tea. You have $9 to spend on your meal and don't need to leave a tip. What dessert can you order?

23. Name the 4 items chosen from the menu that total $11.18. Explain how you solved the problem.

24. You order a lasagna dinner, a Caesar salad, and a glass of soda. You give the server a tip that is 15% of your total bill. How much did you spend?

4.5 Dividing a Decimal by a Whole Number

What you should learn:

Goal 1 How to divide a decimal by a whole number

Goal 2 How to use decimal division to solve real-life problems

Why you should learn it:

Decimal division can be used to help you split the cost of something with others. An example is finding a person's share of a restaurant bill.

Study Tip

When you divide with decimals, you can use estimation to check whether your answer is reasonable. For instance, in Example 1, the answer seems reasonable because 4.8 is between 4 and 6 and the answer is greater than 4 ÷ 2 or 2 and less than 6 ÷ 2 or 3.

Goal 1 · Dividing Decimals

Example 1 · Dividing by a Whole Number

What is 4.8 ÷ 2?

Solution You can find the answer using base-ten pieces.

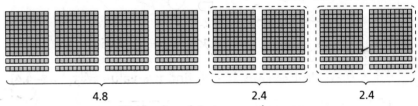

4.8   2.4   2.4

Divide pieces into two equal groups.

From this diagram, you can see that 4.8 ÷ 2 = 2.4. You can show this quotient using a vertical form.

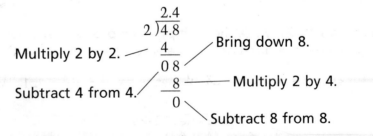

Multiply 2 by 2. —⟍   ⟋— Bring down 8.

$$\begin{array}{r} 2.4 \\ 2\overline{)4.8} \\ \underline{4} \\ 0\,8 \\ \underline{8} \\ 0 \end{array}$$

Subtract 4 from 4. ⟋   ⟍ Multiply 2 by 4.

Subtract 8 from 8.   ∎

Lesson Investigation

■ Investigating Decimal Division

Group Activity For each problem, draw a sketch of base-ten pieces to find the answer. Then use a vertical form to show the quotient.

a. 4.8 ÷ 4   **b.** 4.8 ÷ 6   **c.** 6.4 ÷ 2   **d.** 6.4 ÷ 4

Discuss how you know where to place the decimal point in the solution when using the vertical form.

Example 2 *Dividing Decimals*

Real Life
Restaurant

Two groups of people are in a restaurant. How much should each person pay?

a. 6 people are sharing a bill of $43.08.

b. 12 people are sharing a bill of $118.32.

Solution

a. To find each person's share, divide $43.08 by 6.

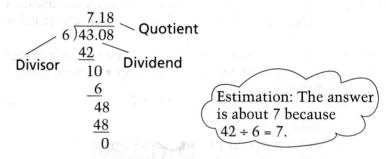

Study Tip

In the investigation, you may have discovered that when you divide a decimal by a whole number, the decimal point is placed directly above the decimal point in the dividend.

Estimation: The answer is about 7 because $42 \div 6 = 7$.

Each person's share is $7.18.

b. To find each person's share, divide $118.32 by 12.

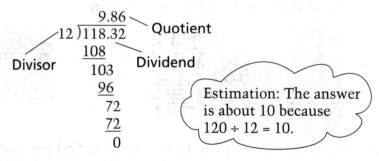

Estimation: The answer is about 10 because $120 \div 12 = 10$.

Each person's share is $9.86. ∎

Communicating about **MATHEMATICS**

Cooperative Learning

▶ **Sharing Ideas about the Lesson**

Partner Activity Example 1 on page 177 shows how to use base-ten pieces to model $4.8 \div 2$. Use grid paper to sketch base-ten pieces to model the following division problems. Then solve.

A. $4.9 \div 2$ **B.** $4.5 \div 5$

EXERCISES

Guided Practice

▶ CHECK for Understanding

1. Write the division problem shown or represented by the base-ten pieces. (Large square = 1 unit)

Think and Discuss

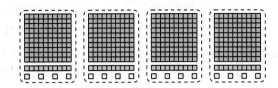

2. Draw a sketch of $4.8 \div 3$. Then solve.

3. *You Be the Teacher* Write an explanation about how to divide a decimal by a whole number in a vertical form.

In Exercises 4–6, estimate the answer. Then draw a sketch to find the exact answer. Write and solve using a vertical form.

4. $10.8 \div 4$ 5. $6.5 \div 2$ 6. $12.25 \div 7$

Independent Practice

In Exercises 7 and 8, write the problem shown or represented by the base-ten pieces. (Large square = 1 unit)

7. 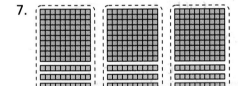   8.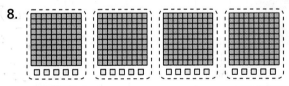

Estimate the answer. Then draw a sketch to find the exact answer.

9. $6.6 \div 3$ 10. $4.6 \div 4$ 11. $4.92 \div 4$ 12. $5.4 \div 2$

In Exercises 13–16, use a vertical form to solve.

13. $8.25 \div 5$ 14. $17.4 \div 3$ 15. $133.6 \div 8$ 16. $100.38 \div 21$

Write a division problem for the area model.

17.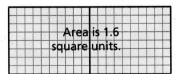
Area is 1.6 square units.

18.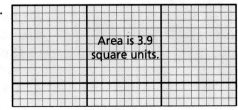
Area is 3.9 square units.

Algebra In Exercises 19–21, use mental math to solve.

19. $x \div 2 = 4.5$ **20.** $12.6 \div y = 4.2$ **21.** $n \div 4 = 2.5$

22. Consider the following division problems. What happens to the quotient when the divisor is doubled?

$48 \div 2, \quad 48 \div 4, \quad 48 \div 8, \quad 48 \div 16$

23. *Error Analysis* Find and correct the error in the division problem shown at the right.

$$
\begin{array}{r}
80.3 \\
7\,)\overline{56.21} \\
\underline{56} \\
0\,21 \\
\underline{21} \\
0
\end{array}
$$

Reasoning In Exercises 24 and 25, complete the statement with *sometimes*, *always*, or *never*. Give an example.

24. A number less than 1 divided by a whole number is ? greater than 1.

25. A decimal divided by a whole number is ? a decimal.

Reading a Table The table at the right shows the amount of money spent per year per person on reading material from 1990 through 1992 in the United States.
(Source: Veronis, Suhler & Associates)

Year	1990	1991	1992
Newspapers	$49.80	$52.44	$54.48
Magazines	$33.12	$33.48	$33.96
Books	$63.96	$68.16	$71.16

26. Find the amount spent *per month* in each category in 1992.

27. Find the amount spent *per week* on books in 1990. (Use 52 weeks in a year.)

28. Which category increased the most from 1991 to 1992?

Consumer Spending You and 3 friends go to a pizza shop for lunch. Individual pieces of cheese pizza cost $1.75 and a medium 8-piece cheese pizza costs $6.80.

29. How much would each of you pay if you decide to split the cost of a medium pizza?

30. Which costs less: buying two individual pieces or splitting the cost of a medium pizza with your 3 friends? Explain.

31. *Geometry* You are building a birdhouse from a piece of wood that is 56.88 inches long and 9.48 inches wide, as shown below. You divide the wood into 6 equal size pieces. What are the dimensions of each piece?

9.48 in.

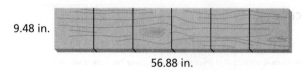

56.88 in.

Complete the statement.

32. $\frac{?}{100} = 0.84$ **33.** $0.77 = \boxed{?}\%$ **34.** $\frac{6}{?} = 60\%$ **35.** $\frac{3}{100} = \boxed{?}$

36. $3^5 = \boxed{?}$ **37.** $4^{\boxed{?}} = 256$ **38.** $\boxed{?}^3 = 1000$ **39.** $2^6 = \boxed{?}$

Exploration and Extension

40. *Building Your Chapter Project*
Hamburger meat loses 20% of its weight when it is cooked. In your restaurant's *Employee Training Manual*, draw a diagram for your employees to explain why they need to begin with 5 ounces of uncooked hamburger meat to end up with one quarter pound of cooked meat. Use the diagram at the right to help you.

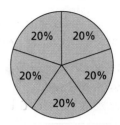

16 ounces = 1 pound

4 ounces = $\frac{1}{4}$ pound

Mixed REVIEW

Algebra   Use mental math to solve. **(1.6)**

1. $x + 15 = 33$ **2.** $54 - y = 45$ **3.** $4.5 \cdot m = 45$ **4.** $n \div 100 = 0.64$

Insert parentheses to make the statement true. **(2.5)**

5. $27 - 9 - 4 + 2 = 24$ **6.** $8 + 2 \times 6 \div 4 = 15$ **7.** $12 \div 6 + 6 \times 7 = 7$

Order the numbers from least to greatest. **(3.5)**

8. $1.13, \quad 1.03, \quad 1.30, \quad 1.02$ **9.** $9.45, \quad 9.4, \quad 9.54, \quad 9.5$

Complete the statement. **(3.7)**

10. $3^4 = \boxed{?}$ **11.** $6^{\boxed{?}} = 216$ **12.** $\boxed{?}^6 = 64$ **13.** $\boxed{?}^3 = 125$

Sketch a model that represents the decimal. **(3.5)**

14. 0.65 **15.** 0.87 **16.** 0.32

4.6

Connections to Algebra: Multiplying and Dividing by Powers of Ten

What you should learn:

Goal 1 How to multiply a decimal by a power of 10

Goal 2 How to divide a decimal by a power of 10

Why you should learn it:

Knowing how to multiply and divide by powers of 10 can help you estimate large sizes. An example is estimating the size of a solar flare on the sun.

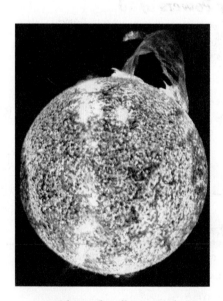

This solar flare on the sun measured 5.8×10^5 km across. How can you write this distance in decimal form?

Goal 1 Multiplying by Powers of 10

In Lesson 3.7, you studied how to use exponents to write powers of 10. Here are some examples.

$$10^2 = 100 \qquad 10^3 = 1000 \qquad 10^4 = 10,000$$

Lesson Investigation

■ **Investigating Multiplying by Powers of 10**

Group Activity Use a calculator to solve each problem. Record each problem and answer.

a. 14×10 **b.** 14×100 **c.** 14×1000

d. 2.73×10 **e.** 2.73×100 **f.** 2.73×1000

With each of the following, try to predict the answer before using your calculator.

g. 300×1000 **h.** 20.9×100 **i.** 0.002×10

In your group, discuss how to mentally multiply a whole number or a decimal by a power of ten.

You may have discovered that you can multiply a number by a power of 10 by moving the decimal point one place *to the right* for each zero in the power of 10.

Example 1 *Multiplying by Powers of 10*

a. $24 \times 1000 = 24,000.$ *1000 has 3 zeros.*
                           Move decimal point 3 places.

b. $3.42 \times 10 = 34.2$ *10 has 1 zero.*
                           Move decimal point 1 place.

c. $0.035 \times 100 = 03.5$ *100 has 2 zeros.*
                           Move decimal point 2 places.

d. $1.04 \times 10^3 = 1040.$ *10^3 or 1000 has 3 zeros.*
                           Move decimal point 3 places. ■

Goal 2 Dividing by Powers of 10

Lesson Investigation

■ Investigating Dividing by Powers of 10

Group Activity Use a calculator to solve each problem. Record each problem and answer.

a. $18 \div 10$ **b.** $18 \div 100$ **c.** $18 \div 1000$

d. $84.3 \div 10$ **e.** $84.3 \div 100$ **f.** $84.3 \div 1000$

With each of the following, try to predict the answer before using your calculator.

g. $600 \div 1000$ **h.** $4.39 \div 100$ **i.** $0.05 \div 10$

With others in your group, discuss how to mentally divide a whole number or a decimal by a power of ten.

Study Tip

Do you move the decimal point to the left or right when dividing by a power of 10? Remember dividing by a power of 10 produces a smaller number, so the decimal point moves to the left.

You may have discovered that you can divide a number by a power of 10 by moving the decimal point one place *to the left* for each zero in the power of 10.

Example 2 *Dividing by Powers of 10*

a. $48 \div 1000 = 0.048$ *1000 has 3 zeros.*
Move decimal point 3 places.

b. $6.57 \div 10 = 0.657$ *10 has 1 zero.*
Move decimal point 1 place.

c. $9.2 \div 10^2 = 0.092$ *10^2 or 100 has 2 zeros.*
Move decimal point 2 places. ■

Communicating about MATHEMATICS

▶ **Sharing Ideas about the Lesson**

 Algebra Use mental math to solve each equation. Then use a calculator to check your solutions.

A. $3.4 \cdot n = 340$ **B.** $42 \cdot m = 42{,}000$

C. $0.51 \cdot y = 5.1$ **D.** $5.6 \div x = 0.56$

E. $234 \div z = 0.234$ **F.** $97.2 \div c = 0.972$

EXERCISES

▶ **CHECK for Understanding**

1. Explain how to multiply and divide a number by a power of ten. Give examples to support your answer.

2. Explain how to remember which way to move the decimal point when multiplying or dividing by a power of ten.

In Exercises 3–6, solve the problem.

3. 0.42×10 4. $56 \div 1000$ 5. $170 \div 100$ 6. 8.3×10^3

7. *Science* Humans have about 90×10^2 taste buds. Write this number in decimal form.

Independent Practice

In Exercises 8–15, solve the problem.

8. $850 \div 10$ 9. $7 \div 1000$ 10. 63×100 11. 2.37×10
12. 0.019×10^2 13. 0.12×10^4 14. $1450 \div 1000$ 15. $12{,}600 \div 100{,}000$

That's a Fact In Exercises 16–21, write the number in decimal form.

16. A 12-ounce jar of peanut butter is made from $5480 \div 10$ peanuts.

17. A half-hour TV cartoon is made up of 18×1000 drawings.

18. Caterpillars have more than 0.2×10^4 muscles.

19. A bee flaps its wings about $25{,}000 \div 100$ times a second.

20. By the time they are 70 years old, most people have slept 220×10^3 hours.

21. Your body has over $40{,}000 \div 1000$ miles of nerves.

This caterpillar from South America will someday become a monarch butterfly.

Algebra and Mental Math In Exercises 22–27, use mental math to solve. Then use a calculator to check.

22. $7 \div x = 0.7$ 23. $y \times 1000 = 39$ 24. $z \times 100 = 51{,}800$
25. $0.55 \times t = 550$ 26. $4600 \div m = 4.6$ 27. $n \div 10{,}000 = 0.09876$

Number Sense   In Exercises 28–31, complete the statement using
>, <, or = .

28. 0.46×10 ⓘ $46 \div 100$

29. 0.018×1000 ⓘ $280 \div 100$

30. $25 \div 100$ ⓘ $30 \div 10$

31. 0.505×1000 ⓘ 50.5×10

32. *Geometry*   A square mile has 640 acres. If a square mile is divided evenly among 100 people, how many acres will each person get?

33. *Science*   Astronomers estimate that there are more than 200 billion billion stars. This number can be written as $200 \times 10^9 \times 10^9$. Write this number in decimal form. How many zeros does it have?

34. *Science*   The nearest star (other than the sun) is about 25 million million miles away. Write this number in decimal form.

Earth and our sun are part of a galaxy called the Milky Way. The universe contains many galaxies.

Integrated Review

Making Connections within Mathematics

Measurement   Complete the statement.

35. ☐ cm = 1 m

36. 18 mm = 1.8 ☐

37. 250 ☐ = 2.5 m

Exploration and Extension

38. *World Populations*   Write each country's population in decimal form. Then order them from least to greatest.

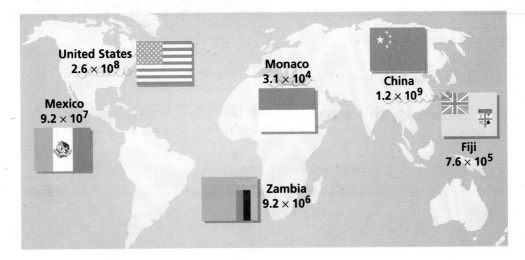

United States
2.6×10^8

Monaco
3.1×10^4

China
1.2×10^9

Mexico
9.2×10^7

Fiji
7.6×10^5

Zambia
9.2×10^6

Materials Needed: calculator, base-ten grid paper, pencils

You can use base-ten grid paper to model division problems. What the model means depends on what you let each small square represent. Here are two examples.

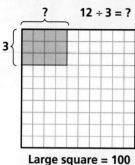

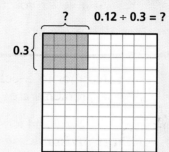

Large square = 100
Each small square = 1

Area of 3-by-4 rectangle
is 12 square units.

So, 12 ÷ 3 = 4.

Large square = 1
Each small square = 0.01

Area of 0.3-by-0.4 rectangle
is 0.12 square units.

So, 0.12 ÷ 0.3 = 0.4.

Part A   *Using Area Models*

1. Write *two* division problems that can be modeled by each base-ten sketch: one with two whole numbers and one with two decimals. For each of your two problems, tell what a large square and a small square represent. Write the answer.

a. 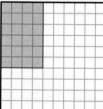   b. 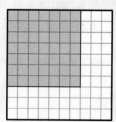   c.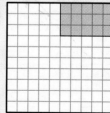

d. 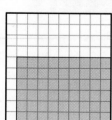   e. 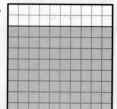   f.

Part B *Looking for Patterns*

2. Use a calculator to divide. With others in your group, discuss any patterns that you see.

   a. $0.012 \div 0.003$ b. $2.1 \div 0.042$ c. $0.00472 \div 0.004$

       $1.2 \div 0.3$ $21 \div 0.42$ $0.0472 \div 0.04$

       $12 \div 3$ $210 \div 4.2$ $0.472 \div 0.4$

                         $2100 \div 42$ $4.72 \div 4$

3. Use the patterns you saw above. Write 3 division problems that have the same answer. Which is easiest for you to solve? Why?

Part C *Making Connections*

4. Solve the division problems. Use a calculator to check your answers. Explain how the two division problems are related.

       Decimal divisor   *Whole number divisor*

   a. $0.02\overline{)84.4}$ $2\overline{)8440}$

   b. $0.7\overline{)2.87}$ $7\overline{)28.7}$

5. You may have discovered that you need to rewrite a division problem that has a decimal divisor. What rules do you need to follow to rewrite the problem so that it has a whole number divisor?

6. Solve each division problem. First write a division problem with a whole number divisor that has the same answer.

   a. $0.03\overline{)25.8}$ b. $0.4\overline{)32.8}$ c. $1.2\overline{)144}$

On Your Own   *Critical Thinking*

In Exercises 7–12, write a division problem with a whole number divisor that has the same answer. Then solve.

7. $1.2 \div 0.6$ 8. $1.2 \div 0.06$ 9. $0.12 \div 0.6$

10. $12 \div 0.6$ 11. $120 \div 0.6$ 12. $12 \div 0.06$

13. Which division problem has the greatest answer? Decide without dividing. Explain your process. Then check by solving each problem.

    a. $3.2 \div 8$ b. $3.2 \div 0.8$ c. $3.2 \div 0.08$ d. $3.2 \div 0.008$

14. Solve using mental math. Use a calculator to check your answers.

    a. $1.6 \div n = 4$ b. $1.6 \div n = 40$ c. $1.6 \div n = 400$ d. $1.6 \div n = 4000$

Dividing Decimals

Goal 1 How to divide decimals

Goal 2 How to use decimal division to solve real-life problems

Why you should learn it:

Decimal division can be used to help you compare the cost of two items that are different sizes. An example is finding the price per ounce of cans of soup.

Goal 1 **Dividing Decimals**

In Lab 4.7, you discovered that to divide by a decimal, solve a division problem with a whole number divisor that has the same answer. The rule is: *In both the divisor and dividend, move the decimal point the same number of places. To do this, multiply both by the power of ten that will make the divisor a whole number.*

Example 1 *Dividing Decimals*

Solve the problem $2.46 \div 0.3$.

Solution

Division by Decimal Divisor

$$0.3\,\overline{)2.46}$$

Move decimal point 1 place to the right.

Related Division by Whole Number Divisor

$$\begin{array}{r} 8.2 \\ 3.\overline{)24.6} \\ \underline{24} \\ 0\,6 \\ \underline{6} \\ 0 \end{array}$$

Check decimal division.

$8.2 \times 0.3 = 2.46$

Check whole number division.

$8.2 \times 3 = 24.6$

Study Tip

Remember, to multiply by powers of ten you move the decimal point to the right. For example, $0.03 \times 100 = 3$ and $84.63 \times 10 = 846.3$.

Example 2 *Dividing Decimals*

a.
$$\begin{array}{r} 1400. \\ 0.02\,\overline{)28.00} \\ 2 \\ \underline{}08 \\ \underline{8} \\ 0 \end{array}$$

Move decimal point 2 places to the right.

b.
$$\begin{array}{r} 0.007 \\ 0.4\,\overline{)0.0028} \\ 28 \\ \underline{}0 \end{array}$$

Move decimal point 1 place to the right.

Real Life
Detective Work

Example 3 *Dividing Decimals*

You are a detective who is investigating a bank robbery. A single thief left the bank carrying a suitcase full of $1 bills. The bank estimates that it lost a million dollars in the robbery. Does this sound reasonable?

Solution One way to decide whether the story is reasonable is to calculate how much 1,000,000 $1 bills weigh. To begin, you could weigh 100 $1 bills and discover that

(Weight of 100 $1 bills) = 0.165 pound.

This means that each $1 bill weighs 0.165 ÷ 100 pound.

Divide to find weight of $1 bill: *Check:*

Weight of $1 bill ⎯ 0.00165   100 × 0.00165
             100)0.165   = 0.165

100 $1 bills

Weight of 100 $1 bills

Because each $1 bill weighs 0.00165 pound, it follows that 1,000,000 $1 bills must weigh

1,000,000 × 0.00165 = 1650 pounds.

This is much more than a person could carry, so the story does not sound reasonable. ∎

100 $1 bills

Communicating about MATHEMATICS

▶ **Sharing Ideas about the Lesson**

Cooperative Learning

Group Activity You estimate that the most the thief could carry in the suitcase is 100 pounds. The number of $1 bills in 100 pounds can be found by dividing 100 by 0.00165.

With only $1 bills, how much money could be in the suitcase? With only $5 bills? With only $10 bills? With only $20 bills? Explain.

EXERCISES

Think and Discuss

▶ **CHECK for Understanding**

Reasoning   In Exercises 1 and 2, explain why the statement is false. Change exactly one word to make it true.

1. Before dividing decimals, you must change the quotient to a whole number.

2. Moving a decimal point two places to the right is the same as multiplying by 1000.

In Exercises 3–6, solve.

3. $13.2 \div 0.6$ 4. $1.32 \div 0.6$ 5. $13.2 \div 0.06$ 6. $1.32 \div 6$

Independent Practice

In Exercises 7–10, write the smallest power of 10 that you would multiply by to make the number a whole number.

7. 9.3   8. 0.12   9. 3.05   10. 12.001

In Exercises 11–19, divide. Check your answer by multiplying.

11. $10.4 \div 0.8$ 12. $0.36 \div 0.9$ 13. $3.14 \div 0.2$
14. $33 \div 0.11$ 15. $24.75 \div 2.25$ 16. $0.816 \div 0.68$
17. $7.85 \div 0.005$ 18. $204.02 \div 5.05$ 19. $500 \div 0.25$

In Exercises 20 and 21, use a calculator to evaluate the expression.

20. $3.34 + 6.4 \div 0.032$ 21. $21.9 \div 0.073 - 40.5 \div 0.5$

Geometry   Find the length of the side labeled *s*.

22.
| Area is 6.88 square meters. |
s | |
4 meters

23.
| Area is 6.25 square kilometers. |
s |
s

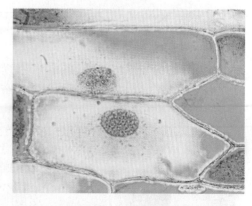

24. *Science*   In the photo, the onion cell is 55 millimeters wide. The actual cell is only 0.04 millimeter wide. Find how many times larger the picture is than the actual cell by dividing 55 by 0.04.

This onion cell is shown many times larger than it is in real life.

Algebra and Mental Math   In Exercises 25–27, use mental math to evaluate the expression when $b = 10$ and when $b = 100$.

25. $6.5 \div b$

26. $b \div 0.5$

27. $3 \times b \div 0.3$

Find the price per meter by dividing by 0.305. (1 foot = 0.305 m)

28. Rope: $1.64 per foot

29. Ribbon: $0.41 per foot

30. Pine board: $2.46 per foot

31. *Largest Vegetables*   Four of the world records for vegetable weights are listed. Find the approximate weights in pounds by dividing by 0.5. (1 pound = 0.5 kg) *(Source: Guinness Book of Records)*

Carrot: 7.00 kg   Onion: 5.05 kg

Radish: 17.21 kg   Zucchini: 29.25 kg

Integrated Review   *Making Connections within Mathematics*

32. *Partner Game: Amazing Decimals*   Place a marker at START. Both players enter 200 in their calculators. The first player chooses a line segment, moves the marker, and does the operation on his or her calculator. The second player chooses a connecting segment, moves the marker, and does the operation on his or her calculator. The game ends when the marker reaches FINISH. The winner is the one with the smallest number on his or her calculator. (You must move up, down, or right without using any segment twice.)

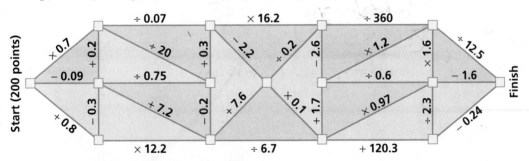

Exploration and Extension

33. *Building Your Chapter Project*   The table shows the weight and price of items your restaurant needs to buy. The price per ounce can be used to find the better buy. To find the price per ounce, divide the price by the weight. In your *Employee Training Manual*, explain how to use the price per ounce to find the better buy. Use the items in the table as samples.

Item	Price	Weight
Soup	$0.92	8 oz
Soup	$1.80	16 oz
Spaghetti	$1.32	16 oz
Spaghetti	$3.60	48 oz

4.8

More Problem Solving Using Decimals and Percents

What you should learn:

Goal 1 How to solve real-life percent problems

Goal 2 How to estimate percents from a bar graph

Why you should learn it:

Percents are used to help you analyze data. An example is reading a bar graph that shows people's favorite hobbies.

Goal 1 **Using Percent in Real Life**

In Lesson 4.4, you learned that you can use decimal multiplication to find a percent of a number.

Question   What is 15% of 60?
Plan   Rewrite 15% as 0.15. Then multiply.
Answer $0.15 \times 60 = 9$

Example 1 *Finding Percents of Numbers*

A school has 420 students. Because of the flu, 20% of the students are absent. How many are absent?

Solution   You can find how many are absent by finding 20% of 420.

$$20\% \times 420 = 0.2 \times 420 \qquad \textit{Rewrite 20\% as 0.2.}$$
$$= 84 \qquad \textit{Multiply.}$$

There are 84 students absent from school.   ■

Example 2 *Buying Something on Sale*

The regular price of a video game is $49.80. It is on sale for 25% off the regular price. What is the discount? What is the sale price?

Solution   Begin by finding 25% of $49.80.

$$25\% \times 49.80 = 0.25 \times 49.80 \qquad \textit{Rewrite 25\% as 0.25.}$$
$$= \$12.45 \qquad \textit{Multiply.}$$

This amount is called the **discount.** To find the sale price, subtract the discount from the regular price.

$49.80	Regular price
−12.45	Discount
$37.35	Sale price

A diagram of the solution is shown at the left.   ■

25%
Discount:
$12.45

75%
Sale Price:
$37.35

$12.45 + $37.35 = $49.80

Real Life
Hobbies

Example 3 *Reading a Bar Graph*

In a survey, 200 people were asked to name their favorite hobbies or activities. The 6 most popular are shown in the bar graph below. Find the number of people who named each hobby or activity.
(Source: Roper Organization)

Favorite Hobbies and Activities
Survey of 200 People

Fishing along the ocean's edge is called "surf-casting." Twilight is the best time of day for surf-casting.

Solution For each activity, multiply the percent by 200.

Activity	Percent	Number Who Named Activity
Reading	43%	$0.43 \times 200 = 86$
Cooking	34%	$0.34 \times 200 = 68$
Music	32%	$0.32 \times 200 = 64$
Gardening	26%	$0.26 \times 200 = 52$
Pets	25%	$0.25 \times 200 = 50$
Fishing	24%	$0.24 \times 200 = 48$ ∎

Communicating about **MATHEMATICS**

Problem Solving
Survey Results

▶ **Sharing Ideas about the Lesson**

Interpreting a Survey In the above survey, people could choose more than one activity. In a different survey of 200 people, they could choose only one favorite activity. The top five activities were reading (28%), cooking (21%), music (18%), gardening (14%), and pets (12%). How many people chose activities other than these? Explain.

EXERCISES

Guided Practice

Think and Discuss

▷ **CHECK for Understanding**

Match the blue portion of the figure with the percent it shows.

a. 25%   b. 10%   c. 50%

1.   2.   3.

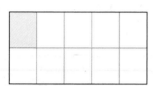

You are given the number that is represented by the whole model. What number is shown by the blue portion?

4.

The whole is 120.

5.

The whole is 75.

6. *Partner Activity*   Write a problem about buying something on sale. Include the regular price and the percent discount. Exchange problems with a partner and solve.

Independent Practice

In Exercises 7–10, find the number.

7. 30% of 80   8. 55% of 125   9. 15% of 240   10. 85% of 300

11. The regular price of a baseball bat is $37.50. It is on sale for 40% off the regular price. How much is the discount? What is the sale price?

12. The drama club is having a dance. The admission is $4, but is increased by 25% if you don't wear a mask. How much is the increase? Without a mask, what is the admission?

13. It costs $8.00 per hour to rent skates at a park. Students get a 20% discount. How much is the discount? How much do students pay?

14. You work at a restaurant for $5 per hour. You are given a 20% raise. What is your new hourly wage?

Pets   In Exercises 15–17, given the percent, find the number of dogs that can perform the trick. About 25,000,000 dogs in the United States can do some type of trick. *(Source: Pet Food Institute Frosty Paws)*

15. Sit: 20%   16. Roll over: 10%   17. Fetch newspaper: 2%

Science The graph below shows the factors, other than parents and teachers, that students in grades 3–12 say influence their interest in science. Find the number of students that listed the factor.
(Source: Purdue University National Science Outreach Survey)

18. Star Trek TV programs
19. Science fiction movies
20. Science TV shows
21. NASA

Rural Living The bar graph below shows the percent of the population that live in rural areas for different states. You are given the population for the entire state. Find the number of people that live in rural areas.

22. Tennessee 4,897,000
23. New Jersey 7,749,000
24. Washington 4,888,000
25. Kansas 2,486,000

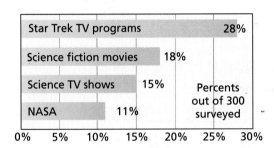

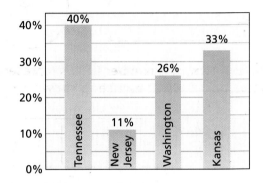

Integrated Review   Making Connections within Mathematics

Which of the four numbers is not equal to the other three numbers? Explain.

26. a. 0.25   b. $\frac{25}{100}$ c. 2.5%   d. 25%

27. a. 0.06   b. $\frac{6}{10}$ c. $\frac{6}{100}$ d. 6%

28. a. 0.89   b. 0.089   c. $\frac{89}{1000}$ d. 8.9%

29. a. 4.5%   b. 45%   c. $\frac{45}{1000}$ d. 0.045

Exploration and Extension

30. **Building Your Chapter Project**
The table shows the number of hours worked by 4 of your employees during a week. In your *Employee Training Manual*, show how your employees can calculate their total pay. Then show them how to find their take-home pay by subtracting 20% from their total pay. Use the 4 employees in the table as samples.

Employee	Position	Hours	Hourly Wage
Sonya	Cook	32.0	$10.60
Tom	Dishwasher	38.5	$8.25
Alicia	Food Server	24.5	$5.75
Luis	Food Server	18.5	$5.75

4

Chapter Summary

What did you learn?

Skills

1. Add decimals. **(4.1)**
2. Subtract decimals. **(4.2)**
3. Estimate sums and differences using rounding and front-end estimation. **(4.3)**
4. Multiply decimals. **(4.4)**
5. Use decimal multiplication to find a percent of a number. **(4.4)**
6. Divide a decimal by a whole number. **(4.5)**
7. Multiply and divide a decimal by a power of 10. **(4.6)**
8. Divide a number by a decimal. **(4.7)**

Strategies

9. Use problem-solving strategies to solve problems. **(4.1–4.8)**

Exploring Data

10. Use tables and graphs to organize data and solve problems. **(4.1–4.8)**

Why did you learn it?

Many real-life problems contain decimals that must be added, subtracted, multiplied, or divided. Here are some of the examples you studied in this chapter.

- Finding the total of a restaurant bill. **(4.1)**
- Finding the amount of change when buying a T-shirt. **(4.2)**
- Finding the sales tax for a purchase. **(4.4)**
- Doing detective work after a bank robbery. **(4.7)**
- Interpreting a bar graph about favorite hobbies. **(4.8)**

How does it fit into the bigger picture of mathematics?

In this chapter, you studied *operations* with decimals. In mathematics, the four basic operations are: addition, subtraction, multiplication, and division.

You now know how to add, subtract, multiply, and divide whole numbers and decimals. In Chapters 7 and 8, you will learn how to add, subtract, multiply, and divide fractions. In Chapter 11, you will learn how to add and subtract integers.

As you study other chapters, remember to look for similarities in the ways different types of numbers are added, subtracted, multiplied, and divided. For instance, adding $13 + 26$ is similar to adding the decimals $1.3 + 2.6$.

Use a vertical form to add or subtract. **(4.1, 4.2)**

1. $0.035 + 8.76$ 2. $2.01 - 0.04$ 3. $22.91 - 7.03$ 4. $36.77 + 2.39$

School Store Use the list of prices at the right. Find the total cost. **(4.1)**

5. Pencil and eraser

6. Pen, pencil, and eraser

7. All 5 items

School Store

Eraser	**$0.33**
Notebook	**$1.89**
Pencil	**$0.22**
Pen	**$1.25**
Binder	**$2.85**

Energy Use In Exercises 8 and 9, use the circle graph. It shows the portions for the different ways electricity is generated in the United States. *(Source: Energy Information Administration)* **(4.2)**

8. Find the difference between the portions generated with coal and with oil.

9. How much larger is the portion generated with nuclear power than the portion generated with hydropower?

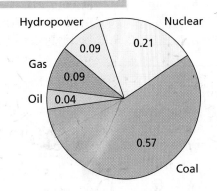

Estimation The table shows the time it takes to complete each task. On Saturday, you want to go to the mall at 10:00. You wake up at 9:00. Use estimation to decide whether you have enough time to do the following. Explain. **(4.3)**

Task	Time
Eat breakfast	12 min
Shower	13 min
Clean your room	26 min
Practice the piano	42 min
Do your homework	37 min

10. Eat breakfast, shower, and do your homework.

11. Eat breakfast, clean your room, and practice the piano.

In Exercises 12–19, multiply or divide. **(4.4, 4.5, 4.7)**

12. 3.4×0.8 13. $2.24 \div 8$ 14. $14.55 \div 5$ 15. 5.67×2.2

16. $3.65 \div 0.02$ 17. 4.52×12.35 18. $13.625 \div 6.25$ 19. $2.89 \div 0.08$

Algebra and Mental Math In Exercises 20–22, solve. **(4.6)**

20. $1000 \times m = 36.2$ 21. $45 \div c = 0.45$ 22. $9.8 \times b = 9800$

23. *Geometry* Find the length of the side labeled s. **(4.7)**

Area is 48.4 square meters. s

8.8 meters

Restaurant Sales In Exercises 24 and 25, use the table below. It shows the sales (in billions of dollars) for restaurants from 1988 to 1993. Decide whether the statement is true or false. *(Source: United States Census Bureau)*

Year	1988	1989	1990	1991	1992	1993
Sales	87.2	91.8	98.2	102.1	104.4	109.0

24. In 1992 and 1993, sales totaled 213.4 billion dollars.

25. The increase in sales from 1988 to 1993 was less than 20 billion dollars.

Food and Nutrition In Exercises 26–28, you are given the percent of people who eat take-out food at different places. Out of 300 people, find the number of people who eat take-out food at each place. *(Source: Beef Industry Council)* **(4.8)**

Rex Bird and William Warren own Macheesmo Mouse, a restaurant in Oregon that serves healthy Mexican-style food.

26. At home: 53% 27. At work: 14% 28. In the car: 19%

29. *Restaurant Words* The clues for the crossword are given below. Evaluate the expression and look up the answer in the table to find the word.

Bill	Cafe	Cook	Diner	Dish	Food	Hostess
3.03	1700	25.215	1.205	8.05	6.69	420

Lunch	Menu	Plate	Tip	Seat	Soup	Waiter
2.201	54.439	5.148	200	22.26	8.49	34.06

ACROSS

4. $5.89 + 2.6$

6. $3.401 - 1.2$

8. 5.24×6.5

10. $25.5 \div 0.015$

12. $8.98 + 13.28$

13. $34.06 - 8.845$

14. $49.91 \div 6.2$

DOWN

1. 9.8×5.555

2. $0.88 + 2.15$

3. $8.21 - 7.005$

5. 0.99×5.2

7. $10.5 \div 0.025$

9. $12.48 \div 0.0624$

11. 111.5×0.06

In Exercises 1–8, simplify.

1. $3.45 + 7.02$ 2. $14.75 - 4.52$ 3. $4.55 + 5.401$ 4. $16.001 - 4.98$
5. 3.5×6.15 6. $46.8 \div 8$ 7. 2.25×4.45 8. $19.08 \div 2.65$

Geometry   In Exercises 9–11, find the indicated measurement.

9. Perimeter = ⬜?   10. Area = ⬜?   11. $s =$ ⬜?

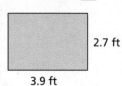

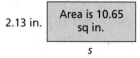

In Exercises 12–15, complete the statement using >, <, or =.

12. 0.88×100 ⊙? $888 \div 100$ 13. 0.603×100 ⊙? $603 \div 10$
14. $98 \div 10$ ⊙? 0.098×10 15. 0.011×100 ⊙? $111 \div 100$

In Exercises 16–18, find the number.

16. 40% of 120   17. 15% of 280   18. 65% of 80

Nutrition   The bar graph at the right shows the average percents of meat, poultry, and fish that a person in the United States eats per year. The total amount is about 187 pounds. *(Source: United States Department of Agriculture)*

19. Find the amount of chicken eaten.
20. Which two items have the same percent? What amount is this?

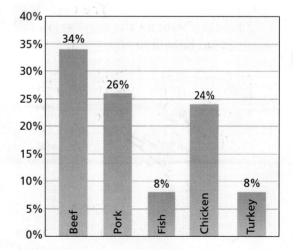

21. *Consumer Spending*   On the average, Americans spend $60.00 per month for telephone service. Of this amount, 24% is spent local and 76% is spent long distance. How much is spent for each service? *(Source: Chilton Research)*

22. You have a coupon for 25% off the price of a mystery book that sells for $7.00. You also have one for 20% off the price of a science fiction book that sells for $6.25. You have $5.00. Which book can you afford to buy? Explain.

Statistics and Graphs

Students gather data about the size, color, shape, and presence of seed coats from seeds of different plants. They can use this data to look for patterns between seed characteristics and plant type.

Real Life
Data Collection

Perform the following experiment. Cut a hole in a sheet of paper. Hold the paper at arm's length and look through the hole at a small object. Close only your right eye, then only your left eye. Through which eye did you see the object? This is called your dominant eye. Collect the class' results.

Think and Discuss

1. How many of your classmates are right-handed? Left-handed? How many people in your class have their left thumb on top when they fold their hands? Their right? Compare these results with the dominant-eye results. Do you see any patterns?

2. How could you best display these results? Explain your reasoning.

SNAP SHOT of our Class

Theme: Data Collection Have you ever answered a survey? What kinds of questions were asked? What organization wanted this information? Surveys are important sources of information to find out what services or products people want and need.

In this project, you will answer 6 survey questions and use the data to do the following.

➡ **In Lesson 5.1:** Make a line plot of the number of letters in first names. (page 210)

➡ **In Lesson 5.2:** Use a stem-and-leaf plot to order the days of the month on which birthdays occur. (page 215)

➡ **In Lesson 5.3:** Find the average rating when students rate how often they read for enjoyment. (page 221)

➡ **In Lesson 5.4:** Find the mean, median, and mode of handspans. (page 226)

➡ **In Lesson 5.5:** Make a bar graph of favorite sports. (page 233)

➡ **In Lesson 5.6:** Write a question for a survey, collect the data, and make a line graph of it. (page 237)

GETTING STARTED

Materials: poster board, paper, colored pencils or markers, pens, centimeter rulers

You will be given 5 sheets of paper. Answer each of the following 5 questions, one on each sheet of paper.

How many letters are in your first name?
What day of the month is your birthday?
How often do you read for enjoyment? Use this rating: As much as possible–1, often–2, sometimes–3, seldom–4, never–5.
What is your handspan in centimeters?
Which of these sports do you like to do best? Choose one.

Football	*Softball*	*Baseball*
Field Hockey	*Soccer*	*Gymnastics*
Tennis	*Basketball*	

Work in groups. Each group should tally the results of one question. These results should be shared, so that each group has the results for each question.

Each group should get a piece of poster board and write the title "A Snapshot of Our Class" on it. By the end of the chapter, the results of all 5 questions plus an additional question that the group decides on will be displayed on it.

Materials Needed: paper, pencils

Part A *Conducting a Survey*   Niki read that the top 5 ice cream flavors are vanilla, chocolate, strawberry, butter crunch, and chocolate chip. She wondered what the favorite flavors are in her class. To find out, she asked each classmate to name his or her favorite flavor. Everyone gave an answer. She recorded the results on a tally sheet like the one shown below.

Tally Sheet

Favorite Flavor	Tally
Vanilla	IIII
Chocolate	HHT I
Strawberry	III
Butter Crunch	I
Chocolate Chip	HHT HHT
Peppermint Stick	I

Frequency Table

Favorite Flavor	Frequency
Vanilla	4
Chocolate	6
Strawberry	3
Butter Crunch	1
Chocolate Chip	10
Peppermint Stick	1

After making the tally sheet, Niki counted the tallies and made a table like the one shown above.

1. How many students are in Niki's class?

2. What observations can you make from the frequency table?

3. Do the results in Niki's class agree with those she read? If not, why do you think they are different?

Part B *Organizing Data*   Randy asked his class about favorite fruits. Two students in the class were absent and did not answer. His tally sheet is shown at the right.

4. Use Randy's tally sheet to make a frequency table.

5. How many students are in Randy's class?

6. Which fruit is the most popular in Randy's class?

7. The next day, Randy asked the two students who missed class. The results changed the favorite fruit. Which fruit did they choose? Explain.

Banana	HHT HHT III
Apple	HHT HHT II
Watermelon	III
Orange	HHT IIII
Cantaloupe	IIII

Part C *Organizing Data*   Loren asked his classmates about favorite zoo animals. The results are shown below.

Janna	*Elephant*	Manuel	*Monkey*	Kelley	*Lion*
Juanita	*Giraffe*	Phyllis	*Elephant*	Jason	*Zebra*
Kim	*Gorilla*	Kanya	*Monkey*	Elaine	*Bear*
Loren	*Lion*	Consuelo	*Giraffe*	Aaron	*Monkey*
Raphael	*Zebra*	Anita	*Zebra*	Tanya	*Elephant*
Jay	*Monkey*	Mary Ellen	*Bear*	Bill	*Monkey*
Matthew	*Lion*	Sarah	*Giraffe*	Tom	*Lion*
Monica	*Zebra*	Carly	*Gorilla*	Steve	*Monkey*
Lin	*Elephant*	Fredrica	*Lion*	Jiang	*Lion*
Lita	*Zebra*	Isra	*Bear*	Maria	*Monkey*

8. Organize the results with a tally sheet.

9. Use your tally sheet to help you make a frequency table.

10. How many different animals were selected?

11. In Loren's class, which zoo animal is most popular?

12. Suppose 200 more people are surveyed. Name three other animals you think might be selected. Explain why you chose those three animals.

On Your Own

Critical Thinking

Collecting Data   In Exercises 13 and 14, use the following information.

The twelve most commonly used words in written English are

the, of, and, a, to, in, is, you, that, it, he, for.

13. Choose a portion of a newspaper, magazine, or novel. The portion should have at least 300 words. Tally each time one of these twelve words is used. Then make a frequency table that shows your results.

14. Which of the twelve words occurred most often?

15. Which five letters of the alphabet do you think are the most commonly used? Describe how you could test your answer. Then test it.

5.1

Line Plots

What you should learn:

Goal 1 How to draw a line plot

Goal 2 How to interpret a line plot

Why you should learn it:

Line plots can help you organize sports data, such as the number of games played in the World Series from 1970 through 1993.

Real Life
Baseball

Goal 1 **Drawing a Line Plot**

Many real-life problems contain unorganized data or numbers. In Lab 5.1, you learned how to use a tally sheet and a frequency table to organize data. Another way to organize data is with a **line plot.**

Example 1 *Drawing a Line Plot*

Each year, in the World Series, two baseball teams play from 4 to 7 games. The first team to win 4 games wins the World Series. The numbers of games played in the World Series from 1970 through 1993 are shown below.

1970 5	1974 5	1978 6	1982 7	1986 7	1990 4
1971 7	1975 7	1979 7	1983 5	1987 7	1991 7
1972 7	1976 4	1980 6	1984 5	1988 5	1992 6
1973 7	1977 6	1981 6	1985 7	1989 4	1993 6

Use a line plot to organize the numbers of games played.

Solution To begin, draw a number line that includes the numbers in the data: 4, 5, 6, and 7. Below the number line, write a title that explains what is being counted.

Number of Games in the World Series (1970 – 1993)

Next, read through the data. As you read each number, draw an × above the number.

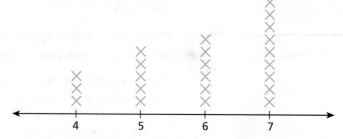

Number of Games in the World Series (1970 – 1993) ∎

Fenway Park in Boston, Massachusetts is home to the Boston Red Sox, four time world champions. The left-field wall in Fenway Park has gained the nickname "The Big Green Monster."

Interpreting a Line Plot

Real Life
Spelling

Example 2 *Comparing Two Data Sets*

The line plots below show a student's spelling quiz scores for the fall and the spring. What is the range of each data set? Compare the student's performance in the fall and in the spring. (Each score is the number of words spelled correctly out of 10 words.)

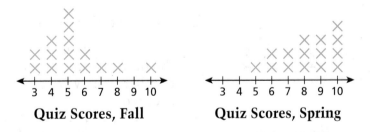

Quiz Scores, Fall   **Quiz Scores, Spring**

Need to Know

The difference between the greatest number and the least number in a set of data is called the **range** of the data. For instance, in Example 1, the range is $7-4$ or 3.

Solution   The ranges of the two sets of scores are:

Range $= 10 - 3 = 7$ *Range for fall*

Range $= 10 - 5 = 5$ *Range for spring*

The range for the spring is smaller. So you can conclude the student was more consistent in the spring.

There are other ways to use the line plots to see that the student did better in the spring. For example, in the fall the student scored 5 or less ten times. But in the spring, the student scored 5 or less only once. What are other ways to compare the scores?   ■

Example 3 · Interpreting a Line Plot

Example 3 · Interpreting a Line Plot

You work for the Park Service at the Bonneville Dam on the Columbia River. During one hour of spawning season, the sockeye salmon that climbed one of the fish ladders were netted, weighed, and returned to the fish ladder. The weights are shown in the line plot. From this line plot, what can you tell about sockeye salmon?

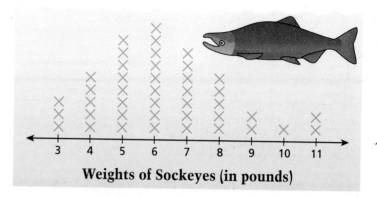

Weights of Sockeyes (in pounds)

A fish ladder is a series of ponds that allows a fish to "climb" over a dam.

Solution   You can tell these things from the line plot.
- During the hour, 42 sockeye salmon were weighed.
- The weights ranged from 3 pounds to 11 pounds. Therefore, the range of the data is 8 pounds.
- The most common weight was 6 pounds.
- Over half the fish weighed 5, 6, or 7 pounds.   ∎

Communicating about MATHEMATICS

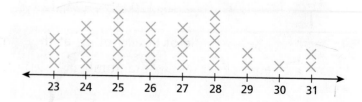

Cooperative Learning

▶ **Sharing Ideas about the Lesson**

Mystery Graph Describe a real-life setting that might be represented by the line plot. Compare your description with your partner's description.

EXERCISES

Think and Discuss

▶ CHECK for Understanding

In Exercises 1–3, match the description of the data with the line plot of the data.

a. Most common number is 5.   b. Has a range of 4   c. Includes 10 numbers

1.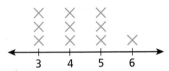

2.

3.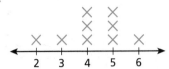

4. *It's up to You* Describe real-life data that you could organize using a line plot.

Cartoons You asked the ages of 25 people who watch Saturday morning cartoons. The ages are listed below.

14, 8, 6, 12, 9, 7, 11, 16, 15, 18, 12, 13, 8,
10, 8, 18, 10, 7, 19, 6, 19, 8, 11, 12, 13

5. Make a line plot of the data. Include a title for the line plot.
6. What is the range of the data? The most common age?

Independent Practice

In Exercises 7–10, make a line plot of the data. Find the most common number, the smallest number, the largest number, and the range of the data.

7. 6, 8, 5, 7, 11, 7, 10, 8, 5, 7

8. 36, 37, 36, 35, 37, 37, 36, 35, 38, 36

9. 14, 16, 16, 11, 16, 13, 14, 17, 16, 14

10. 121, 126, 130, 129, 129, 126, 120, 126, 126, 129

Braille Letters Use the table of Braille letters at the right.

11. Create a line plot that shows the numbers of dots in each letter.
12. What are the two most common numbers of dots?
13. Write two statements that describe the data.

Science Use the line plot below. It shows the numbers of teeth that meat-eating mammals have. *(Source: Peterson Field Guide: Mammals)*

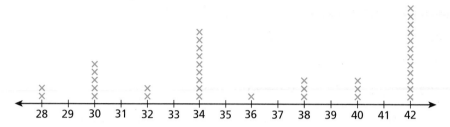

14. What are the two most common numbers of teeth for meat-eating mammals?

15. Why do you think there are no odd numbers of teeth in the data?

16. Could one of the numbers represent human beings? Explain.

17. *Flags of the World* Study the flags to make a line plot that shows the number of colors used in each flag. What is the range of the number of colors?

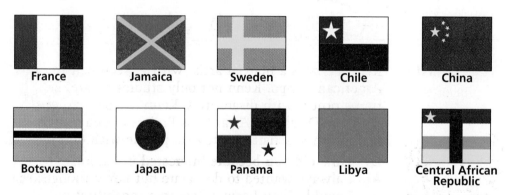

| France | Jamaica | Sweden | Chile | China |

| Botswana | Japan | Panama | Libya | Central African Republic |

Integrated Review   *Making Connections within Mathematics*

18. *Stars and Stripes* Use the information below about the history of the United States flag. Create a time line.

1777: 13 stripes and 13 stars   1795: 15 stripes and 15 stars

1818: 13 stripes and 20 stars   1861: 13 stripes and 34 stars

1912: 13 stripes and 48 stars   1960: 13 stripes and 50 stars

Exploration and Extension

19. *Building Your Chapter Project* The first question of your class survey was *How many letters are in your first name?* Use the results to make a line plot of the data. What is the most common number of letters? How many letters are in the shortest name? The longest name?

Write an equation to solve the problem. Then solve. **(1.6)**

1. What number can you add to 5 to get 27?
2. What number can you multiply by 4 to get 48?

Write the number in expanded notation. **(2.1, 3.1)**

3. 3205   4. 602,920   5. 8.25   6. 12.044

Measurement   Write the measurement in meters. **(3.2)**

7. 440 cm   8. 0.03 km   9. 1250 mm   10. 22 mm

Write the number as a fraction. **(3.4)**

11. 0.54   12. 0.095   13. 87%   14. 12%

Career Interview

Martial Artist

Kenn Perry is a martial artist with a green belt in American Kenpo. Kenn not only studies karate, he trains others with disabilities. Kenn is also involved with the Disability Awareness Project aimed at improving students' sensitivity toward people with disabilities.

Q: How did you become interested in karate?
A: I always wanted to do karate but never thought that I could. Then I saw a flyer in a rehabilitation hospital offering a class for people with disabilities. After taking that class, I continued training in a regular class.

Q: What math skills do you apply in karate?
A: I always use logic. My math teacher told me that math is a perfectly logical science. She was right. I use logic to take apart the moves that an able-bodied person does and rebuild them for a person using a wheelchair.

Q: Do you use any other math concepts in karate?
A: Yes, I was taught that there are 18 ways to attack. They can be described using a coordinate plane on which you are the origin and different lines through the origin represent different angles of attack. Geometry is a useful tool when describing motion.

5.2 Stem-and-Leaf Plots

What you should learn:

Goal 1 How to draw a stem-and-leaf plot

Goal 2 How to use a stem-and-leaf plot to solve real-life problems

Why you should learn it:

Stem-and-leaf plots can help you organize historical data, such as ordering the ages of people who served as First Ladies.

Goal 1 Drawing a Stem-and-Leaf Plot

Example 1 *Drawing a Stem-and-Leaf Plot*

Use a stem-and-leaf plot to order the following ages of family members at a reunion.

12, 42, 36, 43, 18, 24, 39, 21, 47, 55, 51, 26,

30, 45, 40, 27, 16, 28, 32, 29, 29, 22, 35, 44

Solution

1. The tens digits of the ages form the stem. Order the digits. Draw a line to the right of the stem.

```
     1 |   The tens digits of
  ╱  2 |   12, 42, 36, 43, 18, 24,
 Stem 3 |   39, 21, 47, 55, 51, 26,
     4 |   30, 45, 40, 27, 16, 28,
     5 |   32, 29, 29, 22, 35, 44
            are 1, 2, 3, 4, and 5.
```

2. Write the ones digit of each age to the right of the stem. The ones digits form the leaves.

```
       1 | 2 8 6
       2 | 4 1 6 7 8 9 9 2  ←
 Stem  3 | 6 9 0 2 5        ← Leaves
       4 | 2 3 7 5 0 4
       5 | 5 1
```

Need to Know

Once you have drawn an ordered stem-and-leaf plot, you should include a **key** that tells people what the stem and leaves represent.

3. Order the digits in the leaves from least to greatest.

```
       1 | 2 6 8
       2 | 1 2 4 6 7 8 9 9   Leaves
 Stem  3 | 0 2 5 6 9
       4 | 0 2 3 4 5 7        Key
       5 | 1 5                2 | 4 = 24 years
```

4. Use the ordered stem-and-leaf plot to order the ages.

12, 16, 18, 21, 22, 24, 26, 27, 28, 29, 29, 30,

32, 35, 36, 39, 40, 42, 43, 44, 45, 47, 51, 55

Stem-and-Leaf Plots in Real Life

Real Life
History

The youngest woman to serve as First Lady was Frances Cleveland. She married President Grover Cleveland one year after he was elected in 1884.

Example 2 *Drawing a Stem-and-Leaf Plot*

From 1885 through 1996, the age of each First Lady, when she became the First Lady, is listed below. Use a stem-and-leaf plot to help you order the ages.

Frances Cleveland	21	Elizabeth Truman	60
Caroline Harrison	56	Mamie Eisenhower	56
Ida McKinley	49	Jacqueline Kennedy	31
Edith Roosevelt	39	Claudia Johnson	50
Helen Taft	48	Thelma Nixon	56
Ellen Wilson	52	Elizabeth Ford	56
Florence Harding	60	Rosalynn Carter	49
Grace Coolidge	44	Nancy Reagan	57
Lou Hoover	54	Barbara Bush	63
Eleanor Roosevelt	48	Hillary Clinton	45

Solution

First, make an unordered plot.

```
2 | 1
3 | 9 1
4 | 9 8 4 8 9 5
5 | 6 2 4 6 0 6 6 7
6 | 0 0 3
    ↑           ↖
  Stem       Leaves
```

Then, make an ordered plot.

```
2 | 1
3 | 1 9
4 | 4 5 8 8 9 9
5 | 0 2 4 6 6 6 6 7
6 | 0 0 3

4 | 8   means 48 years
```

You can use the ordered plot to order the ages. You are asked to do that below. ∎

Communicating about MATHEMATICS

Cooperative Learning

▶ **Sharing Ideas about the Lesson**

Partner Activity: Extending the Example Use the ordered stem-and-leaf plot above to write the First Ladies' ages from least to greatest. Write 3 questions you could ask about the stem-and-leaf plot. Exchange questions with a partner.

EXERCISES

▶ CHECK for Understanding

1. Describe how to make the stem and leaves of a stem-and-leaf plot.

2. Use the stem-and-leaf plot at the right. Redraw it so that it is ordered. Then write the data from least to greatest.

3. The stem-and-leaf plot at the right represents *decimals,* not whole numbers. The stem represents the ones digits and the leaves represent the tenths digits. Write the numbers in increasing order.

Think and Discuss

```
0 | 5 2 1
1 | 1 0 8 4 6
2 | 6 2 1 7 9    Key
3 | 3 9 3 5         1 | 6 = 16
```

```
7 | 1 2 7
8 | 2 5 6 8 9    Key
9 | 0 3 4 4 8      9 | 3 = 9.3
```

Independent Practice

In Exercises 4–6, match the data with its stem-and-leaf plot.

a. 58, 61, 39, 55, 53, 32, 42, 67, 38, 43, 52, 41, 54, 42

b. 42, 55, 41, 56, 67, 52, 43, 46, 58, 42, 54, 61, 53

c. 67, 56, 43, 52, 42, 54, 42, 39, 61, 32, 55, 41, 53, 38

```
4. 3 | 2 8 9
   4 | 1 2 2 3
   5 | 2 3 4 5 6
   6 | 1 7
```

```
5. 4 | 1 2 2 3 6
   5 | 2 3 4 5 6 8
   6 | 1 7
```

```
6. 3 | 2 8 9
   4 | 1 2 2 3
   5 | 2 3 4 5 8
   6 | 1 7
```

In Exercises 7–9, use the data at the right.

7. Which numbers are missing from the stem?

8. Are any numbers missing from the leaves? How can you tell?

9. Copy and complete the stem-and-leaf plot.

10. *Basketball* The stem-and-leaf plot at the right shows unordered data of the heights (in inches) of players on a high school basketball team. Order the data in a new stem-and-leaf plot.

17, 42, 2, 24, 31, 5, 30, 15, 56, 9, 31, 59, 34, 10, 16, 38, 59, 39, 23, 3

```
0 | 2 5
  | 0 5
  | 4
  | 1 8
4 |
  | 9 9
```

```
5 | 9 8
6 | 5 2 3 8 6 9 4 5 4 4 6 2 4
7 | 0 2 1 0 1 1 0 0    Key
                  7 | 0 = 70 inches
```

Weather The list below shows the record-high temperatures (°F) in December for each state in the U.S.

AL: 81	CO: 75	HI: 89	KS: 83	MA: 73	MT: 69	NM: 72	OK: 86	SD: 61	VA: 80
AK: 54	CT: 74	ID: 65	KY: 76	MI: 68	NE: 72	NY: 74	OR: 64	TN: 81	WA: 63
AZ: 88	DE: 74	IL: 71	LA: 84	MN: 63	NV: 70	NC: 77	PA: 74	TX: 88	WV: 80
AR: 80	FL: 87	IN: 74	ME: 69	MS: 84	NH: 68	ND: 79	RI: 70	UT: 67	WI: 63
CA: 94	GA: 79	IA: 69	MD: 77	MO: 76	NJ: 75	OH: 77	SC: 83	VT: 65	WY: 69

11. Use a stem-and-leaf plot to order the temperatures. Make sure to include a title.

12. Which state has the highest record-high temperature?

13. What is the most common record-high temperature?

14. *Geometry* The dimensions of the rectangles that can be drawn on a 7-by-7 grid of dot paper are shown below. Use the grid at the right to help you find the perimeter of each rectangle. Then order the perimeters in a stem-and-leaf plot.

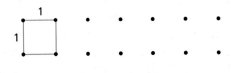

1×1

1×2 2×2

1×3 2×3 3×3

1×4 2×4 3×4 4×4

1×5 2×5 3×5 4×5 5×5

1×6 2×6 3×6 4×6 5×6 6×6

Integrated Review   *Making Connections within Mathematics*

Working Backward Copy and complete the diagram.

15.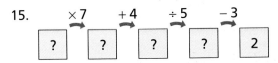

16.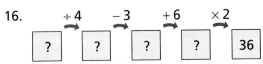

17.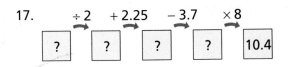

18.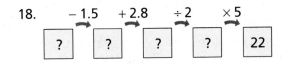

Exploration and Extension

19. *Building Your Chapter Project* The second question of your class survey was *What day of the month is your birthday?* Use a stem-and-leaf plot to order the data. How many other people have a birthday on the same day of the month as yours?

Materials Needed: counters or coins, plain paper, pencils

Part A *Averages* One way to think about the *average* of two numbers, such as 16 and 10, uses coins. Suppose you have two stacks: one with 16 coins and one with 10 coins. You want to make two stacks that have the same number in each.

 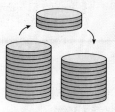 

One stack has 16 coins and one has 10 coins.   **Move 3 coins from the first stack to the second stack.**   **Both stacks now have 13 coins.**

Move 3 coins from the first stack to the second. You get two stacks with 13 coins each. This shows that the average of 16 and 10 is 13.

1. Use counters or coins to model the average of the two numbers. Sketch your results. Write the average.

   a. 6 and 10   b. 11 and 5   c. 9 and 3

2. *Communicating* Another way to think about the average of two numbers uses a number line. Explain how to use the number line below to model the average of 11 and 5. Do you get the same average you got in (b) above?

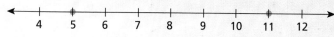

3. *Modeling Decimal Averages* Use the number line below. Find two whole numbers whose average is 3.5. Is there more than one answer? Explain.

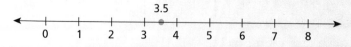

4. Use a number line to find the average of the numbers.
   a. 6 and 11   b. 7 and 8   c. 10 and 13

Part B *Modeling the Average of Three Numbers* Here is a way to model the average of three numbers: 17, 13, and 12. You have three stacks of coins: one with 17 coins, one with 13 coins, and one with 12 coins. You want to make three stacks that have the same number of coins in each stack.

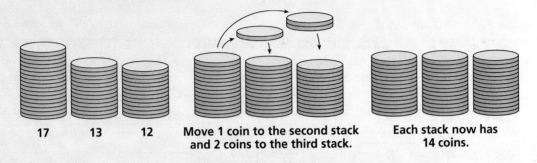

17   13   12   **Move 1 coin to the second stack and 2 coins to the third stack.**   **Each stack now has 14 coins.**

By moving 1 coin from the first stack to the second stack, and 2 coins from the first stack to the third stack, you get three stacks with 14 coins each. This shows you that the average of 17, 13, and 12 is 14.

5. Use counters or coins to model the average of the numbers. Sketch the steps you used. Then write the average of the three numbers.

   a. 4, 8, 9   b. 8, 11, 14   c. 6, 13, 20

On Your Own   *Critical Thinking*

6. Draw a sketch to help you find the average of the numbers.

   a. 7 and 15   b. 7 and 16   c. 8, 12, 13

7. If possible, find two numbers that fit the description.

   a. Two even numbers whose average is 10

   b. Two odd numbers whose average is 10

   c. Two numbers, one even and one odd, whose average is 10

8. *Looking for a Pattern*   Consider three numbers, 4, ?, and 12.

   a. Find a value for ? so that the average is 9.

   b. Find a value for ? so that the average is 10.

   c. Find a value for ? so that the average is 11.

   d. What is the pattern for the numbers found in (a), (b), and (c)?

5.3

Computing Averages

What you should learn:

Goal 1 How to find the average or mean of two or more numbers

Goal 2 How to use averages to solve real-life problems

Why you should learn it:

Averages can help you make decisions about scores. An example is finding the score you need on an English test.

Goal 1 **Finding an Average or Mean**

In Lab 5.3, you learned how to find the average of two or three numbers by leveling out stacks of coins. Here is another way to look at the average of 8, 3, and 7, which is 6.

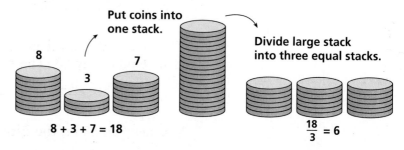

Put coins into one stack.

Divide large stack into three equal stacks.

8   3   7

8 + 3 + 7 = 18

$\frac{18}{3} = 6$

Finding an Average or Mean

To find the **average** of a set of numbers, add the numbers and divide the sum by how many numbers are in the set. The average is also called the **mean.**

Example 1 *Finding Averages or Means*

Find the average or mean of the numbers.

a. 34 and 48   b. 94, 93, 87, 82   c. 102, 145, 168, 169

Solution

a. Average $= \frac{34 + 48}{2} = \frac{82}{2} = 41$

b. Average $= \frac{94 + 93 + 87 + 82}{4} = \frac{356}{4} = 89$

c. You can use a calculator as follows.

102 $\boxed{+}$ 145 $\boxed{+}$ 168 $\boxed{+}$ 169 $\boxed{=}$

The display is 584, so the average or mean is

Average $= \frac{584}{4} = 146.$ ■

Study Tip
You can check that an average is reasonable by checking that it is between the least and greatest numbers in the set. For instance, in Example 1(b), the average is between 82 and 94.

Real Life
School

Example 2 *Guess, Check, and Revise*

So far in English class, your test scores are 82, 75, 91, and 94. What score do you need on the fifth test to get an average or mean of 85?

Solution One way to solve the problem is to use the Guess, Check, and Revise strategy and a calculator. You could guess that you need an 80 on the fifth test. Then the mean score would be

$$\text{Mean} = \frac{82 + 75 + 91 + 94 + 80}{5} = \frac{422}{5} = 84.4.$$

This is a little less than 85, so you can revise your guess to be larger—say 83. The new mean is now

$$\text{Mean} = \frac{82 + 75 + 91 + 94 + 83}{5} = \frac{425}{5} = 85.$$

You need an 83 on the fifth test. ■

Communicating about MATHEMATICS

Problem Solving
Using a Graph

▶ **Sharing Ideas about the Lesson**

Extending the Example A bar graph for the five test scores is shown below. Compare the total points above the mean with the total points below the mean. Explain how the bar graph is similar to the coin-stacking problem described on page 218.

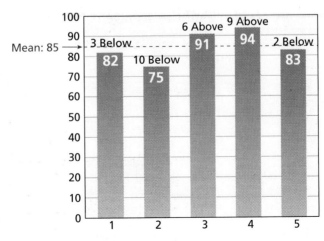

EXERCISES

Think and Discuss

▶ CHECK for Understanding

1. Use the number line to help you find the average or mean of 3 and 11.

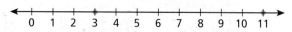

2. Use the model at the right to complete the statement.

   The average or mean of ? and ? is ?.

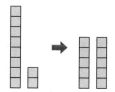

In Exercises 3–5, find the mean of the numbers. Then check whether your answer is reasonable.

3. 14, 26, 59   4. 35, 38, 45, 46   5. 81, 97, 106, 125, 161

Independent Practice

In Exercises 6–8, use the model. Write a statement about the average or mean of the two or three numbers.

6. 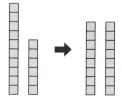   7. 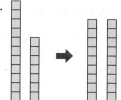   8.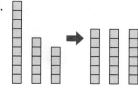

Reasoning   In Exercises 9–14, find the mean of the numbers. Then check whether your answer is reasonable.

9. 52, 68   10. 29, 41, 38   11. 90, 105, 117
12. 63, 68, 34, 51   13. 22, 36, 143, 95   14. 79, 85, 92, 103, 106

In Exercises 15–17, use a calculator to find the mean.

15. 11, 513   16. 90, 176, 304   17. 43, 266, 521, 910

In Exercises 18 and 19, use Guess, Check, and Revise to find ?.

18. $\dfrac{84 + ?}{2} = 57$ 19. $\dfrac{30 + ? + 6}{3} = 21$

20. *Reasoning*   Find a set of five different numbers whose mean is 10. Explain how you arrived at your list of numbers.

21. You are practicing for a cross-country championship race. The bar graph shows the number of miles you ran each week for 6 weeks. Use the bar graph to estimate the average number of miles you ran in a week. Then compute the average. How close was your estimate?

At age 10, Rachael Sanford of Kentucky became the youngest person to win a state high school athletic competition.

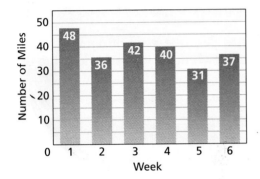

22. You are in a bowling league. So far this season you have bowled 6 games with scores of 110, 134, 129, 148, 116, and 155. What is your bowling average? What score do you need on your 7th game to achieve an average of 135?

Integrated Review — *Making Connections within Mathematics*

Write the division problem that is shown by the model.

23.

24.

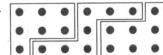

25.

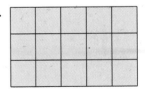

Algebra Evaluate the expression.

26. $32 - 9 \times 3$

27. $(6 \times 8) - 2^4 \div 2$

28. $2^3 + 4 \times 5 - 4^2$

Exploration and Extension

29. *Building Your Chapter Project* You used the ratings below to conduct a class survey that asked *How often do you read for enjoyment?* Find the average class rating. How does the class average compare with the average of the five numbers of the survey?

As much as possible	Often	Sometimes	Seldom	Never
1	2	3	4	5

5.4

Exploring Median and Mode

What you should learn:

Goal 1 How to find the median of a set of numbers

Goal 2 How to find the mode of a set of numbers

Why you should learn it:

For some sets of numbers, the mean or average does not describe the set very well. The median or mode may describe the set better.

Goal 1 The Median of a Set of Numbers

A mean is one way to describe a set of data. In this lesson, you will study two other ways to describe data: the median and the mode.

Finding a Median

To find the **median** of a set of numbers, first write the numbers in order. The median is the middle number or the mean of the two middle numbers.

Example 1 *Finding a Median*

a. 32, 35, 36, 37, 41, 41, 51   *Odd number of numbers*

Median is middle number.

b. 32, 35, 36, 37, 41, 41, 51, 53   *Even number of numbers*

Median is mean of middle numbers: $\frac{37 + 41}{2} = 39.$ ∎

Example 2 *Finding a Median*

You are a teacher and give a test to your students. The scores are shown below. Find the median score.

82, 99, 33, 88, 37, 84, 68, 74, 75, 83,
24, 84, 72, 84, 14, 85, 89, 81, 93

Solution To find the median, order the numbers.

14, 24, 33, 37, 68, 72, 74, 75, 81, 82,
83, 84, 84, 84, 85, 88, 89, 93, 99

The median is 82, the middle number. What is the mean score of this set? Which score better describes how your students did? Why? ∎

Real Life
Teaching

```
1 | 4
2 | 4              9 | 3 = 93
3 | 3 7
6 | 8
7 | 2 4 5  Median
8 | 1 2 3 4 4 4 5 8 9
9 | 3 9
```

In Example 2, you could use a stem-and-leaf plot to order the numbers and to find the median. The tenth leaf is the median.

The Mode of a Set of Numbers

Finding a Mode

To find the **mode** of a set of numbers, put the numbers in order. The mode is the number that appears most often.

Some sets of data do not have a mode. For instance, the set 4, 7, 9, 11, 13 does not have a mode because no number occurs more often than the others.

Real Life
Restaurant

Need to Know

Some sets may have more than one mode. For example, the set

5, 5, 7, 7, 9

has two modes:

5 and 7.

Example 3 *Finding a Mode*

The ages of the employees at an ice cream parlor are shown below. What is the mode of this data?

16, 34, 17, 16, 19, 23, 17, 18, 16, 17,
20, 16, 16, 18, 16, 17, 53, 17, 16, 18

Solution Begin by ordering the ages.

16, 16, 16, 16, 16, 16, 16, 17, 17, 17,
17, 17, 18, 18, 18, 19, 20, 23, 34, 53

From the ordered data, you can see the age that occurs most often is 16. Therefore, the mode is 16. ∎

About one third of the ice cream sold in the United States is vanilla. Chocolate and strawberry are the next most popular.

Example 4   *Finding a Mean, Median, and Mode*

The numbers of months of service of the 20 employees in the ice cream parlor are shown in the line plot. Use the line plot to find the mean, median, and mode of the lengths of service.

Months of Service for Employees

Solution   The months of service are as follows.

1, 2, 2, 4, 5, 5, 5, 5, 5, 7, 7, 7,
9, 9, 10, 12, 12, 15, 19, 21

The sum of these numbers is 162, so the mean is

$$\text{Mean} = \frac{162}{20} = 8.1 \text{ months.}$$

The two middle numbers are both 7, so the median is

Median = 7 months.

The number that occurs most often is 5, so the mode is

Mode = 5 months. ∎

Communicating about MATHEMATICS

Cooperative
Learning

▶ **Sharing Ideas about the Lesson**

Partner Activity Which of the following do you think best describes the ages of the 20 employees in Example 3? Why?

   Mean: 20   *Median:* 17   *Mode:* 16

The hourly wages of the 20 employees are shown below. Find the mean, median, and mode. Which best describes the wages of the employees? Why?

   $6, $9, $7, $7, $6, $6, $7, $8, $6, $6,
   $6, $7, $6, $12, $7, $6, $38, $6, $8, $6

EXERCISES

Guided Practice

▶ CHECK for Understanding

1. *Science* Use the table at the right. It shows the longest recorded life spans (in years) of several animals. Find the mean, median, and mode of the data.

Reasoning Decide whether the statement is true or false. If false, explain.

2. The median and the mean of the data set 21, 27, 27, 29, 31 are both 27.

3. The mode of the data set 5, 7, 11, 18, 21 is 11.

4. The median of the data set 4, 5, 6, 7, 8, 9 is 7.

Think and Discuss

Animal	Age	Animal	Age
Tortoise	152	Lobster	50
Clam	100	Cow	40
Whale	90	Pigeon	35
Oyster	80	Cat	34
Cockatoo	70	Dog	29
Condor	70	Sheep	20
Elephant	70	Goat	18
Ostrich	62	Rabbit	18
Horse	62	Hamster	10
Chimpanzee	50		

Independent Practice

In Exercises 5–7, find the median and mode of the data.

5. Numbers of square feet in closets
45, 36, 38, 48, 42, 45, 60, 54, 72, 45, 48, 42, 66, 54

6. Lengths of movies in minutes
151, 175, 188, 140, 117, 155, 122, 135, 113, 122, 125, 133

7. Ages of players on a school soccer team
11, 13, 11, 12, 12, 12, 12, 11, 13, 12, 11, 12, 10

In Exercises 8–10, match the description with the data set.

a. 50, 49, 49, 54, 46, 45, 57   b. 50, 52, 48, 47, 43, 52, 51   c. 50, 57, 50, 56, 46, 53, 52

8. The mode is 50.   9. The median is 50.   10. The mean is 50.

Music Use the data below. It shows the lengths in seconds of the songs on the CD *Aladdin*. **(Source: Walt Disney Music Company)**

79, 85, 143, 113, 60, 146, 99, 171, 160, 163, 68, 95, 111, 175, 46, 156, 297, 111, 218, 251, 247

11. Find the mean, median, and mode of the lengths.
12. Which do you think best represents the length of a song? Why?

13. *Basketball* The data at the right shows the number of wins of the National Basketball Association teams for the 1992–93 season. Find the mean, median, and mode of the data. *(Source: National Basketball Association)*

48, 35, 57, 22, 55, 19, 60, 41, 28, 49, 11, 62, 44, 26, 39, 47, 43, 54, 34, 25, 41, 40, 55, 43, 36, 51, 41

14. *Number Riddle* There are 5 numbers in a set. One of the numbers is 25. The mode is 28. The median and mean are both 26. What are the numbers?

15. The ages of students on a bus are listed below. Find the mean, median, and mode of the ages. Explain why the mean is not the best way to describe the ages.

12, 13, 12, 10, 13, 10, 12, 52, 12, 13, 11, 10, 10, 10, 12, 12

16. *Homework Time* You keep a list of the numbers of minutes you spend doing homework for 10 days. Find the mean, median, and mode of the numbers. Explain why the mode is not the best way to describe the time spent.

25, 20, 29, 40, 40, 18, 21, 23, 24, 20

Integrated Review

What's in a Name? In a survey, 400 boys and 400 girls ages 13–17 were asked *How important to you is the brand name of the clothes you buy?* *(Sources: USA Today, CNN, Gallup Poll)*

17. About how many boys answered "Somewhat important"?

18. About how many girls answered "Not at all important"?

Making Connections within Mathematics

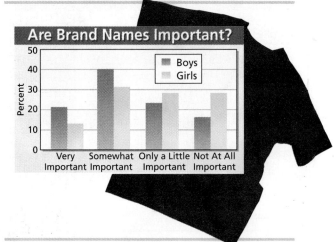

Are Brand Names Important?

19. *Group Activity* Use a telephone book. Choose 40 last names, each from a different page. Choose the names randomly. Then count the letters in the last names. Find the median and mode of the number of letters. Which best describes the number of letters? Share your results with other groups.

20. *Building Your Chapter Project* The fourth question of your class survey was *What is your handspan in centimeters?* Find the mean, median, and mode of the data. Which best describes the typical handspan of students in your class? Explain.

Using a Computer Spreadsheet

Technology
Spreadsheet

Sorting Data with a Spreadsheet

You asked 20 people to state which day of the month they were born. The days are shown below. Use a spreadsheet to write these numbers in order.

5,   21,   7,   4,   25,   17,   14,   24,   11,   1,
19,   24,   24,   15,   30,   28,   9,   24,   20,   14

Solution

First, enter the numbers in a column in the spreadsheet.

Then, select the Sort feature. To sort from least to greatest, select Ascending. To sort from greatest to least, select Descending.

#		#		#	
1	5	1	1	1	30
2	21	2	4	2	28
3	7	3	5	3	25
4	4	4	7	4	24
5	25	5	9	5	24
6	17	6	11	6	24
7	14	7	14	7	24
8	24	8	14	8	21
9	11	9	15	9	20
10	1	10	17	10	19
11	19	11	19	11	17
12	24	12	20	12	15
13	24	13	21	13	14
14	15	14	24	14	14
15	30	15	24	15	11
16	28	16	24	16	9
17	9	17	24	17	7
18	24	18	25	18	5
19	20	19	28	19	4
20	14	20	30	20	1

Ascending Order

Descending Order

DID YOU KNOW? When 20 people are asked to write the day of the month that their birthday occurs, there will almost always be duplicates. For instance, in the list of birthdays at the right, 4 of the people were born on the 24th and 2 of the people were born on the 14th.

Exercises

1. In Exercise 19 on page 215, you conducted a survey to find the days of the month that your classmates have birthdays. Use a spreadsheet. Write the days in ascending and in descending order.

2. Write about three other times you may want to order data using a spreadsheet.

Take this test as you would take a test in class. The answers to the exercises are given in the back of the book.

In Exercises 1–3, match the description with the data. **(5.1–5.4)**

a. The data includes 12 numbers.   b. The mode of the data is 12.

c. The average of the numbers is 21.

1.

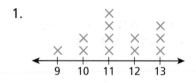

2. 31, 16, 7, 12, 37, 25, 22, 12, 39, 16, 14

3.
```
0 | 8 9
1 | 2 2 2 4
2 | 3 7 5
3 | 1 6 6
4 | 5 5
```

Super Bowl Winners   The table below shows the number of Super Bowls (through 1995) won by each team and the number of points by which they beat their opponent. **(5.1, 5.2)**

4. Make a line plot of the number of Super Bowls won by each team.

5. Write a description of the data in the line plot.

6. What is the most common number of Super Bowls won by a team?

7. Use a stem-and-leaf plot. Order the number of points by which each team beat its opponent.

8. Which team beat its opponent by the most points?

9. Which team won the closest scoring game? Explain.

Team	No. of Super Bowls	Points Won by
Packers	2	25, 19
Chiefs	1	16
Colts	1	3
Cowboys	4	21, 17, 35, 17
Dolphins	2	7, 17
Steelers	4	10, 4, 4, 12
Raiders	3	18, 17, 29
49ers	5	5, 22, 4, 45, 24
Redskins	3	10, 32, 13
Bears	1	36
Giants	2	19, 1
Jets	1	9

Number Sense   In Exercises 10–12, use Guess, Check, and Revise to find the unknown number. **(5.3)**

10. $\dfrac{54 + \boxed{?}}{2} = 49$

11. $\dfrac{\boxed{?} + 26 + 21}{3} = 25$

12. $\dfrac{40 + 53 + \boxed{?} + 41}{4} = 52$

13. *Food and Nutrition*   The table at the right shows the number of calories in one serving of vegetables commonly found in salads. Find the mean, median, and mode of the data. Which best describes the data? Explain. **(5.4)**

Broccoli	40	Celery	20
Carrot	30	Cucumber	20
Cauliflower	32	Lettuce	18
Onion	40	Tomato	40

5.5 Bar Graphs

What you should learn:

Goal 1 How to draw a bar graph

Goal 2 How to choose a scale for a bar graph

Why you should learn it:

A bar graph helps you quickly see information about data.

Goal 1 Guidelines for Drawing Bar Graphs

You already know how to *read* information from bar graphs. In this lesson, you will study guidelines for *drawing* bar graphs.

Example 1 *Drawing a Bar Graph*

Here are typical daily sleep requirements for 6 animals: rabbit, 8 hours; hamster, 14 hours; rat, 13 hours; guinea pig, 9.5 hours; cat, 12.5 hours; dog, 10 hours. Show this data with a bar graph.

Solution One way to draw the bar graph is shown below.

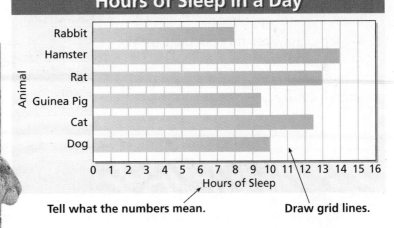

Write a title for your graph.

Hours of Sleep in a Day

Tell what the numbers mean. Draw grid lines.

Real Life
Pets

This rabbit's ability to camouflage, or blend into the background, keeps it safe while it takes a nap.

Guidelines for Drawing a Bar Graph

Bars should have the same widths.

Grid lines should be evenly spaced.

Grid lines should start at 0.

Choosing a Scale

The numbers on a bar graph are its **scale.** In Example 1, the scale increases by ones. When data contains large numbers, it is better to choose a scale that increases by fives, tens, hundreds, or some other number.

Real Life
Buildings

Example 2 *Drawing a Bar Graph*

The heights of the 6 tallest buildings in Charlotte, North Carolina, are shown below. Draw a bar graph for this data.

NationsBank Center	871 ft	Interstate Tower	462 ft
1 First Union Center	580 ft	2 First Union Center	433 ft
NationsBank Plaza	503 ft	Wachovia Center	420 ft

Solution One way to draw the bar graph is shown below.

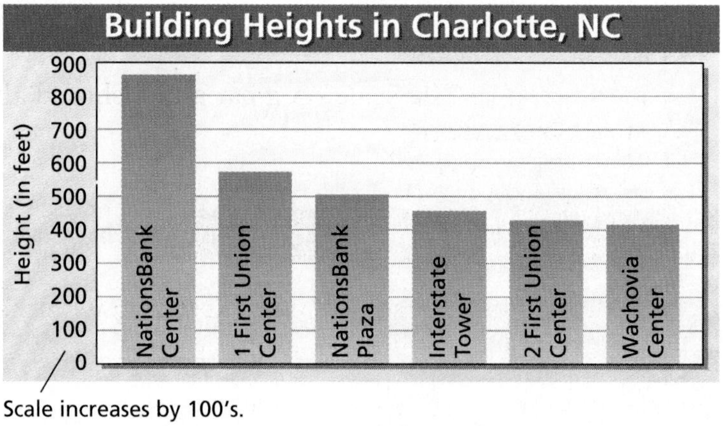

Study Tip

There are many ways to make bar graphs. The bar graph in Example 1 is a **horizontal bar graph.** But you could also have used a **vertical bar graph** like that shown in Example 2.

Building Heights in Charlotte, NC

Scale increases by 100's.

■

Communicating about MATHEMATICS

Cooperative
Learning

▶ **Sharing Ideas about the Lesson**

Partner Activity: Extending the Example Draw a bar graph to show the heights of the 6 tallest buildings in Chicago, Illinois. Compare your graph with other pairs' graphs. How are they alike? How are they different?

Sears Tower	1454 ft	311 S. Wacker	970 ft
Amoco	1136 ft	Prudential	901 ft
John Hancock	1127 ft	AT&T Center	891 ft

EXERCISES

Guided Practice

▶ **CHECK for Understanding**

Hobbies In Exercises 1–3, suppose you surveyed 328 people about their favorite winter activity. You want to show the results below with a bar graph.

Skiing: 62   Ice Skating: 89
Sledding: 120   Snowmobiling: 57

1. What scale should you use?
2. Draw a bar graph of the data.
3. Give the bar graph a title.
4. Which should you *not* do when making a bar graph?
   a. Start the grid lines at 0.
   b. Choose a title for the graph.
   c. Make bars wider for larger numbers.
   d. Space grid lines evenly.
5. *True or False?* The scale on a bar graph should always increase by ones.

Think and Discuss

Independent Practice

Error Analysis In Exercises 6–8, what is wrong with the bar graph?

6.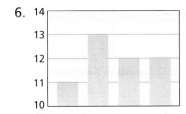

7.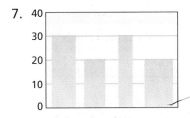

8.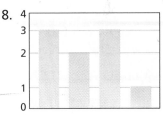

In Exercises 9–11, match the data with the scale that fits best.

a. 550, 330, 570, 225, 100   b. 975, 1050, 2450, 825, 4100   c. 45, 62, 88, 10, 32
9. Increase by 100's   10. Increase by 10's   11. Increase by 1000's

Consumer Spending Use the data at the right about different age groups. It shows the amount of money spent per person per week. *(Source: Teenage Research Unlimited)*

12. What scale best represents the data?
13. Draw a bar graph of the data.

Age	Average Weekly Spending
6–8	$3.80
9–11	$4.80
12–14	$22.00
15–17	$43.00

14. *Geography*   The table below shows the lengths (in miles) of some of the world's rivers. Make a bar graph of the data. *(Source: U.S. Department of Commerce)*

River	Length
Nile	4145
Amazon	4000
Mississippi	2348
Rio Grande	1885
Arkansas	1450

15. *Weather Patterns*   The table below shows the numbers of clear days per year for some cities in the United States. Make a bar graph of the data. *(Source: PC USA)*

City	Clear Days
Baltimore, MD	106
Cincinnati, OH	80
Detroit, MI	75
Memphis, TN	118
Chicago, IL	94
Milwaukee, WI	96

The Nile River, which flows through northern Africa, is the longest river in the world.

16. *Principal for a Day*   Use the data below. It shows the results of a survey of students who responded to the question *What changes would you make if you were principal for a day?* Explain why a bar graph is a better representation of this data than a line plot. Then make a bar graph of the data. *(Source: BKG Youth/Nintendo)*

Raise money for homeless   935   Cancel classes for the day   845
Have a pizza party for lunch 890   Get new equipment and books 725

Algebra   In Exercises 17–22, use mental math to solve.

17. $5 \cdot m = 45$ **18.** $28 + t = 48$ **19.** $3 \cdot b = 75$

20. $s + 210 = 411$ **21.** $n \times 7 = 63$ **22.** $25 + d = 60$

23. Find the mean, median, and mode of the set.

    7, 8, 12, 14, 8, 9, 10, 12, 8, 13, 10, 11, 7, 8, 13

24. Make a stem-and-leaf plot to help you write the numbers in increasing order.

    18, 25, 29, 19, 41, 30, 37, 25, 43, 22, 27, 36, 41, 45, 35, 38, 26

Exploration and Extension

25. *Building Your Chapter Project*   The fifth question of your class survey was *Which of these sports do you like to do best? Choose one from among football, softball, baseball, basketball, field hockey, soccer, gymnastics, or tennis.* Make a bar graph of the data. What is the most popular sport? What is the least popular sport?

Mixed REVIEW

Algebra   Evaluate the expression when $t = 3$. **(2.6)**

1. $4 \cdot (6 - t)$ **2.** $4 \cdot t + 12$ **3.** $30 - t \cdot 4$ **4.** $45 \div 9 \cdot t$

Round the decimal to the nearest tenth. **(3.6)**

5. 34.54   **6.** 1.05   **7.** 3.761   **8.** 5.549

Find the missing number. **(3.7)**

9. $49 = 7^{\boxed{?}}$ **10.** $125 = \boxed{?}^3$ **11.** $\boxed{?} = 3^3$ **12.** $1000 = 10^{\boxed{?}}$

Add or subtract. **(4.1, 4.2)**

13. $5.34 + 8.98$ **14.** $13.76 - 3.22$ **15.** $9 - 0.23$ **16.** $5 + 0.08$

Number Sense   Is the statement true or false? If false, change the right side of the equation so the statement is true. **(4.6)**

17. $48 \div 1000 = 48{,}000$ **18.** $48 \times 100 = 4800$

19. $4.8 \div 10 = 0.48$ **20.** $4.8 \times 100 = 4800$

5.6

Connections to Algebra: Line Graphs

What you should learn:

Goal 1 How to draw a line graph

Goal 2 How to use a line graph to recognize a trend in real-life data

Why you should learn it:

A line graph helps you analyze data over time. An example is comparing the prices of pairs of sneakers from 1985 to 1995.

The average price of sneakers increases from year to year. Inflation is the word used to describe increasing prices.

Goal 1 Drawing a Line Graph

In this lesson, you will learn how to use a **line graph** to represent data that is changing over time.

Example 1 *Drawing a Line Graph*

The average prices for a pair of sneakers are shown for the years 1985 through 1995. Draw a line graph for this data. Which two-year period had the greatest increase?

1985 $32.37	1989 $36.56	1993 $41.22
1986 $32.65	1990 $38.26	1994 $43.16
1987 $34.10	1991 $39.68	1995 $45.32
1988 $35.58	1992 $40.66	

Solution One way to draw the line graph is shown below.

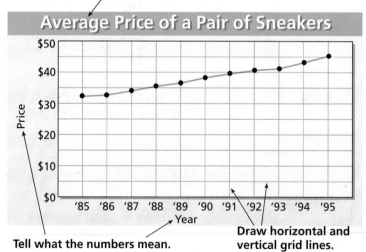

Write a title for your graph.

Average Price of a Pair of Sneakers

Tell what the numbers mean.

Draw horizontal and vertical grid lines.

The greatest increase was from 1993 to 1995, when the average price went up $4.10 from $41.22 to $45.32. ■

When you are drawing a line graph, be sure your grid lines are evenly spaced. For instance, in Example 1, the grid lines that represent the years are evenly spaced.

Goal 2 Using a Line Graph

Line graphs can be used to approximate prices or other values that will occur in the future.

Real Life
Wages

Example 2 *Using a Line Graph*

The average hourly wages for manufacturing workers from 1985 through 1995 are shown below. Draw a line graph for this data. Use the graph to approximate the average hourly wage in 1997.

1985 $ 9.54	1989 $10.48	1993 $11.76
1986 $ 9.73	1990 $10.83	1994 $12.05
1987 $ 9.91	1991 $11.18	1995 $12.34
1988 $10.19	1992 $11.46	

Solution   One way to draw the line graph is shown below.

From the graph, you can approximate that the average hourly wage in 1997 would be about $13. ■

Communicating about MATHEMATICS

Problem Solving
Making a Table

▶ **Sharing Ideas about the Lesson**

Making Connections Make a table that shows how many hours it took a manufacturing worker to earn enough to buy a pair of sneakers from 1985 to 1995. For example, in 1985, it took about $32.37 ÷ $9.54 or about 3.4 hours. Then make a line graph of the data. What can you conclude?

EXERCISES

▶ **CHECK for Understanding**

1. What type of data is best represented by a line graph?

Error Analysis   In Exercises 2 and 3, describe the error.

2.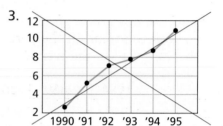

3.

Cable TV   Use the line graph at the right. It shows the numbers of cable subscribers in millions from 1975–1994.

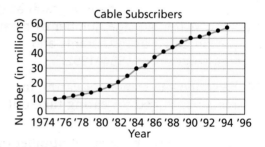
Cable Subscribers

4. Which two-year period had the greatest increase in subscribers?

5. Approximate the number of subscribers in 1995.

Independent Practice

In Exercises 6 and 7, approximate the amount for 1993.

6.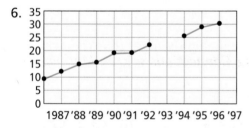

7.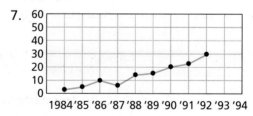

Drink Up   Use the line graph at the right. It shows the gallons of fruit juice that the average person in the United States consumes per year.

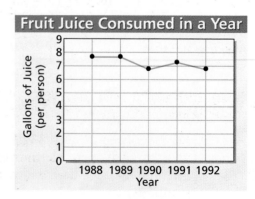
Fruit Juice Consumed in a Year

8. How did the amount of juice consumed change from 1991 to 1992?

9. Explain why it would not be good to use the line graph to approximate the amount of juice consumed in 1993.

10. The table below shows the percents of Americans who have refused to answer at least one survey each year from 1983 through 1992. Draw a line graph for the data. Use the graph to find which years decreased from the previous year.

Year	1983	1984	1985	1986	1987	1988	1989	1990	1991	1992
Percent	18%	20%	22%	24%	30%	34%	35%	36%	33%	31%

11. *Population Trends*   The table below shows the percents of the population who are 10–14 years old each year from 1983 through 1992. Draw a line graph for the data. Write a sentence about the trend in the percents. How does the line graph help you see the trend?

Year	1983	1984	1985	1986	1987	1988	1989	1990	1991	1992
Percent	7.6%	7.4%	7.2%	6.9%	6.8%	6.7%	6.8%	6.9%	7.0%	7.1%

For Here or to Go?   The line graph at the right shows the average number of meals per person eaten at restaurants and ordered to go from 1984–1992.

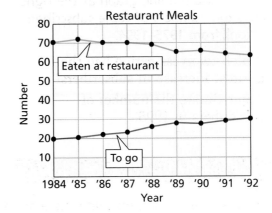

12. Describe the trends for eating in restaurants and for eating take-out food.

13. Approximate the average number of take-out meals in 1995.

14. Do you think the number of meals ordered to go will ever be greater than the number of meals eaten at restaurants? Explain your reasoning.

Integrated Review

Making Connections within Mathematics

Algebra   Solve. Then describe any patterns you see.

15. $20 - x = 19$
$20 - x = 17$
$20 - x = 15$
$20 - x = 13$

16. $x + 15 = 25$
$x + 16 = 25$
$x + 18 = 25$
$x + 21 = 25$

17. $x \cdot 2 = 4$
$x \cdot 3 = 9$
$x \cdot 4 = 20$
$x \cdot 5 = 40$

18. $x \div 1 = 1$
$x \div 2 = 2$
$x \div 3 = 3$
$x \div 4 = 4$

Exploration and Extension

19. *Building Your Chapter Project*   Think about a survey question you would like to ask your classmates. Collect your data. Draw a line graph of the data and name 3 things you can tell from the graph.

Lab 5.7

Misleading Graphs

Materials Needed: paper, pencils

Part A *Data Analysis* Forty people were asked to name their favorite sport on television. The results are shown in the bar graph below.

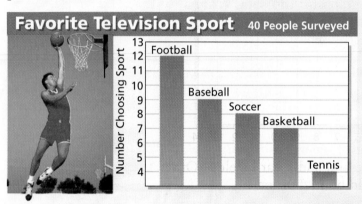

1. Why is this graph misleading?
2. Draw a bar graph that shows the results of the survey but is not misleading.
3. In the misleading graph, it looks like 9 times as many people chose football as tennis. Compare the sizes of the football and tennis bars in your graph.

Part B *Education* Forty people were asked to name their favorite school subject. The results are shown in the bar graph below.

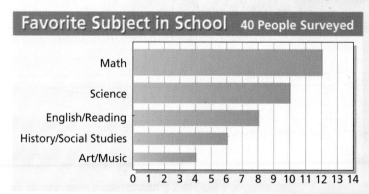

4. Why is this graph misleading?
5. Draw a bar graph that shows the results of the survey but is not misleading.

Part C *Birds and Animals* Fifty people were asked to name their favorite zoo bird. The results are shown in the bar graph.

6. Why is this graph misleading? (*Hint:* Add the totals represented by the bars.)

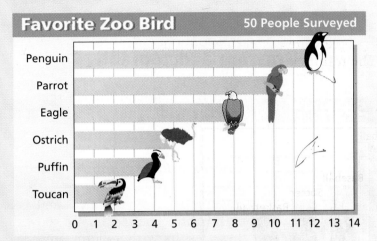

7. Redraw the bar graph above and add a bar labeled "Other." How many responses should be in "Other"?

On Your Own   *Critical Thinking*

Travel Forty people were asked to name their favorite way to travel. The results are shown in the bar graph below.

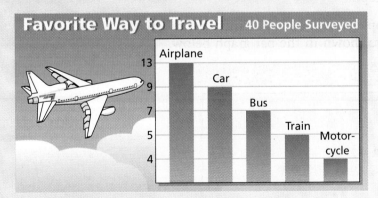

8. Why is this graph misleading?

9. Draw a bar graph that shows the results of the survey and is not misleading.

10. In the misleading graph, it looks like 5 times as many people chose airplanes as motorcycles. Compare the sizes of the airplane and motorcycle bars in your graph.

5.7

Choosing an Appropriate Graph

What you should learn:

Goal 1 How to draw a pictograph

Goal 2 How to choose an appropriate graph

Why you should learn it:

There are many ways to represent data with a graph. By choosing an appropriate graph, you make the data easier to understand.

Unlike fruit, most vegetables are **annuals**—*plants that live for only one growing season.*

Goal 1 **Drawing a Pictograph**

A **pictograph** is similar to a bar graph except that a pictograph represents data with symbols instead of bars.

Example *Drawing a Pictograph*

Sixty people were given a list of 6 vegetables and asked to choose their *least* favorite. The results are shown below. Represent these results with a pictograph.

Mushrooms	18	Tomatoes	8
Beets	14	Broccoli	7
Cabbage	9	Onions	4

Solution One way to draw the pictograph is shown.

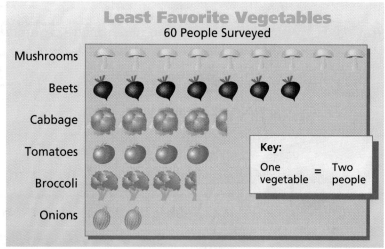

Here are some guidelines for making pictographs.

• Use symbols that are about the same size. For instance, the mushrooms are about the same size as the beets.

• If each symbol represents more than 1 item, include a key to show how many items it represents. For instance, one vegetable symbol represents 2 people.

In this chapter, you have studied 5 types of plots or graphs. Here is an example of each.

Line Plot
(See page 208.)

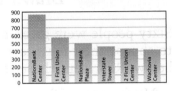

Stem-and-Leaf Plot
(See page 212.)

```
1 | 2 6 8
2 | 1 2 4 6 7 8 9 9
3 | 0 2 5 6 9
4 | 0 2 3 4 5 7
5 | 1 5
```

Bar Graph
(See page 230.)

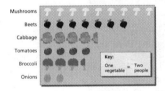

Line Graph
(See page 234.)

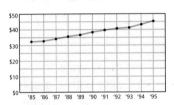

Pictograph
(See page 240.)

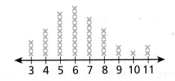

Communicating about MATHEMATICS

Cooperative Learning

▶ **Sharing Ideas about the Lesson**

Choosing an Appropriate Graph With others in your group, review the 5 graphs shown above. For each type of graph, discuss some ways that it can help you organize or understand data. Here are a few things to consider.

- Is the plot or graph used to organize data or is it used to display the data after it is organized?

- Does the data describe yearly changes?

EXERCISES

Think and Discuss

▶ **CHECK for Understanding**

In Exercises 1–3, decide whether the pictograph is misleading.
If the pictograph is misleading, explain why.

1.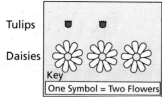

2.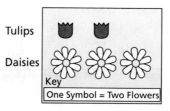

3.

In Exercises 4–6, name the type of graph. Then describe a real-life
situation that the graph could represent.

4.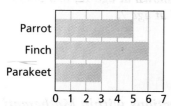

5.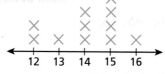

6.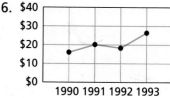

Independent Practice

In Exercises 7–11, match the type of graph with its description.

a. Line plot   b. Stem-and-leaf plot   c. Bar graph
d. Line graph   e. Pictograph

7. Used to represent data that describes changes over time

8. Represents data with symbols   9. Uses an ✕ to represent a number

10. Used to order data   11. Can be horizontal or vertical

12. *Vacations*   In a survey, 20 people were asked how they
    got to their summer vacations. The results were: car, 13;
    plane, 4; bus, 2; train, 1. Draw a pictograph of this data.

13. *Musicians*   The number (in millions) of people who play a
    musical instrument are: piano, 24; guitar, 10; flute, 4; drum,
    3; clarinet, 2. Draw a pictograph of this data. (*Source: American
    Music Conference*)

14. In a survey, students were asked if they had attended a
    professional sports event. The results were: baseball, 372;
    basketball, 162; football, 162; hockey, 90. Draw an
    appropriate graph of the data. (*Source: Sports Illustrated for Kids*)

15. **Games**   The data below is the number of board games owned by 30 students. Organize the data using a stem-and-leaf plot *or* a line plot. Why did you select the graph that you did?

    5, 3, 3, 5, 10, 2, 4, 3, 3, 4, 5, 4, 7, 2, 1, 3, 4, 3, 6, 3, 1, 3, 3, 4, 4, 3, 6, 8, 3, 3

16. The data below shows the average amount of money (per person) spent on reading materials for 1986–1991. Draw a graph of the data. *(Source: U.S. Bureau of Labor Statistics)*

    1986: 140   1987: 142   1988: 150

    1989: 157   1990: 153   1991: 163

17. The data below shows the average daily high temperatures for Baltimore, Maryland, for each month. Use a stem-and-leaf plot to organize the data. *(Source: National Oceanic and Atmospheric Administration)*

    53, 83, 87, 79, 68, 45, 44, 74, 86, 56, 41, 65

Nicholas Woo, shown at age 12, had his first book published at age 7.

Integrated Review   Making Connections within Mathematics

Geometry   Estimate the length of the side labeled *s*.

18. Perimeter = 8.7   19. Perimeter = 4.67   20. Perimeter = 7.6

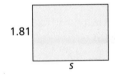

1.81

s

1.56   1.49

s

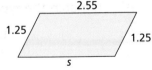

2.55

1.25   1.25

s

Exploration and Extension

Attribute Diagram   Use the diagram at the right. It shows three attributes of shapes—small, red, and triangular. Small shapes belong in Region 1, and small red shapes belong in Region 2. Write the number of the region where each shape belongs.

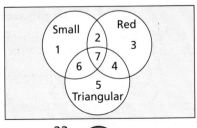

21.   22.   23.

24.   25.   26.

5 Chapter Summary

What did you learn?

Why did you learn it?

Many real-life problems contain sets of data. When the data is unorganized or simply written in a list, it can be difficult to interpret. Organizing the data and representing it with a graph can help you understand the data. Here are some of the examples you studied in this chapter.

- Organize the weights of salmon going over a fish ladder. **(5.1)**
- Compare the ages of workers in a restaurant. **(5.4)**
- Compare the numbers of hours that animals sleep. **(5.5)**
- Compare the average prices of sneakers from 1985–1995. **(5.6)**
- Display the results of a survey about vegetables. **(5.7)**

How does it fit into the bigger picture of mathematics?

As mathematics has developed over the past several hundred years, its different parts have been given special names, such as *arithmetic*, *geometry*, and *algebra*. In this chapter, you studied *statistics*. It is the part that deals with the analysis of data.

As you continue your study of mathematics, you will encounter other parts, such as *probability* and *coordinate geometry*.

Each time you study a different part of mathematics, try to see how they all fit together. In this chapter, you saw how arithmetic (adding and dividing) is used to find the mean of a set of numbers.

Weather The table at the right shows the record-low temperatures in July for 8 cities. **(5.1, 5.2, 5.4)**

City	Temperature (°F)
Denver, CO	43
Miami, FL	69
Boise, ID	35
Wichita, KS	51
Portland, ME	40
Duluth, MN	35
Omaha, NE	44
Raleigh, NC	35

1. Make a line plot of the numbers of letters in the cities' names. (For example: Denver = 6)
   a. What is the most common number of letters?
   b. What is the smallest number of letters?
2. Use a stem-and-leaf plot to order the temperatures.
   a. Which city has the highest record-low temperature?
   b. What is the most common record-low temperature?
   c. Find the median of the data.

In Exercises 3–5, compute the mean. **(5.3)**

3. 48, 56, 25   4. 211, 30, 140, 35   5. 22, 98, 67, 18, 20

6. Find the median and mode of the data. **(5.4)**
   Number of minutes you read per day
   15, 10, 20, 10, 15, 30, 15, 20, 25, 15, 15, 10

7. *Statistics* In a survey, 500 students were asked which they would most like to be: athletic, attractive, smart, or wealthy. The results are shown below. Make a graph of the data. *(Source: BKG Youth/Nintendo)* **(5.5)**
   Smart: 240   Wealthy: 100   Athletic: 125   Attractive: 35

8. *Consumer Spending* The table shows the average price per pound for fish from 1983 to 1992. Make a line graph of the data. Which year had the greatest increase? *(Source: U.S. National Oceanic and Atmospheric Administration)* **(5.6)**

Year	1983	1984	1985	1986	1987	1988	1989	1990	1991	1992
Price	$0.37	$0.37	$0.37	$0.46	$0.45	$0.49	$0.38	$0.38	$0.36	$0.38

9. The average numbers of pieces of sports equipment bought in a day in the United States are: hockey sticks, 3000; bowling shoes, 4000; soccer balls, 6000; skateboards, 8000; and basketballs, 9000. Draw a pictograph of the data. (Let one symbol = 1000.) *(Source: National Sporting Goods Assoc.)* **(5.7)**

Reasoning   In Exercises 10–13, each graph represents a set of data. What do you think the data set could be? Make up a story about the data and how it was collected.

10.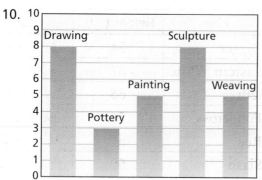

11.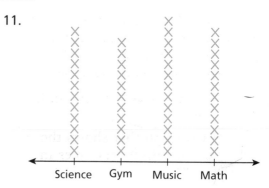

12.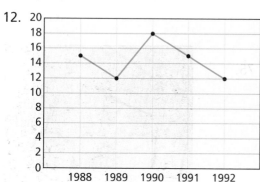

13.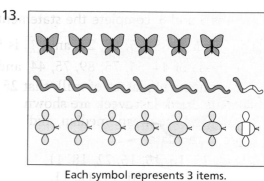

Each symbol represents 3 items.

Detect the Detective   In Exercises 14–27, a clue is given. Use the graphs above to find the number that the clue represents. Then use the key at the right to find the letter that goes with the number. When you have completed the problems, you will discover the name of a famous detective.

14. _____   15. _____   16. _____   17. _____
Worms   Sculpture   Painting   Butterflies

18. _____   19. _____   20. _____   21. _____
Math   1991   Pottery   Gym

22. _____   23. _____   24. _____   25. _____
Drawing   1988   Science   Music

26. _____   27. _____
Weaving   Bees

1-A	14-N
2-B	15-O
3-C	16-P
4-D	17-Q
5-E	18-R
6-F	19-S
7-G	20-T
8-H	21-U
9-I	22-V
10-J	23-W
11-K	24-X
12-L	25-Y
13-M	26-Z

Use the number of days in each month of the year.

1. Make a line plot of the data.

2. List two features of the data.

Science The table at the right shows the 6 tallest pine trees in the United States, their heights, and the state in which they grow. *(Source: American Forestry Assoc.)*

Pine	Height (yd)	State
Digger	54	California
Eastern White	67	Michigan
Jeffrey	66	California
Ponderosa	74	California
Red	51	Michigan
Slash	50	S. Carolina

3. Make a stem-and-leaf plot to order the heights.

4. Draw a bar graph that shows the height of the tallest pine trees in each state.

In Exercises 5 and 6, complete the statement.

5. The mean of 85, 45, 66, 21, and ? is 52.

6. The mode of 44, 54, 75, 89, 75, 44, and ? is 75.

7. The numbers of glasses of milk that 25 students drank last week are shown below. Find the mean, median, and mode of the data.

   10, 14, 25, 16, 15, 16, 22, 18, 11,
   5, 14, 16, 17, 21, 10, 14, 12, 11,
   12, 15, 22, 20, 16, 18, 20

8. *Caves* The table below lists some of the world's deepest caves. Construct a bar graph of the data.

Country	France	Spain	Mexico	Austria	Italy
Depth (ft)	5256	4728	4439	3999	3986

Leah Brown, 12, spelunker (cave explorer), holds the women's world record for a 120-meter climb.

9. The average number of pieces of mail sent by each person is listed in the table for every 5 years from 1970 to 1990. Make a line graph of the data. What 5-year period had the greatest increase? *(Source: U.S. Postal Service)*

Year	1970	1975	1980	1985	1990
Mail	411	411	463	584	662

10. *Gardening* The data lists the numbers out of 100 surveyed who grew each type of flower in their gardens: marigolds, 60; roses, 60; geraniums, 58; impatiens, 56; and tulips, 52. Draw a pictograph of the data.

CHAPTER 6

Exploring Fractions, Ratios, and Proportions

Architecture is an art as well as a profession. A good example is this creatively designed private home in Colorado.

One measure of the country's economic growth is linked to the construction and sale of new homes.

New Housing Starts

Year	1986	1987	1988	1989	1990	1991	1992	1993
Number (in thousands)	1807	1623	1488	1376	1193	1014	1200	1288

(Source: Department of Commerce)

Think and Discuss

1. What kind of graph would you use to display this data? Why?
2. What does this data tell you about the nation's economy during these years?

CHAPTER THEME:

Architecture

Architect for a Day

Chapter Theme: Architecture Have you seen a blueprint of your home? It is a scale drawing. It shows what your home would look like if you sliced off the ceiling and looked at the arrangement of rooms from above.

In this project, you will design an apartment that has five rooms: a kitchen, a bathroom, a living room, and two bedrooms. In Lesson 6.1 you will make a scale drawing of the design. Then you will use the scale drawing to solve the following problems.

- **In Lesson 6.2:** Compare the length-to-width ratios in the blueprint of the rooms. (page 263)

- **In Lesson 6.3:** Compare the length-to-width ratios in the blueprint and in the actual apartment. (page 268)

- **In Lesson 6.4:** Find the number of rolls of wallpaper you need. (page 275)

- **In Lesson 6.5:** Graph data about the amount of time people spend in each room. (page 282)

- **In Lesson 6.6:** Find the number of boxes of tiles needed to cover the floors. (page 287)

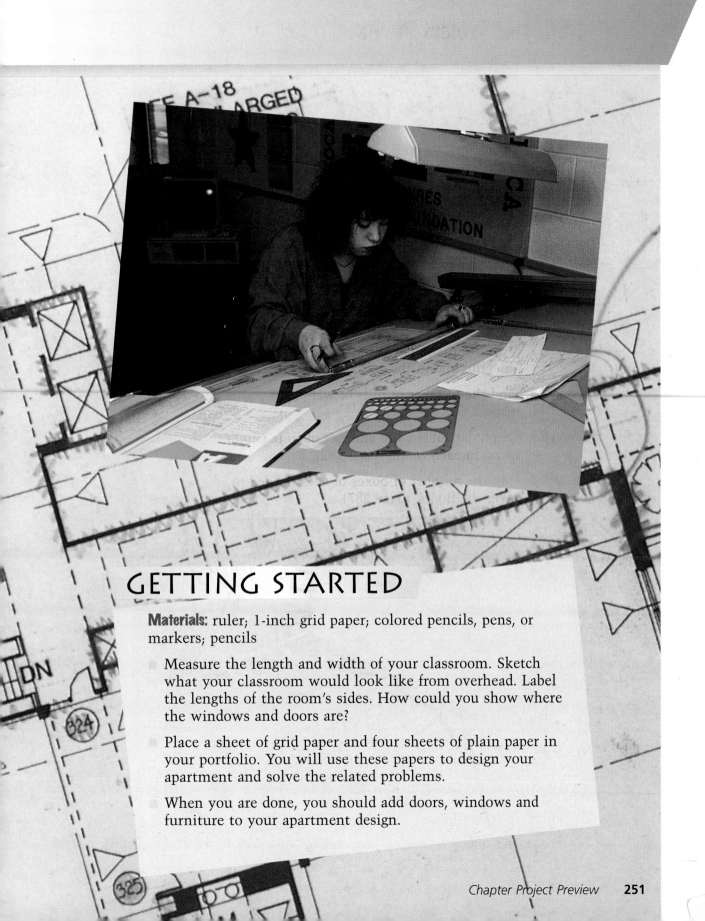

GETTING STARTED

Materials: ruler; 1-inch grid paper; colored pencils, pens, or markers; pencils

Measure the length and width of your classroom. Sketch what your classroom would look like from overhead. Label the lengths of the room's sides. How could you show where the windows and doors are?

Place a sheet of grid paper and four sheets of plain paper in your portfolio. You will use these papers to design your apartment and solve the related problems.

When you are done, you should add doors, windows and furniture to your apartment design.

Materials Needed: plain paper, centimeter ruler, colored pencils, pens, or markers

Part A *Folding Paper in Halves* Fold a sheet of paper in half. Then fold it in half a second and third time. Finally, unfold the paper. Two ways to do this are shown below.

 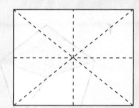

> What other ways can you find to fold a sheet of paper in half 3 times and get *different* patterns?

1. How many small regions are on your sheet? Are all the regions the same size?

2. What fraction of the whole does each small region represent?

3. Shade 3 of the regions. What fraction of the whole do the shaded regions represent?

Part B *Drawing Part-to-Whole Fraction Models*

4. a. Use a centimeter ruler. Draw a rectangle that is 8 centimeters by 12 centimeters. Divide the rectangle into thirds as shown below at the left. Shade one region as shown. Write the fraction that this model represents.

   b. Copy your model from Exercise 4a. Then divide each region in half as shown in the middle figure below. Write the fraction that this model represents.

   c. Copy your model from Exercise 4b. Divide the rectangle into fourths as shown below at the right. Write the fraction that this model represents.

> Why is it easier to divide the 12-centimeter side into thirds than to divide the 8-centimeter side into thirds?

Fraction = $\dfrac{?}{?}$

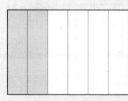

Fraction = $\dfrac{?}{?}$

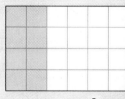

Fraction = $\dfrac{?}{?}$

   d. What can you conclude about the 3 fractions?

Part C *What Do You Think?*

5. Decide whether the figure is a correct part-to-whole model of the fraction $\frac{1}{3}$. Explain your reasoning.

a.

b.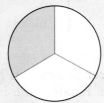

c.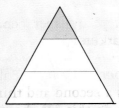

d.

e.

f.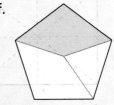

6. Look at the models above. What must be true of a part-to-whole model of the fraction $\frac{1}{3}$?

On Your Own

Critical Thinking

Naming Part-to-Whole Models In Exercises 7–14, write the fraction that is shown by the part-to-whole model.

7.

8.

9.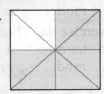

10.

11.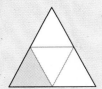

12.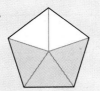

13.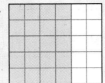

14.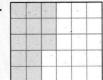

15. For each of the models shown in Exercises 7–14, draw a different part-to-whole model that represents the same fraction. Explain your reasoning.

6.1

Fundamental Fraction Concepts

What you should learn:

Goal 1 How to write fractions

Goal 2 How to use fractions to solve real-life problems

Why you should learn it:

Fractions can help you compare sets. An example is comparing groups of students.

Goal 1 ## Writing Fractions

Lesson Investigation

■ **Investigating Fractions**

Partner Activity Which models represent the fraction $\frac{3}{4}$? Explain your reasoning.

a.  b. c.

Every fraction has two numbers. The top number is the **numerator** and the bottom number is the **denominator**.

Need To Know

In Example 1, the fraction $\frac{5}{4}$ could be written as a mixed number.

$$\frac{5}{4} = 1\frac{1}{4}$$

The fraction tells you that you have five fourths circles. The mixed number $1\frac{1}{4}$ tells you that you have one whole circle, plus one fourth of another circle or $1 + \frac{1}{4}$.

Example 1 *Looking for a Pattern*

Each diagram represents a portion of a circle. Name each fraction as fourths. What do the numerators and denominators represent?

a. b. c. d. 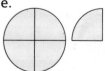 e.

Solution The fractions are

$$\frac{1}{4}, \frac{2}{4}, \frac{3}{4}, \frac{4}{4}, \text{ and } \frac{5}{4}.$$

The denominator of 4 tells you how many pieces are needed to make a whole circle. The numerators tell you how many pieces are in each diagram. ■

Problem Solving
Draw a Diagram

5 out of 6 Groups

5 out of 8 Groups

Example 2 *Representing Portions with Fractions*

You are helping teach 2 first-grade classes how to spell. Each class has 24 students.

a. In the first class, you divide the students into 6 equal groups. Five of the groups spell all the words correctly.

b. In the second class, you divide the students into 8 equal groups. Five of the groups spell all the words correctly.

Did one class do better than the other, or did both classes do the same? Explain.

Solution   A diagram can help you answer the question. From the diagram shown at the left, you can see that $\frac{5}{6}$ of the first class, or 20 students, spelled all the words correctly. You can also see that $\frac{5}{8}$ of the second class, or 15 students, spelled all the words correctly.

This tells you that the first class did better.   ■

Communicating about MATHEMATICS

▶ Sharing Ideas about the Lesson

Number Sense   Write the fraction of the square that is shaded blue. Then classify the fraction as one of the following: equal to 0, equal to $\frac{1}{2}$, equal to 1, close to 0, close to $\frac{1}{2}$, or close to 1.

A.   B.   C.   D.

E.   F.   G.   H.

EXERCISES

Think and Discuss

▶ **CHECK for Understanding**

1. Does the diagram at the right represent the fraction $\frac{4}{6}$? Explain your reasoning.

In Exercises 2–4, complete the statement.

2. In the fraction $\frac{6}{7}$, 6 is the ? and 7 is the ? .

3. The number $2\frac{2}{3}$ is a ? .

4. The denominator of the fraction $\frac{5}{12}$ is ? .

Geometry In Exercises 5–7, match the fraction with its model.

a.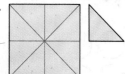

b.

c.

5. $\frac{1}{8}$

6. $\frac{9}{8}$

7. $\frac{4}{8}$

8. *Communicating* Describe 3 situations in real life in which you would use a mixed number.

Independent Practice

Is the diagram a good model to use for a fraction? If it is, what fraction of the model is shaded? If it isn't, explain why.

9.

10.

11.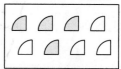

12.

13.

14.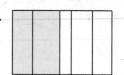

15. *Measurement* Draw a line that is 12 centimeters long. On the line, mark each centimeter. Then shade the part of the line that represents the fraction $\frac{7}{12}$.

16. In 1987, the fraction of cars and vans with driver's side air bags was $\frac{1}{20}$. In 1994, the fraction was $\frac{9}{10}$. Draw a diagram to represent each fraction. *(Source: Insurance Institute for Highway Safety)*

Guinea Pigs Your pet guinea pig had 2 litters. In the first litter, 2 of the 3 babies were brown. In the second litter, 3 of the 4 babies were brown.

17. Write the fraction of baby guinea pigs that were brown for each litter.

18. In which litter was the fraction of brown baby guinea pigs larger? Use the diagram to help you decide.

Guinea pigs can be black, brown, red, white, or a combination of colors.

First
Litter   Second
Litter

19. Write three fractions that are close to 0 and three that are close to 1.

Copy the 20 circles at the right. Group them by 4's. Color 3 of the groups blue. Copy the 20 circles again and group them by 5's. Color 3 of the groups blue.

20. On which copy did you color more circles?

21. Use the result of Exercise 20 to explain which fraction is larger, $\frac{3}{4}$ or $\frac{3}{5}$.

Integrated Review   *Making Connections within Mathematics*

Measurement Use a fraction to complete the statement.

22. One inch is $\boxed{?}$ of a yard.

23. Three cups is $\boxed{?}$ of a quart.

24. Five ounces is $\boxed{?}$ of a pound.

25. Twenty seconds is $\boxed{?}$ of a minute.

Exploration and Extension

26. *Building Your Chapter Project* Draw a model of an apartment on a 5-inch by 5-inch grid of 25 squares. The sizes of the rooms are: kitchen (2 by 2), bathroom (1 by 2), living room (3 by 3), bedroom 1 (2 by 3), and bedroom 2 (2 by 2). The living room should connect to each of the other rooms. For each room, write the fraction that its area is of the apartment's area.

Lab 6.2
Investigating Set Models

Materials Needed: plain paper, colored pencils or markers

Part A *Drawing Set Models*

1. Copy the balls on a sheet of paper. Color $\frac{7}{10}$ of the balls green. Color the rest brown. What fraction of the balls are brown?

2. Copy the cats on a sheet of paper. Color $\frac{1}{4}$ of the cats red. Color the rest blue. What fraction of the cats are blue?

3. Draw 15 triangles of the same size.
   a. Is it possible to color one third of the triangles yellow? Explain.
   b. Is it possible to color one fourth of the triangles yellow? Explain.
   c. Is it possible to color one fifth of the triangles yellow? Explain.

Part B *Problem Solving*

4. Draw a set model to help you solve each problem.

   a. You have 12 model airplanes. One fourth of them have engines. How many have engines?

   b. You have $18. You spend four ninths of it for a T-shirt. How much did the T-shirt cost?

   c. You have 14 people in your club. Three sevenths are girls. What fraction of the group is *boys*?

   d. You have 8 pairs of jeans. One fourth have a hole in the knee. How many *don't* have a hole in the knee?

Part C *Modeling Fractions That Are Greater Than One*

5. You are asked to take one and one-half dozen tortillas to a school picnic. Explain how the set model shown below can help you find how many tortillas you need to take.

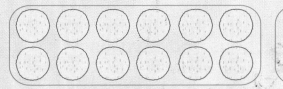

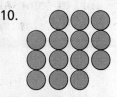

?

6. You have 16 baseball caps in your collection.

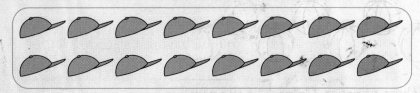

Your friend has $\frac{5}{4}$ as many. Copy the set model and show how it can be used to draw a model for the number of caps your friend has. How many caps does your friend have?

On Your Own   *Critical Thinking*

Identifying Set Models   In Exercises 7–10, write two fractions that are shown by the blue and red parts of the set model.

7.    8.    9. 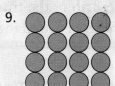   10.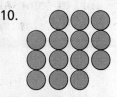

Drawing Set Models   In Exercises 11–14, draw a set model for the fraction. Then write a sentence describing a real-life setting for the set model.

11. $\frac{2}{3}$ 12. $\frac{3}{8}$ 13. $\frac{4}{5}$ 14. $\frac{8}{12}$

15. A softball team has 9 players. You have asked people to sign up for a team. Enough people signed up to form $2\frac{2}{3}$ teams. How many people signed up to play?

6.2 Exploring Division and Ratios

What you should learn:

Goal 1 How fractions are related to division

Goal 2 How to write ratios

Why you should learn it:

Fractions can help you divide things evenly. An example is finding how 5 people can equally share 3 pizzas.

Goal 1 Fractions and Division

Lesson Investigation

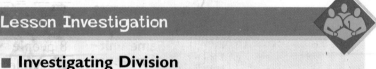

■ **Investigating Division**

Group Activity You are having a sleepover with 4 friends. For supper, you make 3 pizzas. Draw a diagram to show how you could cut the pizzas so that each person would get the same amount. What portion of a whole pizza would each person get?

There are several ways you might have solved the pizza problem above. One way is to use *division*. Because 3 pizzas are shared among 5 people, you could divide 3 by 5 and conclude that each person would get $\frac{3}{5}$ of a pizza.

Need To Know

In earlier chapters you studied three ways to write the result of a division problem.

$5 \div 2 = 2\frac{1}{2}$ Mixed Number

$5 \div 2 = 2 \text{ R1}$ With Remainder

$5 \div 2 = 2.5$ Decimal

Example 1 shows a fourth way to write a division problem: as a fraction.

$5 \div 2 = \frac{5}{2}$ Fraction

Example 1   *Solving Division Problems*

a. Divide 4 hours into 3 equal parts.
b. Divide 5 full glasses of milk into 2 equal parts.

Solution

a. To get the answer, divide 4 by 3.

$$(4 \text{ hours}) \div 3 = \frac{4}{3} \text{ hours}$$

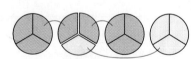

Each of the 3 parts has $\frac{4}{3}$ hours or $1\frac{1}{3}$ hours.

b. To get the answer, divide 5 by 2.

$$(5 \text{ glasses}) \div 2 = \frac{5}{2} \text{ glasses}$$

Each of the 2 parts has $\frac{5}{2}$ glasses or $2\frac{1}{2}$ glasses. ■

Writing a Ratio

A **ratio** is a comparison of two numbers by division. The two numbers must have the same unit of measure.

	Ratios	*Not Ratios*
Same unit of measure	$\dfrac{5 \text{ feet}}{3 \text{ feet}} = \dfrac{5}{3}$	$\dfrac{4 \text{ feet}}{3} = \dfrac{4}{3} \text{ feet}$
Same unit of measure	$\dfrac{8 \text{ people}}{11 \text{ people}} = \dfrac{8}{11}$	$\dfrac{5 \text{ glasses}}{2} = \dfrac{5}{2} \text{ glasses}$

Real Life
Kite

Example 2 *Writing a Ratio*

Your kite is 4 feet wide and 2 feet long. Write the ratio of the width to the length as a fraction.

Solution

$$\frac{4 \text{ feet}}{2 \text{ feet}} = \frac{4}{2}$$

The ratio of the width to the length is $\frac{4}{2}$. ∎

Communicating about MATHEMATICS

Cooperative Learning

▶ **Sharing Ideas about the Lesson**

Partner Activity For each rectangle, write the ratio of the width to the length. Are the ratios the same? If not, which ratio is greatest? Explain your reasoning.

A. Width: 9 feet, Length: 14 feet

B. Width: 9 inches, Length: 14 inches

C. Width: 9 meters, Length: 14 meters

D. Width: 9 yards, Length: 14 yards

EXERCISES

Think and Discuss

▶ **CHECK for Understanding**

1. Suppose there are 4 small pizzas to share equally among 5 people. How could the pizzas be divided equally? What fraction of a pizza does each person get?

2. The model at the right shows how to divide 3 into 2 equal parts. What fraction of the model is each part?

3. Use a diagram to divide 6 apples equally among 4 people. What fraction of an apple does each person get?

4. Explain how to write a ratio. Give an example.

Independent Practice

In Exercises 5 and 6, use a diagram to answer the question.

5. You have 32 one-dollar coins. One fourth are Susan B. Anthony dollars. How many are another type of one-dollar coin?

6. You are flying on a 500-mile trip. You have flown two fifths of the distance. How far have you flown?

Visual Thinking Use the model to divide.

7. Divide 3 into 8 equal parts.

8. Divide 5 into 3 equal parts.

Drawing a Diagram In Exercises 9–12, draw a diagram to help you divide. Write your answer as a fraction.

9. Divide 2 dollars into 4 equal parts.

10. Divide 5 boxes of baseball cards into 7 equal parts.

11. Divide 8 pies into 6 equal parts.

12. Divide 7 packages of beads into 6 equal parts.

Writing Describe a real-life situation that can be represented by the ratio.

13. $\dfrac{16 \text{ miles}}{40 \text{ miles}}$ or $\dfrac{16}{40}$

14. $\dfrac{7 \text{ balloons}}{9 \text{ balloons}}$ or $\dfrac{7}{9}$

15. $\dfrac{8 \text{ meters}}{15 \text{ meters}}$ or $\dfrac{8}{15}$

Geometry In Exercises 16 and 17, write the ratio of the width to the length of the rectangle.

16.

7 inches

18 inches

17.

12 feet

24 feet

Marble Collection The set model below shows a collection of colored marbles.

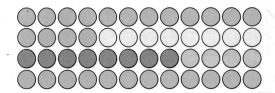

18. What is the ratio of green marbles to total marbles?

19. What is the ratio of red marbles to yellow marbles?

20. What is the ratio of blue marbles to orange marbles?

21. Measure the width and length of the picture at the right to the nearest millimeter. Include the boy's hair. Write the ratio of the width to the length.

Marbles is a game played with small glass balls. Players shoot marbles by flicking a large marble toward smaller ones.

Integrated Review

Making Connections within Mathematics

Solve.

22. $29 \div 4$ 23. $34 \div 5$ 24. $16.1 \div 7$

25. $48.5 \div 5$ 26. $7.68 \div 6.4$ 27. $23.37 \div 1.9$

Looking for a Pattern Describe the pattern. Then write the next 3 fractions.

28. $\frac{1}{2}, \frac{1}{3}, \frac{1}{4}$, ?, ?, ?   29. $\frac{1}{5}, \frac{2}{5}, \frac{3}{5}$, ?, ?, ?   30. $\frac{1}{2}, \frac{1}{4}, \frac{1}{6}$, ?, ?, ?

Exploration and Extension

31. *Building Your Chapter Project* For each of the five rooms in your apartment, write the ratio of the length of the short side to the length of the long side. What can you say about the ratios of the rooms that are square?

Geometry Draw the figure on a 6-by-6 grid of dot paper. **(1.5)**

1. A square with an area of 25 square units

2. Two rectangles, each with a perimeter of 14 units

3. What is 80% of 16? **(4.4)**

4. What is 0.3 of 4.5? **(4.4)**

Visual Thinking Write the fraction of the diagram that is shaded. **(6.1)**

5.

6.

7.

8.

Write the fraction as a decimal. **(3.4)**

9. $\frac{20}{100}$

10. $\frac{45}{100}$

11. $\frac{72}{100}$

12. $\frac{95}{100}$

Milestones   NUMBER PATTERNS

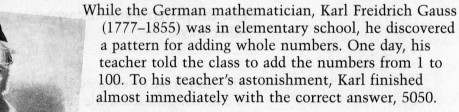

600 B.C. Parthenon, 200 B.C.   A.D. 200   A.D. 600   A.D. 1000   A.D. 1400 Fermat   A.D. 1800
       447 B.C.   Treviso   born,
Pythagoras   Archimedes born,   Arithmetic, 1608 Taj Mahal,
born, 582 B.C.   287 B.C.   1478   1648

While the German mathematician, Karl Freidrich Gauss (1777–1855) was in elementary school, he discovered a pattern for adding whole numbers. One day, his teacher told the class to add the numbers from 1 to 100. To his teacher's astonishment, Karl finished almost immediately with the correct answer, 5050.

He knew that number properties made it possible to add the numbers in any order. So, first he listed the numbers 1-50 one way, then the numbers 51-100 the other way as shown. He quickly realized that each pair of numbers added to 101. Since there were 50 pairs of such numbers, the sum is 50 • 101 = 5050.

- *Can you use the Gauss pattern to find the sum of the even numbers from 1 to 100? The odd numbers from 1 to 100? Try it.*

6.3 Equivalent Fractions and Ratios

What you should learn:

Goal 1 How to decide if two fractions are equivalent

Goal 2 How to decide whether two ratios are equivalent

Why you should learn it:

Fractions can be written in different forms. To be a problem solver, you need to be able to recognize equivalent forms.

Need To Know

The fractions $\frac{10}{12}$ and $\frac{2}{3}$ are not equivalent.

$$\frac{10}{12} = \frac{2 \cdot 5}{3 \cdot 4}$$

Because 5 and 4 are not the same number, $\frac{10}{12}$ and $\frac{2}{3}$ are not equivalent.

Goal 1 Equivalent Fractions

Lesson Investigation

■ Investigating Equivalent Fractions

Group Activity Look at the models and fractions below. What patterns do you see?

a.   b.   c.   d.

a.	b.	c.	d.
$\frac{1}{4}$ or	$\frac{2}{8}$ or	$\frac{3}{12}$ or	$\frac{4}{16}$ or
$\frac{1 \cdot 1}{4 \cdot 1}$	$\frac{1 \cdot 2}{4 \cdot 2}$	$\frac{1 \cdot 3}{4 \cdot 3}$	$\frac{1 \cdot 4}{4 \cdot 4}$

Use the patterns you discovered to write $\frac{1}{4}$ in 2 other ways.

You may have discovered that all the fractions in the investigation are the same size. Such fractions are **equivalent.**

Equivalent Fractions

Multiplying the numerator and the denominator of a fraction by the *same* number produces an **equivalent fraction.**

Example 1   *Equivalent Fractions*

The fractions $\frac{2}{3}$ and $\frac{8}{12}$ are equivalent because

$$\frac{2}{3} = \frac{2 \cdot 4}{3 \cdot 4} = \frac{8}{12}.$$ *Multiply numerator and denominator by 4.*   ■

Ratios are equivalent if they are equivalent as fractions. For instance, the following ratios are equivalent.

$$\frac{3 \text{ inches}}{6 \text{ inches}} = \frac{3}{6} = \frac{1 \cdot 3}{2 \cdot 3} = \frac{1}{2} \text{ and } \frac{1 \text{ foot}}{2 \text{ feet}} = \frac{1}{2}$$

Real Life
Reading Blueprints

Example 2 *Writing Equivalent Ratios*

Find the dimensions of the scale drawing. Compare the width-to-length ratios *of the scale drawing* and *of the actual* kitchen. What can you conclude?

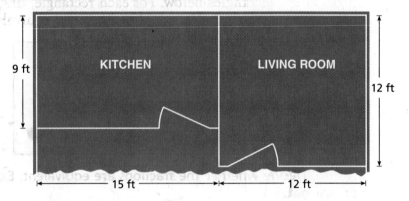

Solution In the scale drawing, the kitchen is 3 cm by 5 cm. The ratio of the width to the length is

$$\frac{3 \text{ centimeters}}{5 \text{ centimeters}} = \frac{3}{5}. \quad \textit{Scale Drawing}$$

The actual kitchen is 9 ft by 15 ft. The ratio of the width to the length is

$$\frac{9 \text{ feet}}{15 \text{ feet}} = \frac{9}{15}. \quad \textit{Actual Kitchen}$$

The two ratios are equivalent because $\frac{3}{5} = \frac{3 \cdot 3}{5 \cdot 3} = \frac{9}{15}$. ∎

The first dollhouses were made during the 1600's for adults. They were scale models of the owners' homes.

Communicating about MATHEMATICS

▶ **Sharing Ideas about the Lesson**

Measurement In Example 2, compare the width-to-length ratios of the scale drawing of the living room and the actual living room. What can you conclude?

EXERCISES

Guided Practice

Think and Discuss

▶ **CHECK for Understanding**

1. Write 2 equivalent fractions represented by the diagram at the right.

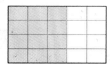

2. Draw a diagram that shows why the fractions $\frac{4}{5}$ and $\frac{8}{10}$ are equivalent.

3. *Geometry* Use a centimeter ruler to measure the width and length of the rectangles below. For each rectangle, find the ratio of the width to the length. Are the ratios equivalent?

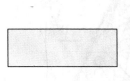 

Reasoning Decide whether the fractions are equivalent. Explain why or why not.

4. $\frac{1}{6}, \frac{2}{12}$ 5. $\frac{1}{2}, \frac{4}{6}$ 6. $\frac{5}{8}, \frac{15}{24}$

Independent Practice

In Exercises 7–10, match the fraction with its diagram. Write an equivalent fraction that is represented by the diagram.

a.   b.   c.   d.

7. $\frac{1}{3}$ 8. $\frac{8}{14}$ 9. $\frac{10}{15}$ 10. $\frac{3}{4}$

Guess, Check, and Revise In Exercises 11–14, find the missing number.

11. $\frac{2}{5} = \frac{?}{25}$ 12. $\frac{3}{18} = \frac{?}{6}$ 13. $\frac{8}{36} = \frac{2}{?}$ 14. $\frac{4}{7} = \frac{24}{?}$

Write 3 equivalent fractions. Tell why they are equivalent.

15. $\frac{7}{8}$ 16. $\frac{4}{11}$ 17. $\frac{15}{18}$ 18. $\frac{4}{36}$

True or False? In Exercises 19–22, is the statement true or false?
If it is false, change the blue number to make the statement true.

19. $\dfrac{2\text{ m}}{3\text{ m}} = \dfrac{4\text{ km}}{9\text{ km}}$

20. $\dfrac{9\text{ feet}}{12\text{ feet}} = \dfrac{18\text{ feet}}{24\text{ feet}}$

21. $\dfrac{4\text{ dogs}}{9\text{ dogs}} = \dfrac{20\text{ dogs}}{45\text{ dogs}}$

22. $\dfrac{5\text{ mm}}{2\text{ mm}} = \dfrac{1\text{ mm}}{4\text{ mm}}$

23. Copy and complete the table. For example, 1 dollar equals 4 quarters. Use the results to write 5 ratios of "quarters to dimes." What can you say about the ratios?

Dollars	1	?	5	?	?
Quarters	4	8	?	?	?
Dimes	?	?	?	80	100

24. *Geometry* The width of a rectangle is 2 inches. The ratio of the width to the length is $\frac{1}{2}$. What is the length of the rectangle?

25. *Ping-Pong™* You are building a Ping-Pong table. The dimensions of the actual table are shown. Use a ruler to find the dimensions of the scale drawing to the nearest millimeter. Find the width-to-length ratio of the scale drawing and of the actual table. What can you conclude?

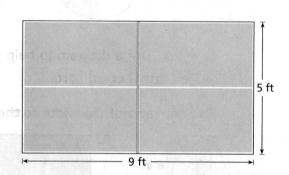

5 ft

9 ft

Integrated Review   *Making Connections within Mathematics*

Write each number as a decimal and as a fraction.

26. 80%   27. 62%   28. 3%   29. 10%

Measurement Complete the statement.

30. $0.36\text{ cm} = 3.6\ \boxed{?}$ 31. $7\text{ cm} = \boxed{?}\text{ m}$ 32. $\boxed{?}\text{ km} = 800\text{ m}$

Exploration and Extension

33. *Building Your Chapter Project* In the scale drawing of your apartment, let each segment represent 6 feet. Label each room with its actual length and width. (This means that the actual apartment is 30 feet by 30 feet.) Copy and complete the table below. What can you conclude?

Room	Kitchen	Living Room	Bathroom	Bedroom 1	Bedroom 2
Model Width-to-Length Ratio	?	?	?	?	?
Actual Width-to-Length Ratio	?	?	?	?	?

Take this test as you would take a test in class. The answers to the exercises are given in the back of the book.

In Exercises 1–4, write the fraction of the figure that is shaded. Then match the fraction with its description. **(6.1)**

a. Close to $\frac{1}{2}$ b. Close to 0   c. Equal to $\frac{1}{2}$ d. Close to 1

1. 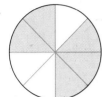   2.   3.    4.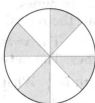

Drawing a Diagram   Use a diagram to help you solve. **(6.2)**

5. Divide 2 cakes into 3 equal parts.   6. Divide 8 apples into 5 equal parts.

Geometry   Find the ratio of the width to the length. **(6.2)**

7.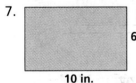
6 in.
10 in.

8.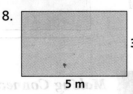
3 m
5 m

9.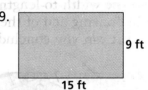
9 ft
15 ft

10. In Exercises 7–9, are any of the ratios equivalent? Explain. **(6.2, 6.3)**

True or False?   In Exercises 11–13, is the statement true or false? If false, change the blue number to make the statement true. **(6.3)**

11. $\dfrac{7 \text{ yards}}{12 \text{ yards}} = \dfrac{21 \text{ yards}}{48 \text{ yards}}$ 12. $\dfrac{1 \text{ cm}}{5 \text{ cm}} = \dfrac{2 \text{ m}}{15 \text{ m}}$ 13. $\dfrac{3 \text{ horses}}{4 \text{ horses}} = \dfrac{27 \text{ riders}}{36 \text{ riders}}$

In Exercises 14–16, use the set model at the right to write the ratio. **(6.2, 6.3)**

14. Yellow cars to total number of cars

15. Yellow cars to blue cars

16. White cars to red cars

17. *Building a Tree House*   You are building a tree house. On your plans, the tree house is 3 inches wide and 4 inches long. The actual tree house is 6 feet wide. How long is the actual tree house? **(6.3)**

Materials Needed: grid paper, pencils

Part A *Graphing Equivalent Fractions* The numerators and denominators of the fractions $\frac{2}{3}$, $\frac{4}{6}$, and $\frac{6}{9}$ are plotted on the first graph below. Notice that all three fractions are equivalent. Also notice that all three points lie on a line, as shown in the second graph.

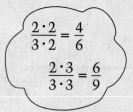

$$\frac{2 \cdot 2}{3 \cdot 2} = \frac{4}{6}$$

$$\frac{2 \cdot 3}{3 \cdot 3} = \frac{6}{9}$$

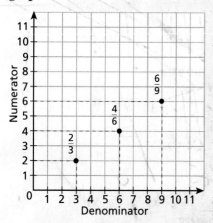
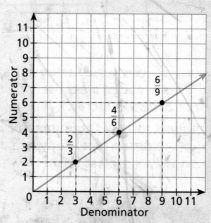

1. Graph the numerators and denominators of the fractions $\frac{1}{2}$, $\frac{3}{6}$, and $\frac{5}{10}$. Are the fractions equivalent? Do all 3 points lie on a line? Draw two other points on the line and label them as fractions. Are these fractions equivalent to $\frac{1}{2}$? Explain.

Part B *Finding Equivalent Fractions*

2. Copy the graph. Label each point with the fraction that it represents. Are all the fractions equivalent? Explain.

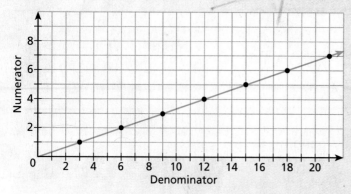

Part C *Finding Simplest Fractions*

3. a. Copy the graph on grid paper. Complete the fractions so that the numerators and denominators are written as products. Explain why all five fractions are equivalent.

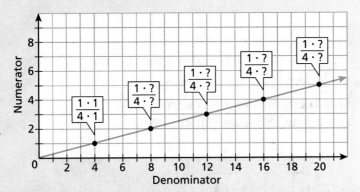

b. Each of the fractions has the same factor in its numerator and denominator. This is called a *common factor*. For each ratio, name the common factor.

c. A fraction is in *simplest form* if its numerator and denominator have no common factor other than 1. Of the five fractions, which is in simplest form?

On Your Own   *Critical Thinking*

Equivalent Fractions Graph the numerators and denominators of the fractions. Which three fractions are equivalent? Explain your reasoning.

4. $\frac{3}{5}, \frac{6}{10}, \frac{8}{12}, \frac{9}{15}$ 5. $\frac{1}{4}, \frac{3}{12}, \frac{4}{16}, \frac{5}{18}$ 6. $\frac{2}{5}, \frac{4}{8}, \frac{4}{10}, \frac{6}{15}$ 7. $\frac{4}{3}, \frac{3}{4}, \frac{6}{8}, \frac{9}{12}$

Complete the statements. Graph the numerators and denominators of the fractions. Which is in simplest form?

8. $\frac{3}{4} = \frac{3 \cdot 1}{4 \cdot 1}$, $\frac{6}{8} = \frac{3 \cdot ?}{4 \cdot ?}$, $\frac{9}{12} = \frac{3 \cdot ?}{4 \cdot ?}$, $\frac{12}{16} = \frac{3 \cdot ?}{4 \cdot ?}$

9. $\frac{3}{5} = \frac{3 \cdot 1}{5 \cdot 1}$, $\frac{6}{10} = \frac{3 \cdot ?}{5 \cdot ?}$, $\frac{9}{15} = \frac{3 \cdot ?}{5 \cdot ?}$, $\frac{12}{20} = \frac{3 \cdot ?}{5 \cdot ?}$

10. $\frac{1}{6} = \frac{1 \cdot 1}{6 \cdot 1}$, $\frac{2}{12} = \frac{1 \cdot ?}{6 \cdot ?}$, $\frac{3}{18} = \frac{1 \cdot ?}{6 \cdot ?}$, $\frac{4}{24} = \frac{1 \cdot ?}{6 \cdot ?}$

11. In Exercises 8–10, what can you say about the location of the point that represents the simplest fraction?

6.4

Exploring Proportions

What you should learn:

Goal 1 How to simplify a fraction

Goal 2 How to solve a proportion

Why you should learn it:

Proportions can be used to find the cost of items. An example is finding the cost of some comic books.

Goal 1 Simplifying Fractions

How many fractions are equivalent to $\frac{4}{8}$? The answer is that there are more than you can count! Here are a few.

$$\frac{1}{2}, \frac{2}{4}, \frac{3}{6}, \frac{4}{8}, \frac{5}{10}, \frac{6}{12}, \frac{7}{14}, \cdots \quad \textit{Equivalent fractions}$$

Of these the **simplest** is $\frac{1}{2}$ because its numerator and denominator have no common factor other than one. Rewriting a fraction as its simplest equivalent fraction is called **simplifying** the fraction.

$$\frac{4}{8} = \frac{1}{2} \qquad \textit{Simplify the fraction } \frac{4}{8}.$$

Four tenths of the balls are red.

Two fifths of the balls are red.

Example 1 *Simplifying Fractions*

Simplify each fraction.

a. $\frac{4}{10}$ b. $\frac{6}{24}$ c. $\frac{10}{5}$

Solution To simplify a fraction, use a common factor to rewrite its numerator and denominator as a product.

a. $\frac{4}{10} = \frac{2 \cdot 2}{5 \cdot 2}$ *Factor numerator and denominator.*

$= \frac{2}{5}$ *Simplify the fraction. (See model at left.)*

b. $\frac{6}{24} = \frac{1 \cdot 6}{4 \cdot 6}$ *Factor numerator and denominator.*

$= \frac{1}{4}$ *Simplify the fraction.*

c. $\frac{10}{5} = \frac{2 \cdot 5}{1 \cdot 5}$ *Factor numerator and denominator.*

$= \frac{2}{1}$ *Simplify the fraction.*

$= 2$ *Write as a whole number.* ∎

Study Tip

In parts (b) and (c) of Example 1, notice that you sometimes need to factor a number as the product of 1 and itself.

A **proportion** is an equation stating that two ratios are equivalent. In real-life problems, proportions sometimes have missing numbers.

$$\frac{3}{7} = \frac{?}{14}$$ ⟵ **Missing number**

Finding the missing number is called **solving the proportion.**

Problem Solving
Drawing a Diagram

Example 2 *Solving a Proportion*

Solve the proportion $\frac{2}{3} = \frac{?}{9}$.

Solution To solve the proportion, you need to find a ratio that is equivalent to $\frac{2}{3}$ and has a denominator of 9. There are many ways to do this. One way is to draw a diagram like that shown at the left.

Another way is to use what you have learned about equivalent fractions.

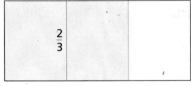

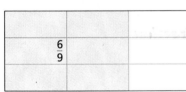

$$\frac{2}{3} = \frac{2 \cdot 3}{3 \cdot 3} = \frac{6}{9}$$

■

Communicating about MATHEMATICS

Cooperative Learning

▶ **Sharing Ideas about the Lesson**

Partner Activity In real life, proportions often occur by setting two ratios equal to each other.

You and Janette both work at the school library. During one week, you worked 2 hours and Janette worked 3 hours. You reshelved 28 books and Janette reshelved 40. Did you both work at the same pace?

$$\frac{\text{Your Books}}{\text{Janette's Books}} \overset{?}{=} \frac{\text{Your Hours}}{\text{Janette's Hours}}$$

If these ratios are equal, then the pace is the same. Is the pace the same? Explain your reasoning.

EXERCISES

Guided Practice

Think and Discuss

▶ CHECK for Understanding

Number Sense   Match the fraction with its model.

a.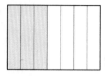

b.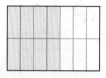

c.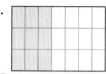

d.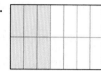

1. $\frac{9}{21}$

2. $\frac{3}{7}$

3. $\frac{8}{14}$

4. $\frac{6}{14}$

5. In Exercises 1–4, which three fractions are equivalent? Of these, which is in simplest form?

6. Write the fraction that is represented by the model at the right. Then simplify the fraction.

7. Solve the proportion $\frac{4}{5} = \frac{\boxed{?}}{15}$ by drawing a diagram.

8. *Partner Activity*   On a sheet of paper, write a proportion that has one missing number. Exchange papers with your partner. Solve the proportion that your partner wrote. Explain your reasoning. Then check each other's work.

Independent Practice

Write the fraction that is represented by the model. Then simplify.

9.

10.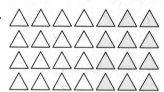

11.

In Exercises 12–19, simplify the fraction.

12. $\frac{3}{18}$

13. $\frac{12}{24}$

14. $\frac{16}{8}$

15. $\frac{9}{9}$

16. $\frac{8}{20}$

17. $\frac{21}{3}$

18. $\frac{32}{36}$

19. $\frac{40}{64}$

True or False?   Is the proportion true or false? Explain.

20. $\frac{3}{5} \stackrel{?}{=} \frac{6}{15}$

21. $\frac{5}{8} \stackrel{?}{=} \frac{7}{16}$

22. $\frac{10}{35} \stackrel{?}{=} \frac{2}{7}$

In Exercises 23–28, solve the proportion.

23. $\dfrac{3}{10} = \dfrac{9}{\boxed{?}}$

24. $\dfrac{16}{28} = \dfrac{4}{\boxed{?}}$

25. $\dfrac{\boxed{?}}{40} = \dfrac{1}{5}$

26. $\dfrac{6}{\boxed{?}} = \dfrac{30}{55}$

27. $\dfrac{2}{9} = \dfrac{\boxed{?}}{54}$

28. $\dfrac{\boxed{?}}{72} = \dfrac{7}{8}$

Geometry In Exercises 29 and 30, the two rectangles have equivalent width-to-length ratios. Write a proportion that allows you to find the missing length. Then solve the proportion.

29.

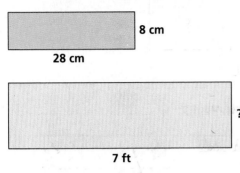

8 cm

28 cm

?

7 ft

30.

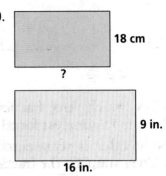

18 cm

?

9 in.

16 in.

31. *Reasoning* Is the following statement true? Explain your reasoning.

If $\dfrac{10}{12} = \dfrac{5}{6}$ and $\dfrac{15}{18} = \dfrac{5}{6}$, then $\dfrac{10}{12} = \dfrac{15}{18}$.

32. *Comic Books* You buy 2 comic books for $4. Use a proportion to find the cost of 6 comic books. Explain your reasoning.

Integrated Review   Making Connections within Mathematics

Complete the statement using $>$, $<$, or $=$.

33. $1.01 \; \boxed{?} \; 1.1$

34. $0.018 \; \boxed{?} \; 0.18$

35. $\dfrac{1}{4} \; \boxed{?} \; \dfrac{1}{5}$

36. $\dfrac{4}{2} \; \boxed{?} \; \dfrac{12}{6}$

37. $4.90 \; \boxed{?} \; 4.9$

38. $13.24 \; \boxed{?} \; 13.14$

39. $0.6 \; \boxed{?} \; 6\%$

40. $7\% \; \boxed{?} \; 0.07$

41. $15\% \; \boxed{?} \; \dfrac{15}{100}$

Exploration and Extension

42. *Building Your Chapter Project* You are ordering wallpaper for the living room in your apartment. One roll of wallpaper will cover $\dfrac{2}{3}$ of each wall. How many rolls will you need to cover all four walls? Use a diagram to help you answer the question. Ignore any doors or windows in the walls.

Materials Needed: plain paper, pencils

Part A *Comparing Fractions*

1. Which fraction is greater: $\frac{1}{3}$ or $\frac{2}{5}$? One way to decide is to draw a rectangular model for each fraction. To make the comparison easier, look at the denominators. Draw each model with 3 units on one side and 5 units on the other side.

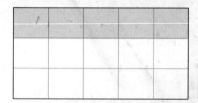 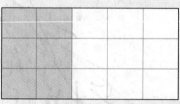

Model for $\frac{1}{3}$ Model for $\frac{2}{5}$

Explain how to decide which fraction is greater.

Part B *Making Connections*

2. Copy the two fraction models below. Write the fraction for each model. Look at the denominators. Add lines to each model so that both models have the same number of regions. Then compare the two fractions. Which is greater?

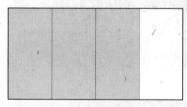 

Model for $\frac{?}{?}$ Model for $\frac{?}{?}$

Draw a rectangular model for each fraction. Then use the models to decide which fraction is greater.

3. Which is greater:

$\frac{3}{4}$ or $\frac{4}{5}$?

Use 4 units on one side and 5 units on the other.

4. Which is greater:

$\frac{3}{8}$ or $\frac{2}{5}$?

Use 8 units on one side and 5 units on the other.

5. Another way to compare fractions is to rewrite them as decimals. To see which decimal is greater, plot them on a number line. Label each point with its decimal and its fraction name.

Which is greater: $\frac{6}{10}$ or $\frac{5}{8}$? Use the number line below to help you decide. Explain your reasoning.

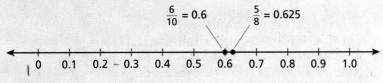

$\frac{6}{10} = 0.6$ $\frac{5}{8} = 0.625$

You can use a calculator to rewrite $\frac{5}{8}$ as 0.625.

5 ÷ 8 =

6. Copy the following number line. Using a calculator, rewrite the fractions $\frac{3}{10}$, $\frac{3}{8}$, $\frac{2}{5}$, $\frac{1}{2}$, and $\frac{7}{16}$ as decimals. Plot and label the decimals on the number line. Answer each question.

```
 ←───┼────┼────┼────┼────┼────┼────┼────┼────┼────┼────→
     0   0.1  0.2  0.3  0.4  0.5  0.6  0.7  0.8  0.9  1.0
```

a. Which is greater: $\frac{3}{10}$ or $\frac{3}{8}$?

b. Which is greater: $\frac{2}{5}$ or $\frac{7}{16}$?

c. Which is greater: $\frac{3}{8}$ or $\frac{1}{2}$?

d. Which is greater: $\frac{1}{2}$ or $\frac{7}{16}$?

On Your Own   *Critical Thinking*

Comparing Fractions In Exercises 7 and 8, draw a model for each fraction. Then use the result to decide which fraction is greater.

7. Which is greater: $\frac{3}{7}$ or $\frac{1}{2}$? Use rectangular models that have 7 units on one side and 2 units on the other side.

8. Which is greater: $\frac{3}{5}$ or $\frac{5}{8}$? Use rectangular models that have 5 units on one side and 8 units on the other side.

Using a Number Line Model   Use a number line to help you answer the question.

9. Which is greater: $\frac{7}{10}$ or $\frac{5}{8}$?

10. Which is greater: $\frac{7}{10}$ or $\frac{4}{5}$?

11. Which is greater: $\frac{3}{4}$ or $\frac{4}{5}$?

12. Which is greater: $\frac{13}{16}$ or $\frac{3}{4}$?

6.5

Comparing and Ordering Fractions

What you should learn:

Goal 1 How to compare and order fractions

Goal 2 How to compare fractions to solve real-life problems

Why you should learn it:

Comparing fractions can help you be a smart consumer. An example is comparing the prices of two remote control cars that are on sale.

Goal 1 Comparing and Ordering Fractions

When you decide that one fraction is greater than another, you are **comparing** the fractions.

Example 1 *Comparing and Ordering Fractions*

Order the fractions from greatest to least.

a. $\frac{2}{5}$ and $\frac{3}{5}$ b. $\frac{2}{3}$ and $\frac{2}{4}$ c. $\frac{3}{5}$, $\frac{4}{9}$, and $\frac{1}{2}$

Solution

a. These fractions have the same denominator. The one with the greater numerator is greater. So $\frac{3}{5} > \frac{2}{5}$.

b. These fractions have the same numerator. But thirds are greater than fourths, so $\frac{2}{3} > \frac{2}{4}$.

c. The fraction $\frac{4}{9}$ is less than $\frac{1}{2}$, and the fraction $\frac{3}{5}$ is greater than $\frac{1}{2}$. So from greatest to least the fractions are $\frac{3}{5}$, $\frac{1}{2}$, and $\frac{4}{9}$. ∎

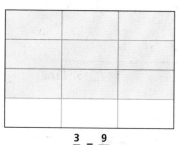

$$\frac{3}{4} = \frac{9}{12}$$

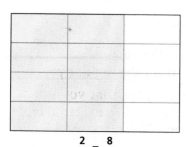

$$\frac{2}{3} = \frac{8}{12}$$

Example 2 *Comparing Fractions*

Compare the fractions $\frac{3}{4}$ and $\frac{2}{3}$.

Solution   One way to compare these is to make a list of equivalent fractions and find two that have the same denominator.

Original Fraction	*Equivalent Fractions*
$\frac{3}{4}$	$\frac{3}{4} = \frac{6}{8} = \frac{9}{12} = \frac{12}{16}$
$\frac{2}{3}$	$\frac{2}{3} = \frac{4}{6} = \frac{6}{9} = \frac{8}{12}$

Using the fractions $\frac{9}{12}$ and $\frac{8}{12}$, it follows that $\frac{3}{4} > \frac{2}{3}$. ∎

Real Life
Shopping

Example 3 *Comparing Fractions*

You want to buy a remote control car. You find one that you like at two stores. The regular price is $48, but both stores are having a sale. Which is the better buy?

Solution One way to answer the question is to use a set model. At *Car Land,* you get one third off, so the sale price is $32. At *Toy Land,* you get one fourth off, so the sale price is $36. This means that the better buy is at *Car Land.*

Remote control systems have a variety of uses—from entertainment to controlling aircraft.

$32   Car Land $36   Toy Land ■

Communicating about MATHEMATICS

Problem Solving
Logical Reasoning

▶ **Sharing Ideas about the Lesson**

Extending the Example In Example 3, the fractions $\frac{1}{3}$ and $\frac{1}{4}$ represent the *discount* from the regular price. What fractions represent the amounts that you must pay? Which of these is smaller? How does that relate to the car that is the better buy? Explain your reasoning.

EXERCISES

Think and Discuss

▶ **CHECK for Understanding**

1. *Communicating*   Describe 3 ways to compare and order fractions. Which way do you prefer? Explain.

2. Name the fractions shown below. Which is greater?

 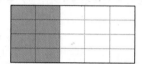

3. *Drawing a Diagram*   Draw a diagram to explain why $\frac{1}{5}$ is greater than $\frac{1}{6}$. What does this tell you about $\frac{4}{5}$ and $\frac{4}{6}$? Explain.

Reasoning   In Exercises 4–6, compare each fraction to $\frac{1}{2}$. Then use the result to decide which fraction is greater.

4. $\frac{4}{9}$ and $\frac{5}{9}$

5. $\frac{1}{3}$ and $\frac{3}{4}$

6. $\frac{2}{3}$ and $\frac{3}{7}$

Independent Practice

Geometry   In Exercises 7 and 8, name the fractions that are shown by the models. Which is greater?

7.

8.

Number Sense   In Exercises 9–12, compare each fraction to $\frac{1}{2}$. Then use the result to decide which fraction is greater.

9. $\frac{2}{4}$ and $\frac{3}{4}$

10. $\frac{3}{5}$ and $\frac{3}{6}$

11. $\frac{4}{6}$ and $\frac{3}{8}$

12. $\frac{5}{9}$ and $\frac{6}{13}$

Copy the number line. Locate and label the four fractions on the line. Then order the fractions from least to greatest.

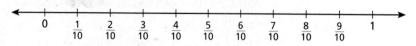

13. $\frac{2}{5}, \frac{5}{10}, \frac{4}{5}, \frac{3}{10}$

14. $\frac{3}{5}, \frac{1}{2}, \frac{4}{10}, \frac{1}{5}$

15. $\frac{6}{10}, \frac{1}{10}, \frac{4}{5}, \frac{1}{2}$

In Exercises 16–19, complete the statement using > or <.

16. $\frac{2}{6}$? $\frac{3}{4}$

17. $\frac{5}{6}$? $\frac{2}{3}$

18. $\frac{3}{8}$? $\frac{1}{2}$

19. $\frac{5}{9}$? $\frac{3}{6}$

Number Sense In Exercises 20–23, find a fraction that makes the statement true.

20. $\boxed{?} < \frac{1}{2}$

21. $\boxed{?} > \frac{8}{10}$

22. $\frac{5}{7} < \boxed{?}$

23. $\frac{6}{11} > \boxed{?}$

Number Sense In Exercises 24–26, find a fraction that is between the two fractions.

24. $\frac{1}{6}, \frac{3}{6}$

25. $\frac{3}{8}, \frac{5}{8}$

26. $\frac{3}{10}, \frac{1}{2}$

27. Of the fractions $\frac{7}{8}, \frac{7}{9}, \frac{7}{10}, \frac{7}{11}$, which is closest to 1? Explain.

28. Of the fractions $\frac{1}{4}, \frac{1}{5}, \frac{1}{6}$, and $\frac{1}{7}$, which is closest to 0? Explain.

In Exercises 29–31, write the fraction that is shown by the model.

29.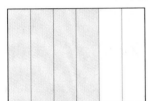

30.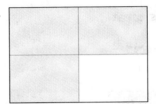

31.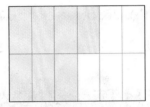

32. Order the three fractions in Exercises 29–31 from least to greatest.

Statistics Use the following information. A survey asked 24 students to name their favorite school subject. One fourth chose science, one third chose English, and one sixth chose computer science. The rest chose math.

33. Use a set model to determine the number of students who chose each subject as their favorite.

34. Write the fraction of students who chose math.

35. Which subject or subjects did most students choose as their favorite?

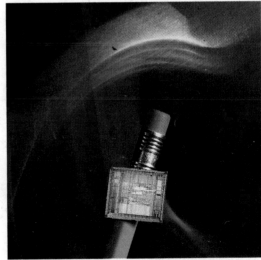

This photo shows a computer chip named Alpha, which was developed by Digital Equipment Corporation. It can process 400 million instructions per second.

Visual Thinking   Write the fraction that is represented by the model.
Then simplify the fraction.

36.

37.

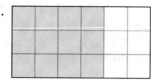

38.

X X X X X X X
X X X X X X X
X X X X X X X
X X X X X X X

Exploration and Extension

39. *Building Your Chapter Project*   The
table at the right shows the fraction
of a day that a person spends in each
room of an apartment. Order the
fractions from greatest to least. Show
one way to graph the data.

Living room	$\frac{1}{6}$
Kitchen	$\frac{1}{12}$
Bedroom	$\frac{5}{12}$
Bathroom	$\frac{1}{24}$

Mixed R E V I E W

Mental Math   Solve. **(2.6)**

1. $2(x + 6) = 18$

2. $8(5 + y) = 48$

3. $4(n + 9) = 64$

Geometry   In Exercises 4–6, solve for x. **(3.7, 4.1–4.4)**

4. Area = x

11

11

5. Perimeter = 30.24

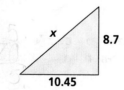

x

8.7

10.45

6. Area = x

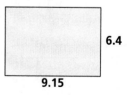

6.4

9.15

Write the number as a fraction. Then simplify. **(3.4, 6.4)**

7. 0.48

8. 0.6

9. 32%

10. 150%

Order the numbers from least to greatest. **(3.5)**

11. 2.12, 2.2, 2.02, 2.3, 2.19

12. 8.32, 8.53, 8.45, 8.35, 8.3

13. 0.19, 0.09, 0.6, 0.05, 0.009

14. 2.15, 2.105, 2.05, 2.015, 2.01

Using a Calculator

One way to compare fractions is to rewrite them as decimals. After you do this, you need to look at the place value of the digits. Compare the digits from left to right until the digits are different.

Technology
Calculator

Example   *Ordering Numbers with a Calculator*

Use a calculator to help you decide which fraction is greater: $\frac{1}{3}$ or $\frac{3}{8}$.

Solution

Fraction	Key Strokes	Display
$\frac{1}{3}$	1 ÷ 3 =	0.333333
$\frac{3}{8}$	3 ÷ 8 =	0.375

To decide which is greater, compare the digits from left to right. From the hundredths place, you can tell that $\frac{3}{8}$ is greater than $\frac{1}{3}$. ■

Exercises

In Exercises 1–8, use a calculator to decide which fraction is greater. Which decimal place did you use to decide?

1. $\frac{8}{11}, \frac{13}{18}$ 2. $\frac{5}{16}, \frac{6}{19}$ 3. $\frac{3}{22}, \frac{2}{15}$ 4. $\frac{5}{12}, \frac{7}{17}$

5. $\frac{4}{7}, \frac{11}{19}$ 6. $\frac{10}{7}, \frac{13}{9}$ 7. $\frac{8}{21}, \frac{9}{23}$ 8. $\frac{1}{12}, \frac{2}{23}$

In Exercises 9–12, use a calculator to help you decide whether the fractions are equivalent. Explain your reasoning.

9. $\frac{7}{9}, \frac{14}{18}$ 10. $\frac{9}{17}, \frac{10}{19}$ 11. $\frac{6}{7}, \frac{18}{21}$ 12. $\frac{12}{22}, \frac{5}{9}$

13. *Statistics*   You and a friend each gave a survey about watching television. You surveyed 37 people and found 14 who watched television 3 or more hours per day. Your friend surveyed 31 people and found 12 who watched 3 or more hours per day. Which survey had a larger fraction of people who watched television 3 or more hours per day? Explain.

6.6

Modeling Fractions Greater Than One

What you should learn:

Goal 1 How to rewrite improper fractions and mixed numbers

Goal 2 How to use fractions greater than one to solve real-life problems

Why you should learn it:

Fractions that are greater than one often occur in cooking. An example is in recipes for baking bread.

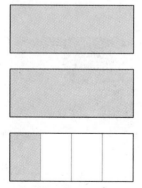

Model for 2$\frac{1}{4}$

Goal 1 **Fractions and Mixed Numbers**

A fraction that is greater than or equal to one is called **improper.** Here are some examples.

$$\frac{9}{4}, \frac{12}{10}, \frac{3}{2}, \frac{6}{6}$$ *Improper fraction: Numerator is greater than or equal to denominator.*

$$\frac{3}{4}, \frac{7}{10}, \frac{1}{2}, \frac{5}{6}$$ *Proper fraction: Numerator is smaller than denominator.*

Lesson Investigation

■ **Investigating Mixed Numbers**

Group Activity The diagram at the left is a model for the mixed number 2$\frac{1}{4}$. Copy the model and add lines so that each whole is divided into four equal parts. Then rewrite 2$\frac{1}{4}$ as an improper fraction.

Draw a model for each mixed number. Then rewrite each mixed number as an improper fraction.

a. 1$\frac{1}{2}$ **b.** 1$\frac{2}{3}$ **c.** 2$\frac{1}{5}$ **d.** 3$\frac{1}{4}$

Example 1 *Rewriting Improper Fractions*

Rewrite the improper fraction $\frac{8}{3}$ as a mixed number.

Solution Draw some rectangles to represent wholes. Divide each rectangle into 3 parts. Then shade 8 parts. From the result, you can see the model represents 2$\frac{2}{3}$.

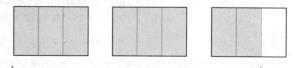

$$2\frac{2}{3}$$

Real Life
Baking

Boston brown bread is baked in a can and typically served with baked beans.

Example **2** | *Rewriting a Mixed Number*

The recipe below makes five loaves of Boston brown bread. You have fourth-cup, half-cup, and third-cup measures, but you can't find the one-cup measure. How many third-cup measures of raisins do you need?

Boston Brown Bread

$2\frac{1}{2}$ cups whole wheat flour		5	eggs
$1\frac{1}{4}$ cups white flour		$2\frac{1}{2}$	cups buttermilk
$1\frac{1}{4}$ cups corn meal		$1\frac{1}{4}$	cups molasses
$2\frac{1}{2}$ teaspoons baking powder		1	tablespoon oil
$1\frac{1}{4}$ teaspoons salt		$\frac{3}{4}$	cup sugar
$2\frac{1}{2}$ teaspoons baking soda		$1\frac{2}{3}$	cups raisins

Solution You need to fill the third-cup measure 5 times. This is the same as saying that the mixed number $1\frac{2}{3}$ is equal to the improper fraction $\frac{5}{3}$.

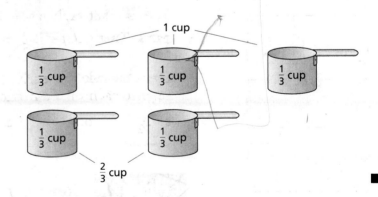

■

Communicating about MATHEMATICS

Problem Solving
Draw a Diagram

▶ **Sharing Ideas about the Lesson**

Extending the Example Use only a fourth-cup measure and a half-cup measure. Explain how you could measure the following ingredients.

A. Whole wheat flour   **B.** White flour   **C.** Sugar

EXERCISES

Guided Practice

Think and Discuss

▶ **CHECK for Understanding**

1. What is an improper fraction? How is it different from a proper fraction?

Geometry In Exercises 2 and 3, use the diagram below.

2. Write the mixed number represented by the model. Explain how each part of the mixed number relates to the model.

3. Write the improper fraction represented by the model.

4. Draw a model to represent $2\frac{1}{4}$. Then use the model to rewrite $2\frac{1}{4}$ as an improper fraction. Explain your steps.

5. Rewrite $\frac{17}{3}$ as a mixed number.   6. Rewrite $4\frac{3}{4}$ as an improper fraction.

Independent Practice

Reasoning In Exercises 7–9, complete the statement using *sometimes, always,* or *never.*

7. A mixed number is ⟨?⟩ greater than 1.

8. A proper fraction is ⟨?⟩ greater than 1.

9. An improper fraction is ⟨?⟩ a whole number.

Making Connections In Exercises 10 and 11, write the mixed number and the improper fraction represented by the model.

10.
            11.

Number Sense In Exercises 12–15, match the mixed number with its improper fraction.

a. $2\frac{3}{4}$ b. $1\frac{6}{8}$ c. $3\frac{1}{2}$ d. $6\frac{1}{4}$

12. $\frac{14}{4}$ 13. $\frac{11}{4}$ 14. $\frac{25}{4}$ 15. $\frac{7}{4}$

In Exercises 16–19, draw a model to represent the improper fraction. Then rewrite the fraction as a mixed number.

16. $\frac{16}{3}$ 17. $\frac{11}{8}$ 18. $\frac{23}{7}$ 19. $\frac{29}{6}$

In Exercises 20–23, draw a model to represent the mixed number. Then rewrite the mixed number as an improper fraction.

20. $2\frac{1}{2}$ 21. $1\frac{3}{4}$

22. $2\frac{3}{5}$ 23. $3\frac{2}{3}$

24. **Footbag** You practice with your footbag half an hour every day for 9 days. Write an improper fraction that shows the total number of hours you practiced. Rewrite the improper fraction as a mixed number. Which number best represents the answer? Explain.

25. **The Stock Market** The closing stock for Toys R Us on January 9, 1995, was $29\frac{1}{2}$ per share. This means that at the end of the day on January 9, 1995, each share of stock was worth $29.50. Rewrite $29\frac{1}{2}$ as an improper fraction. What does the improper fraction mean?

13-year old Adrian Verhoef of Vancouver, British Columbia, practiced 5 hours a day to become a champion footbag player. (Source: Sports Illustrated for Kids)

Integrated Review	**Making Connections within Mathematics**

Perform the operation.

26. $14.6 + 0.92$ 27. $8.05 - 3.71$ 28. $24.1 - 6.92$

29. 12.6×0.34 30. $9.38 \div 6.7$ 31. $12.95 \div 0.25$

Exploration and Extension

32. **Building Your Chapter Project** In your apartment, it takes $2\frac{1}{2}$ boxes of tile to cover the bathroom floor. How many boxes of tile would it take to cover the floor of each of the other four rooms? Explain your reasoning.

Introduction to Probability

What you should learn:

Goal 1 How to use ratios to find probabilities

Goal 2 How to interpret probabilities

Why you should learn it:

Probability can be used to predict outcomes. An example is predicting on which color a spinner will land.

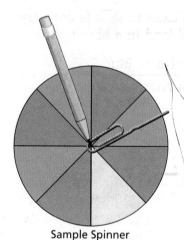

Sample Spinner

Need To Know

The probabilities found in the investigation are *experimental*. To find *theoretical probabilities*, find the ratio of the favorable outcomes to possible outcomes. This is shown in Example 1.

Goal 1 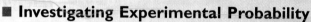 **Using Ratios to Find Probabilities**

Lesson Investigation

■ **Investigating Experimental Probability**

Group Activity Make a spinner by dividing a cardboard circle into 8 equal regions. Color 4 of the regions red, 3 blue, and 1 yellow. As shown at the left, spin the paper clip 10 times. Record the number of times the paper clip lands on each color.

Add your results to those of other groups until you have recorded the results for 100 spins. Finally, write each result as a ratio. On which of the colors is the paper clip most likely to land? Least likely to land? Explain.

Color	Red	Blue	Yellow
Number of Spins on Color	?	?	?
Ratio	$\frac{?}{100}$	$\frac{?}{100}$	$\frac{?}{100}$

The ratios you found in this experiment are **probabilities.** The probability of an event tells you how likely it is that the event will happen.

Example 1   *Finding Probabilities*

Find the probability that the spinner will land on the color.

a. Red   b. Blue

Solution In each case, the probability is a ratio.

a. Probability of Red $= \dfrac{\text{Number of Red Regions}}{\text{Total Number of Regions}} = \dfrac{4}{8}$

b. Probability of Blue $= \dfrac{\text{Number of Blue Regions}}{\text{Total Number of Regions}} = \dfrac{3}{8}$ ■

The probability that *any* event occurs is a number from 0 to 1. The closer the probability is to 0, the less likely the event is to occur. The closer the probability is to 1, the more likely the event is to occur.

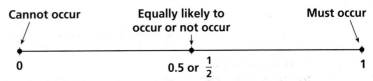

Cannot occur — Equally likely to occur or not occur — Must occur

0   0.5 or $\frac{1}{2}$ 1

Example 2   *Interpreting Probabilities*

A small button is tossed onto regions like those shown at the left. If the button lands on a line, the toss is not counted. Find the probability that the button will land in a blue region. Interpret the results.

Solution

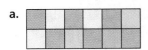
a.

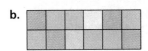
b.

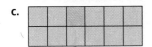
c.

a. Probability of Blue = $\dfrac{\text{Number of Blue Regions}}{\text{Total Number of Regions}} = \dfrac{1}{12}$

Because the probability is close to 0, it is not very likely that the button will land in a blue region.

b. Probability of Blue = $\dfrac{\text{Number of Blue Regions}}{\text{Total Number of Regions}} = \dfrac{6}{12} = \dfrac{1}{2}$

Because the probability is one half, it is equally likely that the button will land in a blue region or on another color.

c. Probability of Blue = $\dfrac{\text{Number of Blue Regions}}{\text{Total Number of Regions}} = \dfrac{11}{12}$

Because the probability is close to 1, it is very likely that the button will land in a blue region. ∎

Communicating about MATHEMATICS

Cooperative Learning

▶ **Sharing Ideas about the Lesson**

Partner Activity Use paper and a button to experimentally find the probabilities in Example 2. Compare your results with those in Example 2.

EXERCISES

Guided Practice

Think and Discuss

▶ **CHECK for Understanding**

Refer to the spinner at the right. Find the probability that the spinner will land on the number described.

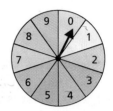

1. An odd number
2. A number divisible by 3
3. A number less than 4

In Exercises 4–6, write an example of each type of event. Then match the event with the probability.

a. 0.02   b. 0.5   c. 0.97

4. Very likely to occur   5. Not likely to occur   6. Equally likely to occur or not

7. *Group Activity* Toss a cup in the air. Did the cup land on its side, upside down, or upright? Repeat the experiment 20 times. Record your results. Use your results to estimate the probabilities of each of the possible outcomes. Compare your results with other groups' results.

8. Tape a penny to the inside bottom of the cup in Exercise 7. Then repeat the experiment. How do your results change?

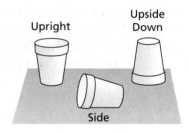

Upright   Upside Down

Side

Independent Practice

Marbles, Marbles In Exercises 9–12, suppose you have a bag that contains the marbles shown. One marble is drawn from the bag. What is the probability that the marble is blue?

9.   10.   11.   12.

Match the event with the letter of its probability.

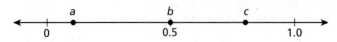

13. You correctly guess the answer to a true-false question.
14. A student you pick from your class is left-handed.
15. You are doing this exercise on a school day.

Make a circular spinner. Divide the spinner into 4 equal pie-cut regions. Color 1 of the regions green and 3 yellow.

16. Find the probability that the spinner will land on green. Write the probability as a fraction and a decimal.

17. Spin the spinner 40 times and record your results. Write the experimental probability of landing on green.

Statistics In a survey, 1000 people were asked which day of the week was their favorite day to shop. The portions of people that chose each day are shown at the right. If one person is chosen from the group, what is the probability that the person gave the following answer? *(Source: International Mass Retail Association)*

Favorite Day to Shop

Thursday 0.13
Friday 0.17
Saturday 0.29
Wednesday 0.12
Tuesday 0.05
Monday 0.04
No preference 0.13
Sunday 0.07

18. Saturday

19. No preference

Science In the 1860's, Gregor Mendel discovered that in pea plants, the color of a flower depends on the colors of the "parent" flowers. The diagram at the right shows the possible flower colors when both parent flowers are light pink. Find the given probability.

20. The flower color is light pink.

21. The flower color is not white.

Integrated Review

Making Connections within Mathematics

 Use a calculator to change each fraction to a decimal. Then complete the statement using $>$, $<$, or $=$.

22. $\frac{3}{12}$? $\frac{1}{5}$

23. $\frac{1}{20}$? $\frac{1}{5}$

24. $\frac{3}{18}$? $\frac{1}{6}$

Exploration and Extension

Random Numbers When you toss a coin, it is equally likely to land heads up or tails up. Such outcomes are *random*. Random numbers are numbers in a set that have equally likely chances of being chosen. Would the following give a random number? Explain.

25. You pick a number between 0 and 9 from a hat.

26. You roll a 6-sided number cube.

27. You pick the *first* digit of a telephone number in your town's phone book.

6 Chapter Summary

What did you learn?

Skills

1. Identify the numerator and denominator of a fraction. **(6.1)**
2. Rewrite a fraction as a division problem. **(6.2)**
3. Use a ratio to compare two values. **(6.2)**
4. Decide whether two fractions or ratios are equivalent. **(6.3)**
5. Simplify a fraction. **(6.4)**
6. Solve a proportion. **(6.4)**
7. Compare and order two or more fractions. **(6.5)**
8. Rewrite mixed numbers and improper fractions. **(6.6)**
9. Find experimental and theoretical probabilities. **(6.7)**

Strategies

10. Use problem-solving strategies to solve problems. **(6.1–6.7)**

Exploring Data

11. Use tables and graphs to organize data and solve problems. **(6.1–6.7)**

Why did you learn it?

Many real-life problems contain fractions. Knowing how to model fractions helps you picture them in your mind. Here are some of the examples you studied in this chapter.

- Compare the performances of 2 first-grade classes. **(6.1)**
- Compare width-to-length ratios of a scale drawing and an actual room. **(6.3)**
- Decide which sale price is a better buy. **(6.5)**
- Rewrite measures that are used in a recipe. **(6.6)**

How does it fit into the bigger picture of mathematics?

Someone once claimed that *"a picture is worth a thousand words."* This is true in mathematics because pictures can help you understand why different rules or formulas work.

For instance, in Chapter 7, you will see how models of fractions can help you understand the rules for adding and subtracting fractions. In Chapter 8, you will see how models of fractions can help you understand the rules for multiplying and dividing fractions.

As you study fraction operations, remember that the "rules of fractions" are a lot easier to understand when you can use models to see why the rules work.

Write the fractions shown by each of the shaded regions. Then order the fractions from least to greatest. **(6.1, 6.5)**

1.    2.

In Exercises 3–6, write 3 fractions equivalent to the given fraction. **(6.3)**

3. $\frac{6}{7}$ 4. $\frac{7}{10}$ 5. $\frac{9}{12}$ 6. $\frac{8}{20}$

Geometry In Exercises 7–9, find the ratio of the rectangle's width to its length. Then simplify. **(6.2, 6.3)**

7. 6 ft, 9 ft

8. 30 in., 36 in.

9. 24 cm, 64 cm

In Exercises 10–15, solve the proportion. **(6.3, 6.4)**

10. $\frac{4}{?} = \frac{16}{28}$ 11. $\frac{?}{36} = \frac{5}{9}$ 12. $\frac{12}{22} = \frac{?}{11}$

13. $\frac{3}{7} = \frac{18}{?}$ 14. $\frac{?}{3} = \frac{9}{27}$ 15. $\frac{39}{?} = \frac{3}{4}$

In Exercises 16–19, match the mixed number with its improper fraction. **(6.6)**

a. $\frac{11}{6}$ b. $\frac{27}{6}$ c. $\frac{31}{6}$ d. $\frac{16}{6}$

16. $4\frac{1}{2}$ 17. $5\frac{1}{6}$ 18. $1\frac{5}{6}$ 19. $2\frac{2}{3}$

20. *Shopping for Sneakers* You go shopping to buy a pair of sneakers. The pair you like is on sale at 3 stores. The regular price for the sneakers is $60. The sneakers are one-fourth off at Store 1, one-third off at Store 2, and two-fifths off at Store 3. Which is the best buy? Explain. **(6.5)**

In Exercises 21–23, complete the statement with 0, $\frac{1}{2}$, or 1. **(6.7)**

21. If an event is impossible, its probability is ?.

22. A probability can be no greater than ?.

23. When flipping a coin, the probability of "heads" is ?.

Use the drawing shown at the right.

24. Use a ruler to draw a 5-by-5 grid of 1-inch squares. Copy the drawing onto the grid by drawing what is shown in each square.

25. What is the ratio of the original drawing to your drawing? Explain.

26. *Scale Drawing*   Find a simple picture in a newspaper or magazine. Use a centimeter ruler to divide it into a grid of 3-cm squares. Then create a grid of 2-cm squares on a sheet of paper. Copy the picture onto the 2-cm grid by drawing what is shown in each square. What are the width-to-length ratios of each drawing? Are they equivalent?

Geography   In Exercises 27–30, use the grid and the pieces below.

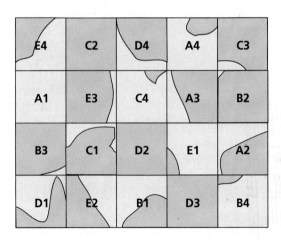

27. Copy the grid. Draw what is shown for each square using the pieces shown at the right. What continent is formed?

28. Each side of a square represents 500 miles. Use your scale drawing to estimate the width of the continent.

29. Estimate the portion of your drawing that is ocean. Explain.

30. Estimate the portion of your drawing that is land. Compare this estimate with the estimate you found in Exercise 29. What do you notice?

Chapter TEST

In Exercises 1–3, write 3 equivalent fractions represented by the blue portion of the figure.

1.

2.

3.

Geometry In Exercises 4 and 5, find the ratio of each rectangle's width to its length. Are the ratios equivalent?

4.

5.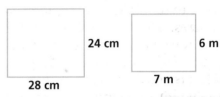

In Exercises 6–9, simplify the fraction.

6. $\frac{8}{16}$

7. $\frac{12}{15}$

8. $\frac{14}{20}$

9. $\frac{6}{27}$

True or False? In Exercises 10–12, tell whether the statement is true or false. If it is false, change the blue number to make the statement true.

10. $\frac{6}{9} = \frac{1}{3}$

11. $\frac{2}{7} = \frac{12}{42}$

12. $\frac{1}{5} = \frac{16}{20}$

In Exercises 13–16, complete the statement using > or <.

13. $\frac{2}{4}$ ⟨?⟩ $\frac{1}{4}$

14. $\frac{5}{8}$ ⟨?⟩ $\frac{5}{7}$

15. $\frac{4}{7}$ ⟨?⟩ $\frac{1}{2}$

16. $\frac{6}{13}$ ⟨?⟩ $\frac{2}{3}$

17. Rewrite $\frac{27}{5}$ as a mixed number.

18. Rewrite $2\frac{3}{8}$ as an improper fraction.

19. *Favorite Foods* A survey asked 24 sixth graders to name their favorite type of food. One sixth chose Mexican, one half chose Italian, one twelfth chose Chinese, and one fourth chose American. Use a set model to find the number who chose each type of food.

Writing In Exercises 20–23, the probability of an event occurring is given. Use the words *impossible, certain, likely,* or *not likely* to describe the probability. Then write an example of a real-life event that could have the probability.

20. 0.95

21. 1

22. 0

23. $\frac{1}{10}$

Algebra and Mental Math In Exercises 1–6, solve. **(1.6, 2.2–2.4, 4.6)**

1. $x + 6 = 18$

2. $20 - y = 9$

3. $12 \cdot n = 60$

4. $m \div 5 = 7$

5. $4(a + 5) = 32$

6. $0.45 \cdot b = 45$

In Exercises 7–12, evaluate the expression. **(2.1, 2.5, 2.7, 3.7)**

7. $(2 \times 3^2) \div 6$

8. $4 + 24 \div 2 - 8$

9. $5 \times 10 - 2^5 - 2$

10. $9 \times 1000 + 5 \times 10$

11. 11011_2

12. 143_5

In Exercises 13–15, write the decimal or fraction shown by the model. **(3.1, 3.3, 6.1)**

13.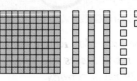

14.

15.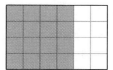

In Exercises 16–21, complete the statement. **(3.2, 3.4, 6.2–6.4, 6.6)**

16. $\boxed{?}$ m $= 2.8$ km

17. $\dfrac{7}{10} = \boxed{?}\%$

18. $\boxed{?}\% = 0.92$

19. $\dfrac{7}{8} = \dfrac{42}{\boxed{?}}$

20. $\dfrac{2 \text{ pears}}{5 \text{ pears}} = \dfrac{2 \text{ pears}}{\boxed{?} \text{ pears}}$

21. $\dfrac{\boxed{?}}{5} = 2\dfrac{4}{5}$

In Exercises 22–25, order the numbers from least to greatest. **(3.5, 6.5)**

22. $3.12, 3.2, 3.02, 3.22, 3.19$

23. $0.02, 0.11, 0.011, 0.01, 0.1$

24. $\dfrac{3}{8}, \dfrac{3}{5}, \dfrac{3}{4}, \dfrac{4}{8}$

25. $\dfrac{4}{7}, \dfrac{4}{5}, \dfrac{1}{2}, \dfrac{2}{3}$

In Exercises 26–31, round each number to the given place value. **(3.6)**

26. 947 (tens)

27. 1620 (hundreds)

28. 83,510 (thousands)

29. 14.8 (ones)

30. 0.53 (tenths)

31. 7.846 (hundredths)

Geometry In Exercises 32–34, find x. **(4.1, 4.2, 4.4, 4.5, 4.7)**

32. Perimeter $= 20.42$

33. Area $= x$

34. Area $= 45.9$

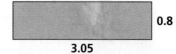

Statistics Find the mean, median, and mode of the data. **(5.3, 5.4)**

35. $15, 12, 12, 16, 14, 15, 14, 11, 17, 14$

36. $43, 39, 37, 41, 41, 39, 39, 42, 39$

37. *Writing* Name 3 ways of organizing or graphing data. Write a sentence about each and the type of data that each would best display. **(1.2, 1.3, 5.1, 5.2, 5.5–5.8)**

Pets and Animals The list below shows the average maximum weights (in pounds) of breeds of sporting dogs. *(Source: American Kennel Club)* **(1.3, 5.2)**

45, 40, 80, 65, 28, 70, 34, 70, 55, 50, 70, 70, 65, 75, 80, 70, 65, 75, 75, 45, 50, 80, 40, 60

38. Organize the data in a stem-and-leaf plot.
39. What is the most common maximum weight of sporting dogs?
40. What is the lightest maximum weight of sporting dogs?

In 1992, the Labrador Retriever was rated the United States top dog with 120,879 registrations.

The table at the right shows the results of a survey that asked 100 people to name their favorite type of movie. **(1.2, 1.4, 3.4, 5.5, 6.4)**

Movie Type	Number
Comedy	32
Action	27
Drama	25
Western	16

41. Represent the data with a bar graph.
42. What percent of the people surveyed chose action?
43. What type of movie was chosen by $\frac{1}{4}$ of the people?

The list at the right shows the number of cellular telephone systems from 1986 through 1993. **(5.8)**

Year	Number of Systems
1986	166
1987	312
1988	517
1989	584
1990	751
1991	1252
1992	1506
1993	1529

44. Choose an appropriate graph to display the data. Explain why you chose that type of graph.
45. Which year had the largest increase in cellular telephone systems?
46. Approximate the number of cellular telephone systems in 1994.

47. You received 18 phone calls on the weekend. One third were on Sunday. How many were on Saturday?

48. You have 32 markers. Three fourths are worn out. How many of your markers are worn out?

CHAPTER 7

Adding and Subtracting Fractions

The White House is the official residence of the President of the United States. It has 132 rooms and is one of the most popular tourist attractions in the country.

The State Dining Room in the White House is where all large dinners are held. The room is 48 ft 8 in. by 34 ft 8 in. and holds 144 people. Planning a dinner includes estimating how much food to buy, making sure there are enough table settings, and deciding how the tables should be arranged.

Think and Discuss

You need to arrange the room for a state dinner for 144 people. You can use any combination of round tables that seat 8 people and rectangular tables that seat 10.

1. How many arrangements with no empty seats can you find? Explain.
2. Sketch the room to scale and show how you would arrange the tables. The area of each table is about 20 square feet.

CHAPTER THEME:

Washington, D.C.

Writing a **Diary** of a Class Trip

Theme: Washington, D.C. Every year thousands of students visit Washington, D.C. What would you like to see if you went there? Some of the most popular sights are the U.S. Capitol, the National Air and Space Museum at the Smithsonian Institution, and the Washington Monument.

In this project, you will imagine that you are visiting Washington, D.C. and its famous sights. You will keep a diary of the sights that you visit and of the math that you use during your visit. These include the following.

▷ **In Lesson 7.1:** The perimeter of the Washington Monument (page 305)

▷ **In Lesson 7.2:** The number of rooms in the White House (page 309)

▷ **In Lesson 7.3:** The length of the walk from the Washington Monument to the White House to the Lincoln Memorial (page 317)

▷ **In Lesson 7.4:** The height of the U.S. Capitol including the Statue of Freedom on top (page 324)

▷ **In Lesson 7.5:** Scheduling a trip to the Vietnam Veterans Memorial (page 331)

▷ **In Lesson 7.6:** Buying souvenirs for your friends (page 337)

The National Air and Space Museum is full of interesting displays about past and present air travel.

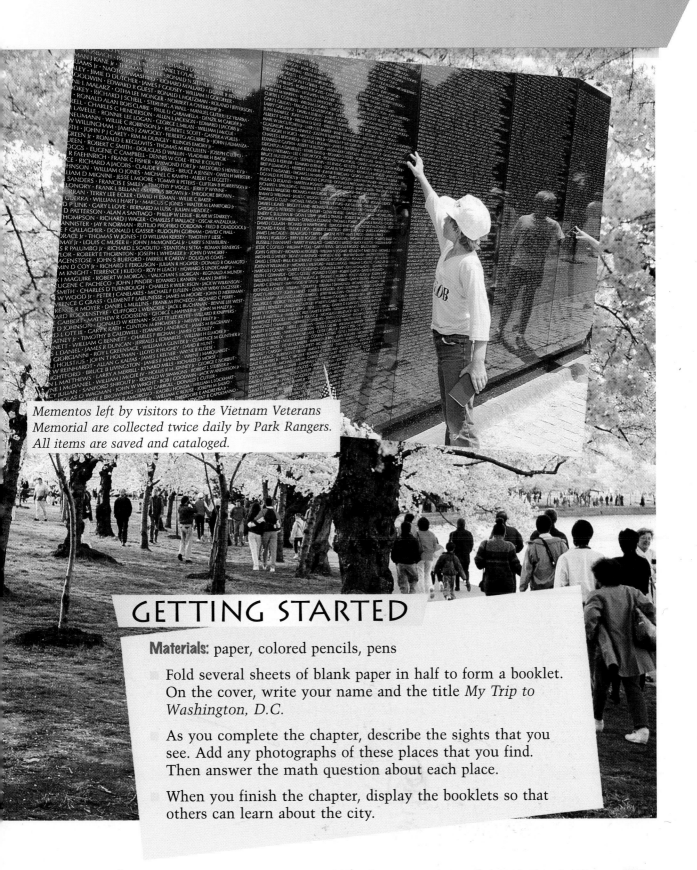

Mementos left by visitors to the Vietnam Veterans Memorial are collected twice daily by Park Rangers. All items are saved and cataloged.

GETTING STARTED

Materials: paper, colored pencils, pens

Fold several sheets of blank paper in half to form a booklet. On the cover, write your name and the title *My Trip to Washington, D.C.*

As you complete the chapter, describe the sights that you see. Add any photographs of these places that you find. Then answer the math question about each place.

When you finish the chapter, display the booklets so that others can learn about the city.

7.1

Measuring Length: The Customary System

What you should learn:

Goal 1 How to measure lengths in the customary system

Goal 2 How to rewrite measurements of length

Why you should learn it:

Knowing how to use the customary system can help you when measuring. An example is measuring a person's height.

Goal 1 Measuring Lengths

In Lesson 3.2, you studied the metric system. In this lesson, you will study the customary system.

Example 1 *Measuring Lengths*

Write the length of each rectangle as a mixed number.

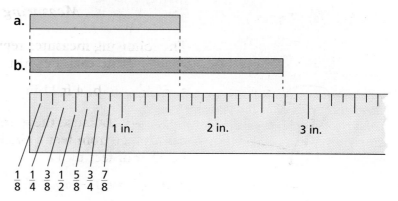

Solution

a. This rectangle is $1\frac{5}{8}$ inches long.

b. This rectangle is $2\frac{3}{4}$ inches long to the nearest $\frac{1}{8}$ in. ■

Study Tip

You can use estimation to check if your answer is reasonable. For example,

$$3\frac{3}{8} + 2\frac{1}{4} \approx 3\frac{1}{2} + 2$$

$$= 5\frac{1}{2}.$$

Is your answer close to $5\frac{1}{2}$?

Lesson Investigation

■ **Investigating Fractional Measures of Length**

Partner Activity Use a ruler to draw line segments that have the following lengths.

a. $\frac{7}{8}$ inch **b.** $1\frac{1}{2}$ inches **c.** $3\frac{3}{8}$ inches **d.** $2\frac{1}{4}$ inches

Explain how you can use the ruler to find the sum of two of these lengths. Give an example.

In the metric system, each unit is 10 times longer than the next smaller unit. For instance, a centimeter is 10 times longer than a millimeter. This is not true in the customary system.

The Customary System
12 inches (in.) = 1 foot (ft)
3 feet = 1 yard (yd)
36 inches = 1 yard

The United States is one of the few countries in the world that still uses the customary system.

Real Life
Heights

Need To Know

The symbol ' represents feet and the symbol " represents inches. For instance, 5' 2" is read as "5 feet, 2 inches."

Example **2** *Measuring a Person's Height*

The following measures represent the heights of three people. Write each height in inches.

a. $5' 4\frac{1}{2}''$ **b.** 4 ft 11 in. **c.** $6' 1\frac{3}{4}''$

Solution Because there are 12 inches in a foot, you can change from feet to inches by multiplying the number of feet by 12.

a. $5' 4\frac{1}{2}'' = 60'' + 4\frac{1}{2}'' = 64\frac{1}{2}''$

b. 4 ft 11 in. = 48 in. + 11 in. = 59 in.

c. $6' 1\frac{3}{4}'' = 72'' + 1\frac{3}{4}'' = 73\frac{3}{4}''$ ■

Communicating about MATHEMATICS

Sharing Ideas about the Lesson

Group Activity Measure the heights of the people in your group. Write each height in feet *and* inches. For instance, a person who is 63 inches tall has a height of 5 feet, 3 inches.

Cooperative Learning

EXERCISES

Guided Practice

Think and Discuss

▶ **CHECK for Understanding**

In Exercises 1 and 2, find the length to the nearest eighth inch.
Write the length as a mixed number and as an improper fraction.

1.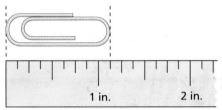

2.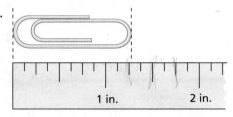

3. Write each of the following as eighths. What is the pattern?

$$\frac{1}{8}, \frac{1}{4}, \frac{3}{8}, \frac{1}{2}, \frac{5}{8}, \frac{3}{4}, \frac{7}{8}, 1$$

4. *Geometry* Use a ruler to measure the dimensions of this
   textbook to the nearest $\frac{1}{8}$ inch. Estimate the perimeter.

5. Complete the statements.

   a. 24 inches = ⟨?⟩ feet   b. $2\frac{1}{2}$ feet = ⟨?⟩ inches

6. Write the height $5' \, 3\frac{1}{2}''$ in words. Then write it in inches.

Independent Practice

Measurement   In Exercises 7–11, write the fraction as a mixed
number. Then match the fraction with its location on the ruler.

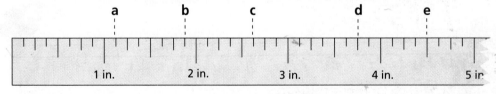

7. $\frac{21}{8}$ in.   8. $\frac{15}{4}$ in.   9. $\frac{9}{2}$ in.   10. $\frac{15}{8}$ in.   11. $\frac{9}{8}$ in.

Measure the length to the nearest eighth inch.

12.

13.

Name a real-life object that could have the given length.

14. 65 inches **15.** 100 yards **16.** 2 feet **17.** 50 feet

In Exercises 18–23, complete the statement.

18. 1 yard = ? feet **19.** 60 inches = ? feet **20.** ? inches = 5 yards

21. ? yards = 27 feet **22.** $\frac{1}{2}$ yard = ? inches **23.** ? inches = $\frac{1}{4}$ foot

In Exercises 24–27, write the height in feet and inches.

24. 75″ **25.** 71 inches **26.** $53\frac{1}{2}''$ **27.** $67\frac{3}{4}''$

Estimation Estimate the perimeter of the figure.

28. 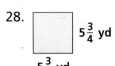 $5\frac{3}{4}$ yd

$5\frac{3}{4}$ yd

29. $1\frac{7}{8}$ ft

$4\frac{3}{8}$ ft

30. 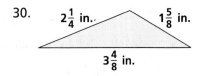 $2\frac{1}{4}$ in. $1\frac{5}{8}$ in. $3\frac{4}{8}$ in.

31. *Bike Riding* You ride your bike 40 yards. The tires on your bike measure 72 inches around. How many times would your tires rotate during your ride? Explain your reasoning.

Integrated Review
Making Connections within Mathematics

32. Copy the grid and the measures. Take turns with a partner crossing off a measure and writing it in a box on the grid. A measure *can't* be next to a measure (not even diagonally) if it is next to it on the ruler on page 302. The game is over when a player is unable to make a move.

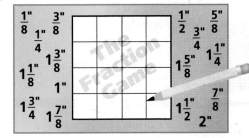

Exploration and Extension

33. *Building Your Chapter Project* On your class trip you visit the Washington Monument. The monument measures $55'1\frac{1}{8}''$ on each of the four sides. Write this number in words. Estimate the perimeter of the monument. Measure the length and width of your classroom. Estimate its perimeter. About how much bigger is the perimeter of the monument than the perimeter of your classroom? In your diary, tell what you learned about the Washington Monument.

7.2

Least Common Denominators

What you should learn:

Goal 1 How to find common denominators of two fractions

Goal 2 How to find the least common denominator of two fractions

Why you should learn it:

Knowing how to find common denominators helps you add and subtract fractions.

Goal 1 **Finding Common Denominators**

Fractions with the same denominator have a **common denominator.** For instance, $\frac{3}{6}$ and $\frac{2}{6}$ have a common denominator of 6.

Lesson Investigation

■ **Investigating Equivalent Fractions**

The models show fractions equivalent to $\frac{1}{4}$. Write the fractions. Describe any patterns.

a.   b. 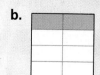   c.

d.   e.   f.

Draw models of $\frac{5}{6}$ and three equivalent fractions. Label each drawing with its fraction.

Study Tip

Remember from Lesson 6.3 that by multiplying the numerator and denominator of a fraction by the same number, you can form equivalent fractions. For instance, the fractions $\frac{2}{3}$ and $\frac{4}{6}$ are equivalent because

$$\frac{2}{3} = \frac{2 \cdot 2}{3 \cdot 2} = \frac{4}{6}.$$

Example 1 **Finding Common Denominators**

Rewrite $\frac{1}{4}$ and $\frac{5}{6}$ with a common denominator.

Solution Here are two equivalent fractions for $\frac{1}{4}$ and $\frac{5}{6}$ that have the same denominator.

$\frac{1 \cdot 3}{4 \cdot 3} = \frac{3}{12}$ ⟍ **Common**
$\frac{5 \cdot 2}{6 \cdot 2} = \frac{10}{12}$ ⟋ **denominator**

$\frac{1 \cdot 6}{4 \cdot 6} = \frac{6}{24}$ ⟍ **Common**
$\frac{5 \cdot 4}{6 \cdot 4} = \frac{20}{24}$ ⟋ **denominator**

Can you think of others? ■

Least Common Denominators

In Example 1, notice that the common denominators of 12 and 24 are multiples of the original denominators 4 and 6.

Least Common Denominator

The **least common multiple** of two numbers is the smallest multiple that they have in common.

The **least common denominator** of two fractions is the least common multiple of their denominators.

Example 2 *Finding Least Common Denominator*

Find the least common denominator of the fractions. Then use the least common denominator to rewrite the fractions.

a. $\dfrac{3}{5}, \dfrac{1}{2}$ b. $\dfrac{5}{8}, \dfrac{1}{6}$

Solution

a. The least common multiple of 5 and 2 is 10.

$$\frac{3}{5} = \frac{3 \cdot 2}{5 \cdot 2} = \frac{6}{10} \quad \textit{Multiply by } \frac{2}{2}.$$

$$\frac{1}{2} = \frac{1 \cdot 5}{2 \cdot 5} = \frac{5}{10} \quad \textit{Multiply by } \frac{5}{5}.$$

b. The least common multiple of 6 and 8 is 24.

$$\frac{5}{8} = \frac{5 \cdot 3}{8 \cdot 3} = \frac{15}{24} \quad \textit{Multiply by } \frac{3}{3}.$$

$$\frac{1}{6} = \frac{1 \cdot 4}{6 \cdot 4} = \frac{4}{24} \quad \textit{Multiply by } \frac{4}{4}.$$ ∎

Study Tip

One way to find the least common multiple of two numbers is to list several multiples of each number. The first multiple that appears in both lists is the least common multiple.

6, 12, 18, 24, 30, 36, 42, 48, . . .

8, 16, 24, 32, 40, 48, 56, 64, . . .

Least common multiple   Common multiple

Communicating about MATHEMATICS

▶ **Sharing Ideas about the Lesson**

Partner Activity Rewrite the 3 fractions using a least common denominator. Explain your steps. How would this help you order these fractions?

$\dfrac{3}{8}, \dfrac{5}{6}, \dfrac{7}{12}$

Cooperative Learning

EXERCISES

Guided Practice

Think and Discuss

▶ **CHECK for Understanding**

1. Which shows a fraction *not* equivalent to $\frac{1}{3}$? Explain.

a.   b.   c.   d.

True or False? Is the statement true or false? Explain.

2. Two common multiples of 3 and 5 are 30 and 45.
3. The least common multiple of 3 and 5 is 30.
4. The least common denominator of $\frac{2}{3}$ and $\frac{2}{5}$ is 15.
5. The least common multiple of any 2 numbers is their product.

6. *It's Up to You* Which is larger, $\frac{3}{10}$ or $\frac{2}{5}$? How did you decide?

Independent Practice

In Exercises 7–10, list the first ten multiples of each number. Then find the least common multiple of the two numbers.

7. 5, 8   8. 10, 4   9. 5, 6   10. 12, 10

In Exercises 11–14, draw models of two fractions that are equivalent to the given fraction.

11. $\frac{1}{6}$ 12. $\frac{3}{8}$ 13. $\frac{4}{5}$ 14. $\frac{5}{12}$

In Exercises 15–18, find the least common denominator. Then use the least common denominator to rewrite the fractions.

15. $\frac{1}{3}, \frac{11}{12}$ 16. $\frac{2}{3}, \frac{7}{8}$ 17. $\frac{1}{6}, \frac{7}{10}$ 18. $\frac{3}{15}, \frac{1}{2}$

19. *Decoding a Message* Order the fractions by rewriting with a common denominator. Then copy the diagram and write the ordered letters in the boxes. What is the message?

$\frac{1}{6}$–E, $\frac{5}{12}$–L, $\frac{11}{12}$–E, $\frac{5}{6}$–O, $\frac{3}{8}$–L, $\frac{7}{8}$–N, $\frac{2}{3}$–D, $\frac{1}{12}$–W

In Exercises 20–22, which fraction is not equivalent? Explain.

20. $\frac{7}{10}, \frac{21}{30}, \frac{12}{15}$

21. $\frac{6}{18}, \frac{3}{8}, \frac{9}{27}$

22. $\frac{9}{12}, \frac{12}{15}, \frac{4}{5}$

Poetry In Exercises 23 and 24, count the number of pronouns in
the poem. Then write the fraction of the words that are pronouns.
In which poem is the fraction of pronouns larger?

23. **Charity**
There is so much good in the worst of us,
And so much bad in the best of us,
That it ill behoves any of us
To find fault with the rest of us.
Author unknown

24. **The Purple Cow**
I never saw a Purple Cow;
I never Hope to See One;
But I can Tell you Anyhow,
I'd rather See than Be One.
Gelett Burgess

25. *Reasoning* It takes you $\frac{3}{5}$ hour to
walk $\frac{5}{8}$ mile. It takes your friend $\frac{2}{3}$
hour to walk $\frac{7}{12}$ mile. Who has
walked farther? A longer time? Faster?
Explain your reasoning.

26. *Probability* Make a circular spinner
that has 10 pie-cut regions of the
same size. Write the following
fractions in the regions.

$$\frac{1}{2}, \frac{1}{3}, \frac{1}{4}, \frac{2}{4}, \frac{2}{6}, \frac{2}{8}, \frac{3}{9}, \frac{3}{12}, \frac{4}{12}, \frac{6}{12}$$

What is the probability that the spinner
will land on a fraction equivalent to $\frac{1}{3}$?
$\frac{1}{4}$? $\frac{1}{2}$?

*In 1992, in a survey of more than 10,000
households, more people participated in
exercise walking than in any other sport.
(Source: National Sporting Goods Assoc.)*

Integrated Review

Making Connections within Mathematics

Write the number as a fraction.

27. 0.45

28. 33%

29. 8%

30. 0.176

Exploration and Extension

31. *Building Your Chapter Project* On your
class trip, you tour the White House. You
see 25 of the 132 rooms. Is this more or
less than $\frac{1}{6}$ of the rooms? In your diary,
explain your reasoning. Also, write all
that you know about the White House.

Ladies Sitting Parlor

Complete the statement using >, <, or = . **(3.2)**

1. 0.75 km (?) 75 m

2. 1.25 m (?) 1250 mm

3. 0.23 cm (?) 2.3 mm

4. 0.2 mm (?) 2.0 cm

Use a vertical form to add or subtract. **(4.1, 4.2)**

5. $4.5 + 3.35$

6. $16 - 3.54$

7. $12.92 + 3.56$

8. $10.66 - 8.98$

Use mental math to solve. Then use a calculator to check. **(4.6)**

9. $m \times 0.03 = 3$

10. $50 \div t = 0.05$

11. $n \div 100 = 0.32$

12. $0.4 \times b = 4000$

13. Make a line plot of the data. Find the mode. Make up a story about what the data could be. **(5.1)**

22, 25, 18, 17, 16, 17, 23, 18, 17, 18, 20, 17

Career Interview

Sound Engineer

Rhea Vogel is the owner of Countdown Studios, a rehearsal and recording studio for musicians. In addition to handling administrative work, Rhea schedules the bands' rehearsals, operates the sound equipment, and employs engineers to do the recordings.

Q: What led you to this career?

A: As a singer, I wanted to understand the equipment used to amplify my voice so that I could control the sound.

Q: Does having a math background help you?

A: Music is described by measures, beats per minute, time signatures, notes, and bars. To understand these terms, I must understand fractions and division and be able to compute quickly in my head.

Q: Has technology changed your job experience?

A: Synthesizers and computers are used to write, perform and record a lot of music today. Digital recording has greatly improved the quality of recorded sound.

In Lesson 7.1, you studied three measures of length in the customary system: inch, foot, and yard. A fourth measure in the system is the mile.

Technology
Calculator

Example   ***Units in the Customary System***

Your friend lives $\frac{3}{10}$ mile from you. Write this distance in feet and in yards.

Solution   One way to do this is to rewrite the distance as a decimal and then multiply.

Need To Know
The number of feet and yards in a mile are as follows.

1 mile = 5280 feet
1 mile = 1760 yards

$\frac{3}{10}$ of a mile = 0.3 of a mile   *Rewrite $\frac{3}{10}$.*

    = 0.3 × (1 mile)   *Multiply.*

    = 0.3 × (5280 feet)   *Rewrite 1 mile.*

    = 1584 feet   *Use a calculator.*

$\frac{3}{10}$ of a mile is 1584 feet.

$\frac{3}{10}$ of a mile = 0.3 of a mile   *Rewrite $\frac{3}{10}$.*

    = 0.3 × (1 mile)   *Multiply.*

    = 0.3 × (1760 yards) *Rewrite 1 mile.*

    = 528 yards   *Use a calculator.*

$\frac{3}{10}$ of a mile is 528 yards. A football field is 100 yards long, so $\frac{3}{10}$ of a mile is about $5\frac{1}{4}$ football fields.   ■

Exercises

Use a calculator. Rewrite the distance in feet and in yards.

1. $\frac{4}{10}$ mile   2. $\frac{1}{10}$ mile   3. $\frac{7}{10}$ mile   4. $\frac{9}{10}$ mile

Use a calculator. Rewrite the distance in feet and in yards.

5. 4 miles   6. 11 miles   7. 32 miles   8. 45 miles

9. *Communicating Math*   You live 3168 feet from the subway station. Write this distance as a fraction of a mile. Explain how to use a calculator to simplify your answer.

Materials Needed: paper, colored pencils, markers, pencils or pens

Part A *Adding Fractions with a Common Denominator*

1. Write the addition problem that each model represents.

   a. ☐ + ☐ = ☐   b. ☐ + ☐ = ☐

2. Draw a sketch of each problem. Find the sum of the two fractions.

   a. $\frac{1}{3} + \frac{2}{3}$ b. $\frac{1}{6} + \frac{4}{6}$ c. $\frac{2}{4} + \frac{3}{4}$

3. Use the results of Exercises 1 and 2. Explain how to add two fractions that have a common denominator. Why do you keep the same denominator in the sum?

Part B *Adding Fractions with Different Denominators*   Here is a model that shows how to add $\frac{1}{4}$ and $\frac{2}{3}$.

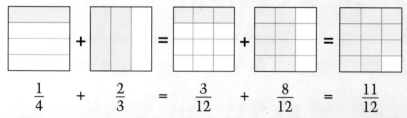

$$\frac{1}{4} \quad + \quad \frac{2}{3} \quad = \quad \frac{3}{12} \quad + \quad \frac{8}{12} \quad = \quad \frac{11}{12}$$

Summary of Steps

$$\frac{1}{4} = \frac{3}{12}$$
$$+ \frac{2}{3} = \frac{8}{12}$$
$$\overline{\quad\quad \frac{11}{12}}$$

4. Write the addition problem that the model represents.

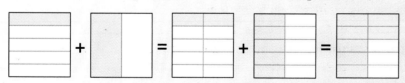

5. Draw a sketch and write the sum of the two fractions.

   a. $\frac{1}{3} + \frac{2}{4}$ b. $\frac{3}{5} + \frac{1}{3}$ c. $\frac{1}{2} + \frac{2}{3}$

6. Use the results of Exercises 4 and 5. Explain how to add two fractions that have different denominators.

Part C *Subtracting Fractions*

7. Write the subtraction problem that each model represents.

a. 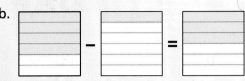   b.

8. Draw a sketch of each problem. Find the difference.

a. $\frac{3}{4} - \frac{1}{4}$ b. $\frac{2}{5} - \frac{1}{5}$ c. $\frac{4}{6} - \frac{3}{6}$

9. Write the subtraction problem that the model represents.

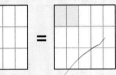

10. Draw a sketch of each problem. Write the difference.

a. $\frac{3}{5} - \frac{1}{2}$ b. $\frac{1}{2} - \frac{1}{3}$ c. $\frac{1}{3} - \frac{1}{4}$

On Your Own   Critical Thinking

Adding and Subtracting Fractions   In Exercises 11–18, draw a sketch of the problem. Then solve.

11. $\frac{3}{6} + \frac{2}{6}$ 12. $\frac{3}{5} + \frac{3}{5}$ 13. $\frac{5}{8} - \frac{3}{8}$ 14. $\frac{4}{5} - \frac{2}{5}$

15. $\frac{1}{2} + \frac{1}{4}$ 16. $\frac{2}{3} + \frac{1}{5}$ 17. $\frac{4}{5} - \frac{1}{2}$ 18. $\frac{2}{3} - \frac{1}{4}$

19. If two fractions are each less than 1, can their sum be greater than 1? Give an example.

20. If you are adding fractions whose denominators are 4 and 5, what denominator might their sum have? Give an example. Illustrate your example with a sketch.

7.3

Adding and Subtracting Fractions

What you should learn:

Goal 1 How to add and subtract fractions with a common denominator

Goal 2 How to add and subtract fractions with different denominators

Why you should learn it:

Fractions may need to be added or subtracted when working with measurements. An example is finding the height of a stack of books.

Goal 1 Using Common Denominators

In Lab 7.3, you may have discovered the following rules for adding and subtracting fractions that have a common denominator.

Fractions with a Common Denominator

To **add** two fractions with a common denominator, add their numerators. To **subtract** two fractions with a common denominator, subtract their numerators.

Example 1 Adding and Subtracting Fractions

a. $\dfrac{1}{8} + \dfrac{3}{8} = \dfrac{1+3}{8}$ *Add numerators.*

$= \dfrac{4}{8}$ *Simplify numerator.*

$= \dfrac{1}{2}$ *Simplify fraction.*

b. $\dfrac{4}{5} - \dfrac{3}{5} = \dfrac{4-3}{5}$ *Subtract numerators.*

$= \dfrac{1}{5}$ *Simplify numerator.*   ■

Example 2 Adding Fractions

Real Life
Measuring Length

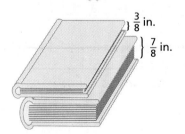

} $\frac{3}{8}$ in.

} $\frac{7}{8}$ in.

Two books are stacked together. One book is $\frac{3}{8}$ inch thick and the other is $\frac{7}{8}$ inch thick. How tall is the stack?

Solution   To find the height of the stack, add the fractions.

$$\frac{3}{8} + \frac{7}{8} = \frac{3+7}{8} = \frac{10}{8} = \frac{5}{4}$$

The stack is $\frac{5}{4}$ inches or $1\frac{1}{4}$ inches high.   ■

Goal 2 Using Different Denominators

In Lab 7.3, you may have discovered the following rules for adding or subtracting fractions that have different denominators.

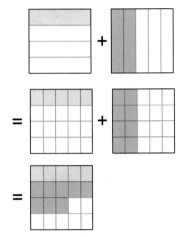

You can use a model to check your work. For instance, this model can be used to check the answer in Example 3(a).

Fractions with Different Denominators

To **add** or **subtract** two fractions with different denominators, first rewrite the fractions using a common denominator. Then add or subtract the numerators.

Example 3 *Adding and Subtracting Fractions*

a. $\dfrac{1}{4} + \dfrac{2}{5} = \dfrac{5}{20} + \dfrac{8}{20}$ *A common denominator is 20.*

$= \dfrac{5 + 8}{20}$ *Add numerators.*

$= \dfrac{13}{20}$ *Simplify numerator.*

b. $\dfrac{3}{4} - \dfrac{1}{6} = \dfrac{9}{12} - \dfrac{2}{12}$ *A common denominator is 12.*

$= \dfrac{9 - 2}{12}$ *Subtract numerators.*

$= \dfrac{7}{12}$ *Simplify numerator.*

Communicating about MATHEMATICS

Problem Solving
Logical Reasoning

▶ **Sharing Ideas about the Lesson**

Partner Activity Here is an example of adding 3 fractions.

$$\frac{1}{4} + \frac{3}{8} + \frac{7}{8} = \frac{2}{8} + \frac{3}{8} + \frac{7}{8} = \frac{2 + 3 + 7}{8} = \frac{12}{8} = \frac{3}{2}$$

How many groups of 3 different fractions can you choose from the list below to get a sum of $\frac{3}{2}$? Compare your answers with your partner's answers.

$$\frac{1}{8}, \frac{1}{4}, \frac{3}{8}, \frac{1}{2}, \frac{5}{8}, \frac{3}{4}, \frac{7}{8}$$

EXERCISES

Think and Discuss

▶ **CHECK for Understanding**

Logical Reasoning In Exercises 1–3, complete the statement with *sometimes*, *always*, or *never*. Give examples to support your answer.

1. The difference of two fractions that are each less than 1 is ⬚? less than 1.

2. The sum of three fractions that are each less than 1 is ⬚? greater than 1.

3. The least common denominator of two fractions is ⬚? the product of the two denominators.

4. *You Be the Teacher* Give an explanation to a partner of how to add or subtract two fractions with a common denominator *and* with different denominators. Give examples to support your explanations.

5. *Error Analysis* Describe and correct the error.

a. $\dfrac{2}{3} + \dfrac{4}{5} = \dfrac{2}{15} + \dfrac{4}{15} = \dfrac{2+4}{15} = \dfrac{6}{15} = \dfrac{2}{5}$ b. $\dfrac{2}{3} + \dfrac{1}{6} = \dfrac{4}{6} + \dfrac{1}{6} = \dfrac{5}{12}$

In Exercises 6 and 7, write the problem that is represented by the model. Then check your answer by using another method.

6.

7.

8. Give 2 real-life examples of adding or subtracting fractions.

Independent Practice

In Exercises 9–11, copy and complete the model. Then check your answer by using another method.

9.

10.

11.

Add or subtract.

12. $\dfrac{3}{6} + \dfrac{5}{6}$

13. $\dfrac{8}{10} - \dfrac{4}{10}$

14. $\dfrac{1}{2} - \dfrac{2}{5}$

15. $\dfrac{7}{8} + \dfrac{2}{4}$

16. $\dfrac{2}{4} - \dfrac{2}{5}$

17. $\dfrac{6}{9} - \dfrac{1}{6}$

18. $\dfrac{1}{9} + \dfrac{5}{9} + \dfrac{2}{9}$

19. $\dfrac{1}{2} + \dfrac{4}{5} + \dfrac{3}{10}$

Geometry In Exercises 20–22, find the value of *x*.

20. Perimeter = *x*

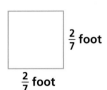

$\frac{2}{7}$ foot

$\frac{2}{7}$ foot

21. Perimeter = *x*

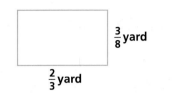

$\frac{3}{8}$ yard

$\frac{2}{3}$ yard

22. Perimeter = $\frac{5}{6}$ in.

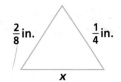

$\frac{2}{8}$ in. $\frac{1}{4}$ in.

x

Algebra and Mental Math In Exercises 23–28, complete the statement. (There may be more than one correct answer.)

23. $\boxed{?} + \frac{3}{7} = 1$

24. $\frac{8}{10} - \boxed{?} = \frac{1}{2}$

25. $\boxed{?} - \boxed{?} = \frac{2}{3}$

26. $\boxed{?} + \boxed{?} = \frac{1}{4}$

27. $\boxed{?} - \frac{1}{4} = \frac{1}{8}$

28. $\frac{1}{3} + \boxed{?} = \frac{1}{2}$

Music In $\frac{4}{4}$ time, the sum of the names of musical notes in a measure must equal 1. The names of 5 types of notes are shown at the right. Decide whether the sum of the given notes is 1.

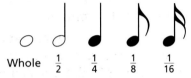

Whole $\frac{1}{2}$ $\frac{1}{4}$ $\frac{1}{8}$ $\frac{1}{16}$

29.

30.

31.

Integrated Review

Making Connections within Mathematics

Use a vertical form to help you find the sum or difference.

32. $9 + 0.9$

33. $18.12 - 5.3$

34. $6.4 - 0.07$

35. $5.46 + 3.08$

36. $10 - 0.06$

37. $20.1 - 19.97$

Exploration and Extension

38. *Building Your Chapter Project*
During your class trip to Washington, D.C., you walked $\frac{2}{6}$ mile to the Washington Monument and $\frac{1}{2}$ mile to the White House. Then you walked $\frac{7}{8}$ mile to the Lincoln Memorial. What is the sum of these three distances? Write an entry about the Lincoln Memorial in your diary.

The Lincoln Memorial has 36 columns—one for each state at the time that Lincoln died.

Materials Needed: paper, colored pencils, markers, pencils or pens

Part A *Adding and Subtracting with a Common Denominator*

Here is a model that shows how to add $1\frac{1}{4}$ and $1\frac{2}{4}$.

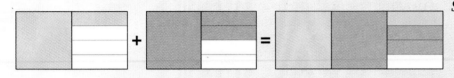

Summary of Steps

$$1\frac{1}{4}$$
$$+\ 1\frac{2}{4}$$
$$\overline{\ 2\frac{3}{4}}$$

1. Draw a model for each problem. Then find the sum or difference.

   a. $1\frac{1}{5} + 1\frac{3}{5}$ b. $1\frac{3}{6} + 1\frac{2}{6}$ c. $2\frac{5}{6} - 1\frac{3}{6}$

2. Use the results of Exercise 1. Explain how to add two mixed numbers that have the same denominator.

3. In the model shown above, what would the sum be if an additional $\frac{1}{4}$ were added?

Part B *Adding and Subtracting with Different Denominators*

Here is a model that shows how to add $1\frac{1}{4}$ and $1\frac{2}{3}$.

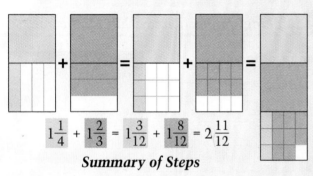

$$1\frac{1}{4} + 1\frac{2}{3} = 1\frac{3}{12} + 1\frac{8}{12} = 2\frac{11}{12}$$

Summary of Steps

4. Use the result shown above to help you find the sum of $1\frac{1}{4}$ and $2\frac{2}{3}$.

5. Draw a model for the problem. Then find the sum or difference.

   a. $1\frac{1}{3} + 1\frac{1}{2}$ b. $1\frac{1}{4} + 1\frac{2}{5}$ c. $2\frac{5}{6} - 1\frac{1}{2}$

6. Use the results of Exercises 4 and 5. Explain how to add two mixed numbers that have different denominators.

7. Write the mixed-number addition problem that the model represents.

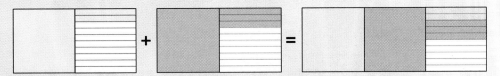

8. Write the decimal addition problem that the above model represents.

9. Write each decimal problem as a mixed-number problem. Solve each version. Compare your answers.

   a. 3.2 + 1.4   b. 1.25 + 1.6   c. 4.7 + 2.5

10. Write the mixed-number subtraction problem that the model represents.

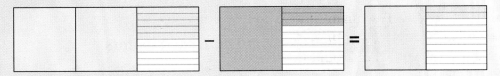

11. Write the decimal subtraction problem that the above model represents.

On Your Own   *Critical Thinking*

Adding and Subtracting Mixed Numbers In Exercises 12–15, draw a sketch of the problem. Then solve.

12. $1\frac{3}{6} + 1\frac{2}{6}$ 13. $2\frac{3}{5} - 1\frac{3}{5}$ 14. $1\frac{1}{2} + 1\frac{1}{4}$ 15. $2\frac{4}{5} - 1\frac{1}{2}$

Estimation In Exercises 16–19, estimate the answer. Explain your reasoning.

16. $8\frac{2}{3} + 4\frac{1}{6}$ 17. $5\frac{4}{5} + 3\frac{1}{4}$ 18. $7\frac{2}{3} - 4\frac{1}{4}$ 19. $2\frac{7}{8} - 1\frac{5}{6}$

20. *Reasoning* Write the problem 2.8 − 1.4 in vertical form. Then solve the problem. How does "lining up the decimal points" relate to the subtraction problem $2\frac{8}{10} - 1\frac{4}{10}$?

7.4

Adding and Subtracting Mixed Numbers

What you should learn:

Goal 1 How to add and subtract mixed numbers

Goal 2 How to use addition and subtraction of mixed numbers to solve real-life problems

Why you should learn it:

Addition and subtraction of mixed numbers is often used in woodworking. An example is finding dimensions to complete a project.

Study Tip

You can write addition and subtraction problems with fractions vertically. Then you can see that the whole numbers "line up" and the fractions "line up."

$$8\frac{2}{6}$$
$$+\,4\frac{1}{6}$$
$$\overline{12\frac{3}{6}}$$

This is similar to lining up the decimal points when you add or subtract decimals.

Goal 1 Add and Subtract Mixed Numbers

In Lab 7.4, you may have discovered the following rules for adding and subtracting mixed numbers.

> ### Adding and Subtracting Mixed Numbers
>
> To **add** or **subtract** two mixed numbers, (1) add or subtract the fractions, (2) add or subtract the whole numbers, and (3) simplify as necessary.

Example 1 *Common Denominators*

a. (1) Add fractions. (3) Simplify mixed number.

$$3\frac{5}{8} + 4\frac{6}{8} = 7\frac{11}{8} = 7 + \frac{8}{8} + \frac{3}{8} = 8\frac{3}{8}$$

(2) Add whole numbers.

b. (1) Subtract fractions.   (3) Simplify mixed number.

$$5\frac{7}{9} - 3\frac{4}{9} = 2\frac{3}{9} = 2\frac{1}{3}$$

(2) Subtract whole numbers. ∎

Example 2 *Different Denominators*

a. (1) Add fractions. (3) Simplify mixed number.

$$8\frac{1}{3} + 4\frac{1}{6} = 8\frac{2}{6} + 4\frac{1}{6} = 12\frac{3}{6} = 12\frac{1}{2}$$

(2) Add whole numbers.

b. (1) Subtract fractions.

$$12\frac{4}{5} - 7\frac{1}{2} = 12\frac{8}{10} - 7\frac{5}{10} = 5\frac{3}{10}$$

(2) Subtract whole numbers. ∎

Example 3 *Subtracting Mixed Numbers*

Real Life
Woodworking

You are designing a wooden box with an inlaid design. Three measurements of the box lid are shown below. What is the height of the flowered part of the lid?

$1\frac{3}{8}$ in.

$4\frac{1}{2}$ in.

$1\frac{3}{4}$ in.

An inlaid wood design is usually made with many kinds of wood. The different types of wood are set into a surface in a decorative design.

Solution One way to answer the question is to first add the heights of the top and bottom parts of the lid.

$$1\frac{3}{8} + 1\frac{3}{4} = 1\frac{3}{8} + 1\frac{6}{8} = 2\frac{9}{8} = 2 + \frac{8}{8} + \frac{1}{8} = 3\frac{1}{8}$$

The sum of the heights of the top and bottom parts is $3\frac{1}{8}$ inches. To find the height of the flowered part of the lid, subtract $3\frac{1}{8}$ inches from $4\frac{1}{2}$ inches (the overall height of lid).

$$4\frac{1}{2} - 3\frac{1}{8} = 4\frac{4}{8} - 3\frac{1}{8} = 1\frac{3}{8}$$

The height of the flowered part is $1\frac{3}{8}$ inches. ∎

Communicating about MATHEMATICS

Sharing Ideas about the Lesson

Cooperative Learning

Partner Activity Use a ruler to check the result obtained in Example 3. Draw a line segment that is about 5 inches long. Then mark off three line segments whose lengths are $1\frac{3}{8}$ inches, $1\frac{3}{8}$ inches, and $1\frac{3}{4}$ inches. Use your ruler to find the total length of the three segments. Check your work by adding the three mixed numbers.

EXERCISES

Think and Discuss

▶**CHECK for Understanding**

1. *Measurement*   Use a ruler to find the sum and difference of $5\frac{5}{8}$ and $3\frac{1}{4}$. Sketch and measure line segments of each length. Explain your methods.

In Exercises 2 and 3, describe each step of the solution.

2. $2\frac{5}{7} + 6\frac{4}{7} = 8\frac{9}{7}$

$= 8 + \frac{7}{7} + \frac{2}{7}$

$= 9\frac{2}{7}$

3. $4\frac{5}{6} - 2\frac{1}{3} = 4\frac{5}{6} - 2\frac{2}{6}$

$= 2\frac{3}{6}$

$= 2\frac{1}{2}$

Copy and complete the model. Then check your answer using another method.

4.
+ = ?

5.
− = ?

Independent Practice

Estimation   In Exercises 6–9, match the sum or difference with the numbers you can use to make an estimate.

a. $9 - 1$ b. $4 + 2$ c. $7 + 1$ d. $5\frac{1}{2} - \frac{1}{2}$

6. $3\frac{9}{10} + 2\frac{1}{8}$ 7. $6\frac{5}{6} + \frac{7}{8}$ 8. $5\frac{4}{9} - \frac{4}{7}$ 9. $9\frac{1}{6} - \frac{7}{8}$

In Exercises 10–13, write the problem represented by the phrase. Then solve the problem.

10. The sum of two and three fifths and five and one fourth.

11. The difference of six and eight ninths and two and four ninths

12. The difference of seven and three sixths and four and one sixth

13. The sum of three and six eighths and one and one half

Add or subtract.

14. $7\frac{3}{5} + 5\frac{1}{5}$ 15. $6\frac{5}{8} - 3\frac{1}{8}$ 16. $8\frac{2}{3} - 1\frac{2}{9}$ 17. $2\frac{7}{10} + 8\frac{1}{2}$

18. $3\frac{2}{3} + 4\frac{3}{4}$ 19. $6\frac{2}{5} - 2\frac{1}{3}$ 20. $9\frac{3}{6} - 4\frac{1}{4}$ 21. $6\frac{5}{8} + 3\frac{1}{6}$

Describing Patterns   In Exercises 22–24, solve each problem. Look for patterns. Then name the problem that does not belong in the list. Explain why it does not belong.

22. $2\frac{1}{6} + 7\frac{2}{3}$, $10\frac{3}{8} - 1\frac{1}{4}$, $6\frac{7}{9} - 3\frac{1}{2}$, $5\frac{6}{7} + 3\frac{3}{7}$

23. $4\frac{7}{8} - 1\frac{3}{8}$, $7\frac{3}{4} - 4\frac{2}{4}$, $6\frac{5}{9} - 2\frac{2}{9}$, $5\frac{5}{6} - 3\frac{1}{6}$

24. $1\frac{2}{3} + 3\frac{2}{3}$, $9\frac{3}{4} + 2\frac{3}{8}$, $4\frac{7}{9} + 4\frac{1}{3}$, $6\frac{2}{5} + 5\frac{1}{2}$

Algebra and Mental Math   In Exercises 25–30, solve.

25. $7\frac{6}{7} - x = 1\frac{6}{7}$

26. $y + 1\frac{1}{3} = 10\frac{2}{3}$

27. $m + 2\frac{1}{8} = 3\frac{3}{8}$

28. $4\frac{3}{4} - n = 4\frac{1}{2}$

29. $3\frac{4}{5} + a = 4$

30. $4\frac{1}{2} - b = 2$

Finding a Pattern   In Exercises 31–33, solve each problem. Then describe any patterns that you see.

31. $6\frac{7}{8} - 5\frac{1}{8} = \boxed{?}$

$6\frac{7}{8} - 5\frac{1}{4} = \boxed{?}$

$6\frac{7}{8} - 5\frac{3}{8} = \boxed{?}$

32. $9\frac{5}{6} - 1\frac{1}{6} = \boxed{?}$

$9\frac{5}{6} - 1\frac{1}{3} = \boxed{?}$

$9\frac{5}{6} - 1\frac{1}{2} = \boxed{?}$

33. $12 - 3\frac{4}{5} = \boxed{?}$

$12 - 3\frac{3}{5} = \boxed{?}$

$12 - 3\frac{2}{5} = \boxed{?}$

Number Riddles   In Exercises 34 and 35, solve the riddle.

34. I am a number between 4 and 5. When added to myself, I equal a whole number. What number am I?

35. The sum of two mixed numbers is $5\frac{4}{5}$. The difference of the numbers is $1\frac{2}{5}$. Both numbers have a denominator of 5. Find the numbers.

36. *Cooking*   You are making tuna noodle casserole. The recipe calls for $6\frac{1}{8}$ oz of tuna. You want to double the recipe. How many ounces of tuna should you use?

37. *Gymnastics*   The diagram below shows a set of uneven parallel bars, used in gymnastics. What is the height from the floor to the lower bar?

Shannon Miller, 17, won more medals than any other United States athlete at the 1992 Summer Olympics. One was a silver medal in the balance beam.

Match the mixed number with its improper fraction.

a. $\frac{26}{8}$ b. $\frac{20}{8}$ c. $\frac{15}{8}$ d. $\frac{41}{8}$ e. $\frac{38}{8}$

38. $4\frac{3}{4}$ **39.** $2\frac{1}{2}$ **40.** $3\frac{2}{8}$ **41.** $1\frac{7}{8}$ **42.** $5\frac{1}{8}$

Exploration and Extension

43. *Building Your Chapter Project* On your class trip to Washington, D.C., you visit the United States Capitol. The bronze Statue of Freedom on top of the Capitol stands $6\frac{1}{2}$ yards tall. The building portion of the Capitol is $93\frac{1}{6}$ yards tall. How tall is the United States Capitol including the statue? The average height of a sixth grader is 4 feet 10 inches. In your diary, explain how to estimate how many "sixth graders tall" the Capitol is. Also, record your estimate.

The United States Capitol is the building where Congress meets. It has 540 rooms which contain paintings of events in American history.

Mixed REVIEW

You are shown a model for a portion of a whole. Describe a model for the whole. **(3.3)**

1.

[model of 6 squares] } 0.6

2.

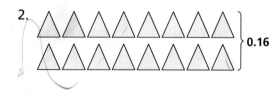

} 0.16

Statistics Use a calculator to find the mean. **(5.3)**

3. 56, 89, 23 **4.** 111, 123, 90 **5.** 192, 533, 250 **6.** 89, 95, 77, 87

Simplify the fraction. **(6.4)**

7. $\frac{6}{54}$ **8.** $\frac{15}{30}$ **9.** $\frac{35}{7}$ **10.** $\frac{12}{60}$

Write the mixed number as an improper fraction. **(6.6)**

11. $2\frac{4}{5}$ **12.** $4\frac{1}{9}$ **13.** $3\frac{11}{12}$ **14.** $6\frac{7}{10}$

Take this test as you would take a test in class. The answers to the exercises are given in the back of the book.

In Exercises 1 and 2, measure the length of the object to the nearest $\frac{1}{8}$ inch. Write the length as a mixed number and as an improper fraction. **(7.1)**

1.

2.

3. *History*   The tallest president was Abraham Lincoln. His height was 6 feet 4 inches. Write Lincoln's height in inches. **(7.1)**

In Exercises 4–7, decide whether the fractions are equivalent. **(7.2)**

4. $\frac{9}{36}, \frac{1}{3}$

5. $\frac{10}{16}, \frac{15}{24}$

6. $\frac{15}{25}, \frac{8}{10}$

7. $\frac{18}{27}, \frac{6}{9}$

In Exercises 8–13, match the pair of fractions with their description. **(7.2–7.4)**

a. Difference is four sevenths.   b. Both can be simplified.   c. They are equivalent.

d. Both are mixed numbers.   e. Sum is 2.   f. Sum is 1.

8. $\frac{7}{9}, 1\frac{2}{9}$

9. $\frac{3}{8}, \frac{9}{24}$

10. $1\frac{2}{3}, 2\frac{1}{8}$

11. $\frac{5}{7}, \frac{1}{7}$

12. $\frac{1}{4}, \frac{6}{8}$

13. $\frac{4}{12}, \frac{6}{12}$

In Exercises 14–22 add or subtract. **(7.3, 7.4)**

14. $\frac{7}{12} + \frac{5}{12}$

15. $\frac{11}{15} - \frac{7}{15}$

16. $\frac{1}{2} - \frac{1}{9}$

17. $\frac{1}{6} + \frac{3}{4}$

18. $\frac{1}{2} + \frac{1}{3} + \frac{1}{6}$

19. $\frac{1}{12} + \frac{1}{6} + \frac{1}{8}$

20. $3\frac{1}{8} + 2\frac{7}{8}$

21. $4\frac{1}{3} + 3\frac{1}{6}$

22. $5\frac{7}{10} - 1\frac{1}{10}$

23. *Teeth*   When your cousin was six years old, she lost one fifth of her baby teeth. When she was seven years old, she lost one fourth of her baby teeth. During the two years, did she lose more or less than half her baby teeth? Explain your reasoning. **(7.3)**

Lab 7.5 Connections to Algebra:

Investigating Number Properties

Materials Needed: paper, colored pencils or markers, pencils or pens

Part A *Addition and Order*

1. Write the addition problem shown. Then write the sum.

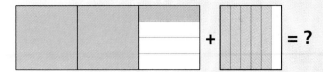

2. Write the addition problem shown. Then write the sum.

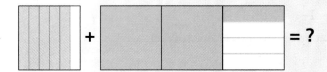

3. Compare your results from Exercises 1 and 2. What can you conclude?

Part B *Subtraction, Addition, and Order*

4. Your friend drew the following model for the problem "subtract $1\frac{2}{3}$ from $2\frac{3}{4}$." Is the model correct? Explain.

> When you subtract numbers, the order is important. For instance, $5 - 3$ is not the same problem as $3 - 5$.

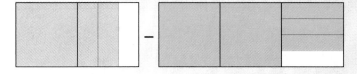

5. The word *commute* means to change the order. Addition has a Commutative Property. Subtraction does not.

> **Commutative Property of Addition** You can add two numbers in either order. For instance, $3 + 5$ and $5 + 3$ have the same sum, which is 8.

Give an example of the Commutative Property of Addition that uses **(a)** a proper fraction and a mixed number and **(b)** two mixed numbers.

Part C *Subtracting with Whole Numbers* Here is a model for the subtraction problem $2 - 1\frac{1}{4}$.

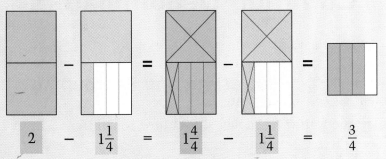

$$2 \quad - \quad 1\frac{1}{4} \quad = \quad 1\frac{4}{4} \quad - \quad 1\frac{1}{4} \quad = \quad \frac{3}{4}$$

Summary of Steps

6. Draw models to help you solve each of the following. Then write a summary of steps for each problem.

   a. $3\frac{1}{2} - 2$ b. $2\frac{3}{4} - 1$ c. $2 - 1\frac{1}{3}$ d. $4 - 1\frac{2}{5}$

   With others in your group, discuss how the problems in (a) and (b) differ from those in (c) and (d).

On Your Own   *Critical Thinking*

7. *Subtraction and Order* Choose the correct model for the problem "subtract $1\frac{1}{2}$ from 2." Then solve the problem.

   a. 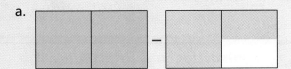   b.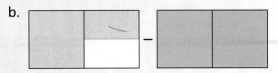

In Exercises 8–11, match the subtraction problem with the first step for solving it. Then draw a model to help you finish solving the problem.

   a. Rewrite 1 as $\frac{3}{3}$.   b. Rewrite 1 as $\frac{2}{2}$.   c. Rewrite 1 as $\frac{4}{4}$.   d. Rewrite 1 as $\frac{5}{5}$.

   8. $1 - \frac{4}{5}$ 9. $1 - \frac{1}{3}$ 10. $1 - \frac{1}{2}$ 11. $1 - \frac{3}{4}$

12. Use the results of Exercises 7–11 to explain how to subtract a fraction or a mixed number from a whole number.

7.5

Subtracting and Regrouping: Common Denominators

What you should learn:

Goal 1 How to regroup in order to subtract

Goal 2 How to use subtracting and regrouping to solve real-life problems

Why you should learn it:

Knowing how to regroup when subtracting can help you when budgeting your time. An example is finding the amount of free time you have on a class trip.

Goal 1 Subtracting and Regrouping

The following model shows how to subtract $\frac{3}{5}$ from $2\frac{2}{5}$.

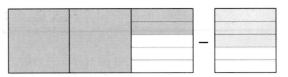

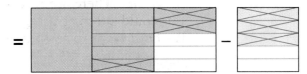

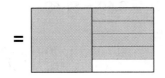

Summary of Steps

$$2\frac{2}{5} - \frac{3}{5} = 1\frac{7}{5} - \frac{3}{5} = 1\frac{4}{5}$$

Rewriting $2\frac{2}{5}$ as $1\frac{7}{5}$ is called **regrouping.** Notice how regrouping is used in the examples below.

Example 1 *Subtracting and Regrouping*

a. $3 - 1\frac{3}{4} = 2\frac{4}{4} - 1\frac{3}{4}$ *Regroup 3 as $2\frac{4}{4}$.*

$= 1\frac{1}{4}$ *Subtract mixed numbers.*

b. $2\frac{1}{3} - \frac{2}{3} = 1\frac{4}{3} - \frac{2}{3}$ *Regroup $2\frac{1}{3}$ as $1\frac{4}{3}$.*

$= 1\frac{2}{3}$ *Subtract numbers.*

c. $5\frac{1}{4} - 2\frac{3}{4} = 4\frac{5}{4} - 2\frac{3}{4}$ *Regroup $5\frac{1}{4}$ as $4\frac{5}{4}$.*

$= 2\frac{2}{4}$ *Subtract mixed numbers.*

$= 2\frac{1}{2}$ *Simplify.*   ∎

Study Tip

In the subtraction problem

$$4 - 2\frac{5}{8}$$

there are many ways to regroup 4. However, regrouping it as $3\frac{8}{8}$ is best for this problem. Why? What is the answer to this subtraction problem?

Real Life
Checking Accounts

Example 2   *Comparing Check Amounts*

Roberta wrote two checks to Susan. How much more is the larger amount than the smaller amount?

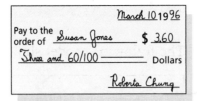

Need To Know

The amount of a check is written two ways: as a decimal and in words with a fractional amount.

Solution   There are two ways to answer this question. You could subtract using decimals or using fractions. Try both ways to see if you get the same amount.

Using Decimals:

$$5.20 - 3.60 = \$1.60 \qquad \text{\textit{Subtract decimals.}}$$

Using Fractions:

$$5\frac{20}{100} - 3\frac{60}{100} = 4\frac{120}{100} - 3\frac{60}{100} \qquad \textit{Regroup } 5\frac{20}{100} \textit{ as } 4\frac{120}{100}.$$

$$= 1\frac{60}{100} \text{ dollars} \qquad \textit{Subtract mixed numbers.}$$

In both cases, the difference is $1.60. The larger amount is $1.60 more than the smaller amount.   ∎

Communicating about MATHEMATICS

Cooperative Learning

▶ **Sharing Ideas about the Lesson**

Partner Activity Two check amounts are shown below. How much more is the larger amount than the smaller amount? Answer the question using decimals *and* fractions. Compare your results with your partner's results.

Check 1: $6.35 or Six and $\frac{35}{100}$ dollars

Check 2: $8.10 or Eight and $\frac{10}{100}$ dollars

EXERCISES

Think and Discuss

▶ CHECK for Understanding

In Exercises 1–3, match the subtraction problem with the best way to regroup the whole number.

a. $2\frac{3}{3}$ b. $2\frac{8}{8}$ c. $2\frac{12}{12}$

1. $3 - 1\frac{5}{8}$ 2. $3 - \frac{11}{12}$ 3. $3 - \frac{2}{3}$

4. Subtract $1.35 from $5.00 using fractions and then using decimals. Which method do you like better? Why?

In Exercises 5 and 6, each quilt contains $4\frac{1}{8}$ square yards of fabric. How many square yards of fabric are *not* blue?

5.

$1\frac{3}{8}$ square yards are blue

6.

$2\frac{5}{8}$ square yards are blue

Independent Practice

In Exercises 7–10, complete the statement using regrouping.

7. $3 = 2\frac{\boxed{?}}{8}$ 8. $4\frac{1}{6} = 3\frac{\boxed{?}}{6}$ 9. $6\frac{1}{4} = 5\frac{\boxed{?}}{4}$ 10. $2\frac{3}{5} = 1\frac{\boxed{?}}{5}$

In Exercises 11–14, complete the statement using $<$, $>$, or $=$.

11. $4\frac{3}{4}$ ⓐ $3\frac{7}{4}$ 12. $5\frac{1}{6}$ ⓐ $4\frac{6}{6}$ 13. $3\frac{4}{8}$ ⓐ $3\frac{12}{8}$ 14. $6\frac{3}{5}$ ⓐ $5\frac{8}{5}$

15. *Sports and Fitness* Use the diagram of a regulation basketball court. Find the difference between the length and the width of the court.

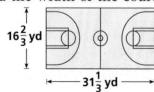

Basketball was invented in 1891 and was originally played with a soccer ball.

In Exercises 16–23, subtract. Then simplify, if possible.

16. $3 - 1\frac{1}{8}$ 17. $4 - 1\frac{7}{12}$ 18. $3\frac{1}{4} - \frac{3}{4}$ 19. $2\frac{2}{5} - \frac{3}{5}$

20. $1\frac{5}{8} - \frac{7}{8}$ 21. $7\frac{4}{9} - 5\frac{5}{9}$ 22. $6\frac{1}{6} - 3\frac{5}{6}$ 23. $9\frac{3}{10} - 6\frac{7}{10}$

You Be the Teacher You asked four music students to keep track of the number of hours they practiced during the week. Find the difference between the practice times for the students.

24. Thelma and Leroy

25. Thelma and Caitlin

26. Arnold and Leroy

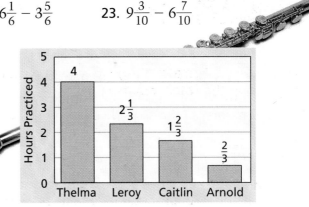

Algebra In Exercises 27–30, evaluate the expression when $n = 2\frac{3}{5}$.

27. $4 - n$ 28. $n - \frac{4}{5}$ 29. $4\frac{1}{5} - n$ 30. $n - 1\frac{4}{5}$

31. *Gym Bags* You and your friend are buying canvas to make gym bags. Each bag uses $2\frac{5}{8}$ yards. The store has $5\frac{3}{8}$ yards of blue canvas. If you buy enough for a gym bag, will there be enough canvas for your friend to make a blue bag also? Explain.

32. *Horseback Riding* You are horseback riding on a 6-mile trail. The trail is marked every $\frac{1}{10}$ mile. The marker you have just passed says $3\frac{7}{10}$ miles. How much farther do you need to ride? Solve the problem using both fractions and decimals.

Integrated Review   *Making Connections within Mathematics*

Fraction Words Make a new word using fractional parts of words. For example, the first $\frac{2}{5}$ of *green* plus the last $\frac{3}{4}$ of *neat* makes the word *great*.

33. First $\frac{3}{6}$ of *muscle*, last $\frac{2}{5}$ of *tonic*   34. First $\frac{2}{5}$ of *money*, last $\frac{3}{5}$ of *amuse*

35. Make a fraction word of your own.

Exploration and Extension

36. *Building Your Chapter Project* On your class trip, you have 4 hours of free time. You want to view the Vietnam Veterans Memorial. It takes you $1\frac{1}{8}$ hours to walk from the Capitol. How much time do you have left? Write in your diary about what you might do during your free time.

Materials Needed: paper, colored pencils, markers, pencils or pens

Part A *Subtracting and Regrouping*   Here is a model that shows how to subtract mixed numbers that have different denominators.

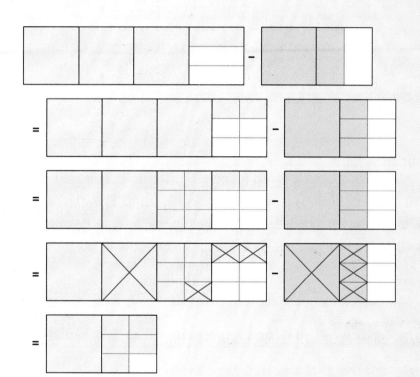

Steps

1. *Original Problem*

$$3\frac{1}{3} - 1\frac{1}{2}$$

2. *Rename with common denominator.*

$$3\frac{2}{6} - 1\frac{3}{6}$$

3. *Regroup.*

$$2\frac{8}{6} - 1\frac{3}{6}$$

4. *Subtract 1 whole piece and 3 sixths pieces.*

5. *Answer*

$$1\frac{5}{6}$$

Summary of Steps

$$3\frac{1}{3} - 1\frac{1}{2} = 3\frac{2}{6} - 1\frac{3}{6} = 2\frac{8}{6} - 1\frac{3}{6} = 1\frac{5}{6}$$

1. Explain Step 2. Why is 6 used as a common denominator?

2. Explain Step 3. Why is $3\frac{2}{6}$ regrouped as $2\frac{8}{6}$?

3. Explain Step 4. Which parts of the model are crossed out? Why?

4. Explain Step 5. What would the answer be if it were written as an improper fraction?

Part B *Subtracting and Regrouping*

5. Write the summary of steps for the subtraction problem that is modeled below. Explain each step.

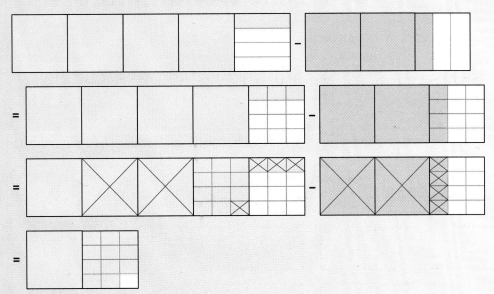

Part C *Subtracting and Regrouping*

6. Use a model to help you solve each subtraction problem. Write a summary of steps.

   a. $3\frac{1}{4} - 2\frac{2}{3}$ b. $2\frac{2}{5} - 1\frac{3}{4}$ c. $4\frac{1}{3} - 3\frac{3}{4}$ d. $6\frac{1}{6} - 4\frac{1}{4}$ e. $5\frac{2}{5} - 3\frac{1}{2}$

7. With others in your group, discuss how to tell that a subtraction problem needs renaming (with a common denominator) *and* regrouping.

On Your Own   *Critical Thinking*

Match the subtraction problem with the phrase that describes it. Then use a model to help you solve the problem. For each problem, write a summary of steps.

a. Needs renaming but *not* regrouping.   b. Needs regrouping but *not* renaming.

c. Needs renaming *and* regrouping.   d. Doesn't need renaming or regrouping.

8. $3\frac{2}{3} - \frac{1}{3}$ 9. $3\frac{3}{4} - 2\frac{2}{3}$ 10. $3\frac{2}{3} - 2\frac{3}{4}$ 11. $3\frac{1}{3} - 2\frac{2}{3}$

7.6 Subtracting and Regrouping: Different Denominators

What you should learn:

Goal 1 How to regroup to subtract

Goal 2 How to use subtraction and regrouping to solve real-life problems

Why you should learn it:

Subtraction and regrouping can help you compare measurements. An example is comparing the lengths of birds.

Goal 1 Subtracting and Regrouping

Example 1 Subtracting, Renaming, Regrouping

$$4\frac{1}{2} - 2\frac{5}{8} = 4\frac{4}{8} - 2\frac{5}{8} \qquad \textit{Rename } \frac{1}{2} \textit{ as } \frac{4}{8}.$$

$$= 3\frac{12}{8} - 2\frac{5}{8} \qquad \textit{Regroup } 4\frac{4}{8} \textit{ as } 3\frac{12}{8}.$$

$$= 1\frac{7}{8} \qquad \textit{Subtract mixed numbers.} \blacksquare$$

The subtraction problem in Example 1 can also be solved with a vertical form. Which form do you like best?

Rename Regroup

$$
\begin{array}{ccc}
4\frac{1}{2} & 4\frac{4}{8} & 3\frac{12}{8} \\
-2\frac{5}{8} & -2\frac{5}{8} & -2\frac{5}{8} \\
\hline
 & & 1\frac{7}{8}
\end{array}
$$

In this example, notice how you can tell that you need to rename *and* regroup.

1. You need to rename because the denominators are different.
2. You need to regroup because $\frac{4}{8}$ is less than $\frac{5}{8}$.

Example 2 Subtracting, Renaming, Regrouping

$$10\frac{1}{6} - 8\frac{1}{4} = 10\frac{2}{12} - 8\frac{3}{12} \qquad \textit{Rename with a common denominator of 12.}$$

$$= 9\frac{14}{12} - 8\frac{3}{12} \qquad \textit{Regroup } 10\frac{2}{12} \textit{ as } 9\frac{14}{12}.$$

$$= 1\frac{11}{12} \qquad \textit{Subtract mixed numbers.} \blacksquare$$

Solving Real-Life Problems

| Example **3** | *Subtracting, Renaming, Regrouping* |

The measure on each wrench represents its bolt width in inches. How much wider is the larger measure than the smaller measure?

$\frac{7}{8}$"

$1\frac{1}{16}$"

Solution To find the difference in the measures, subtract $\frac{7}{8}$ from $1\frac{1}{16}$.

$$1\frac{1}{16} - \frac{7}{8} = 1\frac{1}{16} - \frac{14}{16} \qquad \textit{Rename } \frac{7}{8} \textit{ as } \frac{14}{16}.$$

$$= \frac{17}{16} - \frac{14}{16} \qquad \textit{Regroup } 1\frac{1}{16} \textit{ as } \frac{17}{16}.$$

$$= \frac{3}{16} \qquad \textit{Subtract fractions.}$$

The measure of the larger wrench is $\frac{3}{16}$ inch more than the smaller wrench's measure. ■

Real Life
Home Repair

Wrenches with metric measures are needed when dealing with foreign machine parts.

Communicating about **MATHEMATICS**

Cooperative Learning

▶ **Sharing Ideas about the Lesson**

Partner Activity You bought a set of wrenches that have the following measures (in inches). Which pairs of wrenches have measures that differ by $\frac{5}{16}$ inch? Explain how you made your choices.

$$\frac{3}{8}, \frac{7}{16}, \frac{1}{2}, \frac{9}{16}, \frac{5}{8}, \frac{11}{16}, \frac{3}{4}, \frac{13}{16}, \frac{7}{8}, \frac{15}{16}, 1, 1\frac{1}{16}, 1\frac{1}{8}, 1\frac{3}{16}, 1\frac{1}{4}$$

EXERCISES

Think and Discuss

▷ **CHECK for Understanding**

In Exercises 1–3, decide whether you need to rename or regroup. Explain your reasoning. Then solve.

1. $2\frac{2}{3} - \frac{1}{4}$ 2. $1\frac{1}{8} - \frac{5}{8}$ 3. $3\frac{7}{12} - 2\frac{1}{3}$

4. *Reasoning*   Give an example of a subtraction problem in which you need to regroup but not rename.

5. The steps below are those used to solve $5\frac{2}{3} - 3\frac{4}{5}$. Put the steps in the correct order.

   a. $1\frac{13}{15}$ b. $5\frac{10}{15} - 3\frac{12}{15}$ c. $4\frac{25}{15} - 3\frac{12}{15}$ d. $5\frac{2}{3} - 3\frac{4}{5}$

Independent Practice

Reasoning   In Exercises 6–9, match the problem with the phrase that describes it.

   a. Needs renaming only.   b. Needs regrouping only.

   c. Does not need renaming or regrouping.   d. Needs both renaming and regrouping.

6. $4\frac{5}{16} - 3\frac{7}{8}$ 7. $4\frac{5}{16} - 3\frac{3}{16}$ 8. $4\frac{5}{16} - 3\frac{7}{16}$ 9. $4\frac{5}{16} - 3\frac{1}{8}$

In Exercises 10–17, subtract. Then simplify, if possible.

10. $7\frac{2}{5} - 5\frac{7}{10}$ 11. $3\frac{3}{8} - \frac{7}{12}$ 12. $4\frac{3}{10} - 2\frac{4}{5}$ 13. $5\frac{5}{12} - 2\frac{7}{8}$

14. $2\frac{1}{9} - 1\frac{2}{3}$ 15. $12\frac{4}{15} - \frac{4}{5}$ 16. $15\frac{1}{16} - 12\frac{3}{4}$ 17. $14\frac{4}{9} - 9\frac{11}{18}$

Geography   The bar graph at the right shows the approximate heights in miles of the highest points in four states. Find the difference in the heights. *(Source: United States Geological Survey)*

18. Alaska and West Virginia

19. Oregon and North Carolina

20. North Carolina and West Virginia

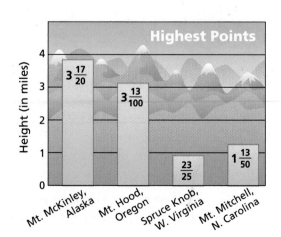

The table at the right shows the lengths of 4 birds. Find the difference in lengths of the given birds. (*Source: Peterson Field Guide*)

Snow Bunting	Ruby-throated Humming-bird	Magnolia Warbler	Saw-whet Owl
$7\frac{1}{4}"$	$3\frac{3}{4}"$	$4\frac{3}{4}"$	$8\frac{1}{2}"$

21. Saw-whet owl and ruby-throated hummingbird

22. Snow bunting and magnolia warbler

23. Saw-whet owl and snow bunting

24. Magnolia warbler and ruby-throated hummingbird

Community Service   The table below shows the hours you spent as a volunteer, reading to preschoolers.

Week	1	2	3	4
Hours	$1\frac{2}{3}$	$1\frac{1}{3}$	$1\frac{1}{6}$	$2\frac{1}{6}$

25. How much longer did you spend during Week 4 than Week 2?

26. You agreed to volunteer 10 hours during a 5-week period. How many hours do you need to volunteer during Week 5?

Reading to children helps them develop their vocabulary which can make learning to read easier.

Integrated Review

Making Connections within Mathematics

27. *Fraction Puzzle*   Copy and cut out the squares. Fit the pieces together so the edges that touch name equivalent fractions.

	$\frac{2}{4}$		2		3			$\frac{6}{16}$		$\frac{6}{8}$		$\frac{10}{12}$		$1\frac{1}{2}$	
1		$\frac{4}{12}$ $\frac{2}{10}$		$\frac{1}{8}$		$\frac{3}{7}$		$\frac{2}{3}$ $\frac{10}{16}$		5	$\frac{12}{24}$		$\frac{1}{5}$ $\frac{6}{14}$		$4\frac{3}{3}$
	$\frac{1}{7}$		$\frac{3}{2}$			$\frac{1}{4}$		$\frac{2}{6}$				$2\frac{6}{6}$			
$\frac{2}{12}$		$\frac{8}{10}$ $\frac{5}{3}$	$\frac{3}{3}$ $\frac{2}{16}$	$\frac{2}{14}$	5 $\frac{1}{8}$ $\frac{1}{2}$	$\frac{1}{3}$	$\frac{4}{6}$	$\frac{17}{9}$	$\frac{2}{8}$	$\frac{4}{5}$ $1\frac{8}{9}$		$\frac{1}{6}$ $\frac{1}{3}$	$\frac{6}{10}$	
	$\frac{3}{5}$	$\frac{6}{3}$		$\frac{3}{4}$				$1\frac{2}{3}$	$\frac{5}{6}$		$\frac{1}{2}$		$\frac{3}{8}$	

Exploration and Extension

28. *Building Your Chapter Project*   On the last evening of your trip, you buy souvenirs. At the shop, you see a figure of the Washington Monument that is $8\frac{3}{8}$ inches tall for $7.29. You then see a figure that is $6\frac{3}{4}$ inches tall for $6.49. Find the difference in the heights and the difference in the prices. Describe in your diary the souvenirs you might buy.

7.7

More Problem Solving with Fractions and Decimals

What you should learn:

Goal 1 How to use addition and subtraction of fractions to solve problems

Goal 2 How to use addition and subtraction of decimals to solve problems

Why you should learn it:

Knowing how to add and subtract fractions and decimals can help you find the value of stocks in the stock market.

Goal 1 Using Fractions to Solve Problems

Example 1 *Following a Treasure Map*

You are following a treasure map on a deserted island.

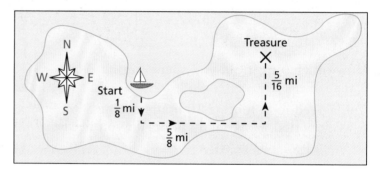

a. Find the total distance to the treasure.

b. At the treasure, how much farther north are you than when you began?

Solution

a. To find the total distance, add the three fractions.

$$\frac{1}{8} + \frac{5}{8} + \frac{5}{16} = \frac{2}{16} + \frac{10}{16} + \frac{5}{16}$$

$$= \frac{2 + 10 + 5}{16}$$

$$= \frac{17}{16}$$

The total distance is $\frac{17}{16}$ miles or $1\frac{1}{16}$ miles.

b. To find how much farther north you are, subtract the distance traveled south from the distance traveled north.

$$\frac{5}{16} - \frac{1}{8} = \frac{5}{16} - \frac{2}{16} = \frac{5 - 2}{16} = \frac{3}{16}$$

You are $\frac{3}{16}$ mile farther north than when you began. ∎

Real Life
Treasure Hunting

Example **2** *Getting the Treasure Back Home*

The buried treasure is a chest that contains 82 gold bars and 15 silver bars. The weight of each bar is shown below. Your boat can hold up to 2000 pounds more. Can you take all the treasure in your boat?

Gold Bar: $22\frac{1}{4}$ pounds   Silver Bar: $5\frac{1}{2}$ pounds

Treasure can be buried on land, or sunk in the ocean. This sunken treasure dates back to the 1600's.

Solution   One way to answer the question is to rewrite the weights as decimals. Each gold bar weighs 22.25 pounds and each silver bar weighs 5.5 pounds.

$$\text{Weight of gold bars} = 82 \times 22.25$$
$$= 1824.5 \text{ pounds}$$

$$\text{Weight of silver bars} = 15 \times 5.5$$
$$= 82.5 \text{ pounds}$$

The total weight of the treasure is

$$\text{Total weight} = 1824.5 + 82.5 = 1907 \text{ pounds.}$$

So you can take all of the treasure back in your boat! ∎

Communicating about **MATHEMATICS**

Cooperative Learning

▶ **Sharing Ideas about the Lesson**

Extending the Example A pound of gold is worth about $5400, and a pound of silver about $84.

A. How much is your treasure worth? Explain.

B. Two friends have come with you on your treasure hunt. You agree that each person will receive $\frac{1}{3}$ of the treasure. How much is each person's share worth?

EXERCISES

Guided Practice

Think and Discuss

▶ **CHECK for Understanding**

In Exercises 1–6, match the problem with its answer.

a. $1\frac{1}{2}$ b. $1\frac{3}{4}$ c. $6\frac{7}{8}$ d. $3\frac{2}{5}$ e. $1\frac{2}{5}$ f. $2\frac{7}{8}$

1. $\frac{3}{5} + \frac{4}{5}$ 2. $2\frac{5}{8} + 4\frac{1}{4}$ 3. $6\frac{7}{10} - 3\frac{3}{10}$ 4. $5 - 2\frac{1}{8}$ 5. $1\frac{9}{10} - \frac{2}{5}$ 6. $7\frac{1}{4} - 5\frac{2}{4}$

Super Bowl The circle graph at the right shows how the tickets are divided up for the Super Bowl. *(Source: National Football League)*

7. Which portion represents the largest number of tickets: the NFL office *or* the remaining teams? Use a model to support your answer.

8. What fraction shows the difference of the tickets of the NFC and AFC champions and the remaining teams? Explain.

9. What is the sum of all the fractions in the circle graph? Explain.

Super Bowl Tickets

NFL Office $\frac{1}{4}$

Host City $\frac{1}{10}$

$\frac{3}{10}$ Divided Among Remaining Teams

$\frac{14}{40}$ NFC and AFC Champions

Independent Practice

The Stock Market On Monday, January 16, 1995, the price of the stock for *Nike Company* was $72\frac{1}{8}$ dollars per share. On Tuesday, the stock rose $\frac{7}{8}$ dollar per share, and on Wednesday, it dropped $\frac{1}{4}$ dollar per share.

(Source: Nike Company)

10. Find the stock's value on Tuesday.

11. Find the stock's value on Wednesday.

12. *World Travels* During your vacation in Italy, you visit the Leaning Tower of Pisa. You learn that the tower is leaning $14\frac{1}{2}$ feet and leans $\frac{1}{12}$ foot more every 20 years. How much will the tower be leaning in 60 years?

To reach the top of the Leaning Tower of Pisa, you must climb more than 300 stairs.

13. *Using a Table* The table below shows the number of inches of snowfall each month for Denver, Colorado, in 1992. What is the total number of inches of snowfall for the year? Write this number in words.

Month	Jan	Feb	Mar	Apr	May	Jun	Jul	Aug	Sep	Oct	Nov	Dec
Snowfall	$8\frac{3}{10}$	$7\frac{3}{10}$	$12\frac{7}{10}$	9	$1\frac{3}{5}$	0	0	0	$1\frac{3}{5}$	$3\frac{7}{10}$	$8\frac{4}{5}$	$7\frac{2}{5}$

Horses The shoulder height of a horse is measured in hands. One hand = 4 inches. American quarter horses have an average shoulder height of 15.25 hands. Thoroughbreds have an average shoulder height of 17 hands.

14. Write each average height in inches.

15. Write each average height in feet and inches.

16. Find the difference in the average heights.

17. An American quarter horse can run $\frac{1}{4}$ mile in $\frac{1}{3}$ minute. A thoroughbred can run 1 mile in $1\frac{1}{2}$ minutes. Which horse is faster? Explain.

Thoroughbreds, weighing from 1000 to 1300 pounds, are among the largest of the saddle horses.

Integrated Review

Making Connections within Mathematics

Complete the statement.

18. $0.8 = \boxed{?}\%$

19. $\boxed{?}\% = 1.2$

20. $3\% = \frac{3}{\boxed{?}}$

21. $\frac{2}{7} = \frac{16}{\boxed{?}}$

22. $0.\boxed{?} = \frac{4}{5}$

23. $5\frac{2}{3} = 4\frac{\boxed{?}}{3}$

24. $3\frac{\boxed{?}}{7} = 4\frac{1}{7}$

25. $0.5 = \frac{1}{\boxed{?}}$

Exploration and Extension

26. *Guess, Check, and Revise* Match the numbers with the letters so that each number is used exactly once.

       7 8 9

a. $\frac{a.}{b.} + \frac{5}{c.} = \frac{7}{8}$

d. $\frac{d.}{e.} + \frac{f.}{12} = 1\frac{1}{12}$

g. $\frac{g.}{h.} + \frac{3}{i.} = 1\frac{1}{2}$

Chapter Summary

What did you learn?

1. Measure lengths in the customary system. **(7.1)**
2. Find the least common denominator of two fractions. **(7.2)**
3. Add and subtract fractions
   - with a common denominator. **(7.3)**
   - with different denominators. **(7.3)**
4. Add mixed numbers. **(7.4)**
5. Subtract mixed numbers
   - without regrouping. **(7.4)**
   - with a common denominator and regrouping. **(7.5)**
   - with different denominators and regrouping. **(7.6)**

6. Use problem-solving strategies to solve problems. **(7.1–7.7)**

7. Use tables and graphs to organize data and solve problems. **(7.1–7.7)**

Why did you learn it?

Many real-life problems can be solved using addition and subtraction of fractions (or mixed numbers). Here are some of the examples you studied in this chapter.

- Compare the heights of people in inches and in feet. **(7.1)**
- Find the dimensions of a wooden box lid. **(7.4)**
- Find the difference in amounts of two checks. **(7.5)**
- Find the weight of a buried treasure. **(7.7)**

How does it fit into the bigger picture of mathematics?

In this chapter, you used one of the most important strategies in all of mathematics. It is called *Rewrite a Difficult Problem as a Simpler Problem*. You learned that it is easy to add or subtract fractions that have a common denominator—you simply add or subtract their numerators and use the common denominator.

To add or subtract fractions that have different denominators, you don't have to learn a whole new set of rules. Instead, you only have to learn how to rewrite two fractions with a common denominator. Then you can use the rule for adding or subtracting fractions that have a common denominator.

In Exercises 1–3, write the length in feet and inches. **(7.1)**

1. Turtle

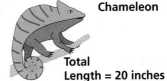

|← 15 inches →|

2. Chameleon

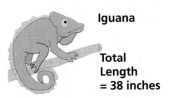

Total
Length = 20 inches

3. Iguana

Total
Length
= 38 inches

In Exercises 4–6, which fraction is not equivalent? **(7.2)**

4. $\frac{2}{9}, \frac{6}{27}, \frac{5}{18}$

5. $\frac{15}{36}, \frac{2}{6}, \frac{10}{30}$

6. $\frac{3}{8}, \frac{15}{32}, \frac{6}{16}$

In Exercises 7–10, find the sum or difference. **(7.3)**

7. $\frac{5}{8} + \frac{1}{4}$

8. $\frac{8}{9} - \frac{1}{3}$

9. $\frac{5}{6} - \frac{2}{5}$

10. $\frac{1}{4} + \frac{3}{8} + \frac{1}{12}$

Algebra and Mental Math   In Exercises 11–13, solve. **(7.4)**

11. $3\frac{4}{10} - m = 1\frac{1}{10}$

12. $s - 1\frac{1}{6} = 3\frac{5}{6}$

13. $n + 3\frac{7}{12} = 9$

In Exercises 14–17, complete the statement with $<$, $>$, or $=$. **(7.5)**

14. $2\frac{5}{5}$ (?) $3\frac{1}{5}$

15. $5\frac{3}{10}$ (?) $4\frac{13}{10}$

16. $1\frac{3}{12}$ (?) $\frac{13}{12}$

17. $4\frac{33}{24}$ (?) $5\frac{9}{24}$

Find the difference between the values of the points given. **(7.6)**

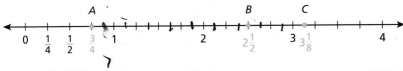

18. B and A

19. C and A

Environment   The circle graph at the
right shows how people use water in the
United States. **(7.7)**

20. Rename each fraction with a
denominator of 40.

21. Find the sum of all the fractions.
What can you conclude?

22. Which uses more water: toilet or
bath and shower?

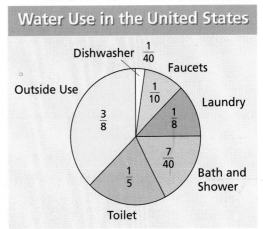

Water Use in the United States

Dishwasher $\frac{1}{40}$
Faucets
Outside Use
$\frac{1}{10}$
Laundry
$\frac{3}{8}$
$\frac{1}{8}$
$\frac{7}{40}$
$\frac{1}{5}$
Bath and
Shower
Toilet

City Planning   The diagram at the right shows Washington, D.C., divided into four regions. The fraction of the city's population for each section is given.

23. What is the sum of the fractions of the population living in the Northeast and Southwest sections?

24. How much greater is the fraction of people who live in the Southeast section than the Southwest section?

25. *Cherry Blossom Festival*   The Cherry Blossom Festival is held each year in Washington, D.C., in early April. You are taking a walking tour and count 25 cherry trees with pink blossoms and 35 cherry trees with white blossoms. Write each as a fraction of the number of trees you counted. How much greater is the fraction of trees that have white blossoms?

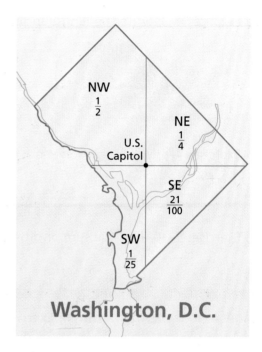

Washington, D.C.

Fraction Puzzle   In Exercises 26–37, find the sum or difference and simplify the answer. Then match each letter to the answer in the spaces below. The letters will spell out the name of a famous person who worked in Washington, D.C.

$$1\frac{19}{24} \quad \frac{11}{12} \quad \frac{1}{9} \quad 3\frac{7}{12} \quad 4\frac{5}{7} \quad \frac{3}{4} \quad 2\frac{17}{24} \quad 3\frac{7}{12} \quad 3\frac{7}{12} \quad 2\frac{17}{24} \quad 2\frac{7}{24} \quad 1\frac{9}{20}$$

26. **D:** $3\frac{5}{8} - 1\frac{1}{3}$ 27. **N:** $2\frac{1}{4} + 1\frac{1}{3}$

28. **H:** $\frac{2}{3} - \frac{5}{9}$ 29. **J:** $3\frac{1}{6} - 1\frac{3}{8}$

30. **E:** $6 - 3\frac{7}{24}$ 31. **N:** $5\frac{5}{6} - 2\frac{1}{4}$

32. **O:** $\frac{7}{24} + \frac{5}{8}$ 33. **E:** $1\frac{1}{8} + 1\frac{7}{12}$

34. **K:** $\frac{5}{12} + \frac{1}{3}$ 35. **Y:** $\frac{7}{10} + \frac{3}{4}$

36. **N:** $5 - 1\frac{5}{12}$ 37. **F:** $4\frac{6}{7} - \frac{1}{7}$

38. *You Be the Teacher*   Use the letters in the name of another famous person who worked in Washington, D.C. Create your own fraction puzzle.

Michigan, not Washington, D.C., grows the most cherry trees, producing 19,000,000 pounds of cherries per year.

Chapter TEST

In Exercises 1–3, complete the statement.

1. 48 inches = [?] feet

2. [?] inches = 4 yards

3. $1\frac{1}{2}$ feet = [?] inches

In Exercises 4–6, find the least common denominator.

4. $\frac{1}{6}$, $\frac{2}{3}$

5. $\frac{3}{8}$, $\frac{5}{6}$

6. $\frac{3}{10}$, $\frac{3}{4}$

Geometry In Exercises 7–9, find the value of *x*.

7.

Perimeter = *x* $\frac{5}{8}$ ft $1\frac{1}{8}$ ft

8.

x $2\frac{1}{4}$ m   Perimeter = $10\frac{1}{8}$ m $2\frac{1}{4}$ m $3\frac{1}{2}$ m

9.

$\frac{9}{10}$ mi $1\frac{1}{5}$ mi   Perimeter = *x* $1\frac{2}{5}$ mi

In Exercises 10–15, find the sum or difference.

10. $\frac{2}{5} + \frac{4}{5}$

11. $\frac{4}{9} + \frac{1}{3}$

12. $\frac{11}{12} - \frac{7}{12}$

13. $\frac{7}{8} - \frac{1}{16}$

14. $\frac{9}{10} + \frac{1}{15}$

15. $\frac{5}{8} - \frac{1}{3}$

In Exercises 16–21, decide whether you need to regroup, rename, both, or neither to subtract. Then find the difference.

16. $3\frac{7}{8} - 2\frac{5}{8}$

17. $5\frac{1}{3} - \frac{2}{3}$

18. $4\frac{4}{5} - 3\frac{1}{2}$

19. $5\frac{1}{12} - 3\frac{2}{3}$

20. $5 - 3\frac{2}{9}$

21. $4\frac{1}{3} - 1\frac{1}{15}$

Hobbies The bar graph shows the numbers sold in millions of five best-selling videos as of 1993. *(Source: Video Store Magazine)*

22. Find the total sold of *Beauty and the Beast* and *The Little Mermaid*.

23. How many more videos of *E.T.* were sold than of *Bambi*?

24. How many more videos of *101 Dalmatians* were sold than of *Bambi*?

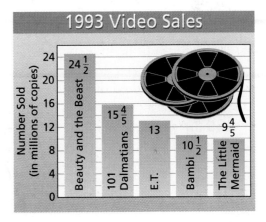

1993 Video Sales

Number Sold (in millions of copies)

Beauty and the Beast $24\frac{1}{2}$; 101 Dalmatians $15\frac{4}{5}$; E.T. 13; Bambi $10\frac{1}{2}$; The Little Mermaid $9\frac{4}{5}$

25. Carl Lewis won three gold medals in long jumping at the Olympics. He jumped 28′ $\frac{1''}{4}$ (1984), 28′ $7\frac{1''}{4}$ (1988), and 28′ $5\frac{1''}{2}$ (1992). How much farther did he jump in 1988 than in 1992?

Multiplying and Dividing Fractions

These rafters are enjoying a thrilling ride in Yosemite National Park. The park is located in eastern California and was established in 1890.

The National Park Service manages recreational and scenic sites covering over 80,000,000 acres of land in the United States.
(Source: Department of the Interior)

National Park Service Total Sites: 367
> Parks (National, Historic, and Military), 110
> Historic Sites and Battlefields, 85
> Monuments and Memorials, 102
> Preserves and Reserves, 16
> Lake shores and Seashores, 14
> Wild and Scenic Rivers, 15
> Other Areas and Trails, 25

Think and Discuss

1. How might you best display this data? Why?
2. Write two questions involving fractions about the data.

CHAPTER THEME:

Outdoor Recreation

Planning A Park Picnic

Theme: Outdoor Recreation Have you ever had a class picnic? What do you remember was the most fun?

A class picnic that is fun for everyone needs careful planning. In this chapter, you will plan the activities needed for a good class picnic. You will use fractions as you do the following:

▷ **In Lesson 8.1:** Change the size of a recipe to feed a larger group. (page 355)

▷ **In Lesson 8.2:** Plan the games for your picnic. (page 361)

▷ **In Lesson 8.3:** Make plans for a sign for your picnic. (page 369)

▷ **In Lesson 8.4:** Plan the prizes for your picnic. (page 375)

▷ **In Lesson 8.5:** Make plans for a fund-raiser to raise money for your picnic. (page 381)

▷ **In Lesson 8.6:** Decide if you have enough table covers for your picnic. (page 385)

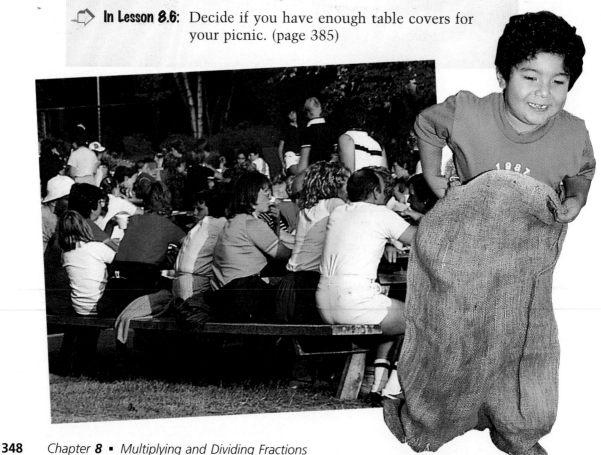

GETTING STARTED

Materials: typing paper, markers or pens

- Make a booklet to record your plans for a picnic. Use five sheets of paper folded in half.

- Write the title "Picnic Planner" and your name on the cover.

- Write these titles at the top of each of the next six pages:

Guests	Food
Publicity	Costs
Games	Other

- On the page titled "Guests", write your guest list. Be sure to include everyone in your class. Will you invite people who are not in your class? Will you invite another teacher or your parents?

- Place the booklet in your portfolio. Now you are ready to add information to it as you complete this chapter.

Lab 8.1 Investigating Multiplication
of Fractions and Whole Numbers

Materials Needed: plain paper, colored pencils or markers, pencils or pens

Part A *Repeated Addition Models* The multiplication problem $3 \times \frac{1}{2}$ means the same as adding $\frac{1}{2}$ three times.

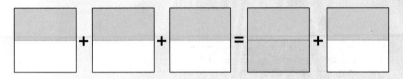

From the model, you can write the following.

$\frac{1}{2} + \frac{1}{2} + \frac{1}{2} = \frac{3}{2}$, or $1\frac{1}{2}$ *Repeated Addition*

$3 \times \frac{1}{2} = \frac{3}{2}$, or $1\frac{1}{2}$ *Multiplication*

1. Use a repeated addition model to solve.

 a. $4 \times \frac{1}{3}$ b. $3 \times \frac{1}{4}$ c. $6 \times \frac{1}{3}$ d. $8 \times \frac{1}{2}$

Part B *Writing Multiplication Problems*

2. Write the repeated addition problem shown by each model. Solve. Then rewrite each problem as a multiplication problem.

 a.  b.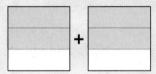

 c.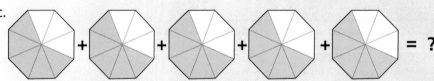

3. Discuss the results of Exercise 2 with others in your group. Did you write each answer as an improper fraction or as a mixed number? Explain.

Part C *Using Area Models* Here is an area model for $\frac{2}{5} \times 4$.

$\frac{2}{5}\Big\{$

4

Summary of Steps

$\frac{2}{5} \times 4 = \frac{8}{5}$

4. Draw an area model for each of the following. Copy and complete the table below. With others in your group, discuss any patterns that you find.

   a. $\frac{2}{3} \times 2$ b. $\frac{3}{4} \times 2$ c. $\frac{5}{6} \times 3$ d. $\frac{4}{5} \times 4$

Problem	Width of Rectangle	Length of Rectangle	Area of Rectangle
Example	$\frac{2}{5}$	4	$\frac{8}{5} = 1\frac{3}{5}$
a.	?	?	?
b.	?	?	?
c.	?	?	?
d.	?	?	?

On Your Own

Critical Thinking

Repeated Addition Models In Exercises 5 and 6, use a repeated addition model to solve the problem.

5. $4 \times \frac{2}{3}$

6. $\frac{2}{5} \times 3$

7. Write the repeated addition problem represented by each model. Solve. How are the models alike? How are they different?

   a.
   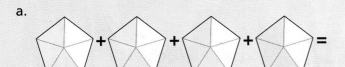
   b.
   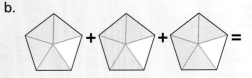

8. Sketch an area model for $\frac{3}{5} \times 4$. Label the dimensions.

   Find the area of the shaded rectangle. Is it easier to count the number of fifths in this model or in the model in Exercise 7(a)? Explain.

9. Explain how to multiply $\frac{3}{7}$ by 4 without drawing a model.

8.1

Multiplying Fractions and Whole Numbers

What you should learn:

Goal 1 How to multiply fractions and whole numbers

Goal 2 How to use multiplication to solve real-life problems

Why you should learn it:

Knowing how to multiply a fraction and a whole number can help you work with data about your class. An example is finding the number of students who went to a water park.

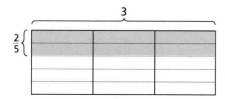

This area model shows the product of $\frac{2}{5}$ and 3. The shaded region of the rectangle has dimensions of $\frac{2}{5}$ and 3. The area of the shaded region is $\frac{6}{5}$, or $1\frac{1}{5}$.

Goal 1 Multiplying with Fractions

In Lab 8.1, you may have discovered the following rule for multiplying a fraction and a whole number.

Multiplying Fractions and Whole Numbers
To multiply a fraction and a whole number, multiply the numerator of the fraction by the whole number. Write the result as a fraction with the original denominator. Simplify, if possible.

Example 1 *Multiplying with Fractions*

a. $\frac{2}{5} \times 3 = \frac{2 \times 3}{5}$ *Multiply 2 times 3.*

$= \frac{6}{5}$, or $1\frac{1}{5}$ *Simplify.*

b. $2 \times \frac{1}{8} = \frac{2 \times 1}{8}$ *Multiply 2 times 1.*

$= \frac{2}{8}$ *Simplify numerator.*

$= \frac{1}{4}$ *Simplify.*

Example 2 *Solving an Equation*

Use mental math to solve for n: $\frac{n}{6} \times 3 = \frac{15}{6}$.

Solution You can solve this problem by asking the question:

"What number can be multiplied by 3 to get 15?"

The answer is 5. This means that the solution of the equation is $n = 5$.

Solving Real-Life Problems

When you are solving real-life problems, remember that the word "of" often means multiplication.

Real Life
Recreation

These visitors are enjoying tubing at Sesame Place in Langhorne, Pennsylvania.

Example 3 *Using a Set Model*

There are 24 students in your class. Two thirds of the students attended a water park last summer. How many students attended a water park last summer?

Solution   One way to solve the problem is to use a set model.

$\frac{1}{3}$ of 24 is 8. $\frac{1}{3}$ of 24 is 8. $\frac{1}{3}$ of 24 is 8.

Another way to solve it is to use multiplication.

$$\frac{2}{3} \text{ of } 24 = \frac{2}{3} \times 24 \quad \textit{Translate "of" as "times."}$$

$$= \frac{2 \times 24}{3} \quad \textit{Multiply 2 times 24.}$$

$$= \frac{48}{3} \quad \textit{Simplify numerator.}$$

$$= 16 \quad \textit{Simplify.}$$

With either solution, you can conclude that 16 of your classmates attended a water park last summer. ∎

Communicating about MATHEMATICS

Problem Solving
Look for a Pattern

▶ **Sharing Ideas about the Lesson**

Finding a Pattern Solve the following problems. Describe any patterns that you see. Then write the next three *answers*.

$$\frac{3}{4} \times 2 = ?, \frac{3}{4} \times 3 = ?, \frac{3}{4} \times 4 = ?, \frac{3}{4} \times 5 = ?, \dots$$

EXERCISES

Think and Discuss

▶ **CHECK for Understanding**

1. Write the multiplication problem shown by the model at the right. Then find the answer.

2. *Error Analysis* Describe and correct the error.

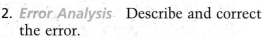

3. What is three eighths of 10?

4. Is $\frac{6}{7} \times 5 = 5 \times \frac{6}{7}$? Explain.

5. *Mental Math* What whole number can be multiplied by $\frac{4}{5}$ to get $\frac{32}{5}$?

Independent Practice

Geometry In Exercises 6 and 7, solve the multiplication problem that is shown by the area model. Simplify, if possible.

6.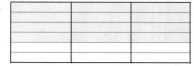

7.

In Exercises 8–15, solve. Simplify, if possible.

8. $\frac{2}{7}$ of 3

9. $8 \times \frac{1}{12}$

10. $\frac{5}{8} \times 2$

11. $\frac{2}{9}$ of 6

12. $5 \times \frac{3}{4}$

13. $4 \times \frac{6}{11}$

14. $\frac{5}{10}$ of 10

15. $\frac{2}{3} \times 9$

Algebra and Mental Math In Exercises 16–18, solve.

16. $\frac{m}{5} \times 2 = \frac{2}{5}$

17. $\frac{5}{9} \times n = \frac{20}{9}$

18. $5 \times \frac{7}{a} = \frac{35}{8}$

Number Sense In Exercises 19–21, write an example of a fraction times a whole number with an answer as described.

19. Greater than 1

20. Less than 1

21. Equal to 1

In Exercises 22–25, use the number line to complete the statement with the correct letter.

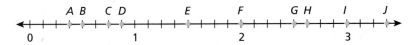

22. $B \times 5 = \boxed{?}$ **23.** $A \times 9 = \boxed{?}$ **24.** $C \times F = \boxed{?}$ **25.** $D \times I = \boxed{?}$

26. *Seasons* A survey asked 36 students which season was their favorite. One sixth chose fall, two ninths chose winter, five eighteenths chose spring, and one third chose summer. How many students chose each season? Check your answer by adding. What should you get for your sum?

27. *Number Puzzle* Use the following clues. Find the length of each fish.

- *Channel Catfish:* Length is 28 inches.
- *Coho Salmon:* Length is $\frac{6}{7}$ of a channel catfish.
- *Rainbow Trout:* Length is $\frac{7}{12}$ of a coho salmon.

The rainbow trout is native to North America and can live up to 11 years.

Integrated Review

Making Connections within Mathematics

Write a multiplication problem you could use to answer the question. Then solve.

28. What is 150% of 48?

29. What is 200% of 7.5?

30. What is $\frac{24}{100}$ of 50?

31. What is $\frac{35}{10}$ of 20?

Exploration and Extension

Geometry In Exercises 32 and 33, show how you can use multiplication of fractions and whole numbers to find the perimeter of the figure.

32.

$\frac{4}{9}$ feet

$\frac{4}{9}$ feet

33.

$\frac{3}{7}$ yard

$\frac{8}{9}$ yard

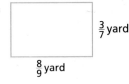

34. *Building Your Chapter Project* Find a recipe that includes fractional measurements and serves 6 or fewer people. Change it so it serves the number of people going to your picnic. Record your results in your Planner.

Lab 8.2 Connections to Geometry:

Investigating Area Models for Multiplication

Materials Needed: grid paper, colored pencils or markers, pencils or pens

Part A *Drawing Area Models with Fractional Dimensions*

Here are three possible area models for $\frac{4}{12}$.

 Model A

 Model B

 Model C

To create each model, a square with an area of 1 square unit was divided into 12 equal parts. Then 4 of the parts were shaded to form a rectangle with an area of $\frac{4}{12}$.

Remember that a square with an area of 1 square unit must have 4 equal sides, each 1 unit long.

1. One way to construct Model A is shown below. Work with a partner and follow these steps to draw Model A on grid paper.

   a. Draw a 6 by 6 square. Why is a square of this size convenient?

   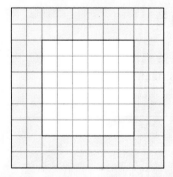

   b. Divide the square vertically into 6 equal parts and horizontally into halves. Label the distances.

   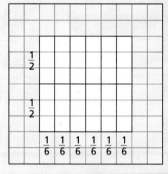

   c. Shade $\frac{4}{6}$ of the square. In a second color, shade half the square.

   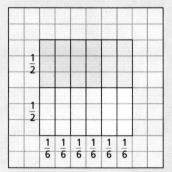

   d. What is the length and width of the rectangle that is shaded in both colors? Label these dimensions.

2. Explain why the area of the two-color rectangle that you made in Exercise 1 is $\frac{4}{12}$.

Part B *Drawing Area Models with Fractional Dimensions*

3. Repeat the process in Exercise 1. Form two-color rectangles for Models B and C. Remember to make your unit squares a convenient size. Find the length and width of each two-color rectangle. Label these dimensions.

4. Copy and complete the table below. Use the area models you have drawn. Do you see any patterns?

Area Model	Length of Two-color Rectangle	Width of Two-color Rectangle	Area of Two-color Rectangle
A	$\frac{4}{6}$	$\frac{1}{2}$	$\frac{4}{12}$
B	?	?	$\frac{4}{12}$
C	?	?	$\frac{4}{12}$

5. Find the length, width, and area of each two-color region. The area of the entire square is 1 square unit.

a.   b.   c.

Part C *Drawing Area Models with Fractional Dimensions*

6. a. Choose a pair of fractions that are not shown above. Use an area model of a unit square to draw a two-color rectangle with these dimensions. Label the dimensions and find the area.

   b. In a table similar to that above, list the results of your group and three other groups. What patterns do you see?

On Your Own   *Critical Thinking*

---

7. On grid paper, draw a square with an area of 1 square unit. Vertically divide the square into fifths. Horizontally divide the square into fourths. How many equal parts are formed? Explain.

8. Explain how to find the area of a $\frac{3}{5}$-by-$\frac{2}{7}$ rectangle *without* drawing a sketch.

8.2

Multiplying Fractions

What you should learn:

Goal 1 How to multiply two fractions

Goal 2 How to use multiplication of fractions to solve real-life problems

Why you should learn it:

Knowing how to multiply two fractions can help you make decisions about nutrition. An example is finding the amount of cheese you ate in two pieces of pizza.

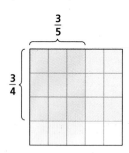

Goal 1 Multiplying Fractions

In Lab 8.2, you may have discovered the following rule for multiplying fractions.

Multiplying Fractions

To multiply fractions, multiply their numerators. Then multiply their denominators. Simplify, if possible.

Example 1 *Multiplying Fractions*

a. $\dfrac{3}{4} \times \dfrac{3}{5} = \dfrac{3 \times 3}{4 \times 5}$ *Multiply.*

$= \dfrac{9}{20}$ *Simplify numerator and denominator.*

The product of $\dfrac{3}{4}$ and $\dfrac{3}{5}$ is $\dfrac{9}{20}$. You can check this by drawing an area model like that shown at the left.

b. $\dfrac{5}{8} \times \dfrac{6}{10} = \dfrac{5 \times 6}{8 \times 10}$ *Multiply.*

$= \dfrac{30}{80}$ *Simplify numerator and denominator.*

$= \dfrac{3}{8}$ *Simplify.*

The product of $\dfrac{5}{8}$ and $\dfrac{6}{10}$ is $\dfrac{3}{8}$. ∎

Problem Solving
Mental Math

Example 2 *Solving an Equation*

Solve for n: $\dfrac{3}{5} \times \dfrac{n}{8} = \dfrac{21}{40}$.

Solution   You need to find a number n such that $3 \times n = 21$. Using mental math, it follows that $n = 7$. Check this result by multiplying $\dfrac{3}{5}$ and $\dfrac{7}{8}$. ∎

Goal 2 Solving Real-Life Problems

Here are two examples of real-life problems that use multiplication of fractions.

Question	Use fractions to find solution.
What is $\frac{1}{2}$ of $\frac{3}{5}$ mile?	$\frac{1}{2} \times \frac{3}{5} = \frac{1 \times 3}{2 \times 5} = \frac{3}{10}$ mile
What is $\frac{2}{3}$ of $\frac{3}{4}$ cup?	$\frac{2}{3} \times \frac{3}{4} = \frac{2 \times 3}{3 \times 4} = \frac{6}{12} = \frac{1}{2}$ cup

Real Life
Nutrition

Over 1 billion pizzas are eaten in the United States each year.

Example 3 *Finding a Serving Size*

You are making a small pizza that has $\frac{3}{4}$ cup of cheese on it. You cut the pizza into 6 pieces and eat 2 pieces. How much cheese did you eat?

Solution You ate $\frac{2}{6}$ of $\frac{3}{4}$ of a cup of cheese.

$\frac{2}{6} \times \frac{3}{4} = \frac{2 \times 3}{6 \times 4}$ *Multiply.*

$\qquad = \frac{6}{24}$ *Simplify numerator and denominator.*

$\qquad = \frac{1}{4}$ *Simplify.*

You ate $\frac{1}{4}$ cup of cheese.   ■

Communicating about MATHEMATICS

▷ **Sharing Ideas about the Lesson**

Checking Your Answer Describe how you can use the following diagram to check the result in Example 3.

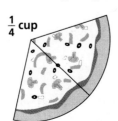
$\frac{1}{4}$ cup

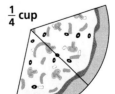
$\frac{1}{4}$ cup

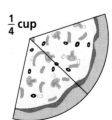
$\frac{1}{4}$ cup

EXERCISES

Think and Discuss

▶ **CHECK for Understanding**

1. *Cookie Baking* A cookie recipe asks for $\frac{3}{4}$ pound of margarine. To make only half a recipe, how much margarine should you use?

2. Multiply $\frac{2}{3}, \frac{1}{2}$, and $\frac{5}{7}$.

3. Find $\frac{3}{5}$ of $\frac{3}{4}$.

4. What multiplication problem is shown by the area model at the right? Find the answer.

5. *Algebra and Mental Math* Solve for n.

$$\frac{5}{9} \times \frac{4}{n} = \frac{20}{63}$$

6. *Error Analysis* Describe and correct the error.

$$\frac{8}{9} \times \frac{2}{9} = \frac{16}{9}$$

Independent Practice

Geometry In Exercises 7–10, match the multiplication problem with the area model. Then find the product. Simplify, if possible.

a.   b.   c.   d.

7. $\frac{2}{3} \times \frac{5}{8}$ 8. $\frac{3}{6} \times \frac{5}{6}$ 9. $\frac{3}{4} \times \frac{1}{2}$ 10. $\frac{3}{5} \times \frac{7}{10}$

In Exercises 11–18, find the product. Simplify, if possible.

11. $\frac{2}{5} \times \frac{4}{5}$ 12. $\frac{1}{6} \times \frac{7}{8}$ 13. $\frac{5}{7} \times \frac{3}{4}$ 14. $\frac{2}{3} \times \frac{2}{3} \times \frac{2}{3}$

15. $\frac{9}{10} \times \frac{4}{10}$ 16. $\frac{4}{8} \times \frac{3}{5} \times \frac{1}{2}$ 17. $\frac{4}{9} \times \frac{1}{2} \times \frac{1}{3}$ 18. $\frac{7}{8} \times \frac{2}{7}$

Algebra and Mental Math In Exercises 19–22, solve the equation.

19. $\frac{4}{5} \times \frac{n}{5} = \frac{12}{25}$ 20. $\frac{2}{7} \times \frac{3}{x} = \frac{6}{28}$ 21. $\frac{3}{8} \times \frac{5}{y} = \frac{15}{56}$ 22. $\frac{1}{9} \times \frac{m}{10} = \frac{7}{90}$

In Exercises 23 and 24, use an area model to help you find the answer.

23. What is $\frac{2}{3}$ of $\frac{3}{4}$?

24. What is $\frac{4}{5}$ of $\frac{2}{3}$?

25. *Reasoning* Is the following statement true or false? Explain.

$$\frac{1}{3} + \frac{1}{3} \text{ is greater than } \frac{1}{3} \times \frac{1}{3}.$$

26. Find four pairs of fractions whose products are $\frac{8}{45}$. Explain your process.

Science An ostrich egg is about $\frac{1}{2}$ foot long. Write the length of the indicated egg in feet.

27. A chickadee egg is about $\frac{1}{6}$ as long as an ostrich egg.

28. A blue jay egg is about $\frac{1}{4}$ as long as an ostrich egg.

29. A bald eagle egg is about $\frac{2}{3}$ as long as an ostrich egg.

30. *Measurement* Explain how to change a measurement in feet to inches. Then copy and complete the table above.

Bird	Egg Length in Feet	Egg Length in Inches
Ostrich	?	?
Chickadee	?	?
Blue Jay	?	?
Bald Eagle	?	?

Integrated Review   *Making Connections within Mathematics*

31. Use the rule for multiplying a fraction by a whole number to find the product of $\frac{2}{3}$ and 2.

32. Think of the whole number 2 as $\frac{2}{1}$. Then use the rule for multiplying two fractions to find the product of $\frac{2}{3}$ and $\frac{2}{1}$. What do you notice about this answer and the answer you got in Exercise 31?

Exploration and Extension

33. *Making Connections* Use fractions to find the area of the two-color region at the right. Then use decimals. Are your results the same? Explain.

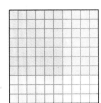

34. *Building Your Chapter Project* Plan at least 3 games to be played at your picnic. Describe the dimensions of the playing fields. Include measurements that are fractions. Find the areas of the fields. Record your results in your Picnic Planner.

1. Write each measurement as a mixed number and as an improper fraction. **(6.6, 7.1)**

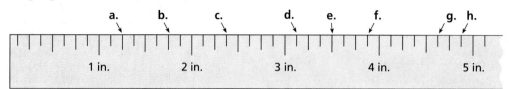

Find the product. **(4.4)**

2. 9.25×1.8

3. 15.5×3.46

4. 75% of 80

5. 125% of 40

Solve the proportion. **(6.4)**

6. $\dfrac{?}{6} = \dfrac{3}{18}$

7. $\dfrac{14}{35} = \dfrac{2}{?}$

8. $\dfrac{16}{?} = \dfrac{4}{7}$

9. $\dfrac{8}{9} = \dfrac{?}{54}$

Simplify. **(7.3)**

10. $\dfrac{1}{3} + \dfrac{4}{3}$

11. $\dfrac{1}{2} + \dfrac{1}{3}$

12. $\dfrac{3}{8} - \dfrac{1}{8}$

13. $\dfrac{3}{8} - \dfrac{1}{4}$

Milestones   BROKEN NUMBERS

| 500 B.C. | | 100 B.C. | 300 A.D. | A.D. 700 | A.D. 1100 | A.D. 1500 | | A.D. 1900 |

Euclid's Elements, 300 B.C.

Magnetic Compass, 1090

Decimal Point, 1492

Decimal Fractions, 1585

Metric System, 1799

The word "fraction" comes from the Latin verb *frangere*, "to break," since they were considered "broken numbers." Early Egyptian writings had symbols for only *unit fractions*, that is, fractions with numerators of 1. So they would write $\frac{3}{4}$ as $\frac{1}{2} + \frac{1}{4}$.

Early *nonunit fractions* were written with the denominator over the numerator. The Hindu mathematician Brahmagupta (about A.D. 628) argued that since fraction models were parts of wholes, the numerator should be over the denominator. By the year 1000, Arab mathematicians had inserted a fraction bar as we do today.

The Egyptian Rhind-Ahmes mathematical papyrus dates back to 1600 B.C.

- In Egyptian fractions, the same unit fraction could not be used more than once. So $\frac{2}{3}$ had to be written as $\frac{1}{2} + \frac{1}{6}$. Find combinations of unit fractions for $\frac{3}{8}$, $\frac{2}{5}$, and $\frac{2}{7}$.

Using a Calculator

Calculators treat fractions in many different ways. Some "fraction calculators" can display fractions, but most calculators display fractions as decimals. Some calculators have parentheses and some don't. If your calculator has parentheses, you can use it to multiply and divide fractions.

Example 1 *Use Parentheses to Multiply Fractions*

Use a calculator with parentheses to multiply $\frac{1}{3}$ by $\frac{3}{8}$.

Solution Use the following keystrokes.

(1 ÷ 3) × (3 ÷ 8) =

The calculator will display 0.125. This is equal to $\frac{1}{8}$. ∎

Example 2 *Parentheses with Mixed Numbers*

Use a calculator with parentheses to multiply $1\frac{2}{3}$ by $\frac{3}{4}$.

Solution Use the following keystrokes.

(1 + 2 ÷ 3) × (3 ÷ 4) =

The calculator will display 1.25. This is equal to $1\frac{1}{4}$. ∎

Exercises

In Exercises 1–8, use a calculator with parentheses to find the products. If necessary, round your answers to thousandths.

1. $\frac{7}{8} \times \frac{2}{7}$

2. $\frac{2}{5} \times \frac{1}{2}$

3. $\frac{2}{3} \times \frac{6}{4}$

4. $\frac{5}{4} \times \frac{3}{8}$

5. $1\frac{1}{2} \times \frac{3}{4}$

6. $2\frac{1}{3} \times \frac{3}{8}$

7. $1\frac{2}{3} \times \frac{3}{4}$

8. $3\frac{3}{4} \times 5\frac{1}{2}$

9. *Error Analysis* A friend of yours used a calculator to multiply $1\frac{1}{2}$ by $\frac{1}{2}$. Your friend used the following keystrokes and got an answer of 1.25.

1 + 1 ÷ 2 × 1 ÷ 2 =

What did your friend do wrong? How could you fix it?

Lab 8.3

Investigating Multiplication of Mixed Numbers

Materials Needed: plain paper, colored pencils or markers, pencils or pens

Part A *Using Area Models for Multiplying Mixed Numbers*

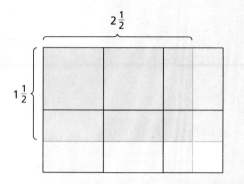

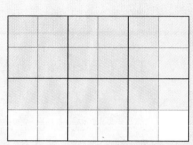

Form a two-color rectangle whose dimensions are $1\frac{1}{2}$ by $2\frac{1}{2}$.

Add grid lines. Then count the number of fourths in the two-color region.

1. Use the area models above to help you find the product of $1\frac{1}{2}$ and $2\frac{1}{2}$. Write a summary of your steps.

2. In Exercise 1, did you write the answer as a mixed number or as an improper fraction? Which form is easier for you to find with a model? Explain.

Part B *Using Area Models for Mixed Numbers*

3. Copy the models shown below. Label the dimensions of the second model as improper fractions.

4. Write the multiplication problem that is shown by the models. Then use either model to help you find the product. Write a summary of your steps.

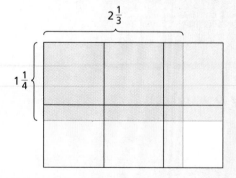

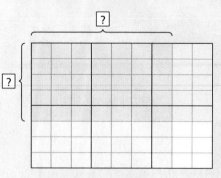

5. Draw an area model for each multiplication problem. Then find the product.

    a. $1\frac{2}{3} \times 2\frac{1}{2}$ **b.** $1\frac{2}{5} \times 1\frac{1}{2}$ **c.** $3\frac{3}{4} \times 2\frac{1}{3}$

6. Use the results of Exercise 5 to copy and complete the table below. Use improper fractions instead of mixed numbers for the length and the width.

Problem	Length of Rectangle	Width of Rectangle	Area of Rectangle
$1\frac{1}{2} \times 2\frac{1}{2}$	$\frac{3}{2}$	$\frac{5}{2}$	$\frac{15}{4}$, or $3\frac{3}{4}$
$1\frac{2}{3} \times 2\frac{1}{2}$	?	?	?
$1\frac{2}{5} \times 1\frac{1}{2}$	?	?	?
$3\frac{3}{4} \times 2\frac{1}{3}$	?	?	?

7. With others in your group, discuss any patterns you see in the table. Record your observations.

On Your Own   *Critical Thinking*

8. Write the multiplication problem that is represented by the model. Then find the product.

   a.
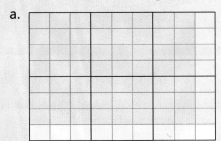
                  b.
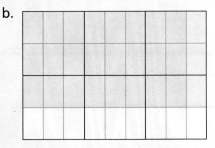

9. Explain how you could find the area of a $2\frac{3}{4}$-by-$1\frac{3}{5}$ rectangle without drawing a sketch.

8.3

Multiplying Mixed Numbers

What you should learn:

Goal 1 How to multiply two mixed numbers

Goal 2 How to use multiplication of mixed numbers to solve real-life problems

Why you should learn it:

Knowing how to multiply two mixed numbers can help you keep records for your sports team. An example is comparing distances people run during track practice.

Goal 1 | Multiplying Mixed Numbers

In Lab 8.3, you may have discovered the following rule for multiplying mixed numbers.

Multiplying Mixed Numbers

To multiply mixed numbers, first rewrite them as improper fractions. Then multiply the numerators and multiply the denominators. Simplify, if possible.

Example 1 | *Multiplying Mixed Numbers*

a. $2\frac{1}{2} \times 1\frac{3}{4} = \frac{5}{2} \times \frac{7}{4}$ *Rewrite as improper fractions.*

$= \frac{5 \times 7}{2 \times 4}$ *Multiply.*

$= \frac{35}{8}$, or $4\frac{3}{8}$ *Simplify.*

The product of $2\frac{1}{2}$ and $1\frac{3}{4}$ is $\frac{35}{8}$. You can use an area model like that shown at the left to check this.

b. $3\frac{1}{2} \times \frac{2}{3} = \frac{7}{2} \times \frac{2}{3}$ *Rewrite $3\frac{1}{2}$ as improper fraction.*

$= \frac{7 \times 2}{2 \times 3}$ *Multiply.*

$= \frac{14}{6}$ *Simplify.*

$= \frac{7}{3}$, or $2\frac{1}{3}$ *Simplify fraction.*

c. $1\frac{5}{6} \times 3 = \frac{11}{6} \times 3$ *Rewrite $1\frac{5}{6}$ as improper fraction.*

$= \frac{33}{6}$ *Multiply.*

$= \frac{11}{2}$, or $5\frac{1}{2}$ *Simplify.* ∎

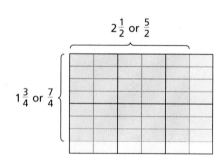

$2\frac{1}{2}$ or $\frac{5}{2}$

$1\frac{3}{4}$ or $\frac{7}{4}$

| Example **2** | *Comparing Products* |

Which person ran the farthest during track practice?

a. Pam ran $4\frac{1}{2}$ times around a $\frac{1}{2}$-mile track.

b. Josh ran 3 times around a $\frac{5}{6}$-mile track.

c. Dionne ran 2 times around a $1\frac{1}{4}$-mile track.

Solution

a. Multiply $4\frac{1}{2}$ times $\frac{1}{2}$.

$$4\frac{1}{2} \times \frac{1}{2} = \frac{9}{2} \times \frac{1}{2} = \frac{9}{4}, \text{ or } 2\frac{1}{4} \text{ miles} \qquad \textit{Pam's distance}$$

b. Multiply 3 times $\frac{5}{6}$.

$$3 \times \frac{5}{6} = \frac{15}{6}, \text{ or } 2\frac{1}{2} \text{ miles} \qquad \textit{Josh's distance}$$

c. Multiply 2 times $1\frac{1}{4}$.

$$2 \times 1\frac{1}{4} = 2 \times \frac{5}{4} = \frac{10}{4}, \text{ or } 2\frac{1}{2} \text{ miles} \qquad \textit{Dionne's distance}$$

From these results, you can see that Josh and Dionne tied for the farthest distance. ■

Real Life
Track

Track and field ranks with soccer as one of the two most popular sports in the world.

Communicating about **M A T H E M A T I C S**

▶ **Sharing Ideas about the Lesson**

Cooperative
Learning

Partner Activity How do the following compare with Pam's, Josh's, and Dionne's distances in Example 2? Write about it.

A. Chun ran $4\frac{1}{2}$ times around a $\frac{3}{4}$-mile track.

B. Charles ran $1\frac{1}{2}$ times around a $1\frac{2}{3}$-mile track.

EXERCISES

Think and Discuss

▶ CHECK for Understanding

Error Analysis   In Exercises 1 and 2, describe and correct the error.

1. $2\frac{2}{3} \times 3\frac{4}{5} = 6\frac{8}{15}$

2. $4 \times 3\frac{3}{4} = 12\frac{3}{4}$

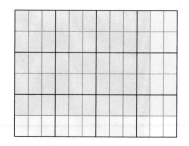

3. Write the multiplication problem that is represented by the model at the right. Then find the product.

4. Multiply: $2\frac{1}{7} \times 2\frac{1}{3}$. Explain each step of your solution.

Measurement   In Exercises 5 and 6, answer the question. Write the answer in hours. Then write the answer in hours and minutes.

5. What is $1\frac{1}{3}$ of 2 hours?

6. What is $\frac{1}{2}$ of $3\frac{1}{2}$ hours?

Independent Practice

In Exercises 7 and 8, write the multiplication problem that is represented by the area model. Then find the product.

7.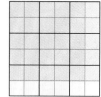

8.

In Exercises 9–16, multiply. Simplify, if possible.

9. $1\frac{1}{2} \times 4\frac{1}{2}$

10. $2\frac{1}{6} \times 2$

11. $4\frac{2}{7} \times \frac{1}{5}$

12. $\frac{3}{4} \times 3\frac{3}{4}$

13. $9 \times 1\frac{7}{9}$

14. $2\frac{1}{3} \times 1\frac{2}{5}$

15. $1\frac{1}{8} \times 5\frac{1}{2}$

16. $6\frac{2}{3} \times 2\frac{1}{2}$

Geometry   In Exercises 17–19, find the area of the rectangle.

17.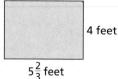
$1\frac{4}{9}$ yards

$1\frac{2}{3}$ yards

18.
4 feet

$5\frac{2}{3}$ feet

19.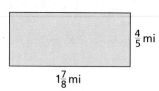
$\frac{4}{5}$ mi

$1\frac{7}{8}$ mi

20. *Reasoning*   Is $2\frac{1}{4} \times 3\frac{4}{5}$ greater than 8? Explain.

In Exercises 21–23, solve each problem. Then describe any patterns that you see. Write and solve the next two problems.

21. $3\frac{1}{2} \times 3 = \boxed{?}$

$3\frac{1}{2} \times 4 = \boxed{?}$

$3\frac{1}{2} \times 5 = \boxed{?}$

22. $1\frac{1}{7} \times \frac{1}{3} = \boxed{?}$

$1\frac{2}{7} \times \frac{1}{3} = \boxed{?}$

$1\frac{3}{7} \times \frac{1}{3} = \boxed{?}$

23. $1\frac{1}{5} \times 1\frac{1}{4} = \boxed{?}$

$2\frac{1}{5} \times 1\frac{1}{4} = \boxed{?}$

$3\frac{1}{5} \times 1\frac{1}{4} = \boxed{?}$

Sailboat Racing To practice for a sailing race, you sailed on 5 different courses. The length of each course and the number of times you sailed it are given in the table below.

Course	1	2	3	4	5
Length (miles)	$9\frac{1}{3}$	$7\frac{1}{2}$	$18\frac{1}{5}$	$5\frac{3}{4}$	$12\frac{3}{5}$
Number of Times Sailed	$2\frac{1}{2}$	$3\frac{1}{5}$	$\frac{6}{7}$	4	$2\frac{1}{7}$

24. On which course did you sail farthest?

25. How many *total* miles did you sail?

Sean Doyle, 13, sailed in the Optimist World Championships, a sailboat racing program for kids.

Integrated Review   *Making Connections within Mathematics*

Write the mixed number represented by the model. Then rewrite the mixed number as an improper fraction.

26.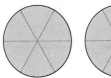

27.

In Exercises 28–31, write the answer as a decimal. Then rewrite the problem using mixed numbers and write the answer as a fraction. Compare your answers.

28. 3.9×4

29. 5.2×0.6

30. 2.5×8.4

31. 10.5×1.6

Exploration and Extension

32. *Building Your Chapter Project* A sign posted for a picnic measures $9\frac{1}{4}$ inches by $7\frac{1}{2}$ inches. Find the area of the sign. Draw plans for a sign with fractional dimensions for *your* picnic. Decide what the sign should say (for example, time and date, directions). Find the area of *your* sign.

Lab 8.4

Investigating Division of Fractions

Materials Needed: plain paper, colored pencils or markers, pencils or pens

Part A *Using Models for Division* You need to measure $3\frac{3}{4}$ cups of water. You have a container that holds $\frac{3}{4}$ cup. How many times do you need to fill the container? To find the answer, divide $3\frac{3}{4}$ by $\frac{3}{4}$, as shown in the following model.

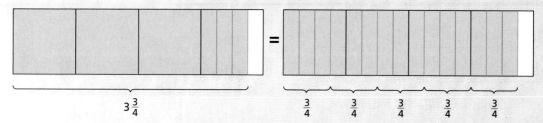

1. Use the above model to help you rewrite the problem $3\frac{3}{4} \div \frac{3}{4}$ with no mixed numbers. Then solve.

   > Dividing $\frac{15}{4}$ by $\frac{3}{4}$ is similar to dividing 15 by 3.

2. The following model represents $2\frac{2}{5}$. Copy the model. Explain how you can use the model to rewrite the problem $2\frac{2}{5} \div \frac{4}{5}$ with no mixed numbers. Then solve.

   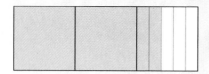

3. Use a model to help you rewrite each division problem with no mixed numbers. Then solve.

   a. $2\frac{4}{7} \div \frac{3}{7}$ b. $2\frac{5}{8} \div \frac{3}{8}$ c. $4\frac{2}{3} \div \frac{2}{3}$

4. Describe any patterns you see in Exercises 1–3. With others in your group, discuss how you could solve these division problems without drawing a model.

Part B *Division and Common Denominators*   Here is a model for $1\frac{1}{2} \div \frac{3}{4}$.

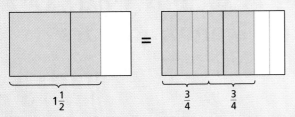

How many times do you need to fill a $\frac{3}{4}$ cup measure to get $1\frac{1}{2}$ cups?

5. Use the above model to help you solve the problem $1\frac{1}{2} \div \frac{3}{4}$.

6. Copy and complete the following.

Mixed Numbers	Improper Fractions	Rewritten with Common Denominators	Solution
a. $2\frac{1}{2} \div \frac{5}{8}$	$\boxed{?} \div \boxed{?}$	$\boxed{?} \div \boxed{?}$	$\boxed{?}$
b. $3\frac{1}{2} \div 1\frac{1}{6}$	$\boxed{?} \div \boxed{?}$	$\boxed{?} \div \boxed{?}$	$\boxed{?}$

Part C *Problems That Don't Divide Evenly*   Here is a model for $2\frac{1}{2} \div \frac{3}{4}$.

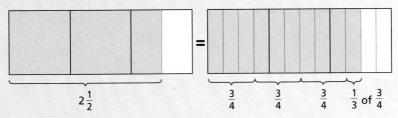

How many times do you need to fill a $\frac{3}{4}$ cup measure to get $2\frac{1}{2}$ cups?

7. Use the above model to help you solve the problem $2\frac{1}{2} \div \frac{3}{4}$.

8. Solve the following problems.

   a. $2\frac{1}{2} \div \frac{3}{8}$ b. $2\frac{1}{6} \div \frac{2}{3}$ c. $3\frac{1}{4} \div \frac{2}{3}$

On Your Own   *Critical Thinking*

In Exercises 9–11, solve.

9. $3\frac{1}{3} \div \frac{2}{3}$ 10. $2\frac{1}{4} \div \frac{3}{8}$ 11. $2\frac{1}{4} \div \frac{2}{3}$

12. Explain how to divide two fractions that have the same denominator. Give some examples.

8.4 Dividing Fractions with Common Denominators

What you should learn:

Goal 1 How to divide fractions that have a common denominator

Goal 2 How to use division of fractions to solve real-life problems

Why you should learn it:

Knowing how to divide fractions can help you find measurements for a construction project. An example is cutting shelves.

Goal 1 Dividing Fractions

In Lab 8.4, you may have discovered the following strategy for dividing fractions that have a common denominator.

Dividing with Common Denominators

To divide fractions that have a common denominator, divide the numerators.

Example: $\dfrac{15}{4} \div \dfrac{3}{4} = \dfrac{15}{3} = 5$

Example 1 *Dividing Fractions*

a. $\dfrac{7}{3} \div \dfrac{1}{3} = \dfrac{7}{1}$ *Divide numerators.*

           $= 7$ *Simplify.*

Use the model at the left to help you check this result.

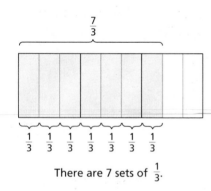

$\dfrac{7}{3}$

$\dfrac{1}{3}\ \dfrac{1}{3}\ \dfrac{1}{3}\ \dfrac{1}{3}\ \dfrac{1}{3}\ \dfrac{1}{3}\ \dfrac{1}{3}$

There are 7 sets of $\dfrac{1}{3}$.

b. $4\dfrac{1}{2} \div \dfrac{3}{4} = \dfrac{9}{2} \div \dfrac{3}{4}$ *Rewrite as improper fraction.*

            $= \dfrac{18}{4} \div \dfrac{3}{4}$ *Rewrite with common denominators.*

            $= \dfrac{18}{3}$ *Divide numerators.*

            $= 6$ *Simplify.*

c. $2\dfrac{1}{3} \div \dfrac{1}{2} = \dfrac{7}{3} \div \dfrac{1}{2}$ *Rewrite as improper fraction.*

            $= \dfrac{14}{6} \div \dfrac{3}{6}$ *Rewrite with common denominators.*

            $= \dfrac{14}{3}$ *Divide numerators.*

            $= 4\dfrac{2}{3}$ *Simplify.* ∎

Solving Real-Life Problems

Real Life
Woodworking

When working with wood, careful planning can prevent mistakes and save time and materials.

Example 2 *Dividing Fractions*

You are cutting shelves from a $7\frac{1}{2}$-foot board. How many shelves can you cut of the given lengths?

a. Each shelf is $2\frac{1}{2}$ feet.   b. Each shelf is $1\frac{3}{4}$ feet.

Solution

a. Divide $7\frac{1}{2}$ by $2\frac{1}{2}$.

$$7\frac{1}{2} \div 2\frac{1}{2} = \frac{15}{2} \div \frac{5}{2} = \frac{15}{5} = 3$$

You get 3 full shelves.

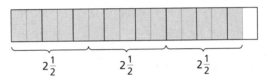

$$2\frac{1}{2} \qquad 2\frac{1}{2} \qquad 2\frac{1}{2}$$

b. Divide $7\frac{1}{2}$ by $1\frac{3}{4}$.

$$7\frac{1}{2} \div 1\frac{3}{4} = \frac{15}{2} \div \frac{7}{4} = \frac{30}{4} \div \frac{7}{4} = \frac{30}{7}, \text{ or } 4\frac{2}{7}$$

You get 4 full shelves. And you would have enough wood left to make $\frac{2}{7}$ of another shelf.

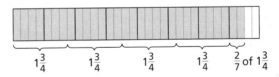

$$1\frac{3}{4} \qquad 1\frac{3}{4} \qquad 1\frac{3}{4} \qquad 1\frac{3}{4} \qquad \frac{2}{7} \text{ of } 1\frac{3}{4}$$

Communicating about MATHEMATICS

Problem Solving
Draw a Diagram

Sharing Ideas about the Lesson

Extending the Example In Example 2, how many shelves can you cut if each shelf is $\frac{3}{4}$ foot long? Answer the question using a model and using division.

EXERCISES

Guided Practice

Think and Discuss

▶ **CHECK for Understanding**

In Exercises 1 and 2, write the division problem that is shown by the model.

1.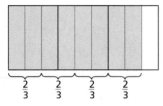

2.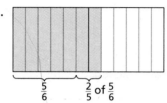

In Exercises 3 and 4, complete the statement.

3. $\dfrac{18}{5} \div \boxed{?} = \dfrac{18}{3}$

4. $\boxed{?} \div \dfrac{4}{9} = \dfrac{15}{4}$

5. Write a real-life problem that can be solved using $\dfrac{5}{2} \div \dfrac{1}{2}$.

Independent Practice

In Exercises 6 and 7, write the division problem that is shown by the model.

6.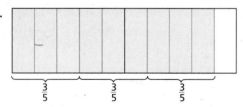

7.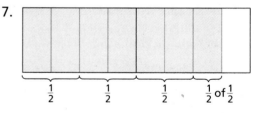

In Exercises 8–15, find the quotient. Simplify, if possible.

8. $3\dfrac{1}{5} \div \dfrac{4}{5}$

9. $\dfrac{2}{3} \div 4\dfrac{2}{3}$

10. $\dfrac{17}{8} \div \dfrac{7}{8}$

11. $1\dfrac{9}{10} \div \dfrac{3}{10}$

12. $2\dfrac{7}{8} \div \dfrac{1}{2}$

13. $\dfrac{16}{3} \div \dfrac{1}{6}$

14. $4\dfrac{5}{6} \div \dfrac{1}{2}$

15. $\dfrac{13}{4} \div \dfrac{2}{3}$

Communicating In Exercises 16–18, use estimation to decide whether the quotient is greater than 1 or less than 1. Explain your reasoning.

16. $\dfrac{4}{5} \div \dfrac{1}{5}$

17. $\dfrac{5}{4} \div 2$

18. $\dfrac{2}{3} \div \dfrac{1}{9}$

Algebra and Mental Math   In Exercises 19–21, solve.

19. $b \div \frac{1}{6} = 11$

20. $b \div \frac{1}{2} = \frac{13}{2}$

21. $1\frac{3}{4} \div b = \frac{7}{3}$

22. *Travel*   You are driving across South Dakota. You stop at the border and plan to stop every 100 miles. The distance across South Dakota on the map is $2\frac{13}{16}$ inches. On the map, $\frac{3}{4}$ inch represents 100 miles. How many times will you stop *in* the state?

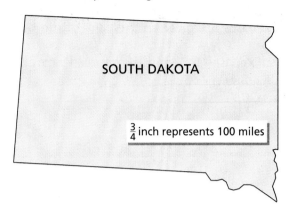

SOUTH DAKOTA

$\frac{3}{4}$ inch represents 100 miles

23. *CD Player*   After the batteries are charged, your portable CD player will run for $4\frac{1}{2}$ hours. An average CD plays for $\frac{5}{6}$ hour. How many CDs can you play before the batteries run down?

24. *Division Puzzle*   Complete the puzzle below by finding the values of *w*, *x*, *y*, and *z*. Name the problem-solving strategy or strategies you used.

$$w \times \frac{1}{2} = x, \ x \times \frac{4}{5} = y, \ y \times \frac{1}{3} = z, \ z \times \frac{3}{4} = \frac{45}{4}$$

Integrated Review

Reading a Graph   The bar graph shows the amount of money spent in vending machines per person per week for different countries. *(Source: Euromonitor Market Direction)*

25. How much more is spent in Japan than in the United States?

26. Which two countries spent about $100 per person per year?

Making Connections within Mathematics

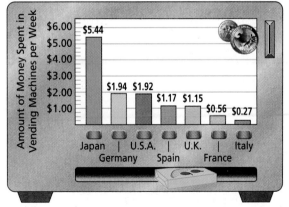

Amount of Money Spent in Vending Machines per Week

$6.00 — $5.44
$5.00
$4.00
$3.00
$2.00 — $1.94 $1.92
$1.00 — $1.17 $1.15 — $0.56 $0.27

Japan | U.S.A. | U.K. | Italy
Germany   Spain   France

Exploration and Extension

27. *Building Your Chapter Project*   You are making prizes for your picnic. Each prize is a small bag that holds $\frac{2}{3}$ cup of fruit and nut mix. You are filling the bags from a container that holds $12\frac{5}{6}$ cups of the mix. How many bags will you fill? Decide on another prize that you will make. Explain how to use division of fractions to make the prize.

Take this test as you would take a test in class. The answers to the exercises are given in the back of the book.

In Exercises 1–8, find the product or quotient. Simplify, if possible. **(8.1–8.4)**

1. $\frac{3}{8} \times 2$

2. $5 \times \frac{4}{7}$

3. $\frac{5}{9}$ of $\frac{1}{2}$

4. $\frac{1}{6} \times \frac{3}{4}$

5. $1\frac{1}{7} \times 3\frac{2}{3}$

6. $\frac{3}{7}$ of $2\frac{4}{5}$

7. $7\frac{1}{5} \div \frac{2}{5}$

8. $6\frac{1}{2} \div \frac{3}{4}$

Algebra and Mental Math In Exercises 9–14, solve. **(8.1, 8.2, 8.4)**

9. $\frac{x}{4} \times 3 = \frac{9}{4}$

10. $y \times \frac{5}{6} = 10$

11. $\frac{1}{5} \times \frac{m}{3} = \frac{2}{15}$

12. $\frac{7}{n} \times \frac{4}{5} = \frac{28}{45}$

13. $a \div \frac{1}{7} = 6$

14. $2\frac{3}{8} \div b = \frac{19}{8}$

Geometry In Exercises 15–17, find the area. **(8.1–8.3)**

15.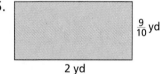
$\frac{9}{10}$ yd

2 yd

16.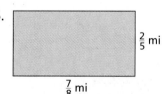
$\frac{2}{5}$ mi

$\frac{7}{8}$ mi

17.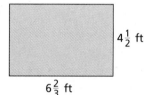
$4\frac{1}{2}$ ft

$6\frac{2}{3}$ ft

In Exercises 18–21, find the product or quotient of the numbers shown on the number line. **(8.1–8.4)**

18. $J \times D$

19. $C \times B$

20. $I \times C$

21. $H \div E$

22. *Statistics* A survey asked 48 students to name their favorite gelatin flavor. One sixth chose grape, three eighths chose blue raspberry, one third chose cherry, and one eighth chose lime. How many students chose each flavor? **(8.1)**

23. *Making Gelatin* You are making gelatin and need $4\frac{1}{2}$ cups of water. You use a $\frac{3}{4}$-cup measuring cup. How many times do you need to fill the measuring cup to get the water you need? **(8.4)**

8.5 Using Reciprocals to Divide Fractions

What you should learn:

Goal 1 How to use reciprocals to divide fractions

Goal 2 How to use division of fractions to solve real-life problems

Why you should learn it:

Knowing how to divide fractions can help you make comparisons of sizes. An example is comparing the sizes of two projects you made in art class.

Goal 1 Using Reciprocals

In Lesson 8.4, you learned one way to divide fractions. In this lesson, you will learn another way to divide fractions. It is called "multiply by the reciprocal."

Two fractions are **reciprocals** if their product is 1. For example, $\frac{2}{5}$ and $\frac{5}{2}$ are reciprocals because $\frac{2}{5} \times \frac{5}{2} = 1$.

Using Reciprocals to Divide Fractions

To divide one fraction by another fraction, multiply the first fraction by the reciprocal of the second fraction.

Example: $\frac{8}{3} \div \frac{2}{5} = \frac{8}{3} \times \frac{5}{2} = \frac{40}{6} = \frac{20}{3}$, or $6\frac{2}{3}$

Example 1 *Dividing Fractions*

a. $\frac{3}{4} \div \frac{3}{8} = \frac{3}{4} \times \frac{8}{3}$ *Multiply by reciprocal.*

$= \frac{24}{12}$ *Multiply.*

$= 2$ *Simplify.*

b. $\frac{5}{3} \div \frac{1}{2} = \frac{5}{3} \times \frac{2}{1}$ *Multiply by reciprocal.*

$= \frac{10}{3}$ *Multiply.*

$= 3\frac{1}{3}$ *Simplify.*

c. $\frac{8}{3} \div \frac{7}{2} = \frac{8}{3} \times \frac{2}{7}$ *Multiply by reciprocal.*

$= \frac{16}{21}$ *Multiply.* ■

Study Tip

Remember that there are usually many ways to solve a problem. For instance, in Example 2 on page 378, you could solve the problem by drawing a diagram and counting the number of tiles. Can you think of another way to solve the problem?

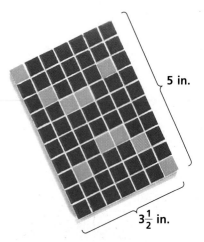

Real Life
Art

Example 2   *Dividing Fractions*

You made two mosaics in art class, as shown at the left.

a. In terms of area, how *much larger* is the blue mosaic than the gold one?

b. In terms of area, how *many times larger* is the blue mosaic than the gold one?

5 in.

$3\frac{1}{2}$ **in.**

Solution   Both of these questions ask you to compare the areas of the two mosaics.

$$\text{Area} = 3\frac{1}{2} \times 4 \qquad \text{\textit{Dimensions of gold mosaic}}$$

$$= 14 \text{ sq in.} \qquad \text{\textit{Area of gold mosaic}}$$

$$\text{Area} = 3\frac{1}{2} \times 5 \qquad \text{\textit{Dimensions of blue mosaic}}$$

$$= \frac{35}{2}, \text{ or } 17\frac{1}{2} \text{ sq in.} \qquad \text{\textit{Area of blue mosaic}}$$

a. To find how *much larger* the blue mosaic is, subtract the area of the gold mosaic from the area of the blue one.

$$17\frac{1}{2} - 14 = 3\frac{1}{2} \text{ sq in.} \qquad \text{\textit{How much larger?}}$$

b. To find how *many times larger* the blue mosaic is, divide the area of the blue mosaic by the area of the gold one.

$$17\frac{1}{2} \div 14 = \frac{35}{2} \times \frac{1}{14} \qquad \text{\textit{Multiply by reciprocal.}}$$

$$= \frac{5}{4}, \text{ or } 1\frac{1}{4} \qquad \text{\textit{How many times larger?}}$$

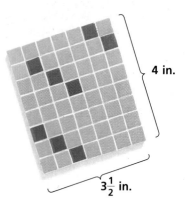

4 in.

$3\frac{1}{2}$ **in.**

Communicating about MATHEMATICS

▶ **Sharing Ideas about the Lesson**

Extending the Example Suppose the blue mosaic had dimensions of $3\frac{1}{2}$ by 10 inches. How would that change the answers to Example 2? Explain.

EXERCISES

Think and Discuss

▶ **CHECK for Understanding**

In Exercises 1 and 2, complete the statement.

1. The reciprocal of $\boxed{?}$ is $\frac{7}{5}$.

2. The reciprocal of $\frac{1}{9}$ is $\boxed{?}$.

Error Analysis In Exercises 3 and 4, describe and correct the error.

3. $\frac{7}{8} \div \frac{5}{6} \cancel{=} \frac{7}{8} \div \frac{6}{5}$

4. $\frac{5}{9} \div \frac{3}{5} \cancel{=} \frac{9}{5} \times \frac{3}{5}$

Auto Racing The lengths of two motor speedways are given below.

Indianapolis, Indiana: $\frac{5}{2}$ miles

Charlotte, North Carolina: $\frac{3}{2}$ miles

5. How *much longer* is the Indianapolis speedway than the Charlotte speedway?

6. How *many times longer* is the Indianapolis speedway than the Charlotte speedway?

Every Memorial Day weekend, approximately 300,000 spectators attend the Indianapolis 500 automobile race at the Indianapolis Motor Speedway.

Independent Practice

In Exercises 7–10, find the reciprocal of the number.

7. $\frac{4}{5}$

8. $\frac{7}{9}$

9. $\frac{11}{6}$

10. $\frac{1}{8}$

Measurement In Exercises 11 and 12, use a ruler to measure both line segments to the nearest $\frac{1}{8}$ inch. Use division to find how many of the shorter line segments it would take to make the longer one.

11. |————————————|

|————|

12. |——————————————|

|————|

13. How many $\frac{1}{4}$-inch pieces of ribbon can you cut from $\frac{7}{8}$ yard of ribbon?

14. How many $\frac{2}{3}$-cup servings are in a box of cereal that contains $12\frac{1}{3}$ cups?

Finding a Pattern In Exercises 15–17, solve the equations. Then describe any patterns that you see.

15. $\frac{7}{8} \div \frac{1}{2} = t$

$\frac{7}{8} \div \frac{1}{3} = t$

$\frac{7}{8} \div \frac{1}{4} = t$

16. $x \div \frac{1}{4} = \frac{36}{2}$

$x \div \frac{1}{5} = \frac{45}{2}$

$x \div \frac{1}{6} = \frac{54}{2}$

17. $\frac{7}{6} \div n = \frac{28}{6}$

$\frac{7}{6} \div n = \frac{21}{6}$

$\frac{7}{6} \div n = \frac{14}{6}$

In Exercises 18–26, find the quotient. Simplify, if possible.

18. $\frac{5}{8} \div \frac{1}{6}$

19. $\frac{9}{10} \div \frac{2}{5}$

20. $\frac{7}{16} \div \frac{1}{4}$

21. $\frac{8}{9} \div \frac{2}{3}$

22. $\frac{14}{5} \div \frac{2}{3}$

23. $\frac{13}{10} \div \frac{3}{4}$

24. $\frac{22}{5} \div \frac{1}{3}$

25. $\frac{15}{4} \div \frac{5}{6}$

26. $\frac{27}{16} \div \frac{5}{8}$

Butterflies Use the list below of the widths of three kinds of butterflies. *(Source: The Audubon Society)*

Monarch	$3\frac{1}{2}$ inches
Tiger Swallowtail	$5\frac{3}{4}$ inches
Metalmark	$1\frac{1}{8}$ inches

Monarch butterflies make long flights south each fall in search of warmer weather. They can migrate from as far north as Canada to Florida or Mexico.

27. How *much wider* is the swallowtail than the monarch?

28. How *many times wider* is the monarch than the metalmark?

29. How *many times wider* is the swallowtail than the metalmark?

30. *You Be the Teacher* You are making flash cards from a sheet of paper that is $\frac{17}{2}$ inches by 11 inches. Each flash card is to be $\frac{17}{8}$ inches by $\frac{11}{4}$ inches. How many flash cards can you make?

Integrated Review

Making Connections within Mathematics

Probability Find the probability that the spinner will land on the given color.

31. Yellow

32. Red

33. Blue

Geometry In Exercises 34–36, copy each diagram. Then label each part of the square using the fractions $\frac{1}{2}, \frac{1}{4}, \frac{1}{8}$, or $\frac{1}{16}$.

34.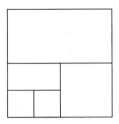

35.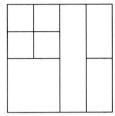

36.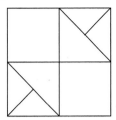

37. *It's Up to You* Make a different square diagram like those shown above. Design it with parts that are the fractions $\frac{1}{2}$, $\frac{1}{4}, \frac{1}{8}$, or $\frac{1}{16}$.

 38. *Building Your Chapter Project* To raise money for the picnic, your class is selling bags of popcorn. Each bag takes $\frac{15}{4}$ minutes to pop. How many bags can you pop in one hour? Choose another item to sell. The time it takes to make each item should be a fraction. Find how many you can make in one hour.

Mixed REVIEW

Working Backward Copy and complete the model. **(1.7)**

1.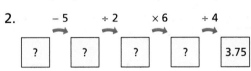

	× 3	÷ 6	+ 9	− 4	
?		?	?	?	8

2.

	− 5	÷ 2	× 6	÷ 4	
?		?	?	?	3.75

Divide. (4.5–4.7, 8.4)

3. $45.9 \div 3$ **4.** $204.05 \div 11$ **5.** $50.32 \div 6.8$ **6.** $76.86 \div 4.5$

7. $680 \div 1000$ **8.** $7500 \div 100$ **9.** $\frac{9}{4} \div \frac{3}{4}$ **10.** $\frac{7}{2} \div \frac{5}{6}$

Find the mean of the numbers. (5.3)

11. 28, 34, 55   **12.** 22, 19, 16, 27   **13.** 100, 46, 80, 81, 43

Find a fraction that is between the two fractions. Explain how you know your answer is correct. (6.5)

14. $\frac{1}{4}, \frac{1}{3}$ **15.** $\frac{5}{8}, \frac{3}{4}$ **16.** $\frac{7}{10}, \frac{4}{5}$

8.6

Dividing Mixed Numbers

What you should learn:

Goal 1 How to divide mixed numbers, fractions, and whole numbers

Goal 2 How to use division of mixed numbers to solve real-life problems

Why you should learn it:

Knowing how to divide mixed numbers can help you gather data for a science project. An example is finding the average length of a breed of squirrel.

Goal 1 **Dividing Mixed Numbers**

In Lesson 8.3, you learned that to multiply mixed numbers you first rewrite them as improper fractions. The same strategy applies to dividing mixed numbers.

Dividing Mixed Numbers

To divide mixed numbers, first rewrite them as improper fractions. Then multiply the first fraction by the reciprocal of the second. Simplify, if possible.

Example 1 *Dividing Mixed Numbers*

a. $6\frac{1}{2} \div 2\frac{1}{2} = \frac{13}{2} \div \frac{5}{2}$ *Rewrite as improper fractions.*

$\qquad = \frac{13}{2} \times \frac{2}{5}$ *Multiply by reciprocal.*

$\qquad = \frac{26}{10}$ *Multiply.*

$\qquad = \frac{13}{5}$, or $2\frac{3}{5}$ *Simplify.*

b. $3 \div 2\frac{1}{2} = 3 \div \frac{5}{2}$ *Rewrite as improper fraction.*

$\qquad = 3 \times \frac{2}{5}$ *Multiply by reciprocal.*

$\qquad = \frac{6}{5}$, or $1\frac{1}{5}$ *Multiply.*

c. $2\frac{1}{2} \div 3 = \frac{5}{2} \div \frac{3}{1}$ *Rewrite as improper fractions.*

$\qquad = \frac{5}{2} \times \frac{1}{3}$ *Multiply by reciprocal.*

$\qquad = \frac{5}{6}$ *Multiply.*

Notice that the reciprocal of a whole number is the fraction that has 1 as its numerator and the whole number as its denominator. For instance, the reciprocal of 3 is $\frac{1}{3}$. ∎

Squirrels eat berries, corn, fruit, nuts, mushrooms, and seeds. They spend most of their time looking for food.

Real Life
Wildlife

Example 2 *Finding an Average*

Your science class is trying to find the average length of an adult gray squirrel. To do this, you measure the lengths (head to tip of tail) of five squirrels, as shown below. What is the average length?

$$1\frac{3}{4} \text{ feet}, \quad 1\frac{2}{3} \text{ feet}, \quad 2 \text{ feet}, \quad 1\frac{5}{6} \text{ feet}, \quad 1\frac{11}{12} \text{ feet}$$

Solution Begin by adding the five lengths.

$$1\frac{3}{4} + 1\frac{2}{3} + 2 + 1\frac{5}{6} + 1\frac{11}{12} = 1\frac{9}{12} + 1\frac{8}{12} + 2 + 1\frac{10}{12} + 1\frac{11}{12}$$
$$= 6\frac{38}{12}, \text{ or } 9\frac{1}{6}$$

To find the average length, divide this total by 5.

$$\text{Average length} = 9\frac{1}{6} \div 5 \qquad \textit{Divide sum of lengths by 5.}$$

$$= \frac{55}{6} \div 5 \qquad \textit{Rewrite as improper fraction.}$$

$$= \frac{55}{6} \times \frac{1}{5} \qquad \textit{Multiply by reciprocal.}$$

$$= \frac{55}{30} \qquad \textit{Multiply.}$$

$$= \frac{11}{6}, \text{ or } 1\frac{5}{6} \qquad \textit{Simplify.}$$

The average length is $1\frac{5}{6}$ feet. ∎

Communicating about **MATHEMATICS**

▶ **Sharing Ideas about the Lesson**

Extending the Example After finding the average length, two more lengths were added to the data: $1\frac{2}{3}$ feet and 2 feet. What is the average length of the seven squirrels? What do you notice? Explain.

EXERCISES

Guided Practice

Think and Discuss

▶ **CHECK for Understanding**

In Exercises 1 and 2, explain each step of the solution.

1. $2\frac{3}{5} \div 6 = \frac{13}{5} \div \frac{6}{1}$

$\quad\quad\quad = \frac{13}{5} \times \frac{1}{6}$

$\quad\quad\quad = \frac{13}{30}$

2. $4\frac{2}{3} \div 3\frac{1}{2} = \frac{14}{3} \div \frac{7}{2}$

$\quad\quad\quad\quad = \frac{14}{3} \times \frac{2}{7}$

$\quad\quad\quad\quad = \frac{28}{21}$

$\quad\quad\quad\quad = \frac{4}{3},$ or $1\frac{1}{3}$

3. Use two different methods to solve $5 \div 3\frac{3}{4}$. Which method do you prefer? Explain.

4. Divide $3\frac{1}{2}$ cakes among 28 students. Explain.

5. Does it matter which fraction you find the reciprocal of when dividing fractions? Give examples to support your answer.

Independent Practice

Chocolate Taste Tests   In Exercises 6–8, divide the hot chocolate evenly among the people.

6. Divide $24\frac{1}{2}$ ounces among 5 people.

7. Divide $4\frac{1}{2}$ cups among 5 people.

8. Divide $5\frac{3}{4}$ cups among 6 people.

9. Copy the model. What mixed number does it represent? Divide the mixed number by 3 and show the results on your sketch.

Artemis and Tami work for a consumer company that did a national taste test for hot chocolate.

In Exercises 10–13, match the problem with an equivalent problem.

a. $\frac{12}{5} \times \frac{3}{7}$

b. $\frac{18}{5} \times \frac{1}{3}$

c. $3 \div \frac{5}{3}$

d. $\frac{7}{3} \div \frac{12}{5}$

10. $3 \div 1\frac{2}{3}$

11. $2\frac{1}{3} \div 2\frac{2}{5}$

12. $2\frac{2}{5} \div 2\frac{1}{3}$

13. $3\frac{3}{5} \div 3$

In Exercises 14–21, divide. Check that your answer is reasonable.

14. $1\frac{2}{5} \div 1\frac{2}{3}$
15. $6\frac{2}{3} \div 1\frac{1}{4}$
16. $7 \div 8\frac{2}{5}$
17. $2 \div 2\frac{3}{8}$

18. $4\frac{1}{6} \div 5$
19. $3\frac{4}{5} \div 4$
20. $4\frac{1}{2} \div 2\frac{1}{3}$
21. $10 \div 5\frac{5}{7}$

Number Sense In Exercises 22–24, complete the statement with *sometimes*, *always*, or *never*.

22. The reciprocal of a fraction is $?$ less than the fraction itself.

23. A whole number divided by a mixed number is $?$ greater than 1.

24. A mixed number divided by a whole number is $?$ greater than 1.

Fitness You and 3 friends go to exercise at the gym. The table at the right shows the number of minutes each of you used a stairclimber and a stationary bicycle.

25. What is the average time for the stairclimber?

26. What is the average time for the stationary bicycle?

27. How *many times more* is the average time on the bicycle than the average time on the stairclimber?

	Stair-climber	Stationary bicycle
You	$10\frac{1}{5}$	$19\frac{1}{4}$
Felicia	$11\frac{7}{10}$	$22\frac{1}{6}$
Enrico	$9\frac{1}{2}$	$22\frac{5}{12}$
Kali	$10\frac{3}{5}$	$20\frac{1}{6}$

Integrated Review   *Making Connections within Mathematics*

Reasoning Name the number that does not belong in the list. Explain.

28. $\frac{8}{3}, \frac{16}{9}, 2\frac{4}{6}, 16 \div 6, 2\frac{2}{3}$

29. $\frac{2}{10}, \frac{11}{2}, \frac{33}{6}, 5\frac{1}{2}, 5.5$

30. $0.2, \frac{2}{10}, 2\%, \frac{1}{5}, 20\%$

31. $1.25, \frac{5}{4}, 125\%, 12.5, 1\frac{1}{4}$

32. $1.8, 18\%, \frac{27}{15}, 1\frac{8}{10}, \frac{9}{5}$

33. $33\frac{1}{3}\%, \frac{7}{21}, \frac{1}{16}$ of $2, \frac{1}{3}, \frac{3}{9}$

Exploration and Extension

34. *Building Your Chapter Project* You have a roll of white paper to cover the tables at your picnic. The roll has $83\frac{3}{4}$ ft of paper on it. Each picnic table is $8\frac{1}{3}$ ft long. How many tables can you cover completely?

Materials Needed: plain paper, colored pencils or pens

In Lesson 2.6 (page 84), you studied the Distributive Property using whole numbers.

$$8(30 + 7) = 8 \times 30 + 8 \times 7 \qquad \textit{The Distributive Property}$$

The property also applies to decimals, fractions, and mixed numbers.

Part A *The Distributive Property: A Whole Number Times a Mixed Number* Here are two ways to find the product $2 \times 1\frac{2}{5}$.

Model 1

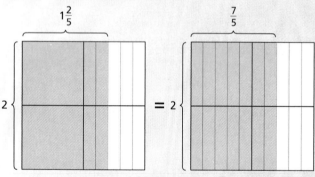

Summary of Steps

$$2 \times 1\frac{2}{5} = 2 \times \left(1 + \frac{2}{5}\right) = 2 \times 1 + 2 \times \frac{2}{5} = 2 + \frac{4}{5} = 2\frac{4}{5}$$

Model 2

Summary of Steps

$$2 \times 1\frac{2}{5} = 2 \times \frac{7}{5} = \frac{14}{5} = 2\frac{4}{5}$$

1. Which of the above models uses the Distributive Property? How can you tell? Use the Distributive Property to find $3 \times 2\frac{1}{4}$. Draw a model to check your result.

2. Which of the above models multiplies by first rewriting as an improper fraction? Use that method to find $3 \times 2\frac{1}{4}$. Draw a model to check your result.

3. Compare Exercises 1 and 2. Which method of finding $3 \times 2\frac{1}{4}$ do you prefer? Why?

Part B *The Distributive Property: A Fraction Times a Mixed Number*

Here is a model for finding the product $\frac{1}{2} \times 2\frac{2}{3}$.

Summary of Steps

$$\frac{1}{2} \times 2\frac{2}{3} = \frac{1}{2} \times \left(2 + \frac{2}{3}\right) = \frac{1}{2} \times 2 + \frac{1}{2} \times \frac{2}{3} = 1 + \frac{1}{3} = 1\frac{1}{3}$$

4. Use the Distributive Property to find each product. Draw a model to check your result.

   a. $\frac{1}{3} \times 3\frac{3}{8}$ b. $\frac{1}{2} \times 4\frac{4}{5}$ c. $\frac{1}{4} \times 4\frac{4}{7}$

Part C *It's Up to You*

5. Copy and complete the following. For each product, decide which method is more convenient for you. Explain your reasoning.

Problem	Distributive Property	Using Improper Fractions
a. $\frac{1}{2} \times 2\frac{4}{5}$	$\frac{1}{2}\left(2 + \frac{4}{5}\right) = \boxed{?}$	$\frac{1}{2} \times \frac{14}{5} = \boxed{?}$
b. $\frac{1}{2} \times 2\frac{3}{5}$	$\frac{1}{2}\left(2 + \frac{3}{5}\right) = \boxed{?}$	$\frac{1}{2} \times \frac{13}{5} = \boxed{?}$
c. $\frac{3}{2} \times 4\frac{2}{3}$	$\frac{3}{2}\left(4 + \frac{2}{3}\right) = \boxed{?}$	$\frac{3}{2} \times \frac{14}{3} = \boxed{?}$

On Your Own   Critical Thinking

In Exercises 6–9, solve the problem in two ways: (1) using the Distributive Property and (2) using an improper fraction.

6. $\frac{1}{2} \times 6\frac{2}{3}$ 7. $\frac{1}{3} \times 6\frac{3}{5}$ 8. $\frac{2}{3} \times 4\frac{1}{4}$ 9. $\frac{2}{5} \times 5\frac{1}{5}$

10. *Error Analysis* What is wrong with the following?

$$2\frac{1}{3} \times 3\frac{1}{4} = (2 \times 3) + \left(\frac{1}{3} \times \frac{1}{4}\right)$$

What is the correct way to solve this problem?

8.7

A Window to Geometry

What you should learn:

Goal 1 How to find the area of a right triangle

Goal 2 How to use the area of a right triangle with problem-solving strategies

Why you should learn it:

Knowing how to find the area of a right triangle can help you solve problems in geometry. An example is finding a pattern for the areas of six triangles.

Goal 1 **The Area of a Right Triangle**

A 90° angle is a **right angle.** A triangle that has a right angle is a **right triangle.**

Lesson Investigation

■ **Investigating the Area of a Right Triangle**

Group Activity Use a ruler to draw a diagonal on a 3-inch by 5-inch card. What is the area of the entire card? Cut the card along the diagonal to form two right triangles. Compare the sizes of the two triangles. What is the area of each triangle? Write a rule for finding the area of a right triangle.

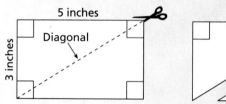

In this investigation, you may have discovered the following.

Area of a Right Triangle

The area of a right triangle is one half the product of its **base** and **height.**

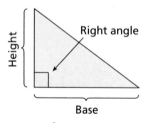

Area = $\frac{1}{2}$ × Base × Height

Example 1 *Finding the Area of a Right Triangle*

Find the area of the triangle at the left.

Solution

Area $= \frac{1}{2} \times 4\frac{1}{2} \times 3\frac{1}{2} = \frac{1}{2} \times \frac{9}{2} \times \frac{7}{2} = \frac{63}{8}$, or $7\frac{7}{8}$ sq cm ■

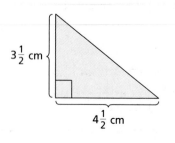

Example 2 *Areas of Triangles*

Find the area of each triangle. Then describe the pattern.

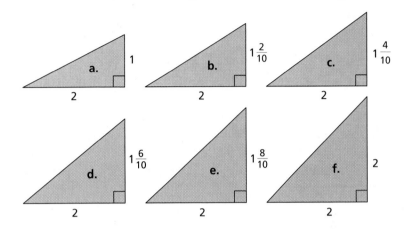

Solution

a. Area $= \frac{1}{2} \times 2 \times 1 = 1$

b. Area $= \frac{1}{2} \times 2 \times 1\frac{2}{10} = 1\frac{2}{10}$

c. Area $= \frac{1}{2} \times 2 \times 1\frac{4}{10} = 1\frac{4}{10}$

d. Area $= \frac{1}{2} \times 2 \times 1\frac{6}{10} = 1\frac{6}{10}$

e. Area $= \frac{1}{2} \times 2 \times 1\frac{8}{10} = 1\frac{8}{10}$

f. Area $= \frac{1}{2} \times 2 \times 2 = 2$

Each area is $\frac{2}{10}$ greater than the previous area. ■

Communicating about MATHEMATICS

Problem Solving
Look For a Pattern

▶ **Sharing Ideas about the Lesson**

Extending the Example Look at the six products in Example 2. There is a quick way to find each product. Can you see what it is? Describe it.

EXERCISES

Guided Practice

Think and Discuss

▶ CHECK for Understanding

In Exercises 1–3, use the triangle at the right to match the measure with its description.

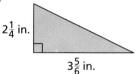

a. base   b. height   c. area

1. $4\frac{5}{16}$ sq in.   2. $3\frac{5}{6}$ in.   3. $2\frac{1}{4}$ in.

Reasoning In Exercises 4–6, decide whether the triangle is a right triangle. Explain.

4.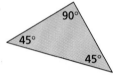

5.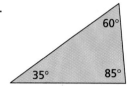

6.

7. Give a real-life example of a right angle.

Independent Practice

In Exercises 8–10, use a centimeter ruler to draw a right triangle that has the given base and height. Then find its area.

8. *Base:* $2\frac{1}{2}$ cm

    Height: 3 cm

9. *Base:* 4 cm

    Height: $3\frac{1}{2}$ cm

10. *Base:* $5\frac{1}{2}$ cm

     Height: $2\frac{1}{2}$ cm

Finding a Pattern In Exercises 11 and 12, find the areas for the triangles. Describe any patterns that you see. Draw the next two triangles that fit the pattern.

11. a. 0.5 / 0.5   b. 1.0 / 1.0   c. 1.5 / 1.5   d. 2.0 / 2.0

12. a. $\frac{1}{2}$ / $\frac{1}{2}$ b. $\frac{1}{2}$ / 1   c. $\frac{1}{2}$ / 2   d. $\frac{1}{2}$ / 4

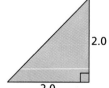
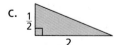

13. *Community Service*   You are planting
    trees in a park shaped like the triangle
    shown at the right. Each tree needs $9\frac{1}{3}$
    square feet of area to grow properly.
    How many trees can you plant?

14. Both dimensions of the park are multi-
    plied by 3. Which of the following is the
    number of trees you can plant? Explain.

    a. 180   b. 270   c. 540

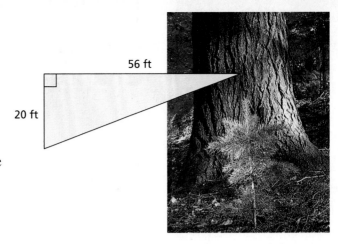

56 ft

20 ft

Algebra and Mental Math   In Exercises 15–17, find the value of *x*.

15. Area = 3 sq in.

x

$\frac{3}{4}$ in.

16. Area = 4.6 sq cm

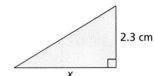

2.3 cm

x

17. Area = 0.18 sq m

x

x

Geometry   In Exercises 18–20, the figure is made of right
triangles. Find the area of the figure.

18.

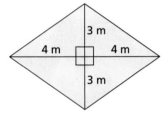

3 m

4 m   4 m

3 m

19.

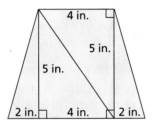

4 in.

5 in.

5 in.

2 in.   4 in.   2 in.

20.

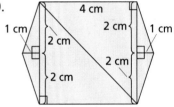

4 cm

1 cm   2 cm   1 cm

2 cm

2 cm

2 cm

Integrated Review

Making Connections within Mathematics

Science   The data below shows the average lengths (in
in.) of 24 species of caterpillars. *(Source: The Audubon Society)*

   2, 1, 2, 2, 2, 4, 1, 2, 2, 3, 3, 2, 1, 5, 4, 1, 2, 3, 3, 4, 4, 6, 1, 1

21. Make a line plot of the data.   22. What is the range of the data?

Exploration and Extension

23. *Think about It*   The large triangle at the
    right is made up of two right triangles.
    Find the area of the figure by finding the
    sum of the areas of the right triangles.
    Describe another way to find the area of
    the large triangle.

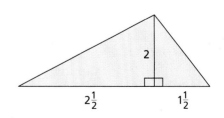

2

$2\frac{1}{2}$ $1\frac{1}{2}$

8 Chapter Summary

What did you learn?

Why did you learn it?

Many real-life problems can be solved using fractions or mixed numbers. Here are some examples you studied in this chapter.

- Find the amount of cheese in 2 pieces of pizza.   **(8.2)**
- Compare the distances run by people in track practice.   **(8.3)**
- Cut shelves from a $7\frac{1}{2}$-foot board.   **(8.4)**
- Compare the sizes of 2 mosaics.   **(8.5)**
- Find the average length of a gray squirrel.   **(8.6)**

How does it fit into the bigger picture of mathematics?

You have now studied operations with decimals and with fractions. Although the rules for adding, subtracting, multiplying and dividing decimals and fractions have differences, they also have similarities. For instance, think about how you would solve $1.3 + 2.4$ and $1\frac{3}{10} + 2\frac{4}{10}$. Do you see any similarities?

Decimals

$$\begin{array}{r} 1.3 \\ + 2.4 \\ \hline 3.7 \end{array}$$

Line up decimal points. Add tenths and add ones.

Mixed Numbers

$$1\frac{3}{10} + 2\frac{4}{10} = 3\frac{7}{10}$$

Add fractions. Then add whole numbers.

Looking for similarities (or differences) in rules for operations with decimals and fractions helps you understand the rules. And understanding the rules helps you to be a better problem solver!

In Exercises 1–4, match the problem with its area model. **(8.1–8.4)**

a. 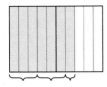 b.  c.   d.

1. $\frac{4}{5} \times \frac{2}{3}$

2. $1\frac{2}{5} \div \frac{3}{5}$

3. $\frac{1}{2} \times \frac{4}{5}$

4. $1\frac{2}{5} \times 1\frac{1}{2}$

In Exercises 5–16, find the product or quotient. Simplify, if possible. **(8.1–8.6)**

5. $7 \times \frac{3}{8}$

6. $\frac{5}{9}$ of 6

7. $\frac{3}{4} \times \frac{1}{6}$

8. $\frac{2}{3} \times \frac{4}{7}$

9. $\frac{1}{5}$ of $7\frac{1}{2}$

10. $2\frac{1}{4} \times 1\frac{1}{7}$

11. $1\frac{1}{5} \div \frac{1}{2}$

12. $3\frac{1}{3} \div \frac{5}{6}$

13. $\frac{10}{9} \div \frac{5}{7}$

14. $\frac{3}{8} \div \frac{2}{5}$

15. $5\frac{2}{3} \div 4\frac{1}{4}$

16. $8 \div 3\frac{4}{5}$

You Be the Teacher   In Exercises 17–22, write two problems:
(a) one with an answer greater than 1 and (b) one with an answer less than 1. **(8.1–8.3, 8.5, 8.6)**

17. fraction × fraction

18. fraction ÷ fraction

19. mixed number ÷ whole number

20. whole number × fraction

21. mixed number × fraction

22. mixed number ÷ mixed number

Geometry   In Exercises 23–25, find the area. **(8.7)**

23.

$\frac{6}{7}$ mi

1 mi

24. $\frac{1}{2}$ ft

$\frac{8}{9}$ ft

25. $5\frac{1}{4}$ km

4 km

26. *Tree Puzzle*   Use the following clues to find the height of each type of broadleaf tree. **(8.3)**

American Elm: Height is $28\frac{1}{8}$ meters.

Red Maple: Height is $\frac{4}{5}$ of American Elm.

Quaking Aspen: Height is $\frac{5}{6}$ of Red Maple.

27. *New Hampshire*   The figure at the right shows the greatest north-south and east-west distances of the state of New Hampshire. Approximate its area. **(8.7)**

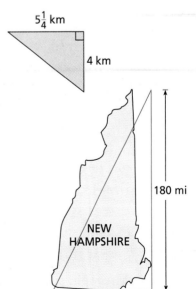

180 mi

NEW HAMPSHIRE

93 mi

In Exercises 28–30, use the following information about the number of visitors (in millions) to national parks in three states. *(Source: National Association of State Park Directors)*

Alabama: $6\frac{3}{50}$ *South Carolina:* $7\frac{24}{25}$ *Wyoming:* $2\frac{1}{50}$

28. As a whole number, Alabama has 6,060,000 park visitors. Write South Carolina's visitors as a whole number.

29. Write Wyoming's park visitors as a whole number.

30. Which of the three states has about 3 times as many park visitors as one of the other three states?

Park Photos   In Exercises 31–35, find the area of each photograph. (The sides are measured in centimeters.)

31.

$4\frac{1}{2}$

$2\frac{4}{5}$

32.

$3\frac{1}{5}$

$4\frac{1}{5}$

33.

$7\frac{1}{5}$

4

34.

$2\frac{3}{5}$

$2\frac{3}{5}$

35.

$4\frac{2}{5}$

$3\frac{1}{2}$ 2

36. *Park Puzzle*   Use the following clues to help you find the names of the national parks shown in the photos above.

- Five times the area of Yosemite's photo is 63.
- The area of Sequoia's photo divided by 36 is $\frac{4}{5}$.
- $\frac{1}{2}$ the area of Everglades' photo is $\frac{168}{25}$.
- The area of Grand Canyon's photo is about $\frac{11}{7}$ the area of Yosemite's photo.
- The area of Yellowstone's photo divided by 13 is $\frac{13}{25}$.

Algebra   In Exercises 1–3, evaluate the product when $n = 3$.

1. $\frac{5}{6}$ of n

2. $n \times 1\frac{9}{10}$

3. $16 \times \frac{n}{12}$

In Exercises 4 and 5, is the statement true or false? Explain.

4. The product of 3 and $\frac{1}{4}$ is $\frac{3}{12}$.

5. The reciprocal of $\frac{1}{7}$ is $\frac{7}{1}$.

In Exercises 6–9, find the product. Simplify, if possible.

6. $\frac{5}{8} \times \frac{1}{5}$

7. $4 \times \frac{3}{5}$

8. $3\frac{1}{6} \times \frac{2}{9}$

9. $2\frac{1}{3} \times 4\frac{3}{8}$

In Exercises 10–13, find the quotient. Simplify, if possible.

10. $\frac{11}{6} \div \frac{5}{6}$

11. $\frac{14}{5} \div \frac{3}{10}$

12. $2\frac{3}{4} \div \frac{3}{5}$

13. $5\frac{1}{2} \div 1\frac{5}{12}$

Geometry   In Exercises 14–16, find the area of the right triangle.

14.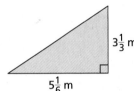

$3\frac{1}{3}$ m

$5\frac{1}{6}$ m

15.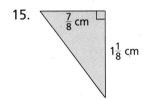

$\frac{7}{8}$ cm

$1\frac{1}{8}$ cm

16.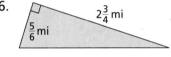

$2\frac{3}{4}$ mi

$\frac{5}{6}$ mi

Health and Nutrition   Use the bar graph at the right. It shows the fraction of people in the United States who take each type of vitamin or mineral. *(Source: NFO Research)*

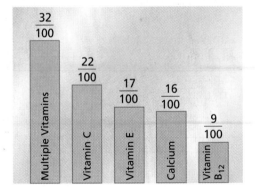

17. One fifth of the people who take multiple vitamins also take iron. What fraction take iron?

18. How *many times more* people take multiple vitamins than take calcium?

Music   Use the figures at the right.

19. How *much longer* is the cello than the violin? How *much wider*?

20. How *many times longer* is the violin than it is wide? Does the cello have the same ratio of length to width as the violin? Explain.

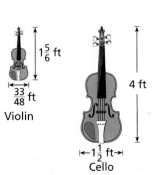

$1\frac{5}{6}$ ft

$\frac{33}{48}$ ft

Violin

4 ft

$1\frac{1}{2}$ ft

Cello

CHAPTER 9

Geometry and Patterns

There are about 100 traditional origami figures, most showing natural forms such as birds, flowers, and fish.

Real Life
Origami

To make the flapping bird shown below, a square piece of paper must be folded along the creases shown in the diagram.

Think and Discuss

1. What are the different shapes that are formed by the creases in the diagram?

2. Which shapes are the same? Which are different?

CHAPTER THEME:

Origami

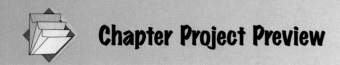
FOLDING Origami Shapes

Theme: Origami Origami is the Japanese art of folding paper to form animals, flowers, and other figures without cutting or pasting the paper. These figures can be very simple or fantastically complex, as the photo on pages 396 and 397 shows.

Even the most complex figures can be made using a series of steps that are simple folds. The steps to making four of these figures are shown on these two pages.

In this project, you will use geometry and the principles of origami to do the following:

➡ **In Lesson 9.1:** Make an origami cat. (page 403)

➡ **In Lesson 9.2:** Make an origami sailboat. (page 409)

➡ **In Lesson 9.3:** Make an origami swan. (page 415)

➡ **In Lesson 9.4:** Make an origami dog. (page 422)

➡ **In Lesson 9.6:** Make an origami airplane. (page 433)

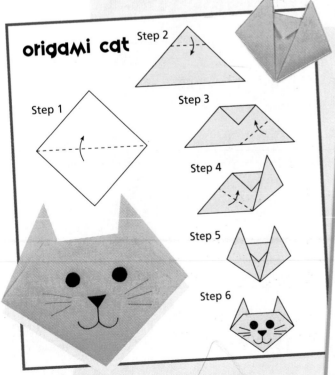

origami cat

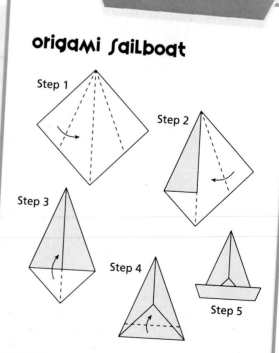

origami sailboat

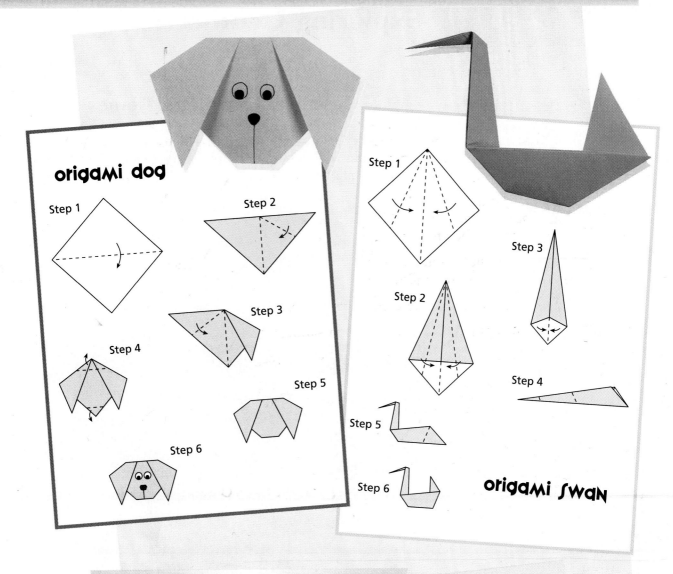

origami dog

Step 1

Step 2

Step 3

Step 4

Step 5

Step 6

origami swan

Step 1

Step 2

Step 3

Step 4

Step 5

Step 6

GETTING STARTED

Materials: plain or origami paper, large envelope, colored pencils or pens

- Place at least five squares of plain or origami paper in a large envelope. Use these materials to complete each portion of the project. You can use the envelope to store your completed figures.

- Decide with your teacher where the figures can be displayed when the project is complete. Plan how the display will be organized.

9.1

Exploring Geometric Figures

What you should learn:

Goal 1 How to describe and estimate with geometric figures

Goal 2 How to identify geometric figures

Why you should learn it:

Knowing how to describe, estimate with, and identify geometric figures can help you describe pieces of art. An example is describing a Moorish floor tiling.

Goal 1 **Describing Geometric Figures**

In geometry, **points** are usually labeled with uppercase letters, such as *A*, *B*, and *C*. **Line segments** and **lines** are labeled as shown below.

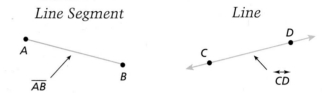

Lesson Investigation

■ **Investigating Geometric Shapes**
Partner Activity Draw a figure on grid paper using line segments. Describe the figure to a partner. (Don't show the figure to your partner.) Ask your partner to use your description to draw the figure. Then compare your partner's drawing to your original figure.

Example 1 *Estimating Lengths*

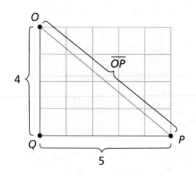

For triangle *OPQ* at the left, describe how to move from point *O* to point *P* by staying on grid lines. Is $\overline{OP}$ longer than $\overline{OQ}$? Longer than $\overline{QP}$? Longer than $\overline{OQ} + \overline{QP}$?

Solution To move from point *O* to point *P*, move 4 units down and 5 units to the right.

By studying the diagram, you can reason that $\overline{OP}$ is longer than $\overline{OQ}$ and $\overline{QP}$, but shorter than $\overline{OQ} + \overline{QP}$. ■

The Alhambra is a palace in Granada, Spain. It was built by the Moors, a Muslim people from northern Africa.

Goal **2** Identifying Geometric Figures

Real Life
Art

Example 2 *Identifying Geometric Figures*

The mosaic at the left was copied from a mosaic at the Alhambra palace. How many different shapes are used in the mosaic? What are the names of the shapes?

Solution The mosaic has 6 different shapes: 3 sizes of triangles, a square, and 2 types of hexagons, or 6-sided figures.

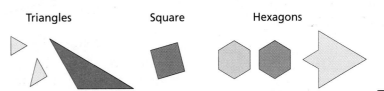

Triangles   Square   Hexagons

■

Communicating about MATHEMATICS

Cooperative
Learning

▶ **Sharing Ideas about the Lesson**

Partner Activity A **polygon** is a geometric figure that has straight sides. The number of sides determines the name of the polygon.

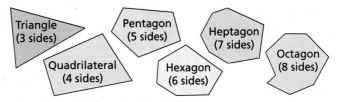

Triangle
(3 sides)

Pentagon
(5 sides)

Heptagon
(7 sides)

Quadrilateral
(4 sides)

Hexagon
(6 sides)

Octagon
(8 sides)

With your partner, use dot paper to create a mosaic. Name the different types of polygons you used.

EXERCISES

▶ **CHECK for Understanding**

In Exercises 1–3, is the figure a polygon? If yes, name it. If not, explain why.

1.   2.   3.

4. *Communicating*   On a sheet of grid paper, copy each figure. Then write a description of how to move from the starting point, clockwise around the figure by staying on grid lines.

a. 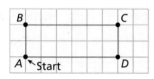   b.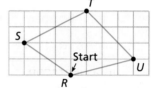

5. Estimate the perimeter of the triangle in Exercise 12.

Independent Practice

In Exercises 6–9, sketch two different polygons of the given shape.

6. Pentagon   7. Quadrilateral   8. Hexagon   9. Octagon

In Exercises 10 and 11, sketch the described figure on grid paper by connecting the points. Then estimate its perimeter.

10. Start at *A*. Move left 3 and down 5 to *B*. Move right 5 and up 1 to *C*. Move up 4 and left 2 to *A*.

11. Start at *V*. Move right 1 to *W*. Move down 3 to *X*. Move left 1 to *Y*. Move left 1 and up 2 to *Z*. Move up 1 and right 1 back to *V*.

Start at the point that is farthest to the left. Then moving counterclockwise, describe how to move around the polygon.

12. 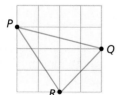   13. 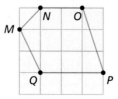   14.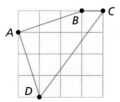

Area In Exercises 15–17, each square in the grid represents 1 square unit. Find the area of the figure. (*Hint:* Count the squares.)

15.

16.

17.

Square Puzzle In Exercises 18 and 19, trace the figure. Show how the figure can be cut once and rearranged to form a square.

18.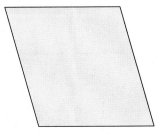

19.

In Exercises 20 and 21, use the figure at the right.

20. Copy the figure and outline a pentagon, a hexagon, and two different sizes of quadrilaterals.

21. How many triangles can you find?

Integrated Review

Making Connections within Mathematics

Perimeter and Area Find the perimeter and area of the figure.

22.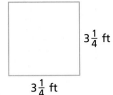

$3\frac{1}{4}$ ft

$3\frac{1}{4}$ ft

23.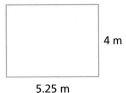

4 m

5.25 m

24.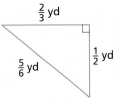

$\frac{2}{3}$ yd

$\frac{1}{2}$ yd

$\frac{5}{6}$ yd

Exploration and Extension

25. **Building Your Chapter Project**
Use the steps on page 398 to make an origami cat. Draw its face. Name the different polygons you see on the front and back of the cat.

Lab 9.2

Investigating Turns and Angles

Materials Needed: grid or dot paper, pencils or pens

Part A *Describing Turns* In the figures below, Felix turns about point *P*.

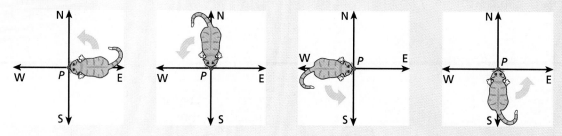

1. To start, which direction is Felix facing?

2. After making $\frac{1}{4}$ of a full turn, which direction is Felix facing? After making another $\frac{1}{4}$ of a full turn? After making another $\frac{1}{4}$ of a full turn?

3. If Felix made a full turn from his starting position, which direction would he be facing?

Part B *Turns and Angles* The triangle at the right is turned $\frac{1}{4}$ of a full turn about point *P*. This turn is called a 90° turn. This is read as a *90 degree turn*.

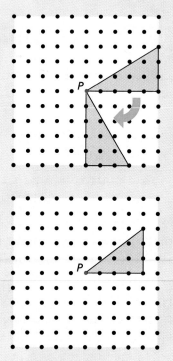

4. Compare the triangle's $\frac{1}{4}$ turn to Felix's $\frac{1}{4}$ turn. Which is clockwise? Which is counter-clockwise?

5. Copy the triangle in the bottom figure on dot paper. Draw the triangle after it has been turned clockwise $\frac{1}{2}$ of a full turn about point *P* and then draw it after another $\frac{3}{4}$ of a full turn.

6. How many degrees is $\frac{1}{2}$ of a full turn? $\frac{3}{4}$ of a full turn? A full turn?

Part C *Drawing Turns*

7. In each drawing, the blue figure has been turned about point *P* to form the red figure. Use degrees to describe the turn. Was the figure turned clockwise or counterclockwise?

a.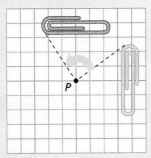

b.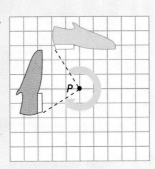

c.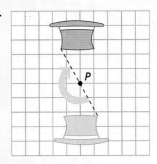

8. Copy each figure on grid or dot paper. Then trace the figure on plain paper. Cut the figure out. Turn each figure about point *P* as indicated and trace each result.

a.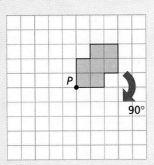

b.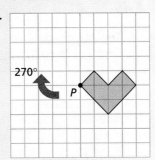

c.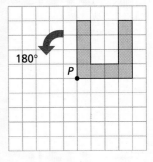

9. Draw a figure on grid or dot paper. Then draw the figure after it has been turned 90° clockwise. Do the same for a 270° counterclockwise turn. What can you conclude?

On Your Own   *Critical Thinking*

Draw a triangle on grid or dot paper. Label one of the corners of the triangle as point *P.* Trace the triangle and cut it out.

10. Turn the triangle 90° clockwise about point *P.* Then turn it another 180° clockwise. Trace the triangle's final position.

11. Turn the triangle 180° clockwise about point *P.* Then turn the triangle another 90° clockwise. Trace the final position of the triangle.

12. Compare the results of Exercises 10 and 11. Are they the same? What can you conclude?

9.2

Angles and Their Measures

What you should learn:

Goal 1 How to identify types of angles

Goal 2 How to use a protractor to measure angles

Why you should learn it:

Knowing how to measure angles can help you work with angles in real life.

Goal 1 — Types of Angles

Definition of Angle

A **ray** is part of a line. It begins at a point and extends in one direction without ending.

An **angle** is formed by two rays that begin at the same point. This point is the **vertex** of the angle, and the rays are the **sides** of the angle.

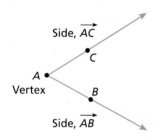

Side, $\overrightarrow{AC}$
C
A — Vertex
B
Side, $\overrightarrow{AB}$

The ray beginning at point A and passing through point B is written $\overrightarrow{AB}$. The two rays at the left are written as $\overrightarrow{AC}$ and $\overrightarrow{AB}$.

The symbol $\angle$ represents an angle. The angle at the left can be named as $\angle A$, as $\angle BAC$, or as $\angle CAB$. Notice that an angle can be named by its vertex, or with 3 letters with the vertex as the middle letter.

Angles can be **acute, right,** or **obtuse.**

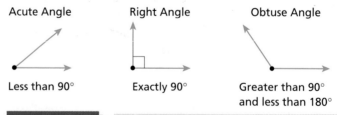

Acute Angle	Right Angle	Obtuse Angle
Less than 90°	Exactly 90°	Greater than 90° and less than 180°

Example 1 — *Types of Angles*

By observation, identify the types of the 4 angles in quadrilateral *DEFG*. Explain.

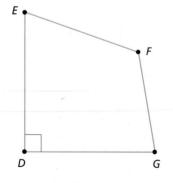

E
F
D
G

Solution

Angle	Type	Comment
$\angle D$, or $\angle EDG$	Right	Measure is 90°.
$\angle E$, or $\angle DEF$	Acute	Measure is less than 90°.
$\angle F$, or $\angle EFG$	Obtuse	Measure is greater than 90°.
$\angle G$, or $\angle FGD$	Acute	Measure is less than 90°. ∎

A **protractor** is used to measure an angle.

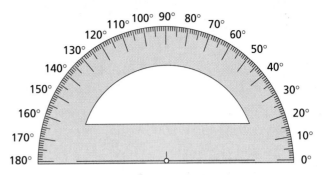

There are lots of angles in this photograph. Use a protractor to measure some of the angles.

Example 2 | *Using a Protractor*

a. Begin by placing the protractor's center on the vertex of the angle.

b. Line up the protrac-tor's 0° line with one ray of the angle.

c. Read the measure on the protractor where the other ray crosses it.

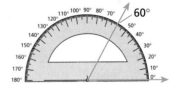

Communicating about MATHEMATICS

▶ **Sharing Ideas about the Lesson**

Partner Activity Draw 4 angles on a sheet of paper. Label the angles as ∠A, ∠B, ∠C, and ∠D. Use a protractor to measure each angle. Write the results on another sheet of paper. Exchange angles with your partner and measure the angles your partner drew. Compare your results. Discuss any differences.

Cooperative Learning

EXERCISES

▶**CHECK for Understanding**

In Exercises 1–3, use the diagram at the right.
Write the given part of the angle.

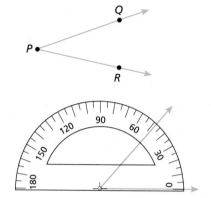

1. The name of the angle
2. The two rays of the angle
3. The vertex of the angle
4. Give a real-life example of an acute angle.
5. Draw a triangle that has one obtuse angle.
6. In the drawing at the right, approximate
   the measure of the angle.

Independent Practice

In Exercises 7–9, use the figure at the right to
match the name of the angle with its
description.

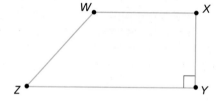

a. ∠Y   b. ∠W   c. ∠Z

7. Obtuse   8. Right   9. Acute

In Exercises 10–12, use a protractor to find the measure of ∠JKL.

10.

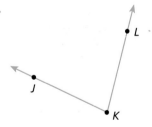

11.

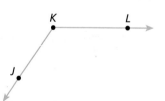

12.

Estimation   In Exercises 13–18, use the figure at the
right. Estimate the measure of the given angle. Choose
from 15°, 45°, 60°, 90°, 95°, or 175°. Do not use a
protractor.

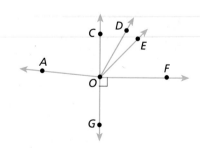

13. ∠DOF   14. ∠COF   15. ∠AOF
16. ∠EOF   17. ∠DOE   18. ∠AOG

19. Find the sum of the measures of angles ∠FOG,
    ∠AOF, and ∠AOG. What can you conclude?

20. Use a protractor to find the measure of
∠*LOM* and ∠*MON*. What is the sum of
the two measures?

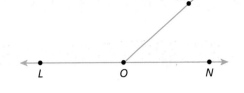

21. *Reasoning* Draw two angles side-by-side
so the sum of their measures is 180°. (The
diagram at the right is an example.)

a. If one of the angles is acute, what must the other one be? Why?

b. If one of the angles is right, what must the other one be? Why?

Detective Work In Exercises 22–24, imagine that you are in a
place that has no right angles. You have a scrap of paper with no
right angles on it. Explain how you can fold the paper twice to
create a right angle. Then use the right angle to help you decide
whether the given angle is acute, right, or obtuse.

22.  23.  24.

25. *Science* Use the photo at the right
of a honeycomb from a beehive. Each
cell of the honeycomb is in the shape
of a hexagon. Use a protractor to
approximate one of the angles of the
hexagon. Is the angle acute, right, or
obtuse?

Integrated Review   *Making Connections within Mathematics*

Measurement Match the animal with its length.

a. 10 mm   b. 0.03 km   c. 25 cm   d. 1.4 m

26. Whale   27. Porpoise   28. Starfish   29. Tadpole

Exploration and Extension

30. *Building Your Chapter Project* Use
the steps on page 398 to make an
origami sailboat. On your sailboat,
use a protractor to measure the 7
angles shown at the right. Classify
them as acute, right, or obtuse.
Compare your measures with others
in your class.

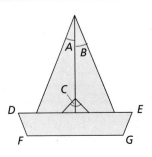

Mixed REVIEW

Write the number as a fraction. **(3.4)**

1. 0.75

2. 0.2

3. 37%

4. 59%

Algebra Use mental math to solve the equation. Then use a calculator to check your answer. **(4.6)**

5. $p \times 100 = 5400$

6. $5900 \div m = 5.9$

7. $y \div 1000 = 0.3$

8. $0.75 \times n = 75$

9. $t \times 100 = 760{,}000$

10. $z \times 1000 = 57$

Find the mean and median of the data. **(5.3, 5.4)**

11. 25, 19, 33, 51

12. 69, 89, 31, 74, 82

13. 7, 10, 4

Decide whether the fractions are equivalent. **(6.3)**

14. $\frac{1}{3}, \frac{4}{12}$

15. $\frac{4}{5}, \frac{8}{15}$

16. $\frac{5}{10}, \frac{1}{2}$

Career Interview

City Planner

Maria Resendiz puts her degree in architecture to work as a city planner. Maria's responsibilities include reviewing permit requests for new construction and designing building plans for local community businesses.

Q: *What math skills do you apply in your work?*
A: Ratios, division, area, and perimeter to name a few. For example, I calculate the square footage of land lots and then figure out how they can be divided into smaller lots.

Q: *Do you use mathematical reasoning?*
A: Yes, I recently had to predict the shadow of a planned office tower using a sun dial and a math formula. I had to decide if the shadow would affect the homes and buildings around it.

Q: *What would you like to tell kids about math?*
A: During my first few years of college, we did a lot of math problems. I couldn't understand why. Then in my last semester, I took a class on architectural technology and I finally saw how everything applied to building. All the time I spent learning math was worth it.

Example **A Number Experiment**

Toss two number cubes (one blue and one red) 10 times. Record the results in a table. For each toss, plot a point on grid paper. Use the point to draw an angle, as shown below. Then use a protractor to measure the angle. Finally, find the average of the 10 angle measures.

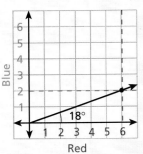

Red number is 6.
Blue number is 2.

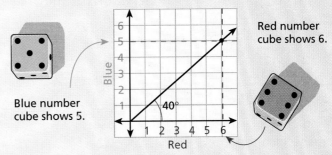

Blue number
cube shows 5.

Red number
cube shows 6.

Solution The first toss of the number cubes is a blue 5 and red 6. This angle is about 40°. The second and third tosses are shown at the left. The fourth through tenth tosses are shown in the table below.

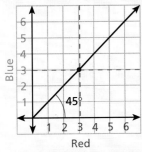

Red number is 3.
Blue number is 3.

Toss	1	2	3	4	5	6	7	8	9	10
Red	6	6	3	4	5	2	3	3	1	2
Blue	5	2	3	5	1	6	5	1	1	1
Angle	40°	18°	45°	51°	11°	72°	59°	18°	45°	27°

You can use a calculator to find the average of the angle measures. Begin by adding the measures to get a sum of 386. Then divide by 10.

386 $\boxed{÷}$ 10 $\boxed{=}$

The average angle measure is 38.6°. ∎

Exercises

1. Try the above experiment for yourself. What average angle measure do you get?

2. If the blue and red numbers are the same, what is the measure of the angle? Explain your reasoning.

3. If you tossed the number cubes 1000 times, what do you think the average angle measure would be? Explain.

9.3

Exploring Congruent and Similar Figures

What you should learn:

Goal 1 How to identify congruent and similar shapes

Goal 2 How to use congruence to solve real-life problems

Why you should learn it:

Knowing how to identify congruent figures can help you compare shapes, such as those used in surveying land.

Goal 1 Congruent and Similar Shapes

Two geometric figures are **congruent** if they have exactly the same shape and the same size. Two figures are **similar** if they have the same shape.

Similar
Congruent

Same size
and shape

Similar
Not Congruent

Same shape but
not same size

Not Similar
Not Congruent

Not same
size or shape

Lesson Investigation

■ Investigating Congruent Figures

Group Activity Trace and cut out the figures below. If possible, draw lines that can be used to divide each figure into 2 congruent parts. Then cut the figure along the lines. Are the 2 pieces congruent?

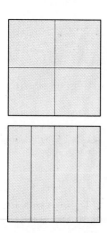

Example 1 *Drawing Congruent Figures*

Show how a square can be divided into 4 congruent parts.

Solution There are many ways to solve this problem. Three are shown at the left. Can you find other ways? ■

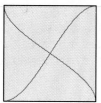

Real Life
Construction

Two polygons are congruent if their angles *and* sides have the same measures. This means that if you place one figure on top of the other, they will match exactly. For example, triangle *ABC* is congruent to triangle *DEF*.

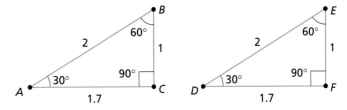

Congruent and similar shapes are often used in construction. What congruent and similar shapes can you see in this photo?

Example **2** *Comparing Quadrilaterals*

You work for a surveying company. You are asked to compare two plots of land shaped like the quadrilaterals below. You measure the sides and discover they have the same lengths. Does this mean the quadrilaterals are congruent? Are they similar?

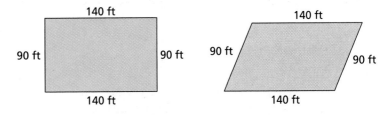

Solution The quadrilaterals are *not* congruent or similar. Their sides have the same lengths. Their angles do not have the same measures. ∎

Communicating about **MATHEMATICS**

Cooperative
Learning

▶ **Sharing Ideas about the Lesson**

Partner Activity Draw a triangle. Don't show your partner the triangle. Use a ruler to measure the triangle's sides. Using only words (no pictures), describe the triangle to your partner. After your partner draws the triangle, cut out both triangles and compare them. Are they congruent? Explain. Then, repeat the activity.

EXERCISES

▶CHECK for Understanding

In Exercises 1–4, match the triangle with a similar triangle.

a.   b.   c.   d.

1.    2.    3.   4.

5. Show one way a rectangle can be divided into 2, 3, and 4 congruent parts.

6. *Reasoning*   Are the figures at the right congruent? Similar? Why or why not?

7. *Communicating*   Sketch two triangles that are congruent. Explain your method. Check your result by measuring the sides and angles of each triangle.

Independent Practice

Math in Nature   Name the pair of figures that are similar.

8. a.   b.   c.   d.

9. a.   b.   c.   d.

Algebra   The two figures are congruent. Find the missing side lengths and angle measures.

10.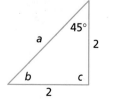

11.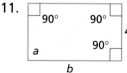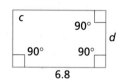

12. Which figures can be divided into 2 congruent parts? Into 3 congruent parts? Sketch your results.

a.   b.   c.   d.   e.   f.

13. *Reasoning* Can two triangles be drawn with the same side lengths and different angle measures? Explain.

Art You are making the stained glass window shown at the right.

14. Copy and color the window. Use a different color for each set of congruent polygons. Make a key that gives the name of each type of polygon.

15. Create your own stained glass window.

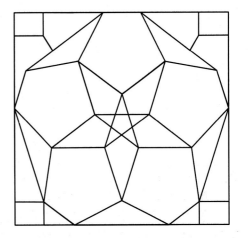

Integrated Review

Making Connections within Mathematics

Measurement Is the statement true or false? If false, change the blue number to make the statement true.

16. 7 mm = 70 cm

17. 5 yd = 15 ft

18. $\frac{1}{2}$ ft = 6 in.

19. 3000 mm = 3 km

20. 24 m = 240 cm

21. 8 ft = 84 in.

22. 1 ft = $\frac{1}{3}$ yd

23. $\frac{1}{2}$ yd = 18 in.

24. *Probability* One piece of glass is selected at random from the stained glass window shown above. What is the probability that the piece is a triangle?

Exploration and Extension

25. *Building Your Chapter Project* Use the steps on page 399 to make an origami swan. The first 2 steps are shown at the right. Compare the swan to the sailboat you have made. During which steps are the swan and the sailboat congruent? Name the congruent triangles labeled in Step 2.

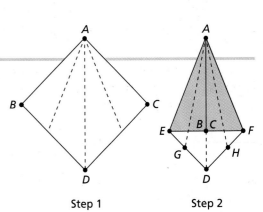

Step 1   Step 2

Materials Needed: grid paper, colored pencils or markers, straightedge and protractor

Part A *Describing and Drawing Flips*

In Exercises 1 and 2, compare the two drawings of Felix. How are drawings A and B alike? Different? Are they congruent?

1.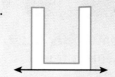

2.

In Exercises 3–6, trace the partial figure. Then draw the other half of the figure by flipping the partial figure about the line.

3.

4.

5.

6.

Part B *Dividing Figures in Half*

In Exercises 7 and 8, trace both figures. Then draw a line about which one figure could be flipped to produce the other figure. Explain how you can check your result by folding the paper.

7.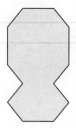

8.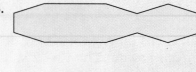

Part C *Comparing Flipped Figures*

In Exercises 9 and 10, copy the figure on grid paper. Imagine what
the figure would look like if it were flipped about the line. Draw
the "flipped" figure. Use a ruler to measure the sides of both
figures. Then use a protractor to measure the angles of both
figures. How do the two figures compare?

9.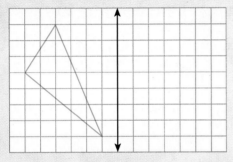

10.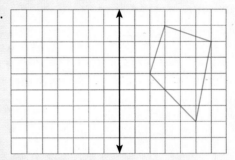

On Your Own

Critical Thinking

In Exercises 11–14, match the blue figure with its red image when
it is flipped about a horizontal line.

a.   b.   c.   d.

11.   12.   13.   14.

15. Which of the squares will "land exactly on themselves" when
they are flipped about the line? Explain your reasoning.

a. 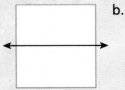   b. 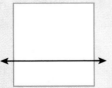   c.    d.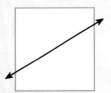

9.4 Line Symmetry

What you should learn:

Goal 1 How to identify line symmetry

Goal 2 How to use line symmetry to solve real-life problems

Why you should learn it:

Knowing how to identify line symmetry can help you create designs, such as company logos.

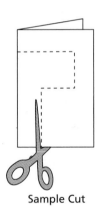

Sample Cut

Real Life
Company Logos

Goal 1 **Identifying Line Symmetry**

A figure has **line symmetry** if it can be flipped about a line and land exactly on itself. The line is the **line of symmetry.**

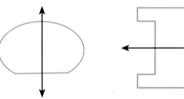

Line Symmetry   *Line Symmetry*   *No Line Symmetry*

Lesson Investigation

■ **Investigating Symmetrical Figures**

Group Activity Fold a sheet of paper in half. Cut from the folded side to make the following figures. Each should have line symmetry about the fold.

a. Heart   **b.** Kite   **c.** Square
d. The letter **T**   **e.** The letter **H**   **f.** The letter **E**

Compare your results with others in your group. Do any of the figures have more than one line of symmetry? Explain.

Example 1 *Identifying Line Symmetry*

Which of the company logos have line symmetry?

a.   b.   c.

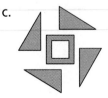

Solution   Figure (b) has line symmetry. Figures (a) and (c) do not. ■

Real Life
Designing Logos

Example 2 *Identifying Lines of Symmetry*

You are working with Alma and Joab to design a company logo. You begin by cutting figures out of folded paper as shown. How many lines of symmetry will each design have?

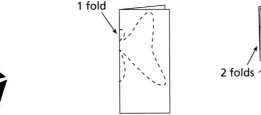

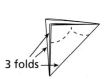

You — 1 fold

Alma — 2 folds

Joab — 3 folds

Company logos are designed to catch your eye. Do you recognize either of these logos?

Solution Your design will have 1 line of symmetry, Alma's will have 2 lines of symmetry, and Joab's will have 4 lines of symmetry.

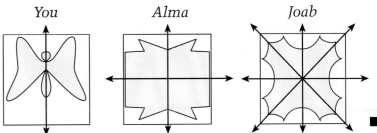

You *Alma* *Joab* ∎

Communicating about MATHEMATICS

Problem Solving
Look for a Pattern

▶ **Sharing Ideas about the Lesson**

Looking for a Pattern In Example 2, 1 fold of a square produced 1 line of symmetry, 2 folds produced 2 lines of symmetry, and 3 folds produced 4 lines of symmetry. How many lines of symmetry do you think 4 folds will produce? Check your answer by actually folding. Discuss your results.

EXERCISES

▶ **CHECK for Understanding**

In Exercises 1–3, draw a figure that has the given symmetry.

1. One line of symmetry
2. Two lines of symmetry
3. No line of symmetry
4. *Science*   Trace the butterfly at the right. Draw any lines of symmetry.
5. Write your first and last names in capital block letters. Which letters, if any, have line symmetry?
6. A sheet of paper was folded in half twice and cut as shown. Draw what you think the paper will look like unfolded. Check your answer by folding and cutting a sheet of paper.

Think and Discuss

This swallowtail butterfly at Butterfly World in Florida is native to India.

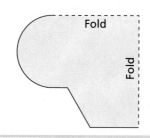

Independent Practice

Decide whether the quadrilateral has line symmetry. If it does, copy the figure and draw the line or lines of symmetry.

7.   8.   9.   10.

Native American Designs   In Exercises 11–13, the designs are from traditional Native American clothing. Decide whether each design has line symmetry. If it does, how many lines of symmetry does the design have?

11.    12. 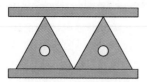   13.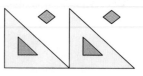

14. *On the Road*   Can you find 3 road signs (such as a stop sign) whose shapes have line symmetry? Draw the shapes of the signs. Draw any lines of symmetry.

Reasoning In Exercises 15–17, decide whether the dashed line is a line of symmetry for the figure. Explain.

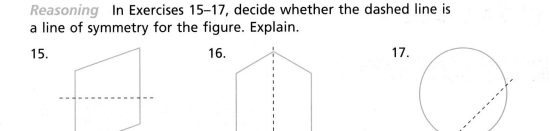

15.   16.   17.

Complete the figure on a 5-by-5 grid of dot paper so that it has line symmetry. Sketch the line or lines of symmetry.

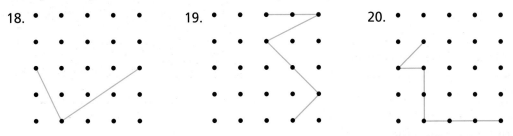

18.   19.   20.

Science In Exercises 21 and 22, the flowers are symmetrical. Find the number of lines of symmetry.

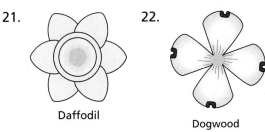

21.   22.

Daffodil

Dogwood

Trace the polygon. Draw its line or lines of symmetry.

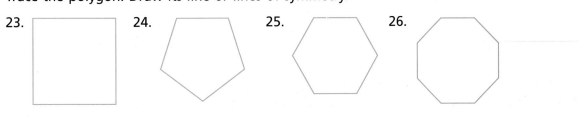

23.   24.   25.   26.

Reasoning You are shown a folded symmetrical figure. Sketch what the figure would look like unfolded.

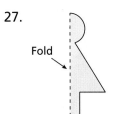

27.   28.   29.

Fold

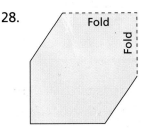

Fold

Fold

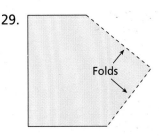

Folds

Integrated Review

 Use a calculator to find the mean.

30. 12, 25, 89, 102

31. 118, 145, 199

32. *Science* The data below shows the number of days for space shuttle flights from 1981 to 1992. Organize the data in a line plot. What is the range of the data? *(Source: NASA)*

2, 2, 8, 7, 5, 5, 6, 6, 10, 8, 8, 6, 7, 7, 2, 6, 7,
6, 7, 7, 2, 7, 7, 5, 4, 4, 4, 4, 5, 5, 5, 10, 6, 5, 4,
6, 9, 6, 5, 10, 8, 5, 7, 8, 9, 9, 14, 8, 8, 10, 7

Astronaut Marsha S. Ivins is shown working in the Space Shuttle Columbia while in orbit around Earth.

Exploration and Extension

33. *Building Your Chapter Project* Use the steps on page 399 to make an origami dog. Does the polygon that makes the dog's face have line symmetry? Does the polygon that makes the dog's ear have line symmetry?

Mixed REVIEW

1. *Making a List* You are making a fruit salad with 4 different kinds of fruit to take to a picnic. You can choose from grapes, pineapple, watermelon, cantaloupe, and strawberries. How many different kinds of fruit salad can you make? **(1.3)**

Order the numbers from least to greatest. **(3.5, 6.5)**

2. 6.15, 6.05, 6.051, 6.5, 6.01

3. $\frac{5}{7}, \frac{1}{2}, \frac{4}{7}, \frac{5}{6}$

Add, subtract, multiply, or divide. **(7.4, 7.5, 8.3, 8.5)**

4. $4\frac{2}{5} + 3\frac{1}{2}$

5. $5 - 2\frac{3}{4}$

6. $1\frac{1}{6} \times \frac{4}{5}$

7. $\frac{2}{3} \div \frac{2}{9}$

Geometry Name the figure and classify its angles. **(9.1, 9.2)**

8.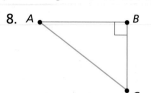

9.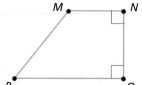

10.

Take this test as you would take a test in class. The answers to the exercises are given in the back of the book.

Describe how to move counterclockwise around the figure by staying on grid lines. Begin at *A*. Estimate the length of $\overline{AB}$. **(9.1)**

1.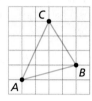

2.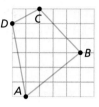

3.

Classify and measure the angle formed by the clock's hands. **(9.2)**

4.

5.

6.

Are the figures congruent? Similar? Why or why not? **(9.3)**

7.

8.

9.

In Exercises 10–12, find the number of lines of symmetry. **(9.4)**

10.

11.

12.

13. *Alphabet*   Copy the letters that have line symmetry. Then draw the line or lines of symmetry. **(9.4)**

ABCDEFGHIJKLM
NOPQRSTUVWXYZ

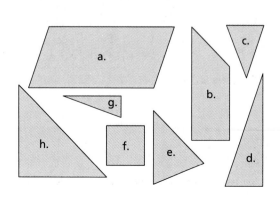

14. Name each figure at the right in as many ways as you can. **(9.1)**

Materials Needed: paper, pencils or pens, ruler, scissors

A *plane* is a flat surface that extends in all directions without ending. A *tiling* or *tessellation* of a plane is a collection of tiles that completely fill the plane with no gaps or overlaps. Two examples of tilings are shown below.

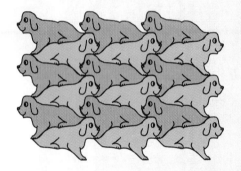 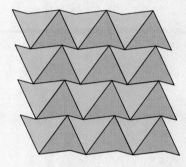

Part A *Making Tilings with Triangles*

1. The tiling shown below is made with congruent triangles.

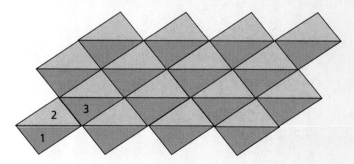

    a. Explain how to move triangle 1 so that it is exactly on top of triangle 3. Do you have to turn or flip the triangle, or can you just slide it?

    b. Explain how to move triangle 1 so that it is exactly on top of triangle 2. Do you have to turn or flip the triangle, or can you just slide it?

2. Have each person in your group draw a different triangle to use as a pattern. Cut out your triangle. Use your triangular pattern to trace a tiling in the plane.

3. Could everyone create a tiling with their triangle? Discuss whether you think *any* triangle can be used to create a tiling.

4. How can quadrilateral 1 be moved so that it is exactly on top of quadrilateral 2? Quadrilateral 3?

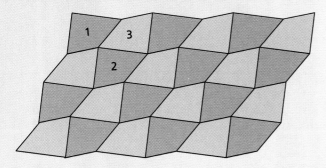

5. With others in your group, decide whether *any* quadrilateral can be used to tile a plane.

6. Decide whether *any* hexagon can be used to tile a plane. If not, find some hexagons that work and some that don't.

Part C *Making Tilings with Animal Shapes*

7. Trace the shape at the right and cut it out. Use it as a pattern to create a tiling. Explain your process. After you have made the tiling, draw features on the shapes so that each looks like an animal. Each tile must have the same features.

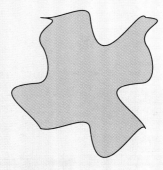

| On Your Own | Critical Thinking |

8. Copy each shape and make a pattern. Then decide whether the shape can be used to make a tiling. If it can, use the pattern to make a tiling.

a. 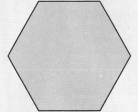   b. 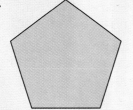   c.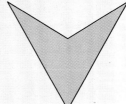

9.5

Connections to Algebra: Slides in a Coordinate Plane

What you should learn:

Goal 1 How to plot points in a coordinate plane

Goal 2 How to identify slides in a coordinate plane

Why you should learn it:

Knowing how to use a coordinate plane can help you draw construction plans. An example is drawing plans for an automobile.

Goal 1 **Points in a Coordinate Plane**

A **coordinate plane** uses **ordered pairs** of numbers to name points. The numbers are the **coordinates** of the point.

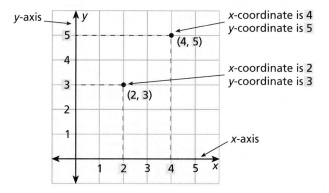

A coordinate plane has two axes, usually called the **x-axis** and the **y-axis.** The first coordinate of a point is the **x-coordinate** and the second coordinate is the **y-coordinate.**

Example 1 *Plotting Points*

Plot the points represented by the ordered pairs (2, 4), (3, 5), and (5, 1).

Solution

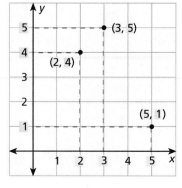

The first coordinate (or x-coordinate) shows the position on the x-axis.

The second coordinate (or y-coordinate) shows the position on the y-axis.

Engineers use coordinate planes to draw plans for buildings, automobiles, and machinery.

Example **2** *Slides in a Coordinate Plane*

Explain how you can **slide** triangle *ABC* to become triangle *DEF*. What are the coordinates of each corner point or vertex of triangle *DEF*?

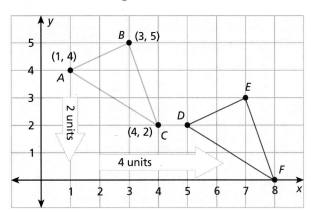

Study Tip

Use these guidelines to draw a coordinate plane.

1. Use grid paper.

2. Draw a horizontal line to be the x-axis. Label the line "x."

3. Draw a vertical line to be the y-axis. Label the line "y."

4. Label the grid lines on each axis with the numbers: 0, 1, 2, 3, 4, . . . The place where the axes cross is the point (0, 0) called the **origin.**

Solution

Each point was moved 2 units down and 4 units to the right.

Point *A*: (1, 4)

Point *B*: (3, 5)

Point *C*: (4, 2)

Move 2 units down.

Move 4 units right.

Point *D*: (5, 2)

Point *E*: (7, 3)

Point *F*: (8, 0)

Communicating about MATHEMATICS

▷ **Sharing Ideas about the Lesson**

Sliding Triangles Plot the points on a coordinate plane to form three triangles. Can one of the triangles be slid to form one of the other triangles? Explain.

A. (1, 2), (0, 5), (1, 6)   **B.** (8, 1), (7, 4), (9, 5)

C. (5, 3), (4, 6), (5, 7)

EXERCISES

Guided Practice

▶ CHECK for Understanding

In Exercises 1–4, use the grid at the right to complete the statement.

1. The grid is called a ?.
2. The vertical line is called the ?.
3. ? is the ordered pair of point *A*.
4. The first number of an ordered pair is called the ?. Why?

Think and Discuss

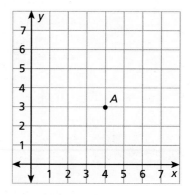

5. *Partner Activity*   You and a partner each draw the same figure on a coordinate plane. Without your partner looking, sketch a slide of the figure. Label the coordinates of each vertex. Describe the slide to your partner. Your partner draws the new figure and names the coordinates of each vertex. Is your partner's slide correct? Repeat.

6. Plot the points *A*(2, 0), *B*(0, 2), *C*(3, 5), and *D*(5, 3) in a coordinate plane. Sketch the sides of figure *ABCD*. Name the figure.

Independent Practice

Match the ordered pair with its point.

7. (2, 2)   8. (3, 4)
9. (5, 0)   10. (0, 1)

In Exercises 11 and 12, plot each set of points in a coordinate plane. Connect the points to form polygons. Which polygons are slides of other polygons?

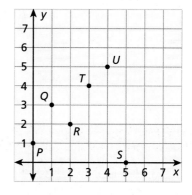

11. *A*(2, 6), *B*(1, 9), *C*(4, 7);   *D*(1, 0), *E*(2, 3), *F*(4, 2);
    G(4, 5), *H*(5, 8), *I*(7, 7);   *J*(6, 1), *K*(5, 4), *L*(8, 2)

12. *A*(0, 2), *B*(2, 3), *C*(2, 1), *D*(0, 0);   *E*(2, 4), *F*(4, 4), *G*(5, 2), *H*(3, 2);
    I(5, 5), *J*(7, 6), *K*(7, 4), *L*(5, 3);   *M*(6, 2), *N*(8, 3), *O*(8, 1), *P*(6, 0)

13. *Communicating*   Is a slide of a figure congruent to the original figure? Explain.

14. Draw a triangle on a coordinate plane. Label the coordinates of each vertex. Multiply the coordinates of each ordered pair by 2. Draw the triangle with the new ordered pairs. Is the new triangle a slide of the original? Explain.

Communicating In Exercises 15–17, the blue figure has been slid to form the red figure. Describe the slide.

15.
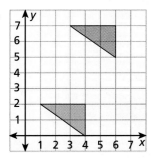

16.
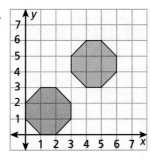

17.
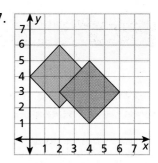

18. A triangle has vertices (1, 4), (1, 2), and (3, 4). Slide the triangle 2 units to the right and 2 units down. Write the new coordinates of each vertex.

19. *Making a Map* You leave home and ride your bike 3 blocks north and 2 blocks east to your friend's house. You both ride 3 blocks east and 5 blocks south to the movies, then 1 block south and 1 block west to the yogurt shop. Then you go home. Your house is located at (2, 5). Make a coordinate map showing the locations of the other places you stopped. On your map, 1 unit should equal 1 block.

Integrated Review   *Making Connections within Mathematics*

Finding a Pattern Describe the pattern. Then sketch the next figure in the pattern.

20.
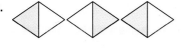

21.

22.

Exploration and Extension

23. *Word Puzzle* The puzzle pieces have been taken apart. Some have been flipped and slid, some have been turned and slid, and some have only been slid. Describe how each piece has been moved from the puzzle to the unattached position.

24. Unscramble the letters in the puzzle to find the hidden word.

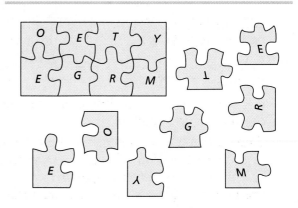

9.6

Triangles

What you should learn:

Goal 1 How to identify triangles by their sides

Goal 2 How to identify triangles by their angles

Why you should learn it:

Knowing how to identify triangles can help you describe structures in real life.

Goal 1 Identifying Triangles by Their Sides

Equilateral, Isosceles, and Scalene

An **equilateral** triangle has three sides of the same length. An **isosceles** triangle has two sides of the same length. A **scalene** triangle has sides of different lengths.

Equilateral
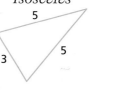

Isosceles

Scalene

Lesson Investigation

■ **Investigating Types of Triangles**

Group Activity Use pieces of straws cut to the following lengths: 1″, 2″, 2″, 3″, 3″, 3″, 4″, 4″. Which lengths can be used to make a triangle? Record your results in a table. Classify each triangle as equilateral, isosceles, or scalene.

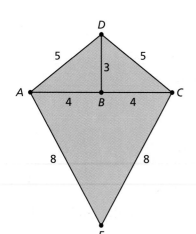

Example 1 *Classifying Triangles*

Classify the triangles in the diagram at the left as equilateral, isosceles, or scalene. Explain.

Solution

Triangle	Side Lengths	Type
ABD	3, 4, 5	Scalene
BCD	3, 4, 5	Scalene
ADC	5, 5, 8	Isosceles
ACE	8, 8, 8	Equilateral

This construction worker is assembling pieces called "trusses." The trusses support the building's roof.

Goal 2 **Identifying Triangles by Their Angles**

Acute, Right, and Obtuse Triangles

An **acute triangle** has three acute angles. A **right triangle** has one right angle. An **obtuse triangle** has one obtuse angle.

Real Life
Construction

Example 2 *Identifying Angles*

In the diagram of the roof truss, identify an acute, a right, and an obtuse triangle.

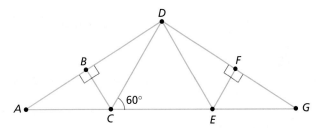

Solution Triangle *ABC* is a right triangle. Triangle *ACD* is an obtuse triangle. Triangle *CDE* is an acute triangle. ∎

Communicating about MATHEMATICS

Problem Solving
Geometry

▸ **Sharing Ideas about the Lesson**

A. Can a triangle have more than one right angle? More than one obtuse angle? Explain.

B. What can you conclude about the other 2 angles in a right or obtuse triangle?

9.6 ▪ *Triangles* **431**

EXERCISES

Guided Practice

▶ CHECK for Understanding

Think and Discuss

In Exercises 1–3, use as many words as possible to describe the triangle: *equilateral, isosceles, scalene, obtuse, right,* or *acute.*

1.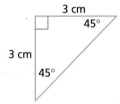
2.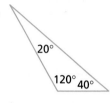
3.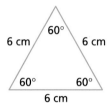

Group Activity Use a 6-foot piece of string to make the indicated triangle. One person should stand at each vertex. Explain how you can determine the side lengths.

4. Scalene   5. Equilateral   6. Isosceles

Independent Practice

Measurement In Exercises 7–9, use a centimeter ruler. Classify the triangle by the lengths of its sides.

7.
8.
9.

In Exercises 10–12, use a protractor to find the three angle measures. Then classify each triangle by the measures of its angles.

10.  11. 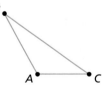 12.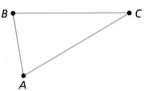

Engineering Use the bridge support at the right. Use as many words as possible to describe each triangle: *equilateral, isosceles, scalene, obtuse, right,* or *acute.*

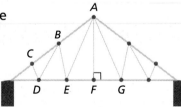

13. Triangle *ABE*

14. Triangle *AEG*

15. Triangle *AFE*

16. *Building Bridges*   Make your own design for a bridge
    support. Identify the triangles that you used.

In Exercises 17–20, sketch a triangle with the given description.

17. Acute and scalene

18. Acute and equilateral

19. Obtuse and isosceles

20. Right and scalene

In Exercises 21–24, decide whether the triangle has line symmetry.
If it does, copy the triangle and draw its line or lines of symmetry.

21.
22.
23.
24.

Reasoning   In Exercises 25 and 26, complete the statement using
the words *sometimes, always,* or *never.*

25. A triangle can [?] have 2 obtuse angles.

26. A right triangle [?] has 2 acute angles.

27. Draw an equilateral triangle. Label each
    vertex using *A, B,* and *C.* What are the
    different types of triangles that you can
    form by drawing a line from *A* to side
    $\overline{BC}$? Sketch your results.

28. *Geodesic Domes*   A geodesic dome is a
    structure made using triangular braces. In
    the photo, what type of triangles appear to
    be used in the structure of the roof?

*Robert Singer owns a company that makes
geodesic dome kits.*

Integrated Review   *Making Connections within Mathematics*

Algebra   Use mental math to find the value of *a.*

29. $\frac{a}{6} \times 5 = \frac{15}{6}$

30. $3 \times \frac{6}{a} = \frac{18}{5}$

31. $\frac{5}{8} \times \frac{a}{3} = \frac{25}{24}$

32. $\frac{3}{a} \times \frac{4}{5} = \frac{12}{25}$

33. $2 \div \frac{1}{a} = 6$

34. $\frac{a}{4} \div \frac{2}{3} = \frac{15}{8}$

Exploration and Extension

35. *Building Your Chapter Project*   Fold an origami airplane.
    (There are many ways to do this.) Then unfold the airplane.
    Use a ruler to trace the triangles. Identify them. Then write
    directions for folding your airplane.

Lab 9.7

Investigating Angles of a Triangle

Materials Needed: paper, pencils or pens, ruler, protractor

Part A *Measuring Angles of Right Triangles*

1. Use a ruler to draw two different right triangles on a sheet of paper. (Use the corners as the right angles.) Label the triangles as Right Triangle 1 and Right Triangle 2. Then label the angles of each triangle as ∠A, ∠B, and ∠C.

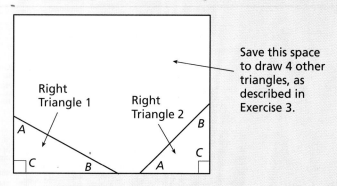

Save this space to draw 4 other triangles, as described in Exercise 3.

Make a table like that shown below. Use a protractor to measure the angles. Complete the first two rows of the table.

Triangle	Measure of ∠A	Measure of ∠B	Measure of ∠C
Right Triangle 1	?	?	?
Right Triangle 2	?	?	?
Acute Triangle 1	?	?	?
Acute Triangle 2	?	?	?
Obtuse Triangle 1	?	?	?
Obtuse Triangle 2	?	?	?

2. What observations can you make about the angles that are not right angles?

Part B *Measuring Angles of Acute and Obtuse Triangles*

3. Use your ruler to draw two different acute triangles and two different obtuse triangles. Label the angles of each triangle as ∠A, ∠B, and ∠C. Measure the angles of the four triangles. Complete your table.

Part C *Investigating the Sum of a Triangle's Measures*

4. Look back at the data in your table. Add a fifth column to the table and label it *Sum of the 3 Angles.* Add the measures of each triangle's angles and record the sum. Compare your group's results with other groups. What can you conclude?

5. Is it possible to draw a triangle that has a 10° angle and a 20° angle? If so, what would the measure of the third angle be?

6. Use a protractor to measure the angles of both triangles. What do you observe? Are the triangles congruent? Similar? Explain.

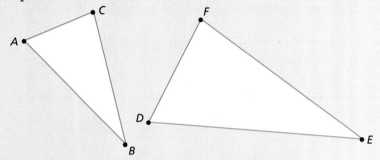

On Your Own   *Critical Thinking*

7. A triangle has angles with the given measures. What is the measure of the third angle?

    a. 30°, 80°   **b.** 30°, 75°   **c.** 20°, 110°

8. Is it possible to draw a triangle that has the same angle measures as the triangle in Exercise 7(a), but is not congruent to that triangle? Explain your reasoning.

9. Without using a protractor, find the measure of ∠C. Then use a protractor to check your answer.

    a.

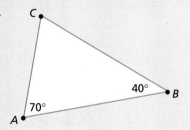

    b.

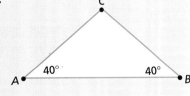

9.7

Exploring the Angles of a Triangle

What you should learn:

Goal 1 How to measure the angles of a triangle

Goal 2 How to use patterns to explore properties of the angles of a triangle

Why you should learn it:

Knowing how to measure the angles of a triangle can help you read maps, such as the map of a hiking route.

Goal 1 **Measuring a Triangle's Angles**

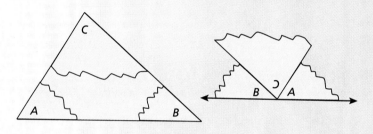

Lesson Investigation

■ **Investigating the Angles of a Triangle**

Cut a triangle out of paper. Tear off the 3 corners and tape them next to each other as shown. What do you observe? Do you get the same result no matter what triangle you use?

In Lab 9.7, or in this investigation, you may have discovered the following property.

Angles of a Triangle

The sum of the measures of the angles of a triangle is 180°.

Example 1 *Finding the Measure of an Angle*

Find the measure of ∠P, shown at the left.

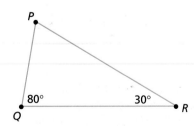

Solution To find the measure of ∠P, subtract the measures of ∠Q and ∠R from 180°.

Measure of ∠P = 180° − 80° − 30°

= 70° ∎

Example 2 *Angles of a Right Triangle*

Make a table showing the measures of the angles for the five right triangles below. Describe any patterns you see.

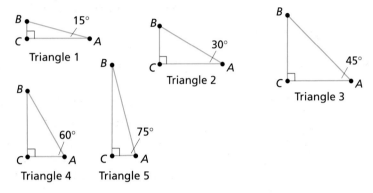

Triangle 1

Triangle 2

Triangle 3

Triangle 4   Triangle 5

Solution   For each triangle, you can find the measure of $\angle B$ by subtracting the measures of $\angle A$ and $\angle C$ from $180°$.

Measure $\angle A$	Measure $\angle C$	Measure $\angle B$
15°	90°	$180° - 15° - 90° = 75°$
30°	90°	$180° - 30° - 90° = 60°$
45°	90°	$180° - 45° - 90° = 45°$
60°	90°	$180° - 60° - 90° = 30°$
75°	90°	$180° - 75° - 90° = 15°$

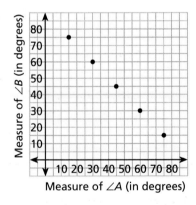

Measure of $\angle B$ (in degrees)

10 20 30 40 50 60 70 80

Measure of $\angle A$ (in degrees)

One way to look for a pattern is to plot the measures of $\angle A$ and $\angle B$ in a coordinate plane, as shown at the left. Notice that as the measure of $\angle A$ increases, the measure of $\angle B$ decreases. ■

Communicating about MATHEMATICS

▶ **Sharing Ideas about the Lesson**

For each triangle above, order the lengths of the sides $\overline{AB}$, $\overline{BC}$, and $\overline{AC}$ from shortest to longest. Order the measures of $\angle A$, $\angle B$, and $\angle C$ from least to greatest. What patterns do you see?

EXERCISES

Think and Discuss

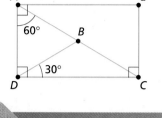

▶ CHECK for Understanding

In Exercises 1–4, use the figure at the right to match the angle with its measure. Explain your reasoning.

   a. 120°   b. 60°   c. 30°   d. 90°

   1. ∠ACD   **2.** ∠CBD   **3.** ∠ABD   **4.** ∠AEC

5. *Reasoning* Draw a right triangle. Use a protractor to measure one of the acute angles. Explain how to find the measure of the third angle without using the protractor. Then use the protractor to check your result.

6. *The Great Pyramid* Each face of the Great Pyramid of Giza in Egypt has one obtuse angle and two 39° angles. What is the measure of the obtuse angle?

The pyramids of Giza are the three largest in the world.

Communicating In Exercises 7–9, decide whether a triangle could have the given angle measures. Explain your reasoning.

   7. 115°, 35°, 30°   **8.** 55°, 90°, 45°   **9.** 61°, 55°, 64°

In Exercises 10–12, use a protractor to measure each angle of the triangle. Then find the sum of the measures.

10. 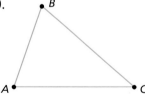   **11.** 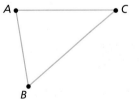   **12.**

Algebra and Mental Math In Exercises 13–15, use mental math to find the measure of the angle marked *x*.

13.   **14.**   **15.**

16. Copy and complete the table below for the measures of triangle *ABC*. Describe any patterns you see.

∠A	85°	80°	75°	70°	65°	60°
∠B	85°	80°	75°	70°	65°	60°
∠C	?	?	?	?	?	?

17. *Hiking*   A diagram of a hiking trail is shown at the right. You begin at point *A* and hike southwest. You then turn and hike directly east. You then turn and hike northwest. To get back to where you began, you make another turn. How many degrees will the last turn be?

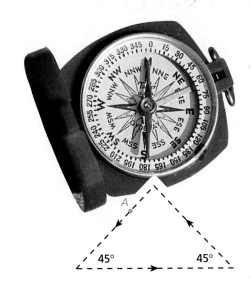

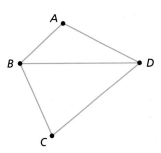

Integrated Review

Making Connections within Mathematics

Using a Graph   The bar graph at the right shows the fractions of people surveyed that answered the question *How often do you feed your pet "people food"?* **(Source: American Animal Hospital Association)**

18. What fraction of people feed their pets "people food" at least once a month?

19. There were 1049 people in the survey. How many people never feed their pets "people food"?

Exploration and Extension

Quadrilaterals   The quadrilateral at the right has been divided into 2 triangles.

20. You know that the sum of the angles of each triangle is 180°. Explain how you can use this information to find the sum of the angles of the quadrilateral.

21. To check the result of Exercise 20, draw your own quadrilateral. Use a protractor to measure the angles. What is the sum?

9

Chapter Summary

What did you learn?

Skills

1. Describe geometric figures and identify polygons. **(9.1)**
2. Identify angles as acute, right, or obtuse. **(9.2)**
3. Use a protractor to measure angles. **(9.2)**
4. Identify congruent shapes and polygons. **(9.3)**
5. Identify similar shapes and polygons. **(9.3)**
6. Identify line symmetry in a figure. **(9.4)**
7. Plot points in a coordinate plane. **(9.5)**
   - Describe slides in a coordinate plane. **(9.5)**
8. Identify triangles as equilateral, isosceles, or scalene. **(9.6)**
   - Identify triangles as acute, right, or obtuse. **(9.6)**
9. Find the sum of the measures of a triangle's angles. **(9.7)**

Strategies

10. Use problem-solving strategies to solve problems. **(9.1–9.7)**

Exploring Data

11. Use tables and graphs to organize data and solve problems. **(9.1–9.7)**

Why did you learn it?

Geometry is used to describe many types of real-life problems. Here are some examples you studied in this chapter.

- Describe a mosaic pattern found in a Moorish palace. **(9.1)**
- Decide whether two plots of land are congruent. **(9.3)**
- Design a logo for a company. **(9.4)**
- Describe the triangles used in the support for a roof. **(9.6)**

How does it fit into the bigger picture of mathematics?

In this chapter, you learned many new words, such as polygon, acute, obtuse, congruent, similar, coordinate, axis, isosceles, and scalene. These words form part of the *vocabulary of geometry.*

Every part of mathematics has its own vocabulary. For instance, the vocabulary of fractions has words like numerator, equivalent, and denominator.

Learning vocabulary words is an important part of studying a new part of mathematics. You need to know vocabulary to be able to communicate with others—and communicating is much of what mathematics is about!

In Exercises 1–3, sketch 2 different polygons of the given shape. **(9.1)**

1. Triangle
2. Quadrilateral
3. Heptagon

Measurement In Exercises 4–6, measure the angles of the polygon. Identify each angle as acute, obtuse, or right. **(9.2)**

4.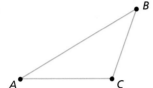

5.

6.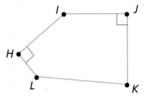

In Exercises 7–10, copy the figure. Show how it can be divided into 4 congruent parts. **(9.3)**

7.

8.

9.

10.

In Exercises 11–14, decide if the figure has line symmetry. If it does, copy the figure. Draw the line or lines of symmetry. **(9.4)**

11.

12.

13.

14.

15. Plot the points in a coordinate plane. Connect the points to form the triangles. Which triangles are slides, flips, or turns of other triangles? **(9.4, 9.5)**

    Triangle 1: A(0, 4), B(4, 4), C(2, 2)   *Triangle 2: D(2, 2), E(6, 2), F(4, 0)*
    Triangle 3: G(6, 7), H(6, 3), I(4, 5)   *Triangle 4: J(7, 7), K(7, 3), L(9, 5)*

In Exercises 16 and 17, sketch a triangle as described. **(9.6)**

16. Acute and isosceles

17. Obtuse and scalene

18. *First Aid* The shape of the bandage used most often in first aid is triangular. It is made by cutting a 40-inch square of cloth in half along the diagonal, as shown at the right. Find the measures of the angles of the triangular bandage. **(9.7)**

40 in.

40 in.

19. *Origami Frog* An origami frog is shown at the right. Its parts are numbered. Name the polygon for each part.

20. Which of the polygons in Exercise 19 are congruent? Similar?

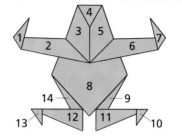

21. *Paper Bracelet* The pattern below is for making the bracelet shown at the right. All the triangles in the bracelet pattern are equilateral. Find the measures of ∠ACB, ∠BAC, and ∠ABC. What can you conclude?

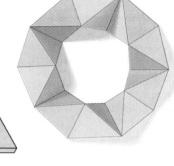

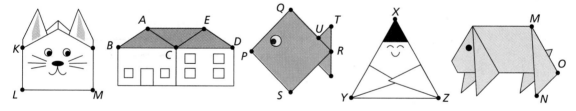

22. Use the origami figures below to complete the crossword.

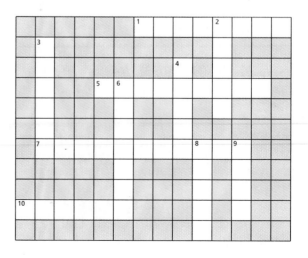

ACROSS
 1. Rabbit face polygon
 5. House triangle *ABC*
 7. Prince triangle *XYZ*
10. ∠BAE of house

DOWN
 2. Rabbit ∠KLM is a right one
 3. Fish polygon
 4. House ∠ABC
 6. Triangle *MON* of pig
 8. Fish ∠TUR
 9. Figure *ABCDE* has
    ? symmetry.

Algebra In Exercises 1–4, match the polygon with its name.

a. Hexagon   b. Octagon   c. Quadrilateral   d. Pentagon

1.
2.
3.
4.

Measurement In Exercises 5–7, use a protractor to measure ∠*DEF*. What type of angle is it: acute, right, or obtuse?

5.
6.
7.

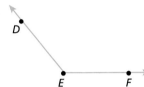
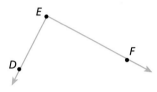
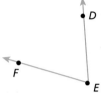

Algebra In Exercises 8 and 9, the figures are congruent. Find the missing side and angle measures.

8.
9.

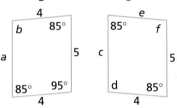
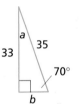

10. The digits from a calculator are shown at the right. Sketch the ones that have line symmetry. Then draw any lines of symmetry.

In Exercises 11 and 12, plot the points in a coordinate plane. Connect the points to form a polygon. Then slide the polygon 3 units to the right and 4 units up. Write the coordinates of the new polygon.

11. $(0, 0)$, $(4, 1)$, $(3, 4)$

12. $(2, 1)$, $(5, 1)$, $(2, 4)$, $(5, 6)$

Kites Each kite is made from triangles. Classify the triangles as *scalene, isosceles,* or *equilateral.* Then find the measure of the angle marked *x*.

13.
14.

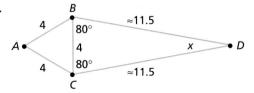
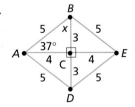

1. Write the measure as a mixed number and as a fraction **(7.1)**

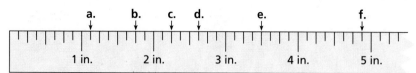

In Exercises 2–9, simplify. **(7.2–7.6, 8.2–8.4, 8.6)**

2. $\frac{5}{6} + \frac{1}{4}$ 3. $2\frac{3}{8} + 4\frac{1}{8}$ 4. $4\frac{1}{5} - \frac{3}{5}$ 5. $3\frac{2}{3} - 1\frac{1}{2}$

6. $\frac{1}{4} \times \frac{4}{5}$ 7. $1\frac{1}{6}$ of 3   8. $2\frac{1}{5} \div \frac{1}{2}$ 9. $6 \div 1\frac{2}{7}$

Algebra In Exercises 10–15, solve to find the value of *x*.
(7.2–7.4, 8.3, 8.6, 8.7)

10. Perimeter = 11 units   11. Perimeter = *x*   12. Area = *x*

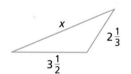   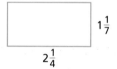

13. Area = $3\frac{3}{5}$ square units   14. Area = *x*   15. Area = *x*

        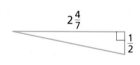

In Exercises 16–19, write the problem represented by the phrase.
Then solve. **(8.1, 8.3, 8.5, 8.6)**

16. The product of nine and one tenth
17. One and one half divided by 6
18. Four fifths divided by three tenths
19. Three and one sixth multiplied by six sevenths

Geometry Name the polygon. Then classify and measure its
angles. **(9.1, 9.2)**

20.   21.   22.

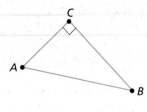   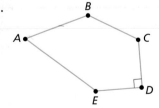   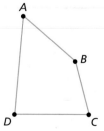

In Exercises 23 and 24, name the pair of figures that are congruent. **(9.3)**

23. a.   b.   c.   d.

24. a.    b. 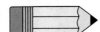   c.    d.

In Exercises 25–27, complete the figure on a 5-by-5 grid of dot paper so that it has line symmetry. How many lines of symmetry does your figure have? **(9.4)**

25.   26.   27.

Copy the figure onto grid paper. Use the description to slide it. **(9.5)**

28. Up 4 and right 3   29. Up 3 and left 4   30. Down 2 and left 1

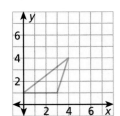   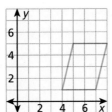   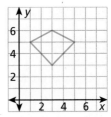

In Exercises 31 and 32, sketch a triangle as described. **(9.6)**

31. Acute and isosceles   32. Obtuse and scalene

33. *Unicycling* Imagine that you are riding a unicycle in the path below. What type of angle is formed at your starting point? How far did you ride? **(7.3, 9.7)**

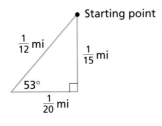

Peter Rosendahl, of Nevada, rode the world's smallest unicycle a distance of 9 ft $9\frac{1}{2}$ inches.

Geometry and Measurement

These professional photographers in Barcelona, Spain, are using special high-tech cameras to capture the moment.

Real Life
Newspapers

As art director for your school newspaper, you are planning an informative 1-page article about the 6 students who are running for school offices. The page is $8\frac{1}{2}$"-by-11". The minimum space between photos is $\frac{1}{2}$ inch. The minimum space between text and photos is $\frac{1}{4}$ inch.

Think and Discuss

1. Use the sample layout figure. Compute the dimensions and the area of the photo area.

2. Assume that the 6 photos all need to have the same dimensions. What size photo would you use? How would you arrange them? Make a "mock layout" for your article on an $8\frac{1}{2}$"-by-11" sheet of paper.

Sample Layout

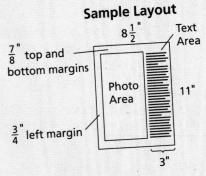

$8\frac{1}{2}$"

Text Area

$\frac{7}{8}$" top and bottom margins

Photo Area

11"

$\frac{3}{4}$" left margin

3"

··· Your School Newspaper ···

Theme: Inside Newspaper Publishing Every major city has a daily newspaper. Have you ever thought about all the tasks to be done before it reaches the newsstand? The publisher must research and write the articles, plan the space on the page for them, make sure the words are typeset correctly, and then get all the pages printed and assembled. Doing this correctly 365 days of the year keeps many people very busy.

In this project, you will learn about some of these tasks by writing and publishing a class newspaper. The tasks you will do are the following:

▷ **In Lesson 10.1 and 10.2:** Make a layout sheet on which all the articles can be pasted. (pages 455 and 459)

▷ **In Lesson 10.3:** Write riddles for your newspaper. (page 467)

▷ **In Lesson 10.4:** Write an article about a "human triangle." (page 474)

▷ **In Lesson 10.7:** Graph the results of a survey and include it in an article. (page 491)

▷ **In Lesson 10.8:** Write an article about a game you have created. (page 495)

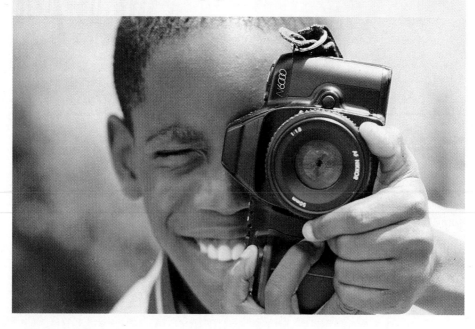

This is the colorful printing of an Australian newspaper.

GETTING STARTED

Materials: paper, ruler, scissors, glue, typewriter or computer

Place two sheets of paper in your portfolio. You will be adding grid lines and your news articles to one sheet as you complete the chapter. Carefully position each article on the paper so that the lines of type are parallel with the top and bottom of the page.

The completed page is called a "page dummy." To print your newspaper, make a second copy of each article. On a clean sheet of paper placed directly over the dummy, position the second copies. Use this new page as your master and photocopy it.

Distribute your newspaper to others in your class.

Materials Needed: dot paper, colored pencils or markers, ruler

Part A *Parallel Lines and Intersecting Lines*

1. Use a ruler to copy the pattern of lines below. Lines that do not meet are *parallel*. Name two lines that are parallel and two that are intersecting.

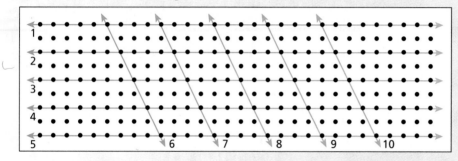

2. Color a small quadrilateral in your pattern of lines.

3. Use a second color to shade a larger quadrilateral.

4. Use a third color to shade a hexagon.

Part B *Drawing Parallel Lines*

5. On dot paper, choose a dot and color it. Move 6 dots to the right and 4 dots up and color that dot. Draw a line through the colored dots. Repeat the process twice, starting at dots that are not on the line you have drawn. What can you conclude about the three lines?

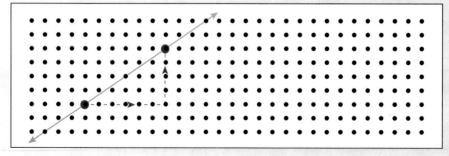

6. Repeat the process in Exercise 5, only begin by moving 8 dots to the right and 5 dots up. What can you conclude about these three lines?

7. With others in your group, create your own pattern of three lines, like those in Exercises 5 and 6. Explain your steps.

Part C *Drawing Perpendicular Lines*

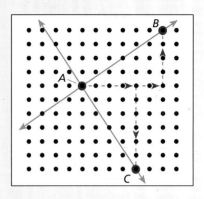

8. On dot paper, color a dot and label it *A*. From point
   A, move 6 dots to the right and 4 dots *up*. Color
   that dot and label it *B*. From point *A*, move 4 dots
   to the right and 6 dots *down*. Color that dot and
   label it *C*. Use a ruler to draw lines $\overleftrightarrow{AB}$ and $\overleftrightarrow{AC}$ as
   shown at the right. Lines that form right angles are
   perpendicular. Tear off a corner of a piece of paper
   and use it to check that lines $\overleftrightarrow{AB}$ and $\overleftrightarrow{AC}$ are
   perpendicular.

9. On dot paper, color a dot and label it *A*. From point *A*, move
   8 dots to the right and 5 dots *up*. Color that dot and label it
   B. From point *A*, move 5 dots to the right and 8 dots *down*.
   Color that dot and label it *C*. Use a ruler to draw lines $\overleftrightarrow{AB}$
   and $\overleftrightarrow{AC}$. What can you conclude about the two lines?

10. With others in your group, create your own pattern of two
    perpendicular lines, like those in Exercises 8 and 9. Explain
    your steps.

On Your Own   Critical Thinking

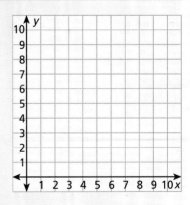

11. **a.** Copy the coordinate plane at the right. Then
        label the following points.

    A(1, 1), *B*(6, 4), *C*(2, 4), *D*(7, 7), *E*(3, 10),
    F(5, 1), *G*(2, 7)

    b. Draw the following lines. Which pairs of lines
        are parallel? Perpendicular? How can you tell?

    $\overleftrightarrow{AB}$, $\overleftrightarrow{CD}$, $\overleftrightarrow{EB}$, $\overleftrightarrow{FG}$

    c. Label points *P* and *Q* so that line $\overleftrightarrow{PQ}$ is parallel
        to $\overleftrightarrow{AB}$.

    d. Label points *R* and *S* so that line $\overleftrightarrow{RS}$ is
        perpendicular to $\overleftrightarrow{AB}$.

Parallel, Intersecting, and Perpendicular Lines

What you should learn:

Goal 1 How to identify parallel and intersecting lines

Goal 2 How to identify perpendicular lines

Why you should learn it:

Knowing how to recognize parallel and perpendicular lines can help you make farming decisions. An example is measuring the distance between parallel crop rows.

Goal 1 **Parallel and Intersecting Lines**

In a plane, two lines that never meet are **parallel.** Any two lines in a plane are either parallel or **intersecting.**

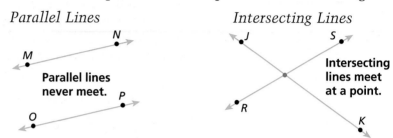

In the above figures, lines $\overleftrightarrow{MN}$ and $\overleftrightarrow{OP}$ are parallel, and lines $\overleftrightarrow{JK}$ and $\overleftrightarrow{RS}$ are intersecting.

Example 1 *Parallel and Intersecting Lines*

In the diagram below, which lines appear parallel? Which lines are intersecting?

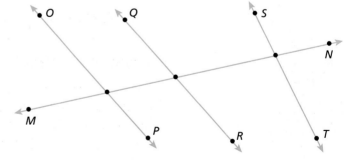

Solution From the diagram, it is clear that line $\overleftrightarrow{MN}$ intersects the other three lines. To decide whether lines $\overleftrightarrow{OP}$, $\overleftrightarrow{QR}$, and $\overleftrightarrow{ST}$ are parallel or intersecting, you can use tracing paper and a ruler to trace the lines. If you trace the lines carefully and extend them far enough, you should find that line $\overleftrightarrow{ST}$ intersects lines $\overleftrightarrow{OP}$ and $\overleftrightarrow{QR}$.

By inspection, you should find that lines $\overleftrightarrow{OP}$ and $\overleftrightarrow{QR}$ are parallel. ∎

Farmers often plant crops in parallel rows. The rows are easy to cultivate because they are the same distance apart at any two points.

Goal 2 · Perpendicular Lines

Two lines that meet at right angles are **perpendicular.**
There are many examples of perpendicular lines in real
life. For instance, adjacent sides of this page are
perpendicular.

Problem Solving
Group Activity

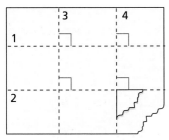

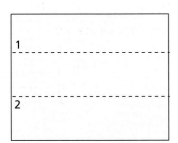

Example 2 *Parallel and Perpendicular Lines*

Fold a sheet of paper twice to produce two parallel lines,
as shown at the top left. Label these lines 1 and 2. Then
fold the sheet of paper twice the other way to produce
two more parallel lines. Label these lines 3 and 4.
Which pairs of lines are perpendicular?

Solution   As shown at the left, the folds produce four
pairs of perpendicular lines.

Line 1 and line 3
Line 1 and line 4
Line 2 and line 3
Line 2 and line 4

You can check that the lines are perpendicular by tear-
ing off a corner of the paper and using it to measure the
angles of intersection. ■

Communicating about MATHEMATICS

▶ **Sharing Ideas about the Lesson**

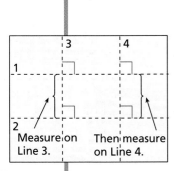

*Cooperative
Learning*

Measuring the Distance between Parallel Lines The
distance between two parallel lines is defined to
be the length of a line segment with ends on the
two lines, that is perpendicular to both parallel
lines.

Use the folded paper from Example 2. To measure
the distance between lines 1 and 2, measure along
line 3 and also along line 4.

With others in your group, discuss what you can
conclude about the distance between two parallel
lines.

EXERCISES

Guided Practice

Think and Discuss

▶ CHECK for Understanding

In Exercises 1–3, match the lines with the description.

a. Perpendicular   b. Intersecting   c. Appear parallel

1.   2.   3.

Logical Reasoning   In Exercises 4 and 5, is the statement true or false? Explain your reasoning.

4. Perpendicular lines always intersect at right angles.

5. Intersecting lines always intersect at right angles.

6. Make a list of as many examples of parallel lines and perpendicular lines that you can see in your classroom.

Independent Practice

In Exercises 7–10, do the lines appear parallel or intersecting? Explain.

7.    8.    9.    10.

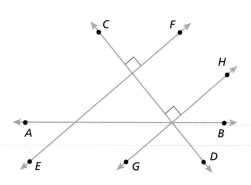

In Exercises 11–13, use the figure at the right to name each of the following.

11. Two lines that appear parallel

12. Two intersecting lines

13. A line that is perpendicular to 2 lines

Reasoning   Complete the statement using *sometimes, always,* or *never.* Explain.

14. Parallel lines [?] meet.

15. Intersecting lines are [?] perpendicular.

16. Perpendicular lines [?] meet at right angles.

Letter Puzzle In Exercises 17–19, use the letter L as shown at the right. When this letter is cut as shown, the pieces can be rearranged to form a square.

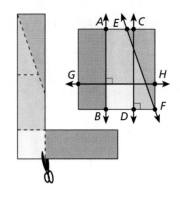

17. Which line appears parallel to $\overleftrightarrow{AB}$?

18. Which line is perpendicular to $\overleftrightarrow{AB}$?

19. Which lines intersect $\overleftrightarrow{AB}$?

20. Draw a rectangle that is 1 inch by $3\frac{1}{4}$ inches. Cut it into pieces that can be rearranged to form a square. Sketch your results.

Road Construction The diagram at the right shows a road map for the downtown portion of a city.

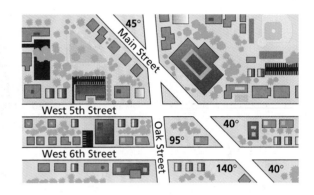

21. What street is parallel to West 5th Street?

22. What streets intersect Main Street?

23. Explain how you know that Oak Street is not perpendicular to West 6th Street.

Integrated Review   *Making Connections within Mathematics*

Measurement Identify the angle as acute, obtuse, or right. Then use a protractor to measure.

24.

25.

26.

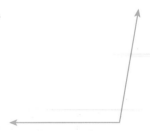

Exploration and Extension

27. *Building Your Chapter Project* Make a layout sheet for your class newspaper. Begin with an $8\frac{1}{2}$-inch by 11-inch sheet of paper. Draw a line parallel to the top edge of the paper that is $1\frac{1}{2}$ inches from the edge. Then draw lines parallel to the sides and bottom of the paper that are 1 inch from the edge. Explain the steps you used to draw the parallel lines.

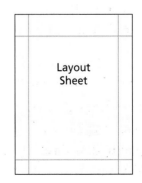

Layout
Sheet

10.2

Angles

What you should learn:

Goal 1 How to identify supplementary and complementary angles

Goal 2 How to draw angles that have a given measure

Why you should learn it:

Knowing how to recognize supplementary and complementary angles can help you with design projects. An example is designing a stained-glass window.

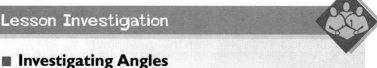

Goal 1 **Special Angles**

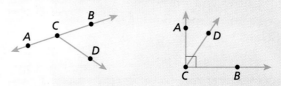

Lesson Investigation

■ **Investigating Angles**

Group Activity Copy the figures below. For each, use a protractor to measure ∠*BCD* and ∠*ACD*. Repeat this process, redrawing each figure with *D* in a different location. What can you conclude?

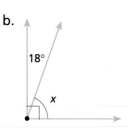

In this investigation, you may have discovered that when two angles form a straight line, the sum of their measures is 180°. These angles are **supplementary.** When two angles form a right angle, the sum of their measures is 90°. These angles are **complementary.**

Example 1 *Algebra Connection*

Solve for *x*.

a.

x

$58°$

b.

$18°$

x

Solution

a. $x + 58 = 180$ *Supplementary angles*

        $x = 122°$ *Mental math*

b. $x + 18 = 90$ *Complementary angles*

        $x = 72°$ *Mental math*   ■

Drawing Angles

In Lesson 9.2, you learned how to use a protractor to *measure* angles. You can also use a protractor to *draw* angles that have a given measure.

Example 2 **Using a Protractor**

Draw an angle whose measure is 55°.

a. Begin by drawing a ray. Mark the point at the end of the ray. This is the vertex of the angle.

b. Line up the protractor's 0° line with the ray. Place the protractor's center on the end of the ray, or vertex.

c. Use the protractor and a pencil to mark a measure of 55°.

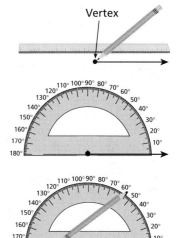

d. Use a ruler to draw the second ray of the angle.

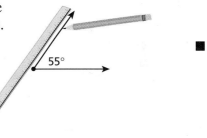

Angle measures are used in the design of stained-glass windows. Before the window is made, an artist sketches the design to be shown in the window.

Communicating *about* MATHEMATICS

▶ **Sharing Ideas about the Lesson**

Drawing Angles Follow the steps shown above to draw angles that have the given measures. Which angles are supplementary? Which angles are complementary?

A. 65°   **B.** 115°   **C.** 25°

EXERCISES

Guided Practice

▶ CHECK for Understanding

Use the figure at the right to complete the statements.

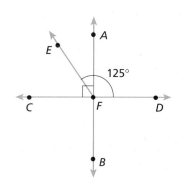

1. Lines $\overleftrightarrow{AB}$ and $\overleftrightarrow{CD}$ are ⬚ .
2. ∠CFE and ∠EFA are ⬚ angles.
3. ∠CFE has a measure of ⬚ .
4. ∠EFA has a measure of ⬚ .
5. In the figure, name 3 sets of supplementary angles.
6. Give a real-life example of two angles that are complementary.
7. *Logical Reasoning*   Use the diagram at the right. The following steps give a logical argument that ∠1 and ∠4 are congruent. Discuss how you know each step is correct.
   - The measure of ∠3 is 55°.
   - The measure of ∠4 is 125°.
   - ∠1 and ∠4 are congruent.

Think and Discuss

Given: • ∠1 and ∠3 are supplementary.
       • ∠3 and ∠4 are supplementary.
       • The measure of ∠1 is 125°.

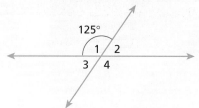

Independent Practice

Algebra and Mental Math   In Exercises 8–11, solve for *x*.

8.

9.

10.

11.

Measurement   In Exercises 12–15, find the measure of the angle that is complementary to the given angle. Then use a protractor to draw both angles.

12. 20°   13. 55°   14. 30°   15. 70°

Find the measure of the angle that is supplementary to the given angle. Then use a protractor to draw both angles.

16. 160°   17. 100°   18. 40°   19. 30°

In Exercises 20 and 21, is the statement true or false? Give examples to support your answer.

20. If two angles are complementary, then both must be acute.

21. If two angles are supplementary, then one must be acute and one must be obtuse.

22. *Reasoning* In the diagram at the right, find the measures of ∠1, ∠2, and ∠3. Explain your reasoning.

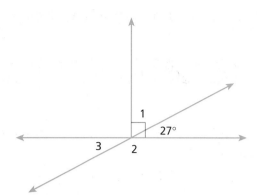

Logical Reasoning A diagram of a billiard table is shown at the right.

23. Find the measure of ∠3. Explain your reasoning.

24. How are ∠1 and ∠2 related?

25. How are ∠2 and ∠3 related?

26. How are ∠1 and ∠3 related?

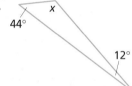

∠1 is congruent to ∠2.

Integrated Review   *Making Connections within Mathematics*

Algebra Find the measure of the angle marked *x*.

27.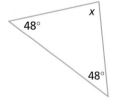

28.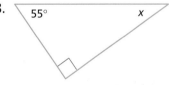

29.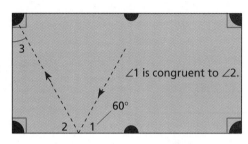

Exploration and Extension

30. *Building Your Chapter Project*
Finish the layout sheet for your class newspaper. Draw a line $5\frac{3}{4}$ inches from the top edge and parallel to the top edge. Then draw 2 lines perpendicular to this line. Each perpendicular line should be $3\frac{3}{4}$ inches from an edge of the paper. Explain the steps you used to draw the perpendicular lines. Create a name for your newspaper and place it in the area as shown at the right.

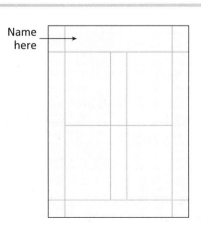

Name here

Mixed REVIEW

Write the number represented by the model. **(2.3, 3.3, 6.1)**

1.

2.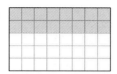

3.

Use a calculator to help you rewrite the fraction as a decimal (round to nearest hundredth) and as a percent. **(3.4)**

4. $\frac{4}{5}$

5. $\frac{3}{8}$

6. $\frac{2}{3}$

7. $\frac{11}{20}$

Algebra and Mental Math   Solve. **(4.1, 4.2)**

8. $5.4 + x = 7$ 9. $y - 4.5 = 2.3$ 10. $11 - m = 10.2$ 11. $n + 6.02 = 9.35$

Statistics   Make a stem-and-leaf plot of the data. **(5.2)**

12. 57, 42, 34, 63, 50, 41, 38, 42, 35   13. 22, 8, 13, 14, 27, 22, 9, 8, 25

Milestones   ALMANACS

300	500	700	900	1100	1300	1500	1700	1900	

Mayan Calendar, 300

Magnetic Compass, 1090

Copernicus Born, Galileo Born, 1564

Sextant, 1731

Greenwich Mean Time, 1884

In 1639, sixty-five years before the first newspaper was published in the United States, almanacs were being printed in the new world.

When Benjamin Banneker, the son of a freed slave, was 57 years old, he became interested in astronomy. Working at his kitchen table on a Maryland farm, he taught himself the mathematics of star charts. Being an unknown author, his work was not accepted by publishers. After joining the surveying team for the newly established District of Columbia, Banneker was able to publish 29 separate editions of almanacs from 1792 through 1797.

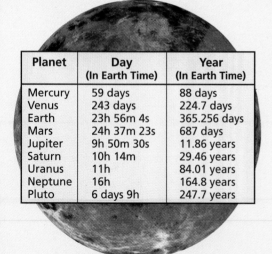

The Planet Venus

Planet	Day (In Earth Time)	Year (In Earth Time)
Mercury	59 days	88 days
Venus	243 days	224.7 days
Earth	23h 56m 4s	365.256 days
Mars	24h 37m 23s	687 days
Jupiter	9h 50m 30s	11.86 years
Saturn	10h 14m	29.46 years
Uranus	11h	84.01 years
Neptune	16h	164.8 years
Pluto	6 days 9h	247.7 years

• *The planet Venus takes 224.7 Earth days (1 Venus year) to travel around the sun. It takes Venus 243 Earth days (1 Venus day) to rotate on its own axis. How many Venus years are in one Venus day?*

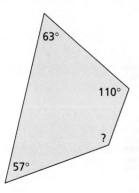

Draw three large quadrilaterals on a sheet of paper. Use a protractor to measure the angles of each quadrilateral. For each quadrilateral, find the sum of the angle measures.

Solution Begin by drawing three quadrilaterals. An example is shown at the left. Then measure the angles of each. You can use a calculator to find the sum of the measures.

Quadrilateral 1

95 + 80 + 130 + 55 =

Quadrilateral 2

60 + 120 + 60 + 120 =

Quadrilateral 3

90 + 90 + 90 + 90 =   ■

Exercises

1. *Partner Activity* Try the above experiment with a partner. Make your quadrilaterals different from those above. Do you get the same results?

2. *Finding a Pattern* From the results of the example and Exercise 1, write a statement about the sum of the measures of the angles of a quadrilateral.

In Exercises 3–5, use a calculator to find the measure of the fourth angle. Then use a protractor to check your answer.

3.

4.

5.
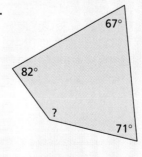

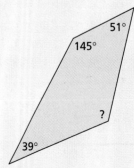

Materials Needed: grid paper, colored pencils or markers, ruler

Part A *Finding Perimeters* The perimeter of a figure is the total distance around the figure.

1. Each small square on the grid is 1 unit by 1 unit. Find the perimeter of each figure. Which figure has the greatest perimeter?

a.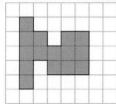
b.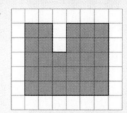
c.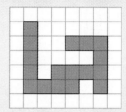

2. *Estimation* Each small square on the grid has a diagonal that is about 1.4 units long. Approximate the perimeter of each figure. Which figure has the greatest perimeter?

a.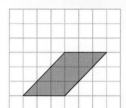
b.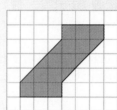
c.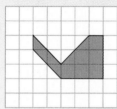

Part B *Drawing Figures*

3. Use grid paper. Draw a polygon with a perimeter in the given range.

   a. Quadrilateral   7–8 units   b. Hexagon   13–14 units
   c. Octagon   13–14 units   d. Triangle   14–15 units

4. Copy the diagrams below on grid paper. Draw a polygon with *A* and *B* as two of its vertices. Stay on the grid lines. Make a polygon so that it has the least possible perimeter.

> The first 3 polygons can be drawn by staying on the grid lines. Is that true of the last polygon?

a.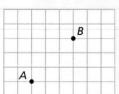
b.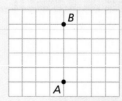
c.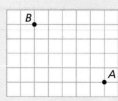

Part C *Finding a Pattern*

5. Copy and complete the table. Describe the pattern.

Figure

Number of Squares (*n*)	Dimensions	Perimeter (*P*)
1	1 × 1	4
2	?	?
3	?	?
4	?	?
5	?	?
6	?	?
7	?	?
8	?	?
9	?	?
10	?	?

6. In Exercise 5, let *n* be the number of small squares. Let *P* be the perimeter of the figure. Complete the following formula.

$$P = \boxed{?} \cdot n + \boxed{?}$$

On Your Own   *Critical Thinking*

7. *Finding a Pattern*   Copy the figures. Describe the pattern and draw the next seven figures.

8. *Finding a Pattern*   Find the perimeter of each figure in Exercise 7. The length of each side of a triangle is 1 unit. List your results in a table. Describe the pattern.

9. *Writing a Formula*   Let *n* be the number of triangles in each figure in Exercise 7. Let *P* be the perimeter of each figure. Does the formula you completed in Exercise 6 work for these figures? If not, what is a formula for the perimeter of these figures?

10. *Solve a Simpler Problem*   Use the result of Exercise 9 to predict the perimeter of the 20th figure in the pattern. Then check your result by drawing the 20th figure and finding its perimeter.

10.3 Parallelograms

Why you should learn it:

Knowing properties of parallelograms can help you find the sum of the angle measures of a parallelogram.

Goal 1 Identifying Parallelograms

A **parallelogram** is a quadrilateral whose opposite sides are parallel. A **rectangle** is a special parallelogram that has four right angles. A **square** is a special rectangle that has four sides of the same length.

These are parallelograms.   *These are not parallelograms.*

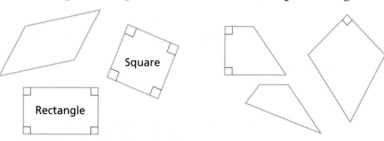

Square

Rectangle

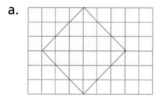

This **Venn diagram shows that (1) all parallelograms are quadrilaterals, (2) all rectangles are parallelograms, and (3) all squares are rectangles.**

Example 1 *Classifying Quadrilaterals*

By inspection, classify each quadrilateral as a parallelogram, a rectangle, and a square.

a.   b.

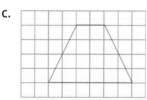   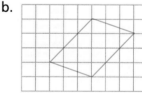

c.   d.

Solution

	Quadrilateral	Parallelogram	Rectangle	Square
a.	Yes	Yes	Yes	Yes
b.	Yes	Yes	No	No
c.	Yes	No	No	No
d.	Yes	Yes	Yes	No	■

Lesson Investigation

■ Investigating Parallelograms

Group Activity Each person in your group should draw two parallelograms on grid paper. (Try to draw parallelograms that are different from others in your group.) Use a ruler and a protractor to measure the sides and angles of your parallelograms. Discuss any patterns that you see.

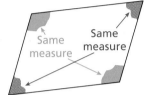

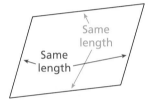

Parallelograms

Properties of Parallelograms

In a parallelogram, opposite sides have the same length, and opposite angles have the same measure.

Example **2** *Using Properties of Parallelograms*

Find the sum of the measures of the angles of the parallelogram at the right.

Solution   Because *ABCD* is a parallelogram, you know that opposite angles have the same measure. This means that the measure of $\angle C$ is 50° and the measure of $\angle D$ is 130°. The sum of the four angle measures is

$$50° + 130° + 50° + 130° = 360°.$$

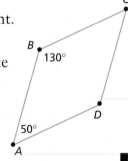

Communicating about MATHEMATICS

▶ **Sharing Ideas about the Lesson**

Angles Draw a parallelogram with a 60° angle. Then use a protractor to measure the other angles. Explain how to find the measures *without* using a protractor.

EXERCISES

▶ **CHECK for Understanding**

In Exercises 1–4, match the polygon with the sentence or sentences that describe it. (You can use each sentence more than once.)

a. It has 4 right angles.

b. It has 4 sides of equal length.

c. It has 4 sides.

d. Opposite sides are parallel.

1. Square   2. Quadrilateral   3. Parallelogram   4. Rectangle

5. *Visual Thinking*   Use the figure at the right. Name as many of each type of polygon as you can. Name each polygon by writing the letter or letters it contains.

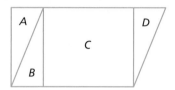

   a. Square   b. Parallelogram

   c. Rectangle   d. Quadrilateral

6. *Group Activity*   Imagine that four straws have been threaded together with a string, as shown at the right. Without bending the straws, can you move them to form a quadrilateral that is not a parallelogram? Can you form a rectangle that is not a square? Explain. (The straws must lie flat.)

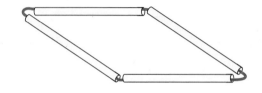

Independent Practice

In Exercises 7–10, use the Venn diagram on page 464 to name the color of the area in which the polygon belongs.

7.    8. 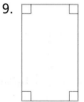   9.    10.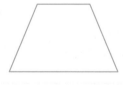

Reasoning   In Exercises 11–14, decide whether the statement is true or false. If false, explain why.

11. All rectangles are parallelograms.   12. All rectangles are squares.

13. All quadrilaterals are parallelograms.   14. All squares are parallelograms.

Symmetry In Exercises 15–18, if the quadrilateral has line symmetry, copy it and draw the line or lines of symmetry.

15. 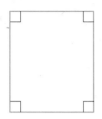   16.    17.   18.

In Exercises 19–21, discuss whether the parallelogram is a rectangle, square, both, or neither. Then find the missing measures.

19. 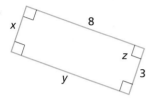   20. 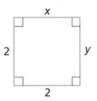   21.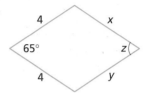

In Exercises 22–24, name the polygon in as many ways as you can.

22. 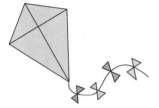   23.    24.

| **Integrated Review** | **Making Connections within Mathematics** |

Measurement Find the area of the given right triangle.

25. Triangle _JOM_   26. Triangle _JLO_
27. Triangle _LNO_   28. Triangle _JKL_

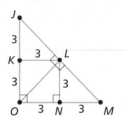

Exploration and Extension

29. _Building Your Chapter Project_ In your newspaper, include one or more riddles about objects that are quadrilaterals. For example:

I am a parallelogram but not a square. I have 4 right angles. I am about 8 inches by 10 inches. What am I?

The answer is the cover of this book! Type your riddles, cut them out, and paste them on your layout sheet.

Materials Needed: grid paper, colored pencils or markers, ruler, scissors

Part A *Cutting Parallelograms into Triangles*

1. Draw a parallelogram on grid paper. (Each person in your group should try to draw a different one.) Cut it out. Draw a *diagonal* on the parallelogram. Cut along the diagonal to form 2 triangles. Compare the triangles. What can you conclude?

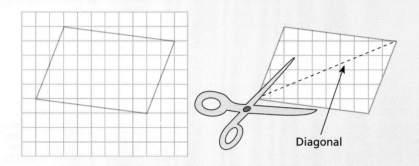

Diagonal

Part B *Forming Rectangles from Triangles*

2. Use the triangles you made in Exercise 1. Fold one of them to form a crease that is perpendicular to the longest side and goes through the opposite vertex. Cut along the crease. Rearrange the 3 pieces to form a rectangle.

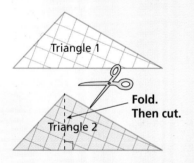

Triangle 1

Fold.
Then cut.

Triangle 2

Rearrange pieces to form a rectangle.

Triangle 1

3. Measure the sides of your rectangle. What is its area?

4. How does the area of Triangle 1 relate to the area of the rectangle? Use the area of the rectangle to find the area of Triangle 1.

5. Compare your results with the results of others in your group. What patterns do you observe?

Part C *Finding the Area of a Triangle*

6.a. Draw an acute triangle on grid paper. Draw the lower side on a grid line. Locate each vertex at a grid point. Then draw a rectangle that encloses the triangle. A sample is shown.

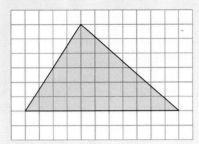 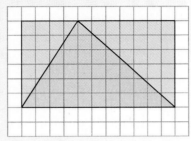

b. Each small square on the grid is 1 unit by 1 unit. Find the area of your rectangle.

c. Cut out your rectangle. Then cut the original triangle out of the rectangle. This should make three triangles: the original and two smaller triangles. Compare the original triangle to the two smaller triangles. What can you conclude? What is the area of the original triangle?

On Your Own   *Critical Thinking*

7. *Finding the Area of a Triangle*   Each small square on the grid is 1 unit by 1 unit. Use the technique described in Exercise 6 to find the area of each triangle.

a. 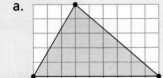   **b.** 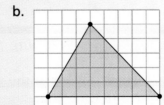   **c.**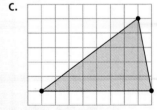

8. *Making Connections*   You already know how to find the area of a *right* triangle. Write a rule for finding the area of *any* triangle.

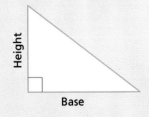 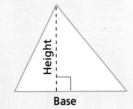

10.4

Area of a Triangle

What you should learn:

Goal 1 How to find the area of a triangle

Goal 2 How to use the area of a triangle to solve real-life problems

Why you should learn it:

Knowing how to find the area of a triangle can help you plan a construction project. An example is finding how much material you need to make a sail for a sailboat.

Study Tip

Even though any side of a triangle can be labeled as its base, there is often one side that is the most convenient. For instance, the side $\overline{AB}$ is most convenient in the triangle below.

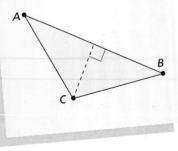

Goal 1 **Area of a Triangle**

Any side of a triangle can be labeled as the triangle's **base.** The **height** of the triangle is the perpendicular distance from the base to the opposite vertex.

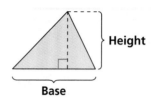 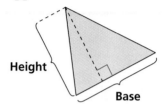

In Lab 10.4, you may have discovered the following rule for finding the area of a triangle.

Area of a Triangle

The **area** of a triangle is one half the product of the base and height of the triangle.

$$\text{Area of Triangle} = \frac{1}{2} \times \text{base} \times \text{height}$$

Example 1 *Finding the Area of a Triangle*

Each small square in the grid is 1 unit by 1 unit. Find the area of each triangle.

a.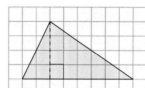

b.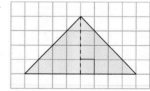

Solution

a. Area $= \frac{1}{2} \cdot 8 \cdot 4 = 16$ square units

b. Area $= \frac{1}{2} \cdot 8 \cdot 4 = 16$ square units

Notice that both triangles have the same area. ■

In 1994, there were about 1,300,000 sailboats in the United States. (Source: National Marine Manufacturers Assoc.)

Solving Real-Life Problems

Real Life
Sailing

Example 2 *Finding the Area of a Triangle*

You are making sails for your sailboat, as shown at the left. How much material is in the two sails?

Solution There are two ways to solve this problem. You can find the area of the right triangle for each sail.

$$\text{Area} = \frac{1}{2} \cdot 4 \cdot 8 \qquad \textit{Triangle formula}$$
$$= 16 \text{ square feet} \qquad \textit{Blue sail}$$
$$\text{Area} = \frac{1}{2} \cdot 2.5 \cdot 8 \qquad \textit{Triangle formula}$$
$$= 10 \text{ square feet} \qquad \textit{Green sail}$$

The total amount of material is 16 + 10 or 26 square feet. Another way to find the total area is to consider both sails as a *single* triangle with base 4 ft + 2.5 ft, or 6.5 ft.

$$\text{Area} = \frac{1}{2} \cdot 6.5 \cdot 8 \qquad \textit{Triangle formula}$$
$$= 26 \text{ square feet} \qquad \textit{Both sails}$$

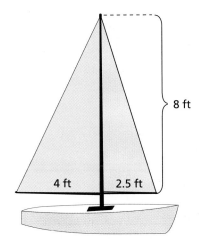

8 ft

4 ft   2.5 ft

Communicating about **MATHEMATICS**

Problem Solving
Guess, Check, and Revise

▶ **Sharing Ideas about the Lesson**

Extending the Example You are designing sails for another sailboat. You want the sails to be 10 feet high and have the same area as in Example 2. How wide should each sail be? Explain.

EXERCISES

Think and Discuss

▶ CHECK for Understanding

In Exercises 1–3, find the area of the triangle.

1. Base = 8, height = 6   2. Base = 8, height = 3   3. Base = 6, height = 3

4. *Error Analysis* Your friend wants to find the area of the triangle at the right. Describe your friend's error.

$$\text{Area} = \tfrac{1}{2} \times \cancel{\text{base}} \times \cancel{\text{height}} = \tfrac{1}{2} \times 6 \times 4 = 12$$

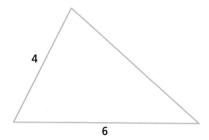

5. *It's Up to You* Sketch a triangle that has an area of 18 square units. Label the base and the height. Describe how you made the triangle.

6. *Cooking* The Greek dessert *baklava* is a walnut-honey pastry that is sometimes cut into a triangle, as shown at the right. Find the area of the triangle.

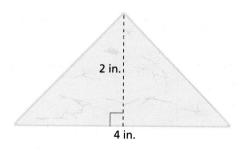

Independent Practice

In Exercises 7–10, find the area of the triangle.

7.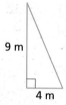

8.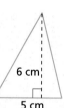

9.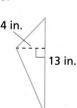

10.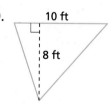

Measurement Use a centimeter ruler to measure the base and the height of the triangle to the nearest centimeter. Find the area.

11.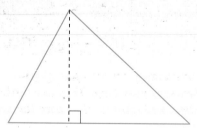

12.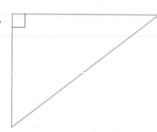

In Exercises 13–15, find the area of each polygon.

13.

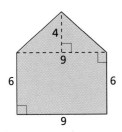

14.

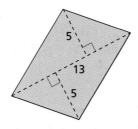

15.

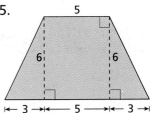

Algebra and Mental Math In Exercises 16–18, find the value of x.

16.

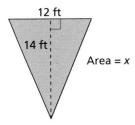

12 ft
14 ft
Area = x

17.

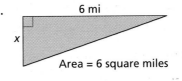

6 mi
x
Area = 6 square miles

18.

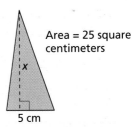

Area = 25 square centimeters
x
5 cm

19. *Geography* The diagram shows the approximate dimensions of Nevada. Approximate the area of the state.

Reasoning In Exercises 20 and 21, complete the statement using the words *sometimes*, *always*, or *never*.

20. Two triangles with the same base and height [?] have the same area.

21. Two triangles with the same area [?] have the same base and height.

22. a. *Greenhouse* You are helping build a greenhouse, as shown in the diagram below. The glass costs $2 per square foot. Find the cost for each of the pieces labeled A, B, C, D, E, F, and G.

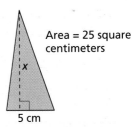

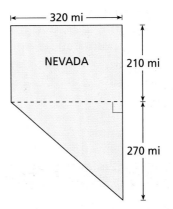

320 mi
NEVADA
210 mi
270 mi

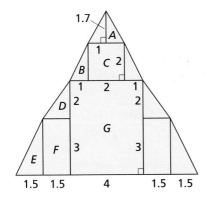

1.7
A
1
C 2
B
1   2   1
D 2   2
G
F 3   3
E
1.5 1.5   4   1.5 1.5

Greenhouses can be used to grow plants all year long. They are "solar collectors," that is, they trap the sun's heat.

b. What is the total cost of the pieces of glass?

23. *Visual Thinking*   Match the polygons that appear to be congruent. Then name each polygon in the first figure.

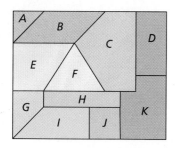
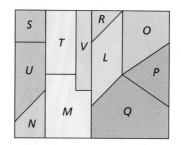

Exploration and Extension

24. *Building Your Chapter Project*   In your classroom, form a "human triangle." The triangle should be a right triangle. Three people should stand along one side of the triangle, 4 people along another side, and 5 people along the third side, as shown at the right. Outline your triangle using string or masking tape. What is the area of the triangle "in people"? This number of people should be able to comfortably stand inside the outline of the triangle. Check to see if they do.

Write an article for your class newspaper about the human triangle. Type your article, cut it out, and paste it on your layout sheet.

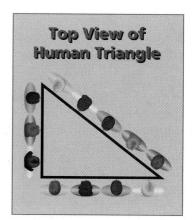

Top View of Human Triangle

Mixed REVIEW

Probability   Describe a real-life situation that has the given probability. **(6.7)**

1. Not likely to occur   2. Certain to occur   3. Equally likely to occur or not

Number Theory   Find the least common multiple of the numbers. **(7.2)**

4. 4, 7   5. 12, 15   6. 6, 8   7. 10, 8

Algebra   Evaluate the expression. **(2.5)**

8. $5 \times (4 + 3)$ 9. $10 \times 5 - 2 \times 7$ 10. $16 - 4 \div 2$ 11. $7 + 3 \times 5$

Take this test as you would take a test in class. The answers to the exercises are given in the back of the book.

In Exercises 1–6, use the figure at the right to name each of the following. **(10.1, 10.2)**

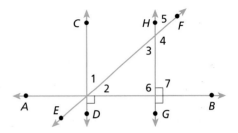

1. Parallel to $\overleftrightarrow{CD}$
2. Perpendicular to $\overleftrightarrow{CD}$
3. Complementary to $\angle 1$
4. Supplementary to $\angle 6$
5. Intersects $\overleftrightarrow{GH}$
6. Supplementary to $\angle 3$ and $\angle 5$

In Exercises 7–10, name the polygon in as many ways as you can. **(10.3)**

7.
8.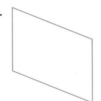
9.
10.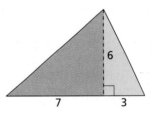

In Exercises 11–13, use the figure at the right. **(10.4)**

11. Find the area of the blue triangle.
12. Find the area of the red triangle.
13. Explain two ways to find the total area of both triangles.

In Exercises 14 and 15, is the statement true or false? Explain. **(10.1, 10.2, 10.3)**

14. All quadrilaterals are parallelograms.
15. All squares are rectangles.

Art In Exercises 16–18, use the painting at the right. The painting is by Piet Mondrian and is titled "Lozenge Composition in a Square." **(10.3, 10.4)**

16. What color is the parallelogram?
17. How many one-color quadrilaterals are there in the painting?
18. The base of the red triangle in the actual painting is 15 inches and the height is 7.5 inches. Find the area of the triangle.

Materials Needed: construction paper, pencils or pens, ruler, scissors, round can

The *diameter* of a circle is the distance across the circle through the center. The *circumference* of a circle is the distance around the circle. Many people have wondered about the relationship between a circle's diameter and circumference. In this investigation, you can repeat experiments that were first tried thousands of years ago. See if you can discover the same amazing result!

The ancient Greeks studied circles. Their letter "pi" describes the ratio of a circle's circumference to its diameter.

Center

Diameter

Circumference

Part A *How Many Diameters Make a Circumference?*

1. Cut two 1-inch wide strips out of construction paper. Use one of the strips to measure the diameter of the can. Cut this strip so it is exactly the length of the diameter. Use the other strip to measure the circumference of the can. Cut this strip so that it wraps around the can exactly once.

2. Use your "diameter strip" to measure your "circumference strip." In terms of diameter strips, about how long is the circumference strip?

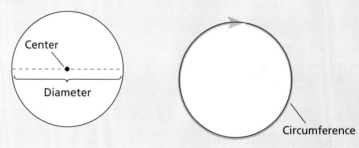

a. **Cut strips.**

b. **Measure diameter.**

c. **Measure circumference.**

d. **Use diameter strip to measure circumference strip.**

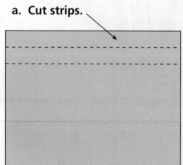

SODA

Part B *An Amazing Quotient*

3. **a.** Cut a sheet of construction paper into eleven 1-inch strips. Mark and cut the strips as shown at the right.

   b. One person should hold each strip so that it forms a circle. Another should use a ruler to measure the diameter of the circle to the nearest one fourth or 0.25 inch.

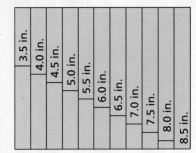

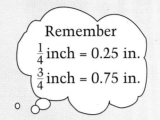

Remember
$\frac{1}{4}$ inch = 0.25 in.
$\frac{3}{4}$ inch = 0.75 in.

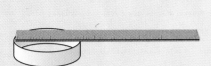

   c. A third person should record the results in a table. Do this for all eleven strips.

Circumference (inches)	3.5	4.0	4.5	5.0	5.5	6.0	6.5	7.0	7.5	8.0	8.5
Diameter (inches)	?	?	?	?	?	?	?	?	?	?	?
Circumference ÷ Diameter	?	?	?	?	?	?	?	?	?	?	?

4. Complete the third row of your table. Round to the nearest tenth. With others in your group, discuss any patterns that you see. Can you see the amazing result that has fascinated people for hundreds of years?

Part C *A Decimal Approximation for Pi*

In Exercises 3 and 4, you may have discovered that the quotient of the circumference and the diameter is about 3 for *any* circle. The ancient Greeks called this quotient "pi." It is written as π.

5. Use the results of your table to write a decimal approximation for π. To do this, find the average of the quotients in your table.

On Your Own   Critical Thinking

6. If you know the diameter of a circle, how can you find its circumference?

7. Find the circumference of each circle as described.
   a. Diameter is 2 inches.   **b.** Diameter is 3 feet.
   c. Diameter is 4 centimeters.   **d.** Diameter is 5 meters.

10.5

Circumference of a Circle

What you should learn:

Goal 1 How to find the circumference of a circle

Goal 2 How to use the circumference of a circle to solve real-life problems

Why you should learn it:

Knowing how to find the circumference of a circle can help you measure distances. An example is finding the distance around the roof of the Superdome.

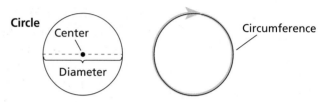

Goal 1 Circumference of a Circle

Every point on a **circle** is the same distance from the **center** of the circle. The **diameter** of a circle is the distance across the circle through the center. The **circumference** is the distance around a circle.

In Lab 10.5, you may have discovered the following.

Circumference of a Circle

To find the circumference of a circle, multiply the diameter by π. The symbol π is the Greek letter "pi." A decimal approximation for π is 3.14.

$$\text{Circumference} = \pi \times \text{diameter}$$

Need To Know

The reason the number *pi* is represented by the special symbol π is because its decimal representation has an unending number of digits that have no pattern. Here are some of the digits.

$\pi = 3.14159265358979\ldots$

Example 1 Finding Circumferences

Find the circumference of each circle.

a.

4 ft

b.

5 cm

Solution To find the circumference, multiply the diameter by 3.14.

a. The diameter is 4 feet.

$\text{Circumference} \approx 3.14 \times 4 = 12.56 \text{ feet}$

b. The diameter is 5 centimeters.

$\text{Circumference} \approx 3.14 \times 5 = 15.7 \text{ centimeters}$ ∎

The roof of the Superdome in New Orleans, Louisiana, is circular. The diameter of the roof is 680 feet.

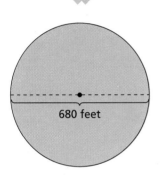

Goal 2 **Solving Real-Life Problems**

Real Life
Architecture

| **Example 2** | *Finding a Circumference* |

You are visiting New Orleans. A friend of yours works on the maintenance crew at the Superdome. She offers to take you up to the roof to walk around its walkway. Use the information with the photo above to find the distance around the walkway.

Solution The diameter of the roof is 680 feet. To find the circumference, multiply the diameter by 3.14.

$$\text{Circumference} \approx 3.14 \times 680$$

$$= 2135.2 \text{ feet}$$

The walkway is about 2135 feet around. There are 5280 feet in a mile, so the walkway is a little less than $\frac{1}{2}$ mile around. ∎

680 feet

Communicating about MATHEMATICS

Cooperative Learning

▶ **Sharing Ideas about the Lesson**

Partner Activity You now know how to find the circumference of a circle when you know the diameter. Explain how to solve the opposite problem. That is, if you know the circumference, how can you find the diameter? Find the diameter of the following circles.

A. Circumference is 14 feet.

B. Circumference is 9 meters.

EXERCISES

▶ **CHECK for Understanding**

In Exercises 1–3, use the diagram at the right to match the part of the circle with its name. Then define the part of the circle.

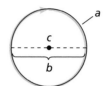

a. a **b.** b **c.** c

1. Diameter   2. Center   3. Circumference

4. Find the circumference of the circle.   5. Find the diameter of the circle.

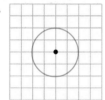

4.5 ft

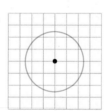

22 in.

Independent Practice

In Exercises 6–9, find the circumference of the circle. Each square on the grid is 1 unit by 1 unit.

6.   7.   8.   9.

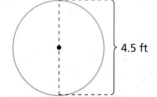

📱 *Measurement*   In Exercises 10–13, find the circumference.

10.   11.   12.   13.

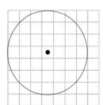
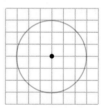
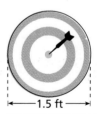

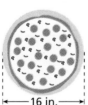
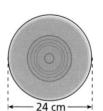

|← 19 mm →| |← 16 in. →| |← 24 cm →| |← 1.5 ft →|

In Exercises 14 and 15, find the circumference of a circle with the given diameter.

14. Diameter is 10 inches.   15. Diameter is 20 inches.

16. *Reasoning*   What happens to the circumference of a circle if you double its diameter? Use the results of Exercises 14 and 15 to support your answer.

Reasoning In Exercises 17 and 18, find the perimeter and area of the quadrilateral.

17.

6.2 cm

18.

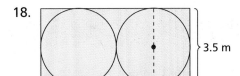

3.5 m

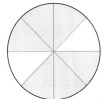 **19.** *Soap Box Derby* You are racing in the Soap Box Derby in a car with wheels 2 feet in diameter. How many times will your wheels rotate in complete circles if the race is $\frac{1}{4}$ mile?

20. *Amusement Park* You are spending the day at an amusement park. You ride a Ferris wheel that has a circumference of 785 feet. Find the diameter of the Ferris wheel.

Danielle Del Ferraro, 14, of Ohio, is the 1st two-time winner of the Soap Box Derby.

Integrated Review   *Making Connections within Mathematics*

Write two fractions shown by the shaded portion of the figure.

21. **22.** **23.** **24.**

 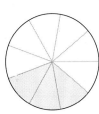 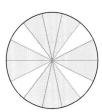

Exploration and Extension

25. *Exploring Circles* The figure shows a 12-sided polygon inside a circle. Find the perimeter of the polygon. Find the circumference of the circle. What can you conclude? Find the perimeter of a 16-sided polygon with each side measuring 0.78 in. surrounded by the same circle. Is the perimeter of the 16-sided polygon closer to the circumference of the circle than the perimeter of the 12-sided polygon? Explain.

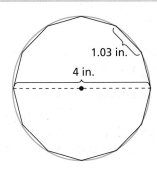

1.03 in.

4 in.

Materials Needed: paper, pencils or pens, scissors, tape

In Lesson 10.5, you learned that the diameter is the distance across the circle through the center. The distance from the center of the circle to a point on the circle is called the *radius* of the circle.

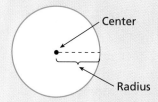

The diameter of a circle is twice its radius.

$$\text{Diameter} = 2 \times \text{radius}$$

Part A *Estimating the Area of a Circle*

1. Begin with a circle whose circumference is shaded. Follow the steps below. When you are done, you will have cut a circle into wedges and rearranged the wedges to form a figure that is almost rectangular.

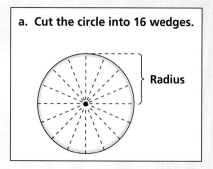

a. Cut the circle into 16 wedges.

Radius

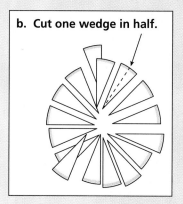

b. Cut one wedge in half.

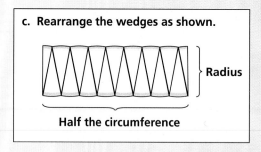

c. Rearrange the wedges as shown.

Radius

Half the circumference

2. With others in your group, discuss how to find the approximate area of the rearranged wedges. What can you say about the area of a circle?

Part B *Finding the Area of a Circle* In Part A, you may have discovered that you can find the area of a circle by multiplying its radius by half the circle's circumference. Half the circumference is equal to multiplying half the diameter or the radius by π.

Area = radius × half the circumference
  = radius × π × radius
  = π × (radius)^2

This is read as "area equals pi times radius squared."

3. Find the area of the circle on the left.

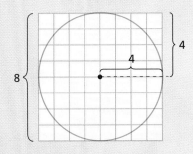
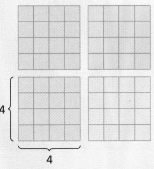
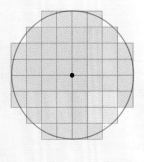

4. If the radius is 4, about how many 4-by-4 squares can you fit in the circle above? How does this relate to your answer from Exercise 3?

Part C *Guess, Check, and Revise*

5. You want to draw a circle whose area is 12 square inches. Estimate the radius of the circle you should draw. Explain your reasoning.

On Your Own   *Critical Thinking*

6. If you know the radius of a circle, explain how you can find the area of the circle.

7. Use your answer to Exercise 6 to find the area of each circle.

a.

b.

c.

d.

10.6

Area of a Circle

What you should learn:

Goal 1 How to find the area of a circle

Goal 2 How to use the area of a circle to solve real-life problems

Why you should learn it:

Knowing how to find the area of a circle can help you compare the sizes of circular areas. An example is comparing the sizes of greens on golf courses.

Goal 1 **Area of a Circle**

The **radius** of a circle is the distance between the center of the circle and a point on the circle. The radius of a circle is half its diameter.

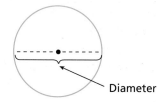

In Lab 10.6, you may have discovered the following.

Area of a Circle

To find the area of a circle, multiply the square of the radius by π. A decimal approximation for π is 3.14.

$$\text{Area} = \pi \times (radius)^2$$

Example 1 *Finding the Area of a Circle*

Find the area of each circle.

a.
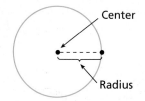

b.
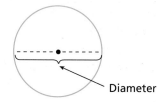

Study Tip

When you are finding the area of a circle, it helps to use a calculator. For instance, to find the area of the circle in Example 1(a), you could use the following keystrokes.

3.14 ☓ 5 ☓ 5 =

Solution To find the area, multiply the square of the radius by π or 3.14.

a. The radius is 5.

   Area $\approx 3.14 \cdot 5^2 = 3.14 \times 25 = 78.5$ square units

b. The diameter of the circle is 6, which means that the radius is 3.

   Area $\approx 3.14 \cdot 3^2 = 3.14 \times 9 = 28.26$ square units ∎

Example 2 *Using the Area of a Circle*

You just bought the circular picture shown below. The mat you will put it in is 24 in. wide and 30 in. high. What is the area of the circular picture?

Solution To begin, draw a diagram, as shown below.

This picture is called "Circle of Life." The name of the artist is Christian Riese Lassen. Many of his paintings have an ocean theme.

From the diagram, you can reason that the radius of the circle is half the diameter, or 11 inches. To find the area of the circle, multiply the square of the radius by 3.14.

Area $\approx 3.14 \times 11^2 = 3.14 \times 121 = 379.94$ square inches

The picture has an area of about 380 square inches. ■

In Example 2, notice you are given more information than you need to answer the question. Part of problem-solving is deciding which information to use.

Communicating about MATHEMATICS

Cooperative Learning

▷ **Sharing Ideas about the Lesson**

Finding Area Find the area of the mat around the circular picture above. Compare your results with others in your group. Explain your reasoning.

EXERCISES

Guided Practice

Think and Discuss

▶ **CHECK for Understanding**

In Exercises 1–5, match the name with the labeled part of the circle.

1. Diameter
2. Radius
3. Center
4. Circumference
5. Area

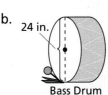

6. *Drums* A snare drum and a bass drum are shown below. The surface that is hit is called the drumhead. Find the area of each drumhead.

a.

Snare Drum

b.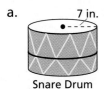

Bass Drum

The drum is the oldest musical instrument. It is a member of the percussion family of instruments.

Independent Practice

Measurement In Exercises 7–9, find the area of each object.

7.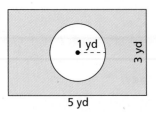

Dinner Plate

8.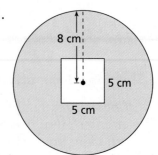

Dime

9.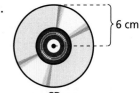

CD

In Exercises 10–12, find the area of the shaded region.

10.

11.

12.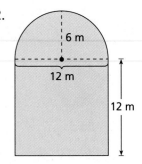

Reasoning In Exercises 13–15, complete the statement using >, <, or =. Use π = 3.14.

13. A circle with a radius of 3 m has an area (?) 27 sq m.

14. A circle with a diameter of 10 inches has an area that is (?) 100 square inches.

15. A circle with a radius of 7 ft has an area (?) a circle with a diameter of 13 ft.

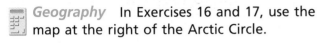 *Geography* In Exercises 16 and 17, use the map at the right of the Arctic Circle.

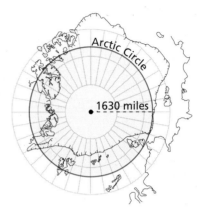

16. What is the area of the circle formed by the Arctic Circle?

17. What is the circumference of the Arctic Circle?

18. *Golf Time* The *green* on a golf course is a circular area of short grass. Your job is to mow the greens. Which will take you longer to mow, a green with a diameter of 80 feet, or a green with a radius of 45 feet? Explain.

19. *Field Trips* Suppose your school's policy is that field trips can be taken only to places within a 50 mile radius of the school. How large is this area? If the policy is changed to be a 100 mile radius, does this area double? Explain.

Integrated Review   *Making Connections within Mathematics*

Reading a Graph The graph at the right shows the most popular car colors for 1994. *(Source: DuPont Automotive)*

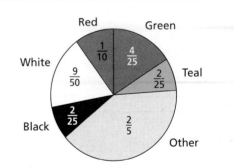

20. Order the colors from most popular to least popular.

21. How much more popular is green than black?

Exploration and Extension

 22. *Surface Area* Calculate the area of the figure. Copy the figure, cut it out, and tape it together to form a three-dimensional figure. Can you name the figure? The area you calculated is the *surface area* of the three-dimensional figure.

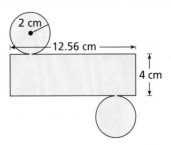

10.7

Statistics and Circle Graphs

What you should learn:

Goal 1 How to make a circle graph

Goal 2 How to use a circle graph to organize real-life data

Why you should learn it:

Knowing how to make a circle graph can help you organize data. An example is organizing the results of a poll.

Goal 1 Making a Circle Graph

A **circle graph** represents data as parts of a circle. The parts are labeled as fractions, decimals, or percents. Because the entire circle graph represents 1 unit, the sum of all the parts must be 1 (or 100%).

To make a circle graph, you need to find the measure of each part's angle. For example, to find $\frac{1}{3}$ of the circle, find $\frac{1}{3}$ of 360°.

$$\frac{1}{3} \text{ of } 360° = \frac{1}{3} \times 360°$$
$$= 120°$$

Sum of the angles is 360°.
45° + 45° + 60° + 120° + 90° = 360°

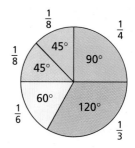

Real Life
Organizing Data

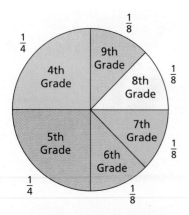

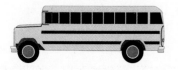

Example 1 *Making a Circle Graph*

Students on a school bus were asked which grade they are in. Organize the results below with a circle graph.

4th Grade: 8 students	5th Grade: 8 students
6th Grade: 4 students	7th Grade: 4 students
8th Grade: 4 students	9th Grade: 4 students

Solution There are 32 students on the bus. The 8 students in 4th grade make up $\frac{8}{32}$ or $\frac{1}{4}$ of the total. The 8 students in 5th grade also make up $\frac{1}{4}$ of the total. Each of the other grades has $\frac{4}{32}$ or $\frac{1}{8}$ of the total.

$$\frac{1}{4} \times 360° = 90° \quad \textit{4th and 5th grades}$$

$$\frac{1}{8} \times 360° = 45° \quad \textit{6th–9th grades}$$

Each part is either 90° or 45°, as shown at the left. ■

To make the angles of a circle graph, you can use a protractor or you can use *circle graph paper.*

| **Example 2** | *Making a Circle Graph* |

Real Life
Taking a Poll

Circle Graph Paper
Each part represents 5°.

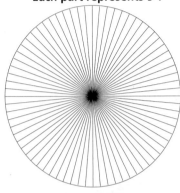

You took a poll of 36 people who made New Year's resolutions last year. Each person was asked to name the month that they broke their resolution. Make a circle graph of the results.

January: 9   July–September: 3
February: 6   October–December: 3
March: 6   Didn't break: 6
April–June: 3

Solution   Because 9 people answered "January," that month represents $\frac{9}{36}$ or $\frac{1}{4}$ of the circle graph. The categories with 6 responses represent $\frac{6}{36}$ or $\frac{1}{6}$ of the circle graph. The categories with 3 responses represent $\frac{3}{36}$ or $\frac{1}{12}$ of the circle graph.

$$\frac{1}{4} \times 360° = 90° \quad \tfrac{1}{4} \textit{ of circle graph}$$

$$\frac{1}{6} \times 360° = 60° \quad \tfrac{1}{6} \textit{ of circle graph}$$

$$\frac{1}{12} \times 360° = 30° \quad \tfrac{1}{12} \textit{ of circle graph}$$

To make the circle graph, you can use circle graph paper, as shown at the left. ■

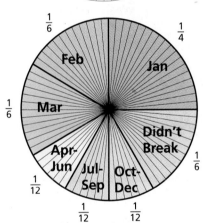

Communicating about MATHEMATICS

Cooperative Learning

▶ **Sharing Ideas about the Lesson**

Group Activity Ask 18 people to name their favorite month. Make a circle graph of the results. Compare your group's results with other groups' results.

Guided Practice

Think and Discuss

▶ **CHECK for Understanding**

Error Analysis In Exercises 1 and 2, describe and correct the error.

1.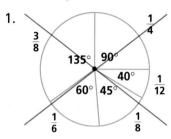

2.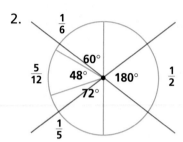

3. The list below shows the unordered steps to make a circle graph. Write the steps in order.

   - Use circle graph paper to draw each part.
   - Find the fraction for each part.
   - Find the degree of each part.
   - Add up the fractions and angle measures.

Sportswear The circle graph at the right shows how people wear sports clothing. *(Source: Sporting Goods Manufacturers Assoc.)*

4. Show that the sum of the parts equals 100%. Change the percents to fractions. Show that the sum of the parts equals 1. Explain.

5. Which part is 126°? Show why.

6. Which clothing use is about $4\frac{1}{2}$ times another? Explain.

Independent Practice

In Exercises 7 and 8, name the fraction or degree measure for each unknown part.

7.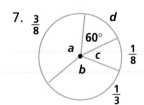

8.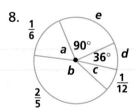

9. Three classes were asked to name their favorite fruit juice. The results were: orange, 24; grape, 18; apple, 12; cranberry, 12; and other, 6. Organize the data with a circle graph.

10. A survey asked 36 people to name their favorite breakfast food. The results were: cereal, 12; pancakes, 9; waffles, 8; eggs, 4; and other, 3. Organize the data with a circle graph.

11. *Reading for Fun*   A survey asked 48 students which type of book they like to read most. The results were: mystery, 18; autobiography, 16; science fiction, 8; and humor, 6. Organize the data with a circle graph.

12. *Rollerskating*   Students at a roller rink were asked which grade they are in. Organize the data with a circle graph. Which two grades make up half the students at the rink? Explain.

Grade	4	5	6	7	8
Number of Students	15	40	30	20	15

13. *At the Beach*   A survey asked 20 people to name what they like to do most at the beach. The results were as follows.

Get a tan	25%
Swim	40%
Play volleyball	20%
Build a sand castle	5%
Other	10%

Organize the data with a circle graph. How many people chose each category?

Integrated Review

Making Connections within Mathematics

Mental Math   Complete the statement.

14. $\frac{2}{10} = \boxed{?}\%$

15. $\frac{\boxed{?}}{100} = 3\%$

16. $\boxed{?}\% = \frac{1}{4}$

17. $\frac{1}{\boxed{?}} \times 9 = \frac{9}{2}$

18. $\frac{\boxed{?}}{7} \times 7 = 6$

19. $\frac{4}{5} \cdot \boxed{?} = 16$

Exploration and Extension

20. *Building Your Chapter Project*   Make up a survey that asks 48 people a question. Organize the data with a circle graph. Then write an article for your newspaper about your survey. Type your article, cut it out, and paste it and your circle graph on your layout sheet.

10.8 Geometric Probability

What you should learn:

Goal 1 How to find geometric probabilities

Goal 2 How to use geometric probability to solve real-life problems

Why you should learn it:

Geometric probabilities can help you when playing games. An example is finding the probability of getting points in a shuffleboard game.

Goal 1 Finding Geometric Probabilities

Example 1 Finding a Geometric Probability

You are playing shuffleboard. You slide your disk into the region shown below. Assume that your disk is equally likely to land anywhere in the region. What is the probability that you will get 10 points?

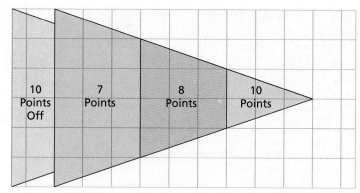

| 10 Points Off | 7 Points | 8 Points | 10 Points |

Each square in the grid is 1 foot by 1 foot.

Solution To find the probability that you will get 10 points, find the area of the "10-point triangle" and divide by the area of the entire rectangular region.

The 10-point triangle has a base of 2 feet and a height of 3 feet, so its area is

$$\text{Area} = \frac{1}{2} \times 2 \times 3 = 3 \text{ square feet.}$$

The entire rectangle is 6 feet by 12 feet, so its area is 6×12 or 72 square feet. The probability of landing on the 10-point triangle is

$$\text{Probability} = \frac{\text{Area of triangle}}{\text{Area of rectangle}} = \frac{3}{72} = \frac{1}{24}.$$

This means that you will get 10 points about 1 out of 24 times you slide your disk. ∎

Solving Real-Life Problems

Example 2 | *Finding a Geometric Probability*

Real Life
Shopping

A friend of yours has forgotten where he parked his car at a shopping mall. The mall has 5 parking zones. You search Zones 1 and 2 and your friend searches Zones 3, 4, and 5. What is the probability that you will find the car? What is the probability that your friend will find the car?

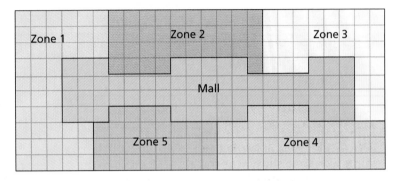

Solution You can use the area of the zones in the model to find each probability. In Zones 1 and 2, there is a total of 80 square units. In Zones 3, 4, and 5, there is a total of 100 square units. The total number of square units of parking space is 80 + 100 or 180 square units.

$$\text{Your probability} = \frac{80}{180} = \frac{4}{9}$$

$$\text{Friend's probability} = \frac{100}{180} = \frac{5}{9}$$

The probability that you will find the car is $\frac{4}{9}$. The probability that your friend will find it is $\frac{5}{9}$. ∎

Communicating about MATHEMATICS

▶ **Sharing Ideas about the Lesson**

Cooperative
Learning

Partner Activity In Example 2, suppose you searched Zones 1, 2, and 3 and your friend searched Zones 4 and 5. What is the probability that you will find the car? Explain your reasoning.

EXERCISES

Think and Discuss

▶ CHECK for Understanding

Carnivals In Exercises 1–3, suppose you are playing a carnival game. To win points you must throw a ball through different areas of a gameboard like that shown at the right. Find the probability of winning the given points.

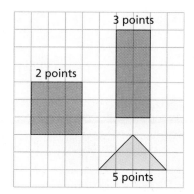

1. 2 points   2. 3 points   3. 5 points

4. *It's Up to You* Design your own carnival game with these points and probabilities.

Points	2	3	5
Probability	$\frac{1}{4}$	$\frac{1}{8}$	$\frac{1}{16}$

Bean Bags You are tossing a bean bag onto a region like that shown at the right. Retoss if the bag lands on a line. The bag is equally likely to land on any point in the region. Find the probability of landing on the given color.

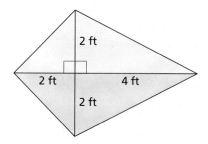

5. Green   6. Yellow

Independent Practice

Sticky Darts A game is played by throwing balls that "stick" to a board. Find the probability of a ball sticking to the red region.

7.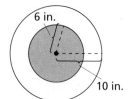

8.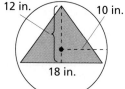

9.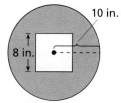

Lost and Found An ad says that a ring was lost in the area of a city like that shown at the right. The ring is equally likely to have been lost at any point. What is the probability of finding the ring in the given place?

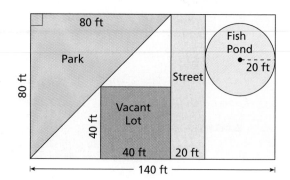

10. The park   11. The fish pond

12. The vacant lot   13. The street

Designing a Game In Exercises 14 and 15, suppose you are designing a game to be played at a fund-raiser. The object of the game is to toss a coin so that it lands in the blue square. In each design, determine the probability of winning the game.

14.

2 ft ← 2 ft →

← 3 ft →

15.

1 ft

2 ft 1 ft

← 3 ft →

16. *Tennis Anyone?* In tennis, a player must serve the ball into the opponent's service court. The service court is a 21-ft by $13\frac{1}{2}$-ft rectangle. The entire area of the tennis court is 2808 square feet. Suppose you are just learning to play tennis and the ball is equally likely to land anywhere on the court when you serve it. What is the probability that it will land in your opponent's service court?

Millions of people throughout the world play tennis for exercise and recreation.

Integrated Review

Making Connections within Mathematics

Order the fractions from least to greatest.

17. $\frac{2}{3}, \frac{7}{6}, \frac{1}{2}$

18. $\frac{1}{3}, \frac{4}{5}, \frac{7}{15}$

19. $\frac{3}{8}, \frac{3}{16}, \frac{1}{4}$

20. $\frac{9}{8}, \frac{11}{12}, \frac{5}{4}$

21. $\frac{4}{9}, \frac{2}{3}, \frac{5}{6}$

22. $\frac{5}{6}, \frac{7}{12}, \frac{3}{4}$

Exploration and Extension

23. *Building Your Chapter Project* A game is *fair* if each player has an equal probability of winning. Use a grid to design a board like the one shown at the right. Two players will toss a coin onto it. Each player chooses a different shape. In order to win, the coin must land on the shape they chose.

Show that the game at the right and your game are fair. Ask some classmates to play your game. Then write and type a short article for your newspaper that describes the results. Paste it on your layout sheet.

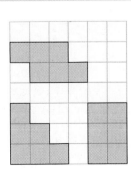

10 Chapter Summary

What did you learn?

Skills

1. Identify parallel, intersecting, and perpendicular lines.   **(10.1)**
2. Identify supplementary and complementary angles.   **(10.2)**
3. Learn how to draw angles.   **(10.2)**
4. Identify parallelograms, rectangles, and squares.   **(10.3)**
   - Use properties of parallelograms.   **(10.3)**
5. Find the area of a triangle.   **(10.4)**
6. Find the circumference of a circle.   **(10.5)**
7. Find the area of a circle.   **(10.6)**

Strategies

8. Use geometric probability to solve problems.   **(10.8)**
9. Use problem-solving strategies to solve problems.   **(10.1–10.8)**

Exploring Data

10. Use a circle graph to organize data.   **(10.7)**
11. Use tables and graphs to organize data and solve
    problems.   **(10.1–10.7)**

Why did you learn it?

Geometry and measurement can be used to solve many types of
real-life problems. Here are some of the examples you studied in
this chapter.

- Design a stained-glass window.   **(10.2)**
- Find the amount of material in a sailboat's sails.   **(10.4)**
- Find the distance around the walkway on the Superdome's
  roof.   **(10.5)**
- Organize data about New Year's resolutions.   **(10.7)**
- Find the probability of getting points in shuffleboard.   **(10.8)**

How does it fit into the bigger picture of mathematics?

In this chapter, you studied many properties and formulas. To be
successful in mathematics, you will need to find a way to
remember the properties and formulas you will be studying. You
could try to memorize every property and formula. For instance,
many people memorize the formula "pi r-squared" for the area of
a circle.

Instead of memorizing, however, we suggest that you try to
understand *why* properties are true. For instance, you learned
that the area of a triangle is "one half the base times the height"
because it is one half of a rectangle.

In Exercises 1–4, use the figure at the right. **(10.1, 10.2)**

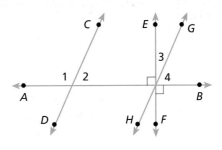

1. Lines $\overleftrightarrow{CD}$ and $\overleftrightarrow{EF}$ are ? lines.
2. Lines $\overleftrightarrow{EF}$ and $\overleftrightarrow{AB}$ are ? lines.
3. $\angle 1$ and $\angle 2$ are ? angles.
4. $\angle 3$ and $\angle 4$ are ? angles.
5. *Visual Thinking* Name as many of each type of polygon in the figure as you can. Name each polygon by writing the letter or letters it contains. **(10.3)**
   a. Square
   b. Parallelogram
   c. Rectangle
   d. Quadrilateral

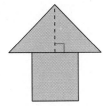

Tangrams In Exercises 6 and 7, use the diagram of tangram pieces at the right. Find the area of the figure. **(10.4)**

6.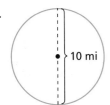

7.

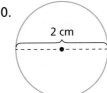

 In Exercises 8–10, find the circumference and the area of the circle. **(10.5, 10.6)**

8.
   10 mi

9. 2 km

10. 2 cm

11. *Making a Circle Graph* A survey asked people to name their favorite meal of the day. The results were: breakfast, 15; lunch, 12; and dinner, 18. Organize the data with a circle graph. **(10.7)**

12. *Scavenger Hunt* You are having a scavenger hunt in your backyard, as shown at the right. You are looking for a golf ball, the last item on the list. What is the probability that the golf ball is in the woods? **(10.8)**

Newspaper Measurements   In Exercises 13–15, use the figure of a layout sheet for a page of a standard newspaper.

13. Explain how you would paste a photograph on the layout sheet so that it is parallel to the bottom edge of the sheet.

14. You are asked to crop (cut) the photograph before pasting it on the layout sheet. Explain how you could be sure the side and top of the photograph are perpendicular to each other.

15. For a page of an average newspaper, advertising fills an area of 207 square inches. Suppose you close your eyes and point to a page of a newspaper. What is the probability that you will point to an ad?

 16. *Numbers of Newspapers*   In 1994, there were 596 morning newspapers, 996 afternoon newspapers, and 891 Sunday newspapers published in the United States. Organize this data with a circle graph. *(Source: Editor and Publisher Company)*

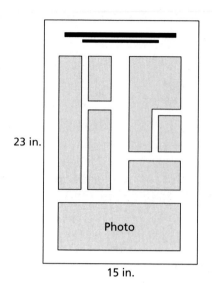

Newspaper Words   Use the figure at the right. Find a description that best fits the clue. Then place the letter of the description in the blank. The words you will spell will be terms used in newspaper publishing.

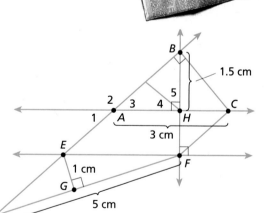

An Exclusive Story

17. ____   18. ____   19. ____   20. ____   21. ____

$\overleftrightarrow{FB}$ and $\overleftrightarrow{DB}$ $\overleftrightarrow{EF}$ and $\overrightarrow{BF}$ $\angle EGF$ $\angle BHC$ $\angle 1$

A Typed Story Ready for Layout

22. ____   23. ____   24. ____   25. ____

$\overleftrightarrow{AC}$ and $\overleftrightarrow{BF}$ $\angle ABC$ $\angle 3$ 2.25 sq cm

An Unimportant Story to Fill Space

26. ____   27. ____   28. ____   29. ____   30. ____

$\overleftrightarrow{AC}$ and $\overleftrightarrow{DB}$ $\angle 5$ 2.5 sq cm $ACFE$ $ACFD$

B	A quadrilateral
C	Perpendicular lines
I	A parallelogram
O	A right angle
P	Supplementary to $\angle 2$
Q	Complementary to $\angle 4$
S	Intersecting lines
U	Area of Triangle DEF
Y	Area of Triangle ABC

In Exercises 1–5, use the figure at the right.

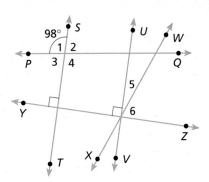

1. Lines $\overleftrightarrow{ST}$ and $\overleftrightarrow{WX}$ are [?] lines.

2. Name two pairs of perpendicular lines.

3. ∠1 and ∠2 are [?] angles.

4. ∠5 and ∠6 are [?] angles.

5. Write an explanation of how you can determine that ∠4 measures 98°.

In Exercises 6–8, name the polygon in as many ways as you can. Then find the missing measures.

6.
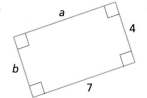

7.
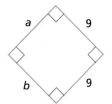

8.
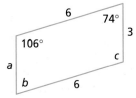

In Exercises 9–11, find the area of the triangle.

9.
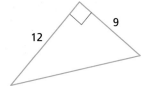

10.
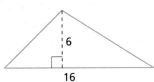

11.
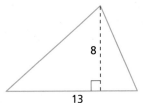

In Exercises 12–14, find the circumference and area of the circle.

12.
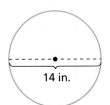

13.
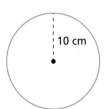

14.
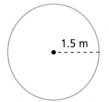

15. *Making a Circle Graph* A survey asked 42 sixth graders the average number of hours they do homework a day. Seven said "less than 1 hour," 21 said "1–2 hours," and 14 said "more than 2 hours." Organize the data with a circle graph.

16. *Dunking Booth* You are at a fair playing the dunking booth game. To dunk the person, you have to throw a ball and hit the circular target, as shown at the right. What is the probability that you will dunk the person?

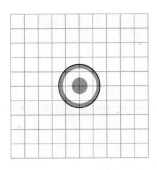

Algebra: Integers and the Coordinate Plane

Most species of penguins build their nests and raise their young in huge colonies called rookeries. *These King penguins are part of a larger rookery.*

Real Life
Antarctica

Antarctica is covered with so much ice that much of the land is below sea level. This ice mantle, which covers Antarctica, is 14 million square kilometers in area and sometimes more than 4000 m thick.

Ice Mantle

Think and Discuss

Trace the ice mantle. Draw one or more shapes that fit around your tracing with the least amount of space left over. Use the shape or shapes you drew to estimate the dimensions of the ice mantle. Explain.

Surfing the Internet

Theme: Antarctica Are you on the Information Superhighway yet? "Information Superhighway" is a way of referring to the *Internet*, which scientists have used to communicate since 1983. Now, with commercial online services, anyone can join in.

In this project, imagine you are using a computer to send messages to scientists in Antarctica. Your online service is offering a program called *Live from Antarctica*. The scientists have you help them do the following things, which you will keep record of in a scientific journal.

⟹ **In Lesson 11.1:** Change temperatures in degrees Celsius to degrees Fahrenheit. (page 510)

⟹ **In Lesson 11.2:** Find the average temperature in Antarctica, when some temperatures are above 0°C and some are below 0°C. (page 517)

⟹ **In Lesson 11.3:** Find the height of an iceberg. (page 524)

⟹ **In Lesson 11.4:** Locate the United States stations in Antarctica in a coordinate plane. (page 532)

⟹ **In Lesson 11.5:** Estimate the distance between two points in Antarctica. (page 537)

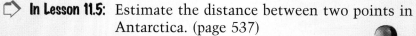

This whale skull was found on the beach of King George Island, Antarctica.

GETTING STARTED

Materials: paper, pencil, research material

Go to your library and look for interesting facts about Antarctica that you can include in your scientific journal.

Design a cover for your scientific journal. It should include the title *Science in Antarctica*, your name, your teacher's name, and your class period.

Materials Needed: calculator, pencils and pens, paper

Part A *Addition and the Number Line*

1. Enter 6 on a calculator. Then repeatedly add 4 and write the numbers the calculator displays. Describe the pattern.

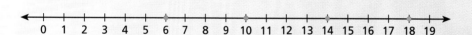

   Keystrokes   6 [+] 4 [=]   [+] 4 [=]   [+] 4 [=]   [+] 4 [=]   [+] 4 [=]   [+] 4 [=] . . .

   Display   10   14   18   22   26   30

2. The number line below shows some answers from Exercise 1. Describe the number line pattern. Is the pattern moving to the right or to the left?

```
  0  1  2  3  4  5  6  7  8  9  10 11 12 13 14 15 16 17 18 19
```

3. Copy and complete the table. Describe any patterns.

Starting Number	Repeated Operation	Example	First 8 Answers
3	Add 2.	3 [+] 2 [=]	5, 7, 9, 11, 13, 15, 17, 19
0	Add 5.	0 [+] 5 [=]	?
9	Add 3.	9 [+] 3 [=]	?

4. Plot the answers in each row of the table on a number line. Describe each pattern. Is each pattern moving to the right or to the left?

5. Complete the statement: *If you add 3 to a number, the result will lie* [?] *units to the* [?] *of the number on the number line.*

Part B *Subtraction and the Number Line*

6. Enter 17 on a calculator. Repeatedly subtract 2 and write the numbers the calculator displays. Describe the pattern.

   Keystrokes   17 [−] 2 [=]   [−] 2 [=]   [−] 2 [=]   [−] 2 [=]   [−] 2 [=]   [−] 2 [=] . . .

   Display   15   13   11   9   7   5

7. The number line below shows some of the answers from Exercise 6. Describe the number line pattern. Is the pattern moving to the right or to the left?

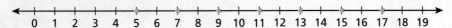

8. Copy and complete the table. Describe any patterns.

Starting Number	Repeated Operation	Example	First 8 Answers
27	Subtract 3.	27 − 3 =	24, 21, 18, 15, 12, 9, 6, 3
45	Subtract 5.	45 − 5 =	?
36	Subtract 4.	36 − 4 =	?

9. Plot the answers in each row of the table on a number line. Describe each pattern. Is each pattern moving to the right or to the left?

10. Complete the statement: *If you subtract 3 from a number, the result will lie* ? *units to the* ? *of the number on the number line.*

11. *Temperatures* On a cold winter day, the temperature is falling 4 degrees each hour. The temperature at 3 P.M. is 8°F. What will the temperature be at 6 P.M.? At 7 P.M.? Use your calculator to help you. What do you notice about the temperatures?

Time	3:00 P.M.	4:00 P.M.	5:00 P.M.	6:00 P.M.	7:00 P.M.
Temperature	8°F	4°F	0°F	?	?

On Your Own   *Critical Thinking*

12. Enter 5 on a calculator. Add 2 eight times and describe the numbers that the calculator displays. Graph the numbers on a number line. Is the pattern moving to the right or to the left?

13. Enter 5 on a calculator. Subtract 2 eight times and describe the numbers that the calculator displays. Graph the numbers on a number line. Where will the next six numbers be?

14. Give an example of how you can get your calculator to display a number that is less than 0.

Graphing Integers on a Number Line

What you should learn:

Goal 1 How to graph integers on a number line

Goal 2 How to use integers to solve real-life problems

Why you should learn it:

Knowing how to use negative integers can help you understand a scientific report. An example is understanding a report about temperatures in Antarctica.

Need To Know

Two numbers are **opposites** of each other if they are the same distance from 0 on a number line. For instance, −4 is the opposite of 4 and 4 is the opposite of −4.

Goal 1 Graphing Integers

The following numbers are **integers.**

. . . , −4, −3, −2, −1, 0, 1, 2, 3, 4, . . . **Integers**

Negative integers   Zero   Positive integers

The three dots (. . .) mean that the numbers continue to the left and to the right. Integers are divided into three categories: **negative integers,** zero, and **positive integers.** On a number line, negative integers are to the left of zero and positive integers are to the right of zero.

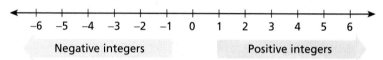

Negative integers   Positive integers

The symbol "−" used to represent negative numbers is a **negative sign.** You read "−4" as "negative four."

Example 1 *Graphing on a Number Line*

Graph −4, −1, 0, 2, and 4 on a number line.

Solution

Begin by using a ruler to draw a straight line.

Then mark several evenly spaced tick marks on the line and label them. Draw arrowheads on each end of the line.

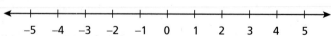

Finally, graph each number on the number line.

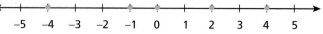

Example 2 *Locating Numbers on a Number Line*

a. Name the integers between -7 and -3.

b. Name the opposites of the integers -3, 0, and 1.

Solution

a. The integers between -7 and -3 are -6, -5, and -4.

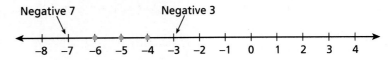

b. The opposites of -3, 0, and 1 are 3, 0 and -1.

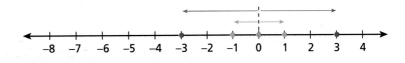

A number line can be used to compare integers. Smaller numbers are to the left. Greater numbers are to the right.

Example 3 *Comparing Integers*

Use a number line to complete the statement with $<$ or $>$.

a. $-5 \,⑦\, -2$ **b.** $3 \,⑦\, -5$

Solution

a. Begin by graphing the numbers on a number line.

Negative 5 is to the left of negative 2.

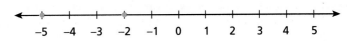

Because -5 is to the left of -2, it follows that $-5 < -2$.

b. Begin by graphing the numbers on a number line.

3 is to the right of negative 5.

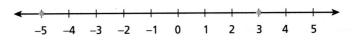

Because 3 is to the right of -5, it follows that $3 > -5$. ■

Study Tip

Whenever you write a mathematical statement, be sure that you can also say it with words. For instance, the statement
$$-5 < -2$$
is read as "negative 5 is less than negative 2." Similarly, the statement
$$3 > -5$$
is read as "3 is greater than negative 5."

The United States has three scientific stations in Antarctica: McMurdo Station, Palmer Station, and Amundsen-Scott Station. Palmer Station, shown at the right, is located on the Antarctic Peninsula.

Goal 2 Solving Real-Life Problems

Connections
Science

Celsius Scale

50
40
30
20
Water 10
freezes. → 0
−10
−20
−30
−40
−50

Example 4 *Measuring Temperatures*

You have just watched a television program called *Live from Antarctica,* which is sponsored by the National Science Foundation. A scientist on the program says that the temperature (on the Celsius scale) is 15 degrees below zero. What does this mean? How would you write this temperature?

Solution A thermometer represents numbers with a *vertical* number line, as shown at the left. So 15 degrees *below zero* means that it is 15 degrees less than zero. In symbols, this temperature is written as −15°C. This is read as "negative 15 degrees Celsius." ■

Communicating about MATHEMATICS

▶ **Sharing Ideas about the Lesson**

Extending the Example You are visiting Palmer Station. During the morning, the temperature is increasing. At 8 A.M., the temperature is −14°C. At 11 A.M., the temperature is −5°C. Use a number line to estimate the temperatures at 9 A.M. and at 10 A.M. Explain your reasoning.

EXERCISES

▶ CHECK for Understanding

1. List the integers in order from −4 to 4.

In Exercises 2–6, match the number with its location on the number line.

2. 4   3. −3   4. 5   5. −4   6. −7

7. Which integer is neither positive nor negative?

8. Name the integers between −6 and −2.

9. *Number Sense* Which integer is the opposite of 4? Which integer is the opposite of −8?

Independent Practice

Finding a Pattern Graph the integers on a number line. Describe the pattern. Then list the next two integers of the pattern.

10. −6, −4, −2, 0, 2, ?, ?   11. −5, −3, −1, 1, 3, ?, ?   12. 2, −1, −4, −7, ?, ?

Number Sense In Exercises 13–18, use a number line to help you complete the statement using > or < .

13. 4 ? 0

14. 0 ? −1

15. −8 ? −6

16. −2 ? 2

17. −2 ? −7

18. −5 ? −4

Number Sense In Exercises 19–21, use a number line to help you order the integers from least to greatest.

19. 6, 1, −3, 3, −4   20. −2, 4, −9, −7, 0   21. −1, −6, −3, 0, −5

Making Connections Match the figure with its description.

a. Three integers that are 1 unit apart   b. Two integers that are 5 units apart

c. Two integers that are opposites   d. Two integers that are 2 units apart

22. ←——+——◆——+——+——◆——+——◆——→
      −3   −2   −1   0   1   2   3

23. ←——◆——+——+——◆——+——◆——→
       −9   −8   −7   −6   −5   −4

24. ←——+——◆——◆——+——→
       −7   −6   −5   −4

25. ←——+——◆——+——◆——◆——+——→
       −5   −4   −3   −2   −1   0

Word Scramble   In Exercises 26–33, write the described integer.

26. **H:** 3 more than −3

27. **A:** between −6 and −4

28. **R:** opposite of 6

29. **G:** opposite of −9

30. **I:** smallest positive integer

31. **P:** largest negative integer

32. **G:** 2 less than −7

33. **N:** 4 less than 10

34. Graph each integer in Exercises 26–33 on the same number line. Label each integer with its letter. What word is spelled?

35. *Science*   The lowest temperature recorded in the United States was 80 degrees below zero on the Fahrenheit scale in Prospect Creek, Alaska. How would you write this temperature? How is it read? How does it compare to the lowest temperature recorded outside of Alaska?

The lowest temperature recorded outside of Alaska was −70°F in Roger Pass, Montana.

36. *Communicating*   Beginning at 0 on a number line, graph the integer that is represented by the expression "one step forward and two steps back." If you repeat the instructions 4 more times, what integer will you end on?

Integrated Review

Making Connections within Mathematics

Number Sense   Plot the fractions on a number line. Then use the result to order the fractions from greatest to least.

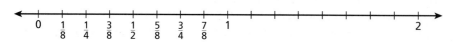

37. $\dfrac{5}{8}, \dfrac{3}{4}, \dfrac{2}{4}, \dfrac{2}{8}$

38. $\dfrac{9}{8}, \dfrac{6}{8}, \dfrac{3}{2}, \dfrac{5}{4}$

39. $\dfrac{8}{4}, \dfrac{7}{4}, \dfrac{3}{2}, \dfrac{11}{8}$

40. $\dfrac{16}{8}, \dfrac{3}{4}, \dfrac{3}{2}, \dfrac{4}{4}$

Exploration and Extension

41. *Building Your Chapter Project*   You are online chatting with a scientist on *Live from Antarctica*. The scientist says that the temperature is −8°C. Copy the thermometers at the right in your scientific journal. Then show how they can be used to estimate the temperature on the Fahrenheit scale.

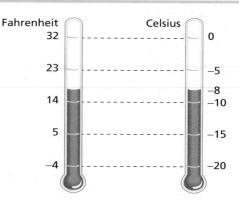

Find the product. **(4.4)**

1. 2.3×0.5 2. 7×1.65 3. 0.36×0.1 4. 0.09×30

Measurement Use a fraction to complete the statement. **(6.1)**

5. Sixteen minutes is ? of an hour.
6. Six inches is ? of a foot.
7. Three pints is ? of a gallon.
8. Four ounces is ? of a pound.

Is the proportion true or false? Explain your reasoning. **(6.4)**

9. $\frac{5}{6} \stackrel{?}{=} \frac{15}{18}$ 10. $\frac{2}{9} \stackrel{?}{=} \frac{5}{27}$ 11. $\frac{15}{45} \stackrel{?}{=} \frac{1}{3}$ 12. $\frac{3}{4} \stackrel{?}{=} \frac{16}{20}$

Find the reciprocal of the number. **(8.5)**

13. $\frac{8}{9}$ 14. $\frac{1}{6}$ 15. $\frac{7}{12}$ 16. $\frac{13}{16}$

Career Interview

Professor Professor Cooper gathers data about how people perform on their jobs. In his research and teaching, he creates mathematical and statistical models to help people understand what they can do to perform better.

Q: *What led you to this career?*
A: I first became interested in business when I was five years old. In eighth grade, my brother and I started our own camping equipment company. We sold certificates representing shares of stock to raise money for our business. With the money we made, we rented an airplane and flew our stockholders around New York State.

Q: *Why are math skills important in your work?*
A: One reason is that to become a successful businessperson, you need to be able to predict your customers' needs. Mathematics and statistics help you do this.

Q: *Can the math concepts you teach be used in everyday situations?*
A: Yes, math and statistics can help you answer questions such as: "How do I succeed in the stock market?" "How can I become a better athlete?" "Will the amount of time I study affect my future career?"

Lab 11.2

Investigating Integer Addition

Materials Needed: number counters, mats, pencils, paper

Part A *Adding Two Integers*   You can use number counters to model integer addition. The examples below show the sum of two positive integers and the sum of two negative integers.

Sum: **5 + 3**

5 + 3 = 8
↘ *Number sentence*

Choose 5 black counters to show positive 5 and 3 black counters to show positive 3.

Place the counters on the mat and count the total number of black counters.

Sum: **−5 + (−3)**

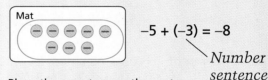

−5 + (−3) = −8
↘ *Number sentence*

Choose 5 red counters to show negative 5 and 3 red counters to show negative 3.

Place the counters on the mat and count the total number of red counters.

1. Use number counters to model the following addition problems. Write a number sentence for each problem.
   a. 4 + 5   b. 7 + 2   c. −3 + (−6)   d. −5 + (−5)

Part B *Zero Pairs*   When you pair one black counter and one red counter, the result is zero. We call this pair of counters a *zero pair*.

Sum: **3 + (−3)**

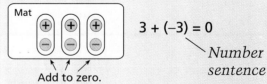

3 + (−3) = 0
↘ *Number sentence*

Add to zero.

Choose 3 red counters to show negative 3 and 3 black counters to show positive 3.

Place the counters on the mat and group pairs of black and red counters.

2. Use number counters to model the following addition problems. Write a number sentence for each problem.
   a. −2 + 2   b. 4 + (−4)   c. 6 + (−6)   d. 1 + (−1)

Part C *Adding Positive and Negative Integers* When you use number counters to add a positive integer and a negative integer, remember that each pair that has one red counter and one black counter adds to zero.

Sum: –5 + 3

–5 ⊖ ⊖ ⊖ ⊖ ⊖

3 ⊕ ⊕ ⊕

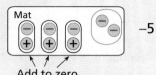

Add to zero.

–5 + 3 = –2

Number sentence

Choose 5 red counters to show negative 5 and 3 black counters to show positive 3.

Place the counters on the mat and group pairs of black and red counters. The remaining counters show the sum.

3. Use number counters to model the following addition problems. Write a number sentence for each problem.

   a. $-4 + 5$ b. $7 + (-2)$ c. $5 + (-8)$ d. $-7 + 2$

4. With others in your group, discuss what you noticed about the sum of a positive integer and a negative integer.

On Your Own   *Critical Thinking*

In Exercises 5–8, use number counters to model the addition problem. Then write a number sentence for the problem.

   5. $-5 + (-2)$ 6. $-3 + (-9)$ 7. $-4 + 3$ 8. $5 + (-5)$

In Exercises 9–11, match the addition problem with the description of its sum. Then use number counters to check your result.

   a. A negative integer   b. Zero   c. A positive integer
   9. $-4 + 5$ 10. $3 + (-4)$ 11. $-4 + 4$

Reasoning In Exercises 12–14, use the words *sometimes, always,* or *never* to complete the statement. Give examples to support your answer.

12. The sum of two positive integers is [?] negative.
13. The sum of two negative integers is [?] negative.
14. The sum of a positive integer and a negative integer is [?] negative.

11.2 Adding Integers

What you should learn:

Goal 1 How to use a number line to add integers

Goal 2 How to use integer addition to solve real-life problems

Why you should learn it:

Knowing how to add integers can help you find averages. An example is finding if your average miniature golf score is over or under par.

Goal 1 — Adding Integers

In Lab 11.2, you used number counters to add integers. Another way to add integers uses a number line.

- When you add a *positive* number, move to the right.
- When you add a *negative* number, move to the left.

Example 1 — Adding Two Integers

Use number lines to solve the addition problems.

a. $3 + 5$ **b.** $-4 + (-2)$ **c.** $-5 + 3$

Solution

a. Begin at 3. Then move 5 units to the right. The final position on the number line is 8. So $3 + 5 = 8$.

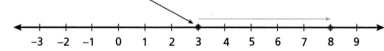

① Begin at 3.   ② Then move 5 units to the right.

③ Because you end at 8, the sum is 8.

b. Begin at -4. Then move 2 units to the left. The final position on the number line is -6. So $-4 + (-2) = -6$.

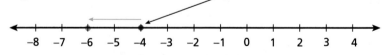

② Then move 2 units to the left.   ① Begin at -4.

③ Because you end at -6, the sum is -6.

c. Begin at -5. Move 3 units to the right. The final position on the number line is -2. So $-5 + 3 = -2$.

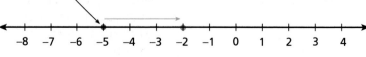

① Begin at -5.   ② Then move 3 units to the right.

③ Because you end at -2, the sum is -2. ∎

Study Tip

Addition of integers is commutative, which means that the order in which you add integers doesn't affect their sum. For instance, try solving the following problems. Do you get the same results as in Example 1?

a. $5 + 3$

b. $-2 + (-4)$

c. $3 + (-5)$

There are many applications of negative integers.

Real-Life Situation	Number Model
A loss of $10	−10 dollars
Five feet below sea level	−5 feet
In football, a yardage loss of 6 yards	−6 yards

Real Life
Miniature Golf

Miniature golf courses often have complex designs, such as this one with a geometric theme.

Example 2   *Adding Integers*

You played two games of miniature golf. On your first game, you scored 3 over par. On your second game, you scored 1 under par. Is your average score over or under par?

Solution   Because the first score is over par, it can be represented by the positive number 3. Because the second score is under par, it can be represented by the negative number −1.

To find the average, add 3 and −1. Then divide by 2.

To find the sum of 3 and −1, you can use a number line, as shown below.

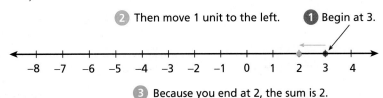

② Then move 1 unit to the left.   ① Begin at 3.

③ Because you end at 2, the sum is 2.

$$\text{Average} = \frac{3 + (-1)}{2} = \frac{2}{2} = 1$$

Because your average is positive 1, your average score is 1 over par. ∎

Communicating about MATHEMATICS

▶ **Sharing Ideas about the Lesson**

Cooperative Learning

Number Counters Lab 11.2 describes how to use number counters to add integers. With others in your group, show how you can use number counters to find the sums in Example 1. Do you get the same results?

EXERCISES

▶ **CHECK for Understanding**

Error Analysis Describe and correct the error. Then write the correct sum.

1. $-2 + 5$

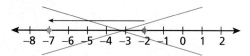

2. $-4 + (-3)$

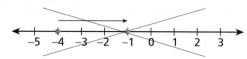

3. Write the addition problem shown by the figure.

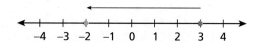

In Exercises 4–7, use a number line to solve the problem.

4. $2 + 8$ **5.** $-4 + 3$ **6.** $-5 + 9$ **7.** $-1 + (-6)$

8. *Making Connections* How can the sum of a positive integer and a negative integer be *positive? Negative? Zero?* Give examples to support your answers.

Independent Practice

Write the addition problem shown by the figure. Then solve.

9.

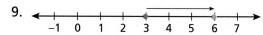

10.

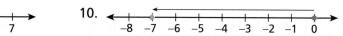

11.

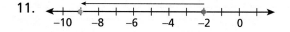

12.

In Exercises 13–16, match the problem with its answer.

   a. 11 **b.** 5 **c.** -5 **d.** -11

13. $3 + 8$ **14.** $-6 + 1$ **15.** $-8 + (-3)$ **16.** $-3 + 8$

Use a number line to solve the problem.

17. $7 + 7$ **18.** $-5 + 5$ **19.** $-2 + 1$ **20.** $-4 + 7$

21. $-9 + (-5)$ **22.** $-4 + (-11)$ **23.** $-6 + 13$ **24.** $-15 + 8$

Communicating Math Use a number line. Write the addition problem described. Then solve.

25. Start at 4. Move 5 units left, then 2 units right.

26. Start at −3. Move 1 unit left, then 5 units right. Move 1 unit left.

27. *Savings Account* In your savings account book, you record a deposit as a positive integer and a withdrawal as a negative integer. You then add to get a new balance. Suppose you begin with $15 in your account. What will the new balance be after you do the following?

a. Deposit $7   b. Then withdraw $11

Use a number line to determine how many yards the tag football team gained or lost overall.

28. The team gains 6 yards, then 9 yards.

29. The team gains 8 yards, then loses 4 yards.

Bank vaults are usually made of steel. They are used to safeguard money, securities, and other valuables.

Integrated Review   Making Connections within Mathematics

Add.

30. $\frac{3}{5} + \frac{1}{5}$

31. $\frac{1}{6} + \frac{2}{3}$

32. $\frac{5}{8} + \frac{1}{2}$

33. $\frac{1}{9} + \frac{4}{9} + \frac{1}{9}$

34. $1\frac{4}{7} + 5\frac{3}{7}$

35. $3\frac{1}{4} + 1\frac{5}{6}$

36. $1\frac{2}{5} + 1\frac{1}{3}$

37. $2\frac{1}{2} + \frac{1}{4}$

Exploration and Extension

38. *Building Your Chapter Project* You are online on *Live from Antarctica* exploring data about temperatures. You find the morning temperatures for a week, as shown below. What is the average morning temperature for the week? In your journal, explain how you found it.

Temperatures			
Sunday	−4°C	Thursday	6°C
Monday	−5°C	Friday	7°C
Tuesday	−1°C	Saturday	9°C
Wednesday	2°C		

This leopard seal is enjoying a stretch in the sun.

Materials Needed: number counters, mats, pencils, paper

Part A *Subtracting Positive Integers*

1. This example shows how to model 5 − 8.

 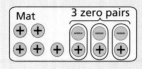 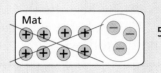

Start with 5 black   Add enough zero   Subtract 8 by removing   5 − 8 = −3
counters.   pairs to get 8 black   8 black counters.
                        counters.   The solution is −3.   *Number
                                                                          sentence*

Use number counters to help you subtract.

   a. 5 − 7   b. 3 − 6   c. 2 − 9   d. 8 − 9

Part B *Subtracting Negative Integers*

2. This example shows how to model −2 − (−4).

 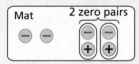 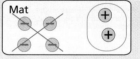

Start with 2 red   Add enough zero pairs   Subtract negative 4 by   −2 − (−4) = 2
counters.   to get 4 red counters.   removing 4 red counters.
                                               The solution is 2.   *Number
                                                                          sentence*

Use number counters to help you subtract.

   a. −3 − (−4)   b. −4 − (−6)   c. −1 − (−5)   d. −5 − (−9)

3. This example shows how to model −6 − (−3).

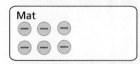 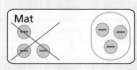

Start with 6 red   Subtract negative 3 by   −6 − (−3) = −3
counters.   removing 3 red counters.
                      The solution is −3.   *Number
                                                   sentence*

Use number counters to help you subtract.

   a. −6 − (−4)   b. −8 − (−3)   c. −7 − (−2)   d. −5 − (−4)

Part C Subtracting Positive and Negative Integers

4. This example shows how to model $5 - (-3)$.

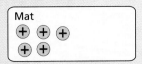

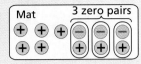

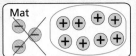

$5 - (-3) = 8$

Number sentence

Start with 5 black counters.

Add enough zero pairs to get 3 red counters.

Subtract negative 3 by removing 3 red counters. The solution is 8.

Use number counters to help you subtract.

a. $6 - (-3)$ b. $4 - (-5)$ c. $2 - (-2)$ d. $1 - (-7)$

5. This example shows how to model $-4 - 2$.

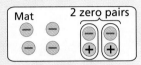

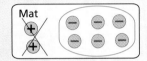

$-4 - 2 = -6$

Number sentence

Start with 4 red counters.

Add enough zero pairs to get 2 black counters.

Subtract positive 2 by removing 2 black counters. The solution is -6.

Use number counters to help you subtract.

a. $-3 - 5$ b. $-2 - 6$ c. $-1 - 3$ d. $-8 - 1$

On Your Own   Critical Thinking

In Exercises 6–13, use number counters to help you subtract.

6. $5 - 3$ 7. $5 - 7$ 8. $-3 - (-2)$ 9. $-4 - (-5)$

10. $-6 - (-5)$ 11. $7 - (-4)$ 12. $-6 - 5$ 13. $-1 - (-2)$

14. Without using number counters, tell whether the result is negative, zero, or positive. Then use number counters to help you subtract.

a. $5 - (-2)$ b. $-3 - (-3)$ c. $7 - 9$ d. $-4 - (-6)$

15. When you are using number counters to subtract, how can you tell when you need to add zero pairs to the mat? Illustrate your answer with two examples, one that needs zero pairs added and one that doesn't.

11.3 Subtracting Integers

What you should learn:

Goal 1 How to use a number line to subtract integers

Goal 2 How to use integer subtraction to solve real-life problems

Why you should learn it:

Knowing how to subtract integers can help you find distances. An example is finding the distance you traveled on an elevator.

Goal 1 Subtracting Integers

In Lab 11.3, you used number counters to subtract integers. Another way to subtract integers uses a number line.

- When you subtract a *positive* number, move left.
- When you subtract a *negative* number, move right.

Example 1 Subtracting Two Integers

Use number lines to solve the subtraction problems.

a. $7 - 3$ **b.** $2 - (-4)$ **c.** $-3 - 2$

Solution

a. Begin at 7. Then move 3 units to the left. The final position on the number line is 4. So $7 - 3 = 4$.

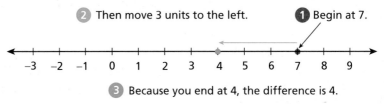

② Then move 3 units to the left.   ① Begin at 7.

③ Because you end at 4, the difference is 4.

b. Begin at 2. Then move 4 units to the right. The final position on the number line is 6. So $2 - (-4) = 6$.

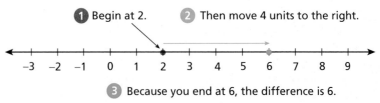

① Begin at 2.   ② Then move 4 units to the right.

③ Because you end at 6, the difference is 6.

c. Begin at -3. Then move 2 units to the left. The final position on the number line is -5. So $-3 - 2 = -5$.

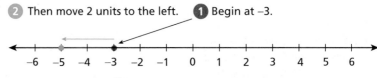

② Then move 2 units to the left.   ① Begin at -3.

③ Because you end at -5, the difference is -5. ∎

Study Tip

Compare the rules for subtracting on a number line with the rules for adding on a number line on page 514. Notice that with subtraction, you move the opposite direction that you move with addition.

In many real-life problems, smaller integers are subtracted from larger integers. When you subtract a smaller integer from a larger integer, the result represents the distance between the two numbers.

Real Life
Temperature

Example 2 *Subtracting Integers*

At 1 P.M. the temperature is 5°C. By 5 P.M. it is −7°C. How many degrees did the temperature drop?

Solution   You can use integer subtraction to solve this problem. The number of degrees the temperature dropped is the difference between 5 and −7.

$$5 - (-7) = 12 \quad \text{\textit{Subtract} −7 \textit{from} 5.}$$

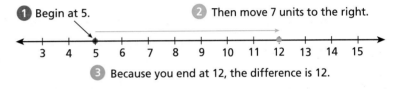

1 Begin at 5.   **2** Then move 7 units to the right.

3 Because you end at 12, the difference is 12.

The temperature dropped 12 degrees.

You can check this result by counting the number of degrees between 5 and −7 on the thermometers below. This represents the distance between 5 and −7.

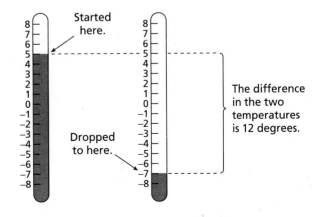

These fishermen are ice fishing through a hole cut in the ice of the frozen Ottawa River in Canada.

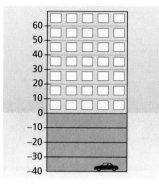
Example 3   *Subtracting Integers*

You enter an elevator 60 feet above ground level. Your car is parked in an underground parking lot, as shown at the left. How many feet must you travel down to reach the level your car is on?

Solution   One way to solve this problem is to use integer subtraction. To do that, you can represent the floor your car is on as −40. The number of feet you must travel is the difference between 60 and −40.

$$60 - (-40) = 100 \quad \textit{Subtract } -40 \textit{ from } 60.$$

You must travel 100 feet. Check this using the diagram below.

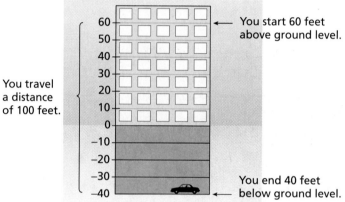

You start 60 feet above ground level.

You travel a distance of 100 feet.

You end 40 feet below ground level.

Communicating about MATHEMATICS

▷ Sharing Ideas about the Lesson

Finding Distances on Number Lines Write a subtraction problem that represents the distance between the 2 numbers shown on the number line. Then solve. For example, the distance on the number line below can be represented by 6 − (−2). The solution is 8.

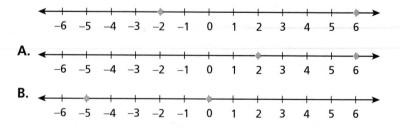

EXERCISES

Think and Discuss

▶ **CHECK for Understanding**

In Exercises 1–4, use a number line. Start at 3. Write whether you should move left or right on the number line to solve.

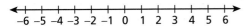

1. Subtract 2   2. Add −2   3. Add 2   4. Subtract −2
5. Repeat Exercises 1–4, starting at −3. Do your answers change? Explain.
6. *Communicating Math* Write a real-life problem that can be modeled by −10 − 25. Then solve the problem.

Independent Practice

In Exercises 7–10, match the number line model with the subtraction problem that it represents.

a. −1 − 3   b. −4 − (−5)   c. 2 − 5   d. 1 − (−2)

7.
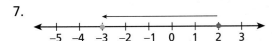

8.
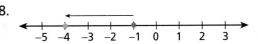

9.
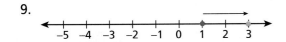

10.
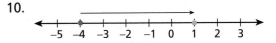

In Exercises 11–16, use a number line to solve the problem.

11. −8 − 2   12. −2 − 5   13. 6 − (−5)
14. 2 − (−6)   15. −4 − (−9)   16. −7 − (−5)

Model Rocket The diagram at the right shows the path of a model rocket.

17. How much higher is the rocket at the parachute release than at burnout stage?

18. How much higher is the rocket at its highest point than at ground level?

19. The countdown to liftoff of your model rocket starts at −5 seconds. The rocket reaches its highest point at 3 seconds after liftoff. How many seconds later is this?

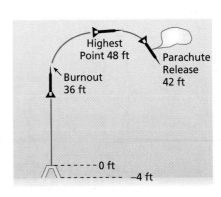

Algebra In Exercises 20–22, evaluate the expression when $s = -5$.

20. $s - 5$ **21.** $6 - s$ **22.** $-3 - s$

Solve each subtraction problem. Describe any patterns you see.

23. $3 - 2 = \boxed{?}$
$3 - 1 = \boxed{?}$
$3 - 0 = \boxed{?}$
$3 - (-1) = \boxed{?}$

24. $3 - (-2) = \boxed{?}$
$2 - (-2) = \boxed{?}$
$1 - (-2) = \boxed{?}$
$0 - (-2) = \boxed{?}$

25. $-6 - 2 = \boxed{?}$
$-6 - 1 = \boxed{?}$
$-6 - 0 = \boxed{?}$
$-6 - (-1) = \boxed{?}$

26. *Integer Game* Describe a strategy for this game. Players take turns joining any 2 dots next to each other. Diagonals are not allowed. When a player makes a square, the box is won and the player's initials are put in the box. When all the squares are completed, calculate the scores by subtracting the numbers in each player's boxes from 25. The player with the highest score wins.

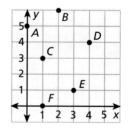

27. *Geography* The height or depth of Earth's surface is measured from sea level. Mount McKinley in Alaska is 20,320 feet above sea level. Death Valley in California and Nevada is 282 feet below sea level. Which estimate better describes the difference in these two heights? Explain.
     a. 20,000   b. 20,600

Integrated Review   *Making Connections within Mathematics*

Geometry Use the coordinate plane at the right to match the ordered pair with its point.

28. $(1, 0)$ **29.** $(0, 5)$

30. $(4, 4)$ **31.** $(3, 1)$

32. $(1, 3)$ **33.** $(2, 6)$

Exploration and Extension

 34. *Building Your Chapter Project* You are online on *Live from Antarctica* exploring data about icebergs. You discover the tip of an iceberg is 100 feet above sea level and the bottom of the iceberg is 500 feet below sea level. In your scientific journal, draw a vertical number line to represent these measures. How could you use integer subtraction to find the total height of the iceberg?

These penguins look tiny compared to the size of this iceberg tip.

Using a Calculator

Most calculators have a special key for negative numbers. This key comes in two versions: a *change-sign key* or a *negative key*.

Change-Sign Key $\boxed{+/-}$ Enter number first, then press key.

Negative Key $\boxed{(-)}$ Press key first, then enter number.

Technology
Calculator

Example   *Adding Integers*

Use a calculator to find the sums.

a. $-3 + 4$ b. $5 + (-2)$ c. $3 + (-6)$ d. $-2 + (-4)$

Solution

Keystrokes	Display	Type of Key
a. 3 $\boxed{+/-}$ $\boxed{+}$ 4 $\boxed{=}$	1	*Change-Sign Key*
$\boxed{(-)}$ 3 $\boxed{+}$ 4 $\boxed{=}$	1	*Negative Key*
b. 5 $\boxed{+}$ 2 $\boxed{+/-}$ $\boxed{=}$	3	*Change-Sign Key*
5 $\boxed{+}$ $\boxed{(-)}$ 2 $\boxed{=}$	3	*Negative Key*
c. 3 $\boxed{+}$ 6 $\boxed{+/-}$ $\boxed{=}$	-3	*Change-Sign Key*
3 $\boxed{+}$ $\boxed{(-)}$ 6 $\boxed{=}$	-3	*Negative Key*
d. 2 $\boxed{+/-}$ $\boxed{+}$ 4 $\boxed{+/-}$ $\boxed{=}$	-6	*Change-Sign Key*
$\boxed{(-)}$ 2 $\boxed{+}$ $\boxed{(-)}$ 4 $\boxed{=}$	-6	*Negative Key* ∎

Study Tip

On most calculators, the subtraction key $\boxed{-}$ cannot be used as a negative key.

Exercises

In Exercises 1–8, use a calculator to find the sum. Then use a number line to check your result.

1. $5 + (-3)$ 2. $4 + (-7)$ 3. $-2 + 4$ 4. $-9 + 6$

5. $-2 + (-3)$ 6. $-7 + (-1)$ 7. $-9 + 7$ 8. $-5 + 8$

9. *Think about It*   Suppose you have a calculator that does not have a negative key. Using only $\boxed{+}$, $\boxed{-}$, $\boxed{=}$, and the number keys, show how you can get the calculator to display -5.

Lab 11.4

Investigating the Coordinate Plane

Materials Needed: graph paper, pencils or pens, ruler

Part A *Plotting Ordered Pairs*   In Lesson 9.5, you plotted ordered pairs in a coordinate plane.

1. Plot the ordered pairs on graph paper. Then use a ruler to connect the points in the order you plotted them. The first three are shown at the right.

    (3, 2) to (6, 2) to (5, 1) to (2, 1) to
    (1, 2) to (3, 2) to (3, 3) to (2, 3) to
    (3, 5) to (5, 3) to (3, 3) to (3, 2)

2. Shade the inside of the 2 shapes you made in Exercise 1. Name the shapes and the object.

3. Which shape do you think has the greater area? Why?

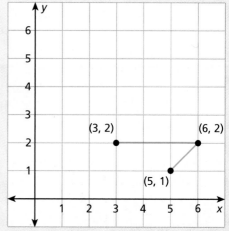

Part B *Integers and the Coordinate Plane*   Now that you have studied integers, you can enlarge the coordinate plane to include points that have negative coordinates.

The ordered pair (0, 0) is the *origin.* Moving to the right is the positive *x*-direction, and moving to the left is the negative *x*-direction. Moving up is the positive *y*-direction, and moving down is the negative *y*-direction.

4. Copy the coordinate plane and the four points at the right. Then plot the following six points.

    $M(-4, 3)$, $N(4, 3)$, $O(4, -3)$,
    $P(0, -3)$, $Q(-4, 0)$, $R(-3, -4)$

5. Name all points that lie in a vertical line.

6. Name all points that lie in a horizontal line.

7. Do the points M, N, O, and R form the vertices of a rectangle? Explain.

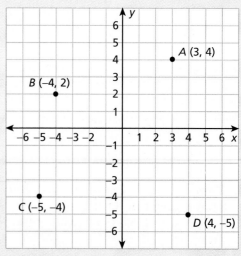

Part C *Slides in a Coordinate Plane*

8. a. Draw a coordinate plane, as shown at the right. Then plot the stick figure. Write the coordinates of the labeled points.
   b. Slide the figure 6 units to the left and 2 units up. What are the new coordinates for points *A*, *B*, *C*, *D*, *E*, *F*, and *G*?
   c. What patterns do you see in the *x*-coordinates? In the *y*-coordinates?

9. Now slide the new figure 2 units to the right and 8 units down. Then describe the slide you would need to move the figure back to its original position.

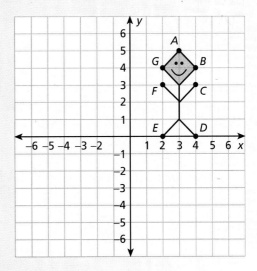

On Your Own

Critical Thinking

10. a. Copy the coordinate grid at the right on graph paper. Write the coordinates of each of the 23 points. For instance, point *A* has coordinates (6, 0).
   b. Connect the points in alphabetical order. Connect *W* to *A*. What animal is formed?
   c. Describe the slide that would move the tip of the animal's tail to the origin.
   d. Describe a slide that would make all of the animal's *x*- and *y*-coordinates negative.

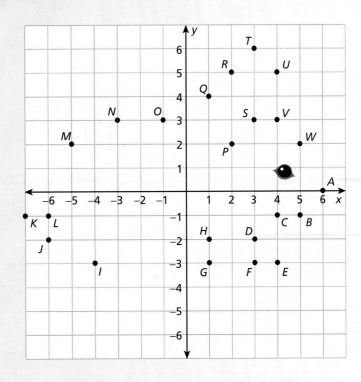

11.4

The Coordinate Plane

What you should learn:

Goal 1 How to plot points in a coordinate plane

Goal 2 How to use a coordinate plane to describe figures that have been slid or flipped

Why you should learn it:

Knowing how to plot points in a coordinate plane can help you understand how a computer works. An example is using a coordinate plane to move figures in a computer drawing program.

Goal 1 Using a Coordinate Plane

In Lesson 9.5, you studied the coordinate plane. But in that lesson, none of the coordinates were negative. Now that you have studied negative integers, you can work with an expanded coordinate plane.

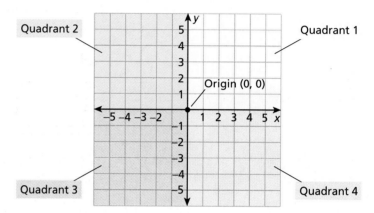

The x-axis and y-axis divide the plane into four regions called **quadrants.**

Study Tip

When plotting a point in a coordinate plane, remember these tips.

- Points with negative x-coordinates are left of the origin. Points with positive x-coordinates are right of the origin.

- Points with negative y-coordinates are below the origin. Points with positive y-coordinates are above the origin.

Example 1 *Plotting Points*

Plot the points $A(-3, 5)$, $B(-2, -4)$, $C(5, -3)$, and $D(-4, 0)$.

Solution

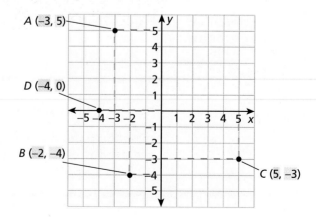

Real Life
Computer Graphics

Example 2   *Moving Points in a Coordinate Plane*

You are using a computer drawing program. The coordinates of the figure on your screen are $A(-1, 2)$, $B(-2, -1)$, $C(-1, -3)$, and $D(-6, -1)$.

   a. What are the new coordinates of the figure if you slide it 5 units to the right and 2 units down?

   b. What are the new coordinates of the figure if you flip it about the y-axis?

Solution   First, draw the figures.

a. 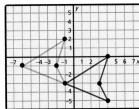   b.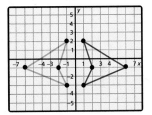

The coordinates of the new figure are $(4, 0)$, $(3, -3)$, $(4, -5)$, and $(-1, -3)$.

The coordinates of the new figure are $(1, 2)$, $(2, -1)$, $(1, -3)$, and $(6, -1)$.

■

Scientists at Mission Control, NASA use computers to track planetary probes. Jupiter is shown on the center screen.

Communicating about MATHEMATICS

Problem Solving
Look for a Pattern

▶ **Sharing Ideas about the Lesson**

   Extending the Example Study the coordinates of the points in Example 2. Do you see any patterns in part (a)? In part (b)?

EXERCISES

Think and Discuss

▶ **CHECK for Understanding**

1. *Error Analysis* Describe the error. Write a statement about how to sketch a coordinate plane.

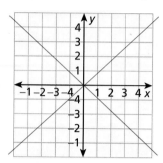

2. Write the ordered pairs for the points shown in the coordinate plane. Which of these points has a special name?

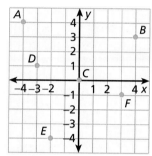

In Exercises 3–6, describe in words how to plot the point.

3. $(-3, 4)$ 4. $(2, 7)$ 5. $(-4, -6)$ 6. $(0, -8)$

7. Plot the points represented by the ordered pairs $A(-2, 2)$, $B(1, 2)$, $C(2, -2)$, and $D(-1, -2)$. Connect the sides of polygon $ABCD$. Then name the type of polygon.

Independent Practice

In Exercises 8–11, name the quadrant that contains the point.

8. $(-9, 5)$ 9. $(1, 3)$

10. $(-7, -3)$ 11. $(2, -2)$

In Exercises 12–14, use the figure at the right.

12. Name the coordinates of the points.

13. Copy the coordinate plane and connect the points in alphabetical order. Then connect G to A. What animal is formed?

14. Describe the slide that would move the tip of the animal's nose to the origin.

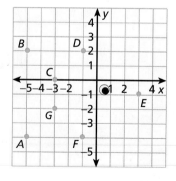

Plot the points represented by the ordered pairs. Connect the sides of the polygon. Then name the type of polygon.

15. $H(-5, -4)$, $I(-5, -2)$, $J(-1, 0)$, $K(-1, -6)$

16. $D(1, 0)$, $E(3, -2)$, $F(3, -5)$, $G(0, -5)$, $H(-2, -3)$

17. Slide the figure 1 unit right and 2 units up.

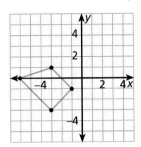

18. Flip the figure about the x-axis.

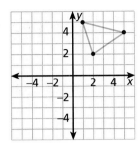

In Exercises 19 and 20, plot the points represented by the ordered pairs. Connect the sides of the polygons. Describe the slide or flip.

19. *Figure:* H(3,−1), I(6,−1), J(4,−3), K(1,−3)
   Slide: L(−4, 1), M(−1, 1), N(−3,−1), O(−6,−1)

20. *Figure:* A(−5, 3), B(−2,−1), C(−7,−1)
   Flip: D(5, 3), E(2,−1), F(7,−1)

21. *Visual Thinking*   Draw a triangle in the first quadrant. Flip the triangle about the y-axis. Compare the coordinates of the vertices of the two triangles.

Using a Map   A city has six Mini-Marts, as shown in the coordinate plane below. Each unit represents 5 miles.

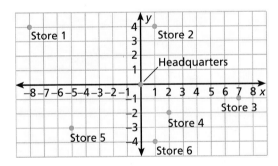

Many convenience stores are part of a chain. The first chain-store company in the United States was established in 1859.

22. Where is the Mini-Mart headquarters located?

23. Which Mini-Mart is closest to the headquarters? Estimate its distance.

24. Which two Mini-Marts are the same distance from the headquarters? Explain.

25. Store 1 decides to move its location to (−9,−1). Describe the slide.

26. A new Mini-Mart is being built 10 miles south and 15 miles east of Store 5. Write its ordered pair.

Area   Find the area of the figure.

27.
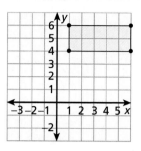

28.
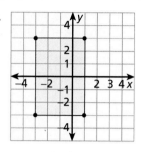

29.
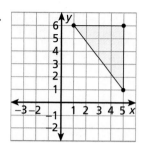

Exploration and Extension

30. *Building Your Chapter Project*   To approximate the locations of the three United States stations in Antarctica, draw a coordinate plane and label the axes from −16 to 16. Let the origin represent the South Pole. The Antarctic Circle is represented by a circle of radius 16, centered at the origin. Each unit on your coordinate plane represents 100 miles. Locate and label each United States station: Amundsen-Scott Station (at South Pole), Palmer Station (1300 miles left and 700 miles up from origin), McMurdo Station (200 miles right and 800 miles down from origin). Record your work in your scientific journal.

Mixed REVIEW

Add or subtract. **(7.4)**

1. $6\frac{2}{5} - 2\frac{4}{5}$

2. $10\frac{5}{8} + 4\frac{1}{4}$

3. $2\frac{7}{8} - 1\frac{1}{3}$

4. $3\frac{3}{4} + 5\frac{1}{6}$

Probability   A square is evenly divided into 9 small squares. Three of the small squares are red, 2 are blue, and 4 are yellow. If a coin is tossed onto the square, what is the probability it will land on the given color? (The coin is retossed if it lands on a line.) **(6.7)**

5. red

6. yellow

7. blue or red

Algebra   Use mental math or paper and pencil to solve. **(8.4)**

8. $t \div \frac{2}{5} = \frac{5}{2}$

9. $\frac{3}{4} \div n = \frac{9}{4}$

10. $\frac{4}{5} \div m = \frac{4}{15}$

11. $p \div \frac{1}{4} = \frac{4}{15}$

Take this test as you would take a test in class. The answers to the exercises are given in the back of the book.

In Exercises 1–4, match the integer with the phrase that describes it. **(11.1)**

a. Opposite of -6 b. 1 less than -7 c. 1 more than -1 d. Between -7 and -5

1. -8 2. -6 3. 0   4. 6

Number Sense   In Exercises 5–8, use a number line to complete the statement using $>$ or $<$. **(11.1)**

5. -9 (?) -5 6. -2 (?) -3 7. -4 (?) 0   8. 1 (?) -1

In Exercises 9–16, use a number line to solve the problem. **(11.2, 11.3)**

9. $-3 + 5$ 10. $-6 + 2$ 11. $-1 + (-9)$ 12. $-8 - (-2)$

13. $7 - 12$ 14. $-5 - 6$ 15. $4 - (-7)$ 16. $9 - (-3)$

Geometry   In Exercises 17–19, write the coordinates of the vertices of the polygon. Then write the coordinates of the polygon after the slide or flip. **(11.4)**

17. Slide 1 unit down and 6 units right.

18. Flip about the *x*-axis.

19. Flip about the *y*-axis.

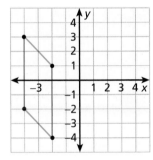

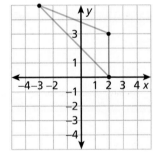

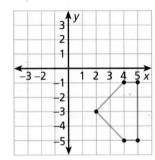

20. *Communicating Math*   Write a summary of what you have learned about integers. **(11.1–11.4)**

21. *Reading a Bar Graph*   You have a job walking dogs for your neighbors. The bar graph at the right shows how much money you earned and spent in 5 days. Find how much money you have at the end of the 5 days. **(11.2, 11.3)**

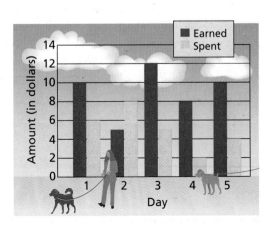

11.5

Connections to Algebra: Patterns in the Coordinate Plane

What you should learn:

Goal 1 How to create and describe patterns by evaluating expressions

Goal 2 How to use a coordinate plane to represent data

Why you should learn it:

Representing data in a coordinate plane can help you find patterns. An example is finding how many inches a corn plant grows each day.

Goal 1 Evaluating Integer Expressions

One of the important uses of algebra is to use expressions to represent patterns. To recognize the pattern, it helps to make a table.

Example 1 *Evaluating Expressions*

Evaluate $x - 2$ for the integers -3 through 3. Complete the table below. Describe any patterns that you see.

x	−3	−2	−1	0	1	2	3
x − 2	?	?	?	?	?	?	?

Solution To complete the table, evaluate the expression $x - 2$ for the given values of x.

Value of x	Substitute.	Simplify.
−3	−3 − 2	−3 − 2 = −5
−2	−2 − 2	−2 − 2 = −4
−1	−1 − 2	−1 − 2 = −3
0	0 − 2	0 − 2 = −2
1	1 − 2	1 − 2 = −1
2	2 − 2	2 − 2 = 0
3	3 − 2	3 − 2 = 1

x	−3	−2	−1	0	1	2	3
x − 2	−5	−4	−3	−2	−1	0	1

You may have noticed that as the numbers in the first row increase by 1, the numbers in the second row also increase by 1. ∎

Evaluating expressions can help you solve equations such as $y = x - 4$. When the value of x is 5, you can evaluate the expression $x - 4$ to find the value for y, which is 1. This solution can be written as the ordered pair (5, 1).

Example 2 *Graphing Solutions*

Make a table of the solutions to the equation $y = 3 - x$ for the integers -3 through 3. Graph the data and describe the pattern.

Solution Begin by evaluating the expression $3 - x$ for the given values of x. Then make a table of the x and y values.

Value of x	Substitute.	Simplify to get y.
-3	$3 - (-3)$	$3 - (-3) = 6$
-2	$3 - (-2)$	$3 - (-2) = 5$
-1	$3 - (-1)$	$3 - (-1) = 4$
0	$3 - (0)$	$3 - 0 = 3$
1	$3 - (1)$	$3 - 1 = 2$
2	$3 - (2)$	$3 - 2 = 1$
3	$3 - (3)$	$3 - 3 = 0$

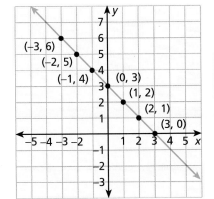

x	-3	-2	-1	0	1	2	3
y	6	5	4	3	2	1	0

Write each pair of x and y values as an ordered pair.

(−3, 6), (−2, 5), (−1, 4), (0, 3), (1, 2), (2, 1), (3, 0)

These ordered pairs are plotted in a coordinate plane at the left. The pattern is that the points lie in a line. ∎

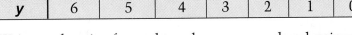

Communicating about **MATHEMATICS**

▷ **Sharing Ideas about the Lesson**

Cooperative Learning

Partner Activity Rewrite the data in Example 1 as ordered pairs. Then plot the ordered pairs. Describe the pattern.

EXERCISES

Guided Practice

Think and Discuss

▶ CHECK for Understanding

1. Order the steps necessary to graph the solutions of an equation in the coordinate plane.
   a. Graph the ordered pairs.
   b. Write as ordered pairs.
   c. Make a table of the data.
   d. Evaluate the expression.

2. Complete the table. Then write the data in the table as ordered pairs.

x	−2	−1	0	1	2
x + 3	?	?	?	?	?

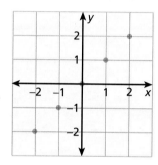

Use the coordinate plane at the right.

3. Describe the pattern of the points.

4. If the pattern continued, which of the following would be on the graph? Explain.
   a. (−15, −15)   b. (15, −15)   c. (−15, 15)   d. (15, 15)

5. *You Be the Teacher*   You are a teacher, and are wondering how to write your policy for late homework. You decide to give a 2-point penalty for each day the homework is late. Complete the table below that shows the number of points a student will receive for a "10-point" homework paper. Then plot the data in a coordinate plane. Describe the pattern.

x	Days Late	0	1	2	3	4	5
y	Score	10	?	?	?	?	?

Independent Practice

Complete the table. Describe any patterns that you see.

6.

x	−3	−2	−1	0	1	2	3
x + 4	?	?	?	?	?	?	?

7.

x	−3	−2	−1	0	1	2	3
6 − x	?	?	?	?	?	?	?

Tables and Solutions   Evaluate the given expression for the integers −3 through 3. Record your results in a table. Graph the data in a coordinate plane. Describe any patterns that you see.

8. $x - 3$

9. $-5 + x$

10. Write 5 ordered pairs that you think lie in a vertical line. Check your work by plotting the points. How can you tell whether two points lie in a vertical line?

In Exercises 11–13, plot the points $L(-2, -1)$ and $M(1, 2)$. Draw a line through the points. Then draw the lines $\overleftrightarrow{JK}$, $\overleftrightarrow{RS}$, and $\overleftrightarrow{YZ}$ through the given points. Match each line with its description.

a. Parallel to $\overleftrightarrow{LM}$

b. Perpendicular to $\overleftrightarrow{LM}$

c. Not parallel or perpendicular to $\overleftrightarrow{LM}$

11. $J(-1, 2)$, $K(1, 0)$

12. $R(-1, -2)$, $S(1, 3)$

13. $Y(-1, -3)$, $Z(1, -1)$

14. *Science*   The table shows the height (in inches) of a corn kernel after it is planted. Write the data as ordered pairs. Then graph the ordered pairs. Use the graph to complete the statement: *A corn plant grows* $\boxed{?}$ *inches each day.*

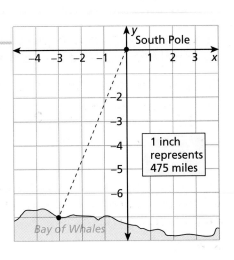

x	Day	1	2	3	4	5
y	Height	-3	-1	1	3	5

Integrated Review

Making Connections within Mathematics

Measurement   Find the area of the figure.

15.
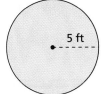
5 ft

16.

6 cm
3 cm

17.
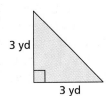
3 yd
3 yd

18.
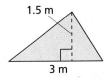
1.5 m
3 m

Exploration and Extension

19. *Building Your Chapter Project*   You are online on *Live from Antarctica*. You are chatting about exploring Antarctica. A scientist explains that an expedition by Admiral Byrd in 1929 began in the Bay of Whales and ended at the South Pole. The location of the South Pole is at $(0, 0)$ on the graph at the right. What ordered pair represents the Bay of Whales? Use a ruler and the scale to estimate how long the expedition was. Record your results in your journal.

11.6

Connections to Geometry: Coordinate Geometry

What you should learn:

Goal 1 How to find areas of figures in a coordinate plane

Goal 2 How to find the midpoint of a line segment

Why you should learn it:

Understanding coordinate geometry can help you when studying maps. An example is finding the area of a parcel of land.

Goal 1 **Areas in the Coordinate Plane**

Coordinate geometry is the study of geometric figures in a coordinate plane. The coordinates of the points in the plane can be used to find lengths, perimeters, and areas.

To measure lengths, use the units given on the axes.

Example 1 *Finding Areas*

Find the area of each figure.

a. 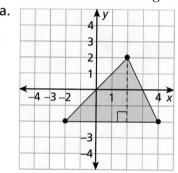 b.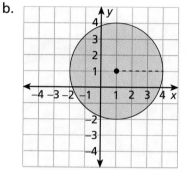

> **Study Tip**
>
> There are two ways to find the length of the base of the triangle in Example 1a. You could count the squares that lie along the base. Or you could use subtraction. On the x-axis, the distance from $x = 4$ to $x = -2$ is $4 - (-2)$ or 6.

Solution

a. This figure is a triangle. The base of the triangle is 6 units long, and the height is 4 units.

$$\text{Area} = \frac{1}{2} \cdot (\text{base}) \cdot (\text{height}) \quad \textit{Area of triangle}$$

$$= \frac{1}{2} \cdot 6 \cdot 4 \quad \textit{Substitute.}$$

$$= 12 \text{ square units} \quad \textit{Simplify.}$$

The area is 12 square units.

b. This figure is a circle. The radius is 3 units long.

$$\text{Area} \approx 3.14 \cdot (\text{radius})^2 \quad \textit{Area of circle}$$

$$= 3.14 \cdot 3^2 \quad \textit{Substitute.}$$

$$= 28.26 \text{ square units} \quad \textit{Simplify.}$$

The area is 28.26 square units. ∎

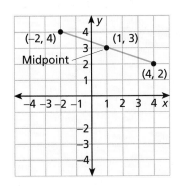

The midpoint of a line segment is halfway between the two endpoints.

The **midpoint** of a line segment is the point on the line segment that is halfway between the two endpoints.

Example **2** | *Finding Midpoints*

By inspection, find the midpoints of the sides of the quadrilaterals. Then connect the midpoints. What type of figure do you get?

a. 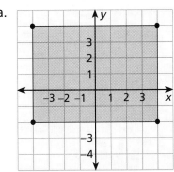   b.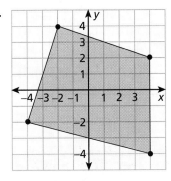

Solution   The figures are shown below.

a. 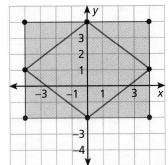   b.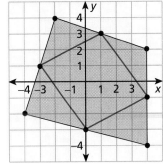

In both cases, you get a quadrilateral that appears to be a parallelogram. ■

Communicating about MATHEMATICS

Cooperative Learning

▶ **Sharing Ideas about the Lesson**

Extending the Example With others in your group, use a ruler to draw several quadrilaterals on grid paper. Find the midpoints of the sides. Then connect the midpoints. Do you always get a parallelogram?

EXERCISES

Think and Discuss

▶ CHECK for Understanding

Use the figure at the right. Match the
point or measurement with its description.

a. Length of $\overline{AB}$

b. Midpoint of $\overline{AB}$

c. Midpoint of $\overline{BC}$

d. Perimeter of rectangle $BDEF$

e. Area of triangle DEF

f. Area of quadrilateral $AEFB$

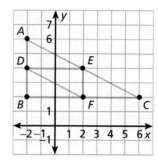

1. 12 square units   2. 4 square units   3. 4 units

4. $(-2, 4)$ 5. 12 units   6. $(2, 2)$

Independent Practice

Area In Exercises 7–9, find the area of the figure.

7.
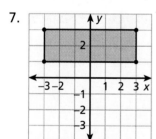

8.
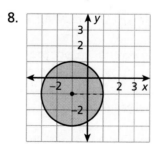

9.
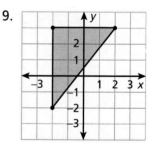

Geometry In Exercises 10 and 11, plot the ordered pairs and
connect them to form a polygon. Find the area.

10. $(2, 5), (-3, 5), (-3, -2), (2, -2)$ 11. $(2, 0), (-1, 3), (-1, -5)$

Reasoning Find the coordinates of the midpoints of $\overline{PR}$ and $\overline{QS}$.
Are the midpoints the same point? Explain.

12.
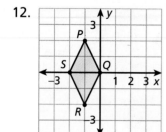

13.
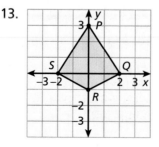

14.
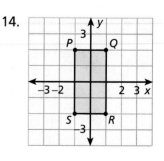

Which is the best estimate of the figure's area? Explain.

15. a. 4 square units
    b. 6 square units

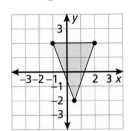

16. a. 9 square units
    b. 7 square units

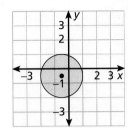

17. a. 12 square units
    b. 14 square units

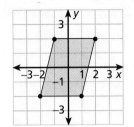

18. *Finding Patterns* In the figure at the right, each smaller triangle is formed by connecting the midpoints of the sides of the next larger triangle. Find the area of each of the 4 triangles. Describe any patterns that you see. What would be the area of the next smaller triangle?

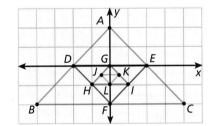

19. *Property Boundaries* A surveyor is using a grid in which each square unit is 2 miles by 2 miles. The coordinates of a parcel of land are $(-3, 3)$, $(1, 3)$, $(-3, -3)$, and $(1, -3)$. What is the area of the parcel in square units? In square miles?

Integrated Review
Making Connections within Mathematics

20. *Health* A survey was taken in which 36 people with a broken bone were asked how old they are. The results are shown in the table. Make a circle graph of the data. *(Source: American Academy of Orthopaedic Surgeons)*

Age	Under 18	18–44	45–64	65 and older
Number	14	12	6	4

Exploration and Extension

21. *Group Activity* Each person in the group should draw a large triangle on cardboard. Find the midpoint of one of the sides of the triangle. Draw a line from the midpoint to the opposite vertex. Repeat this for each of the other 2 sides. The point where the three lines meet is the *balance point* of the triangle. Check it by carefully cutting out the triangle and balancing it on a pencil point.

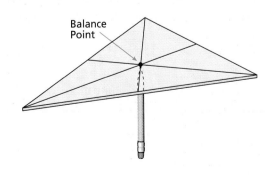

Balance Point

11 Chapter Summary

What did you learn?

Skills

1. Graph integers on a number line.   **(11.1)**
2. Add and subtract integers.
   - Use number counters.   **(Labs 11.2 and 11.3)**
   - Use a number line.   **(11.2, 11.3)**
3. Plot points on a coordinate plane.   **(11.4)**
4. Slide and flip geometric figures in a coordinate plane.   **(11.4)**
5. Use a graph in the coordinate plane to represent data.   **(11.5)**
6. Find the area of a figure in a coordinate plane.   **(11.6)**
7. Find the midpoint of a line segment in a coordinate
   plane.   **(11.6)**

Strategies

8. Use problem-solving strategies to solve problems.   **(11.1–11.6)**

Exploring Data

9. Use tables and graphs to organize data and solve
   problems.   **(11.1–11.6)**

Why did you learn it?

Integers and the coordinate plane can be used to solve real-life problems. Here are some examples you studied in this chapter.

- Measure temperatures in Antarctica.   **(11.1)**
- Compare your miniature golf score to the par score.   **(11.2)**
- Find the number of feet traveled in an elevator.   **(11.3)**
- Move an object on a computer screen.   **(11.4)**

How does it fit into the bigger picture of mathematics?

Throughout history, the number system that humans use has become more and more complicated. Primitive peoples used only a simple number system with counting numbers, such as 1, 2, 3, and 4. Then, other types of numbers were developed to represent more complicated real-life situations. To represent *parts* of things, fractions and decimals were developed. To represent having "no amount" of something, zero was developed.

For hundreds of years, this system (counting numbers, fractions, decimals, and zero) was good enough to model real life. Then, a few hundred years ago, people began finding real-life situations in which they wanted to use numbers that were *less than zero*. Measuring temperatures below zero is an example. To do this, negative numbers were added to the number system.

In Exercises 1–3, order the integers from least to greatest. **(11.1)**

1. $-6, -7, 2, -2, 7$ 2. $0, -5, -1, 1, -4$ 3. $-3, -8, -2, -9, -5$

In Exercises 4–11, evaluate the expression when $t = -3$. **(11.2, 11.3)**

4. $t + 6$ 5. $t + 2$ 6. $-4 + t$ 7. $t + (-12)$

8. $t - (-7)$ 9. $3 - t$ 10. $-5 - t$ 11. $t - 8$

Copy the figure at the right. **(11.5)**

12. Write the coordinates of one point in each quadrant.

13. Connect the points in alphabetical order. Connect P to A. What is formed?

14. Describe the slide that would move the center of the insect to the origin.

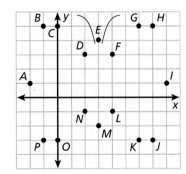

In Exercises 15 and 16, complete the table. Then graph the data. Describe any patterns. **(11.5)**

15.
x	−2	−1	0	1	2
x − 1	?	?	?	?	?

16.
x	−2	−1	0	1	2
4 − x	?	?	?	?	?

In Exercises 17–19, copy the grid and figure. Find the coordinates of the midpoints of the sides of the figure. Then connect the midpoints and name the polygon that is formed. **(11.6)**

17.
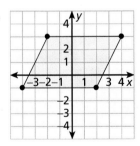

18.
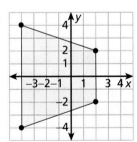

19.
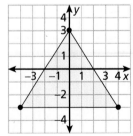

Iowa Use the figure at the right. **(11.4, 11.6)**

20. Write the coordinates of Sioux City and Waterloo. Then approximate the distance (in miles) between the two cities.

21. Estimate the area of Iowa.

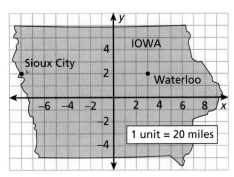

22. *Antarctica Icecap*   The icecap covering the continent of Antarctica is 3 miles thick at the thickest point. How far is it from the top of the ice to a point 2 miles below the surface of the Antarctic Ocean? Explain.

23. *Seasonal Temperatures*   In Antarctica, winter is from May through August. Temperatures in the winter range from −40°F to −94°F inland. Summer is from December through February. Summer temperatures range from 5°F to −31°F. Which season has the greatest difference in temperature? Explain.

These Emperor penguins are standing on the Riiser-Larsen ice shelf in Antarctica.

24. *Ice Shelf*   A broad flat sheet of ice is called an ice shelf. The grid at the right shows the Ross Ice Shelf of Antarctica. Estimate the area of the Ross Ice Shelf. Each square is 143 miles by 143 miles.

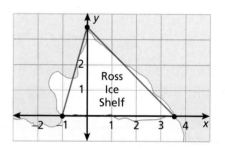

Animals of Antarctica   Copy the number line below. Then use the number line to solve each problem. Each answer represents a letter, as shown on the number line. Unscramble the letters to find the name of a common animal in Antarctica.

```
 A  B  C  D  E  F  G  H  I  J  K  L  M  N  O  P  Q  R  S  T  U  V  W  X  Y  Z
─┼──┼──┼──┼──┼──┼──┼──┼──┼──┼──┼──┼──┼──┼──┼──┼──┼──┼──┼──┼──┼──┼──┼──┼──┼──┼──
   −12   −10   −8   −6   −4   −2    0    2    4    6    8   10   12
```

25. $\underset{12-18}{\boxed{?}}$ $\underset{-6+15}{\boxed{?}}$ $\underset{1-14}{\boxed{?}}$ $\underset{-13-(-4)}{\boxed{?}}$ $\underset{9-11}{\boxed{?}}$

26. $\underset{-10-(-10)}{\boxed{?}}$ $\underset{-2-7}{\boxed{?}}$ $\underset{-3+5}{\boxed{?}}$ $\underset{-13+6}{\boxed{?}}$ $\underset{10-15}{\boxed{?}}$ $\underset{-4+11}{\boxed{?}}$ $\underset{-8+8}{\boxed{?}}$

27. $\underset{-10+8}{\boxed{?}}$ $\underset{-3-6}{\boxed{?}}$ $\underset{3-16}{\boxed{?}}$ $\underset{1-(-4)}{\boxed{?}}$

28. $\underset{-7-5}{\boxed{?}}$ $\underset{-10-3}{\boxed{?}}$ $\underset{-4-(-2)}{\boxed{?}}$ $\underset{2-15}{\boxed{?}}$ $\underset{-5+11}{\boxed{?}}$ $\underset{-1+5}{\boxed{?}}$ $\underset{-5+10}{\boxed{?}}$ $\underset{-1-(-2)}{\boxed{?}}$ $\underset{-13+18}{\boxed{?}}$

Chapter **TEST**

In Exercises 1–4, write the integer described by the phrase.

1. 2 more than -10

2. 4 less than 1

3. Opposite of 7

4. Between 0 and -2

In Exercises 5–12, solve the problem.

5. $-5 + 11$ **6.** $-8 + 8$ **7.** $-6 + (-2)$ **8.** $-4 - (-9)$

9. $-7 - (-3)$ **10.** $-4 - 4$ **11.** $5 - 10$ **12.** $3 - (-1)$

Geometry   In Exercises 13 and 14, plot the points and connect them to form a polygon. Then name the type of polygon.

13. $A(-1, 3)$, $B(2, 0)$, $C(-1, -1)$, $D(-4, 2)$

14. $M(-7, -1)$, $N(-3, 3)$, $O(1, -1)$, $P(-3, -5)$

In Exercises 15 and 16, copy and complete the table. Then copy the graph at the right and use the data in the table to plot the ordered pairs. What do you notice?

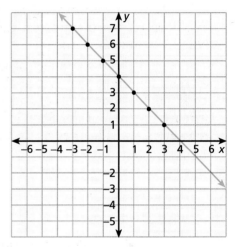

15.

x	-3	-2	-1	0	1	2	3
1 − x	?	?	?	?	?	?	?

16.

x	-3	-2	-1	0	1	2	3
x − 4	?	?	?	?	?	?	?

In Exercises 17–19, find the area of the figure.

17.
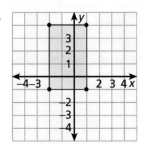

18.
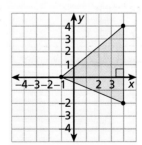

19.
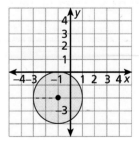

20. *Communicating*   Write a summary about what you have learned in this chapter about the coordinate plane.

21. *Science*   Dry ice is solid carbon dioxide. Its temperature is about 141°F less than the temperature of normal ice, which is 32°F. Which of the following would you use to find the temperature of dry ice? Explain your reasoning.

    a. $141 - 32$ b. $32 - 141$

CHAPTER 12

Algebra: Equations and Probability

These Native American children are enjoying a version of the game Totolospi. They are playing outside their Hopi village in Hotevilla, Arizona.

Real Life Games

One way to model "win-lose" games is to use coin tossing. A tree diagram for the 8 possible outcomes of tossing three coins is shown.

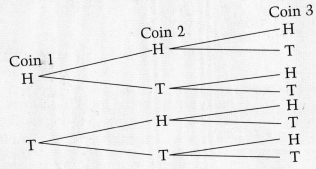

Coin 1 Coin 2 Coin 3
H   H   H
         T
     T   H
         T
T   H   H
         T
     T   H
         T

Think and Discuss

Language meanings are important in translating verbal phrases into mathematical statements.

1. How many outcomes show *exactly* 2 heads? *At least* 2 heads?
2. Extend the tree pattern to show the possible outcomes for tossing 4 coins. How many outcomes are there?

CHAPTER THEME:

Games around the World

Pen Pals Around the World

Theme: Games around the World Do you have a pen pal? Many people enjoy writing to them, because you can find out what people your own age are doing in other parts of the world.

In this project, you will imagine that your pen pals have written to you about games or activities that they like to play. You are to answer a question about each game in a letter back to them. The games and activities that you will find out about are the following.

➡ **In Lesson 12.1:** The Hawaiian game of Lu-lu (page 556)

➡ **In Lesson 12.2:** The Korean game of Ko-no (page 561)

➡ **In Lesson 12.3:** Chinese Magic Squares (page 565)

➡ **In Lesson 12.5:** The Hopi game of Totolospi (page 579)

➡ **In Lesson 12.6:** The Israeli game of Dreidel (page 583)

GETTING STARTED

Materials: paper, pencils or pens

Place five sheets of stationery in your portfolio. Write each letter to your pen pal when it is part of your assignment in this chapter.

When you have finished the chapter, work with a partner to make the pieces for one of the games or activities. Then play it.

Materials Needed: algebra tiles, pencils or pens, paper

Algebra tiles, like those shown below, can be used to model expressions and to solve equations.

The smaller tile is a 1-by-1 square whose area is 1 square unit. It represents the number 1.

The larger tile is a 1-by-x rectangle whose area is x square units. It represents the variable x.

Part A *Modeling Expressions*   Algebra tiles can be used to model expressions. Here are some examples.

$2x + 1$ $2x + 4$ $x + 5$

1. Write the expression that is modeled by the tiles.

   a.   b.    c.

2. Use algebra tiles to model each expression. Sketch each model.

   a. $3x + 4$ b. $4x + 5$ c. $x + 2$

Part B *Solving Equations*   Algebra tiles can also be used to solve equations. The example below shows how to solve the equation $x + 3 = 8$.

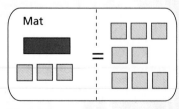   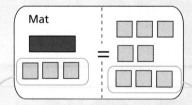   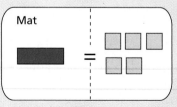

Model the equation with algebra tiles.

You need to get the x-tile by itself on one side of the mat. Remove three 1-tiles from each side.

The solution is $x = 5$.

3. Write the equation that is being modeled. Then remove enough tiles from each side of the mat so that the x-tile is by itself on one side. What is the solution?

a.
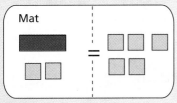

b.
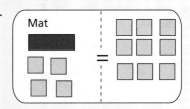

4. Use algebra tiles to solve each equation. Sketch the tiles that you used.

  a. $x + 5 = 12$ b. $x + 8 = 14$ c. $x + 2 = 17$

5. With others in your group, discuss how you knew the number of tiles to remove from each side of the mat in Exercise 4.

6. In the following model, two tiles are removed from each side of the mat. What operation does this represent? Explain your reasoning.

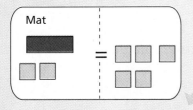
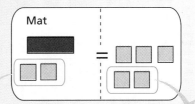

Critical Thinking

In Exercises 7–10, use algebra tiles to solve the equation. Sketch the tiles that you used.

  7. $x + 4 = 8$ 8. $x + 5 = 15$ 9. $x + 1 = 12$ 10. $x + 3 = 10$

11. *Communicating Math*   Which of the following do you think is correct? Explain your reasoning.

  a. To solve $x + 3 = 7$, subtract 3 from the left side of the equation.

  b. To solve $x + 3 = 7$, subtract 3 from each side of the equation.

  c. To solve $x + 3 = 7$, subtract 3 from the right side of the equation.

12.1

Solving Addition Equations

What you should learn:

Goal 1 How to solve addition equations by subtracting the same number from both sides

Goal 2 How to use addition equations to solve real-life problems

Why you should learn it:

Knowing how to solve addition equations can help you find temperature increases. An example is finding the increase in temperature from 12°C to 38°C.

Goal 1 Solving Addition Equations

In Lab 12.1, you may have discovered the following rule for solving addition equations.

Solving an Addition Equation

To solve an addition equation, you subtract the same number from both sides of the equation so that the variable will be by itself on one side of the equation.

Once you solve an equation, you should always check your solution.

Example 1 *Checking Solutions*

Which of the following are solutions of $x + 4 = -2$?

   a. $x = 2$ b. $x = -6$

Solution To **check** a value of x, substitute it into the equation and simplify both sides of the equation.

- If both sides are the same, then the value of x is a solution.
- If both sides are not the same, then the value of x is not a solution.

a. $x + 4 = -2$ *Original equation*

   $2 + 4 \overset{?}{=} -2$ *Substitute 2 for x.*

      $6 \neq -2$ *Both sides are not the same.* $\bigotimes$

Because both sides of the equation are not the same, the value of x does not check. This means $x = 2$ is not a solution.

b. $x + 4 = -2$ *Original equation*

  $-6 + 4 \overset{?}{=} -2$ *Substitute −6 for x.*

     $-2 = -2$ *Both sides are the same.* ✓

Because both sides of the equation are the same, the value of x checks. This means $x = -6$ is a solution. ∎

Study Tip

When you are checking a solution, remember that you can use a number line to add or subtract the numbers. For instance, try using a number line to show that $-6 + 4 = -2$.

Example 2   *Solving an Addition Equation*

Solve each equation.

a. $m + 4 = -8$ b. $3 = n + 5$

Solution

a. Subtract 4 from both sides of the equation.

$$\begin{array}{lll} m + 4 = & -8 & \text{\textit{Original equation}} \\ \underline{-4 \quad -4} & & \text{\textit{Subtract 4 from both sides.}} \\ m = -12 & & \text{\textit{Solution}} \end{array}$$

The solution is -12. Check this as follows.

Check:

$$\begin{array}{ll} m + 4 = -8 & \text{\textit{Original equation}} \\ -12 + 4 \overset{?}{=} -8 & \text{\textit{Substitute} -12 \textit{for m.}} \\ -8 = -8 & \text{\textit{Both sides are the same.}} \checkmark \end{array}$$

b. Subtract 5 from both sides of the equation.

$$\begin{array}{lll} 3 = n + 5 & & \text{\textit{Original equation}} \\ \underline{-5 \qquad -5} & & \text{\textit{Subtract 5 from both sides.}} \\ -2 = n & & \text{\textit{Solution}} \end{array}$$

The solution is -2. Check this as follows.

Check:

$$\begin{array}{ll} 3 = n + 5 & \text{\textit{Original equation}} \\ 3 \overset{?}{=} -2 + 5 & \text{\textit{Substitute} -2 \textit{for n.}} \\ 3 = 3 & \text{\textit{Both sides are the same.}} \checkmark \end{array}$$

■

In Example 2, you can also use a number line to check the solution.

a.   Move 4 units to the right: $-12 + 4 = -8$.

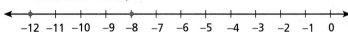

b.   Move 5 units to the right: $3 = -2 + 5$.

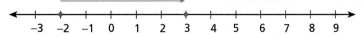

Example **3** *Solving an Addition Equation*

The temperature is 12°C. How many degrees does the temperature have to increase to be 38°C?

Solution   One way to answer this question is to use a **verbal model.** Assign labels. Let *x* represent the unknown amount.

Verbal Model   Original temperature + Increase = New temperature

Labels   Original temperature = 12
Increase = *x*
New temperature = 38

Equation   12 + *x* = 38

To solve this equation, you can subtract 12 from both sides of the equation.

$$12 + x = 38 \quad \textit{Original equation}$$
$$\underline{-12 \qquad -12} \quad \textit{Subtract 12 from both sides.}$$
$$x = 26 \quad \textit{Solution}$$

The solution is 26, so the increase is 26°C. You can check 12 + 26 = 38 by using a number line.

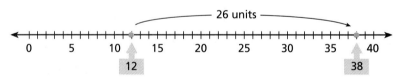

Palm trees typically grow in warm climates. They provide food, clothing, and building materials for people in tropical regions.

Real Life
Temperatures

Communicating about MATHEMATICS

▷ **Sharing Ideas about the Lesson**

Solving Equations Solve each equation by subtracting the same number from both sides of the equation. How do you know which number to subtract? Check your solution.

A. $n + 5 = 12$ **B.** $m + 3 = -7$ **C.** $12 + x = 23$
D. $11 + p = -10$ **E.** $3 + y = -4$ **F.** $t + 7 = 0$

EXERCISES

Think and Discuss

▶ CHECK for Understanding

In Exercises 1–3, describe the steps used to solve the equation.

1. $x + 2 = 9$
   $\underline{-2 \quad -2}$
   $x \quad = 7$

2. $-1 = m + 1$
   $\underline{-1 \qquad -1}$
   $-2 = m$

3. $t + 3 = 0$
   $\underline{-3 \quad -3}$
   $t \qquad = -3$

4. Explain the basic strategy for solving an addition equation.

In Exercises 5–7, solve the equation. Then check your solution.

5. $5 + y = 4$
6. $3 + n = 6$
7. $a + 1 = -7$

8. Write the equation represented by the sentence *The sum of a number and 5 is −10.* Then solve the equation.

Independent Practice

In Exercises 9–12, decide whether the given number is a solution to the equation.

9. $z + 2 = -7$
   $z = -9$

10. $p + 6 = -1$
    $p = -7$

11. $n + 5 = -3$
    $n = -8$

12. $5 = m + 11$
    $m = 6$

In Exercises 13–24, solve the equation. Then check your solution.

13. $x + 8 = 3$
14. $10 + a = 2$
15. $6 + y = 14$
16. $15 = t + 11$
17. $5 = 5 + m$
18. $9 + p = 0$
19. $n + 7 = -7$
20. $13 + b = -6$
21. $-2 + c = 8$
22. $p + 8 = -11$
23. $4 + q = -20$
24. $15 = 14 + z$

Communicating Math In Exercises 25–28, write the equation represented by the sentence. Then solve the equation.

25. The sum of a number and 2 is −10.
26. The sum of a number and 16 is 1.
27. The sum of 5 and a number is 18.
28. The sum of 13 and a number is 0.

In Exercises 29 and 30, use the given numbers to make the equation true. Use each number only once.

29. $\boxed{?} + \boxed{?} = \boxed{?}$
    $-1, 2, -3$

30. $\boxed{?} = \boxed{?} + \boxed{?}$
    $3, -2, 1$

31. *Guess, Check, and Revise* I am a number between -5 and 5. When I am added to 8, the result is a multiple of 2. When I am added to 14, the result is a multiple of 5. What number am I?

32. *Bowling* You are saving money to buy a bowling ball that is $64. You have $38 saved. How much more money do you need to save? Use the verbal model to assign labels and write an equation to represent the problem. Then solve.

$$\boxed{\begin{array}{c}\text{Amount}\\\text{saved}\end{array}} + \boxed{\begin{array}{c}\text{Amount left}\\\text{to save}\end{array}} = \boxed{\text{Cost}}$$

33. The bowling ball in Exercise 32 is on sale for $48. Which of the addition equations represents the amount the bowling ball is discounted from the regular price? Explain your reasoning.

a. $64 + x = 48$ b. $x + 64 = -48$

Jeanne Maiden, of Tacoma, WA, set the Women's International Bowling Congress record of 20 perfect games and a record of 40 consecutive strikes.

Integrated Review   Making Connections within Mathematics

Evaluate the expression when $m = -4$.

34. $m + 1$ **35.** $m + 4$ **36.** $13 + m$ **37.** $-6 + m$

38. $m - 9$ **39.** $8 - m$ **40.** $-5 - m$ **41.** $-m - 7$

Exploration and Extension

42. *Building Your Chapter Project* Your pen pal from Hawaii writes the following in a letter. *Early settlers of Hawaii played the game of Lu-lu. They used playing pieces made from volcanic stone marked on one side as shown. To take your turn, toss the pieces. If all 4 land dot-side up, score 10 points and toss all 4 pieces again. If all 4 do not land dot-side up, pick up the pieces that are dot-side down, and toss them again. Add the number of dots showing on all 4 pieces to your score. The first player to reach exactly 100 wins. If you are playing Lu-lu and your score is 79, can you win on your next turn?* Write an answer that uses an addition equation to your pen pal.

Algebra   Solve the equation using mental math. **(2.2, 4.1, 4.2, 7.3)**

1. $9 + x = 12$

2. $25 - y = 15$

3. $1.3 + m = 4.6$

4. $n - 0.8 = 1$

5. $a + \frac{1}{4} = 1$

6. $b - \frac{2}{7} = \frac{3}{7}$

Working Backward   Copy and complete the model. **(1.7, 11.2, 11.3)**

7.
$$\boxed{?} \xrightarrow{+8} \boxed{?} \xrightarrow{-4} \boxed{?} \xrightarrow{-1} \boxed{?} \xrightarrow{+7} \boxed{3}$$

8.
$$\boxed{?} \xrightarrow{+5} \boxed{?} \xrightarrow{-3} \boxed{?} \xrightarrow{-6} \boxed{?} \xrightarrow{-2} \boxed{-6}$$

Writing   Describe a real-life situation that can be represented by the ratio. **(6.2)**

9. $\dfrac{5 \text{ hours}}{8 \text{ hours}}$ or $\dfrac{5}{8}$

10. $\dfrac{9 \text{ apples}}{14 \text{ apples}}$ or $\dfrac{9}{14}$

11. $\dfrac{3 \text{ yards}}{10 \text{ yards}}$ or $\dfrac{3}{10}$

Milestones   GEOMETRY OF LIFE

| 1700 | 1750 | 1800 | 1850 | 1900 | 1950 | 2000 |

New England Primer, 1690

McGuffey's Eclectic Readers, 1836

Crossword Puzzles, 1913

Monopoly, 1934

Department of Education, 1979

Milton Bradley's first board game was published in 1860.

Friedrich Froebel (1782–1852), a German educator, created a set of wooden objects to teach young children the concepts of geometry. He proposed that schools set aside a children's garden (in German, *Kinder Garten*) where young children could be taught.

In the late 1800's, Milton Bradley, an American game producer, became interested in Froebel's ideas. Bradley came to realize that young children need special equipment and playthings. Anticipating the rise of the kindergarten movement, his company used the profits from its board games, including the *Checkered Game of Life*, to manufacture educational toys, crayons, and child-size tables and chairs.

• *One of Froebel's shapes was a cube that could be broken apart into 27 smaller cubes. Imagine dipping this cube in a bucket of red paint. How many smaller cubes would have red paint on 3 faces? 2 faces? 1 face? 0 faces?*

12.2

Solving Subtraction Equations

What you should learn:

Goal 1 How to solve subtraction equations by adding the same number to both sides

Goal 2 How to use subtraction equations to solve real-life problems

Why you should learn it:

Knowing how to solve subtraction equations can help you with your finances. An example is finding the amount of money you took shopping.

Goal 1 ## Solving Subtraction Equations

In Lesson 12.1, you learned how to write your steps when solving addition equations. The process for solving subtraction equations is similar.

Solving a Subtraction Equation

To solve a subtraction equation, you add the same number to both sides of the equation so that the variable will be by itself on one side of the equation.

Example 1 *Solving a Subtraction Equation*

Solve each equation.

a. $x - 5 = -6$ b. $-2 = m - 7$

Solution

a. Add 5 to both sides of the equation.

$$x - 5 = -6 \quad \text{Original equation}$$
$$\underline{+5 \quad +5} \quad \text{Add 5 to both sides.}$$
$$x \quad = -1 \quad \text{Solution}$$

The solution is -1. Check this as follows.

Check:

$$x - 5 = -6 \quad \text{Original equation}$$
$$-1 - 5 \overset{?}{=} -6 \quad \text{Substitute } -1 \text{ for } x.$$
$$-6 = -6 \quad \text{Both sides are the same.} \checkmark$$

b. Add 7 to both sides of the equation.

$$-2 = m - 7 \quad \text{Original equation}$$
$$\underline{+7 \quad +7} \quad \text{Add 7 to both sides.}$$
$$5 = m \quad \text{Solution}$$

The solution is 5. Check this in the original equation.   ∎

Solving Real-Life Problems

Example 2   *Solving a Subtraction Equation*

You have been shopping downtown. You spent $21 on clothes, and you have $7 left. How much money did you take downtown?

Solution   One way to answer this question is to use a verbal model. Assign labels. Let x represent the unknown amount.

| **Verbal Model** | Original amount | − | Amount spent | = | Amount left |

Labels   Original amount = x
Amount spent = 21
Amount left = 7

Equation $x - 21 = 7$

To solve this equation, you can add 21 to both sides of the equation.

$$
\begin{array}{rcll}
x - 21 &=& 7 & \textit{Original equation} \\
+\,21 & & +\,21 & \textit{Add 21 to both sides.} \\
\hline
x &=& 28 & \textit{Solution}
\end{array}
$$

The solution is 28, so you started with $28. ∎

This shopping district in Boston, Massachusetts is known as Downtown Crossing.

Communicating *about* MATHEMATICS

▶ **Sharing Ideas about the Lesson**

Solving Equations Solve each equation by adding or subtracting the same number from both sides of the equation.

A. $n + 5 = 12$ **B.** $m - 3 = -7$ **C.** $12 + x = 23$
D. $11 + p = -10$ **E.** $-4 = 3 + y$ **F.** $t - 7 = 0$

With others in your group, discuss how you know whether to add or subtract. Also discuss how you know which number to add or subtract.

EXERCISES

▶ **CHECK for Understanding**

In Exercises 1–3, decide whether you should add or subtract to solve the equation. Explain your reasoning. Then solve and check.

1. $t - 3 = 14$
2. $u + 5 = -33$
3. $-14 = s - 12$

In Exercises 4–6, use the following information. The temperature at 8 P.M. was $-8°F$. The temperature had fallen 5 degrees from 5 P.M. What was the temperature at 5 P.M.?

4. Write a verbal model to represent the problem.

5. Let x represent the 5 P.M. temperature. Assign labels. Then write the verbal model as an equation.

6. Solve the equation and answer the question.

Blizzards have strong winds, low temperatures, and large amounts of snow.

Independent Practice

Writing In Exercises 7–9, write a real-life problem that could be solved using the given equation.

7. $n - 14 = 0$
8. $35 = t - 25$
9. $x - 6 = -12$

In Exercises 10–13, decide whether the solution is correct.

10. $x - 12 = 13$, $x = 25$
11. $x - 25 = -1$, $x = 24$
12. $-9 = x - 17$, $x = 26$
13. $-2 = x - 4$, $x = -2$

In Exercises 14–22, solve the equation. Then check your solution.

14. $n - 5 = 16$
15. $t - 7 = 19$
16. $27 = p - 13$
17. $50 = x - 15$
18. $b - 14 = -2$
19. $s - 16 = -12$
20. $-3 = z - 18$
21. $-16 = y - 13$
22. $c - 6 = -20$

23. *Science* A barometer is an instrument used in weather forecasting. It measures the pressure of the atmosphere in inches of mercury. On Wednesday, the barometer read 27 in., which was 2 in. less than the reading on Tuesday. Use the verbal model to assign labels. Write an equation that can be used to find the pressure on Tuesday. Then solve.

Verbal Model $\boxed{\text{Reading on Tuesday}} - \boxed{2 \text{ inches}} = \boxed{\text{Reading on Wednesday}}$

24. *Art* Your class is taking a field trip to an art museum. After driving 35 miles, you see a sign that says the museum is 15 miles away. Write a verbal model using subtraction to find the total distance to the museum. Assign labels. Then write the verbal model as an equation and solve.

These art students are practicing techniques by doing sketches of a painting.

Integrated Review   Making Connections within Mathematics

Find the sum or difference.

25. $23.12 + 8.33$ 26. $3.05 - 1.29$ 27. $\frac{5}{12} + \frac{5}{6}$ 28. $\frac{5}{8} - \frac{1}{4}$

Exploration and Extension

29. *Building Your Chapter Project* Your pen pal from Korea writes the following. *The game of Ko-no is for 2 players. One has 2 black playing pieces (A and B) and the other has 2 white pieces (C and D), as shown. To play the game, take turns moving a playing piece along a line segment to an open space. The game is over when a player is blocked and cannot move. There are many versions of Ko-no. In one version, after you cover spaces with 14 playing pieces you have 11 open spaces. How many total spaces did you start with in this version?* Write an answer that uses a subtraction equation to your pen pal.

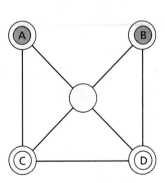

12.3 Solving Equations with Fractions and Decimals

What you should learn:

Goal 1 How to solve equations that have fractions and decimals

Goal 2 How to use equations with fractions and decimals to solve real-life problems

Why you should learn it:

Knowing how to solve equations can help you make a savings plan to buy an item you really want. An example is finding how much more money you need to save to buy a skateboard.

Goal 1 Solving Equations

Example 1 *Solving Equations with Fractions*

Solve $x + \frac{1}{5} = \frac{3}{5}$.

Solution Subtract $\frac{1}{5}$ from both sides of the equation.

$$x + \frac{1}{5} = \frac{3}{5} \quad \textit{Original equation}$$
$$\underline{-\frac{1}{5} \quad -\frac{1}{5}} \quad \textit{Subtract } \tfrac{1}{5} \textit{ from both sides.}$$
$$x \quad = \frac{2}{5} \quad \textit{Solution}$$

The solution is $\frac{2}{5}$. Check this in the original equation. ■

Example 2 *Solving Equations with Decimals*

Solve each equation.

a. $n + 11.4 = 23.1$ b. $p - 7.8 = 12.5$

Solution

a. Subtract 11.4 from both sides of the equation.

$$n + 11.4 = 23.1 \quad \textit{Original equation}$$
$$\underline{-11.4 \quad -11.4} \quad \textit{Subtract 11.4 from both sides.}$$
$$n \quad = 11.7 \quad \textit{Solution}$$

The solution is 11.7. Check this in the original equation.

b. Add 7.8 to both sides of the equation.

$$p - 7.8 = 12.5 \quad \textit{Original equation}$$
$$\underline{+7.8 \quad +7.8} \quad \textit{Add 7.8 to both sides.}$$
$$p \quad = 20.3 \quad \textit{Solution}$$

The solution is 20.3. Check this in the original equation. ■

Study Tip

In Examples 1 and 2, notice that to solve equations that have fractions or decimals, you can use the same strategies you studied in Lessons 12.1 and 12.2. That is, use addition to solve subtraction equations and use subtraction to solve addition equations.

Real Life
Savings Plan

Skateboarding started in California in the 1950's and developed from surfing.

Example 3 *Solving Equations with Decimals*

You are saving money to buy a new skateboard. The cost of the skateboard is $79.95 plus $4.80 sales tax. You have already saved $52.35. How much more do you need to save?

Solution The total cost of the skateboard is $79.95 + $4.80, or $84.75. To find how much more you need to save, you can use a verbal model.

Verbal Model	Amount saved	+	Amount more to save	=	Total cost

Labels Amount saved = 52.35

Amount more to save = x

Total cost = 84.75

Equation 52.35 + x = 84.75

To solve this equation, you can subtract 52.35 from both sides of the equation.

$$52.35 + x = 84.75 \quad \textit{Original equation}$$
$$\underline{-52.35 \qquad -52.35} \quad \textit{Subtract 52.35 from both sides.}$$
$$x = 32.40 \quad \textit{Solution}$$

The solution is 32.40, so you need to save an additional $32.40. ∎

Communicating about MATHEMATICS

▷ **Sharing Ideas about the Lesson**

Error Analysis Describe each error. Then correct the error and solve the original equation.

A. $x + 4.6 = 7.8$
   $\quad -4.6 \quad -7.8$
   $\quad x \quad = \quad 0$

B. $n - 5.6 = 8.8$
   $\quad -5.6 \quad -5.6$
   $\quad n \quad = \quad 3.2$

EXERCISES

Think and Discuss

▶ CHECK for Understanding

Communicating In Exercises 1–3, explain how to solve the equation.

1. $\frac{1}{6} + m = \frac{5}{6}$

2. $12.5 = z + 7.6$

3. $t - 9.4 = 3.8$

4. Write the equation represented by the statement *The difference of a number and one half is two thirds.* Then solve the equation.

In Exercises 5–7, solve the equation. Then check the solution.

5. $n - \frac{3}{8} = 1$

6. $\frac{1}{2} + b = \frac{3}{5}$

7. $18 = x + 2.3$

8. *Fishing* You buy a fishing rod that has a list price of $23.50. The total cost including sales tax is $24.91. Use the verbal model to find the amount you paid in sales tax.

Verbal Model	Total cost	=	List price	+	Sales tax

Independent Practice

In Exercises 9–12, match the equation with its solution.

a. $\frac{3}{5}$ or 0.6

b. $\frac{14}{5}$ or 2.8

c. $\frac{4}{5}$ or 0.8

d. $\frac{1}{2}$ or 0.5

9. $x - \frac{1}{5} = \frac{3}{10}$

10. $x + \frac{1}{5} = 1$

11. $13.5 + x = 14.1$

12. $1.6 = x - 1.2$

It's Up to You In Exercises 13–15, copy and complete the problem.

13.
$$x - \frac{1}{3} = \frac{1}{4}$$
$$\underline{+\ ?\quad +\ ?}$$
$$x \qquad = ?$$

14.
$$\frac{7}{9} = y + \frac{2}{9}$$
$$\underline{-\ ?\quad -\ ?}$$
$$? = y$$

15.
$$11.4 + z = 23.1$$
$$\underline{-\ ?\qquad -\ ?}$$
$$z = \quad ?$$

In Exercises 16–21, solve the equation. Then check the solution.

16. $\frac{2}{7} + y = \frac{6}{7}$

17. $a - \frac{5}{8} = \frac{1}{8}$

18. $m - \frac{2}{3} = \frac{3}{4}$

19. $9.1 = 3.05 + p$

20. $s - 15.2 = 16.19$

21. $b - 32.96 = 7.04$

Finding a Pattern In Exercises 22–24, solve each equation and describe the pattern for t. Then write the next two values of t.

22. $\frac{2}{7} = t + \frac{1}{7}$

$\frac{3}{7} = t + \frac{1}{7}$

$\frac{4}{7} = t + \frac{1}{7}$

23. $10.25 + t = 20.5$
$10.25 + t = 25.5$
$10.25 + t = 30.5$

24. $t - 1.8 = 35.1$
$t - 1.7 = 35.1$
$t - 1.6 = 35.1$

25. *Missouri* The portion of the state of Missouri that is rural is represented by the fraction $\frac{8}{25}$. Which of the equations can be used to find the portion of Missouri that is not rural? Explain.

a. $\frac{8}{25} + u = 1$ b. $100 = 0.32 + u$

c. $u + \frac{8}{25} = 100$ d. $0.32 + u = 1$

26. *Walk-a-thon* Your community is having a volunteer walk-a-thon of 4.25 miles. From 8:30 A.M. to 10:00 A.M., you walk 2.4 miles. Write a verbal model, labels, and an equation to represent the problem. How much farther will you walk?

St. Louis, home of the famous Gateway Arch, is the largest city in Missouri.

Integrated Review

Making Connections within Mathematics

Name the number that does not belong in the list. Explain.

27. 0.4, $\frac{2}{5}$, 40%, $\frac{1}{4}$, $\frac{4}{10}$

28. $\frac{14}{4}$, 3.5, $\frac{35}{10}$, 35%, $3\frac{1}{2}$

29. $1\frac{1}{4}$, $\frac{10}{6}$, 1.25, $\frac{125}{100}$, 125%

30. 0.36, $\frac{18}{5}$, 3.6, 360%, $3\frac{3}{5}$

Exploration and Extension

31. *Building Your Chapter Project* Your pen pal from China writes the following in a letter. *Magic Squares is a one-person game that is played on a square grid. To play, complete the square by finding numbers that when added horizontally, vertically, and diagonally, will produce the same sum.* Complete the magic squares at the right. Then write an explanation to your pen pal that shows how solving an equation can be used to complete a square.

15.8		
	9.5	13.7
		3.2

$\frac{4}{5}$	$\frac{1}{10}$	
$\frac{3}{10}$		$\frac{7}{10}$
$\frac{2}{5}$		

Using a Calculator

Technology
Calculator

| **Example** | **A Number Experiment** |

You tossed two number cubes (one blue and one red) 20 times. You recorded the results in a table. For each toss, you wrote an equation of the form

$x + $ Blue Number $=$ Red Number.

You solved each equation and checked your solutions.

Solution   The first toss of the number cubes was a blue 6 and a red 1. The equation is $x + 6 = 1$ and the solution is $x = -5$. You can check this with a calculator.

Red number cube shows 1.

Blue number cube shows 6.

Keystrokes	Display	Type of Negative Key
5 +/− + 6 =	1	Change-Sign Key
(−) 5 + 6 =	1	Negative Key

The tables summarize all 20 tosses.

Blue	6	4	1	3	5	2	1	4	4	4
Red	1	4	4	5	3	5	1	1	4	1
Solution (x)	−5	0	3	2	−2	3	0	−3	0	−3

Blue	5	3	3	2	2	3	5	1	3	1
Red	3	3	1	4	2	6	6	3	4	5
Solution (x)	−2	0	−2	2	0	3	1	2	1	4

Exercises

1. *Line Plots*   Use a line plot to organize the 20 solutions given in the example above.

2. Perform the experiment in the example to get your own 20 equations and solutions. Then use a line plot to organize the solutions.

3. Copy and complete the table at the right. In each square, write the solution.

   a. What are the possible solutions?

   b. Which solution is most likely? Explain.

12.4

Connections to Algebra: Exploring Functions

What you should learn:

Goal 1 How to evaluate a function

Goal 2 How to write a rule for a function

Why you should learn it:

Knowing how to evaluate functions can help you find patterns in real life. An example is recognizing the pattern for the amount of sales tax.

Goal 1 — Evaluating Functions

In mathematics a **function** is a rule that tells you how to perform one or more operations on a number called the **input** to produce a result called the **output.**

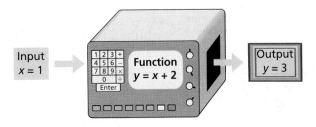

Example 1 — *Making an Input-Output Table*

Make an **input-output table** for the function

$$y = x + 2.$$

Use input values of $x = 1$, $x = 2$, $x = 3$, $x = 4$, $x = 5$, and $x = 6$. What patterns can you see from the table?

Solution To make an input-output table, substitute the x-values into the function. Then compute the corresponding y-values.

Input	Function	Output
x	$y = x + 2$	y
1	$y = 1 + 2$	3
2	$y = 2 + 2$	4
3	$y = 3 + 2$	5
4	$y = 4 + 2$	6
5	$y = 5 + 2$	7
6	$y = 6 + 2$	8

Here are two patterns that you can see from the table.

- The value of y is always 2 more than the value of x.
- Each time x increases by 1, y also increases by 1.

Example 2   *Evaluating a Function*

You are in a state that has a 5% sales tax. Let *c* represent the cost of an item and let *T* represent the total cost including sales tax. A function that gives the total cost is

$$T = c + 0.05 \times c.$$

Use this function to find the total costs of items that cost $1, $2, $3, $4, $5, and $6.

Solution   You can use an input-output table to organize your work.

Input	Function	Output
c	$T = c + 0.05 \times c$	*T*
1	$T = 1 + 0.05 \times 1$	1.05
2	$T = 2 + 0.05 \times 2$	2.10
3	$T = 3 + 0.05 \times 3$	3.15
4	$T = 4 + 0.05 \times 4$	4.20
5	$T = 5 + 0.05 \times 5$	5.25
6	$T = 6 + 0.05 \times 6$	6.30

■

Dollar Stores *are good places to buy discounted items, such as these dominoes which sold for $1!*

After making an input-output table, you can rewrite the data as ordered pairs of the form (Input, Output).

(1, 1.05), (2, 2.10), (3, 3.15), (4, 4.20), (5, 5.25), (6, 6.30)

Then you can graph the ordered pairs in a coordinate plane.

Need to Know

When you write a function that represents a real-life situation, it helps to use letters that remind you of the real-life situation. For instance, in Example 2, *T* is used for the total cost and *c* is used for the cost.

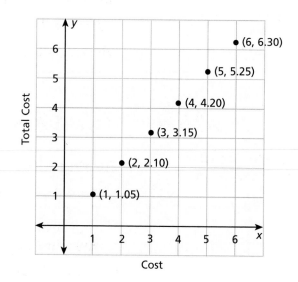

Example 3 *Writing a Function Rule*

Connections
Geometry

Find the perimeter of each rectangle. Organize the results in a table. Describe the pattern and write a rule for the function.

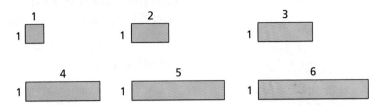

Solution Here is one way to organize your work.

Length	Width	Perimeter
1	1	$1 + 1 + 1 + 1 = 4$
2	1	$2 + 1 + 2 + 1 = 6$
3	1	$3 + 1 + 3 + 1 = 8$
4	1	$4 + 1 + 4 + 1 = 10$
5	1	$5 + 1 + 5 + 1 = 12$
6	1	$6 + 1 + 6 + 1 = 14$

You can organize these results in a table.

Length	1	2	3	4	5	6
Perimeter	4	6	8	10	12	14

When the length is 1, the perimeter is 4. Each time the length increases by 1, the perimeter increases by 2. A rule that gives the perimeter P is

$$P = 2 + 2 \cdot L$$

where L is the length. ∎

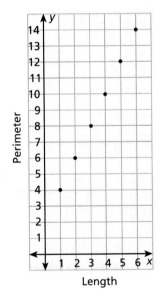

The data in the table can be represented using a coordinate plane.

Communicating about MATHEMATICS

Problem Solving
Making a Table

▶ **Sharing Ideas about the Lesson**

Extending the Example Evaluate the function $P = 2 + 2 \cdot L$ when L is 1, 2, 3, 4, 5, and 6. Organize your results in an input-output table. Then compare your input-output table to the table in Example 3.

EXERCISES

Think and Discuss

▶ CHECK for Understanding

1. Copy and complete the table at the right for $y = x - 8$.

In Exercises 2–4, you measured the daily temperatures (°C) for Oklahoma City from January through June. You found that the average temperature for each month could be found using the function $T = 4 \times m$. The variable m is the number of the month. That is, January = 1, February = 2, and so on.

Input	Output
x	y
9	?
8	?
7	?
6	?
5	?

2. Make a table that shows the temperatures from January through June.

3. Graph the data.

4. Do you think the same function could be a rule for the temperatures from July through December? Explain.

5. Write a function for the rule *For every carton of eggs you buy, you buy 12 eggs.*

6. Use the graph at the right. Make a table of the input and output. Then write a function to represent the data.

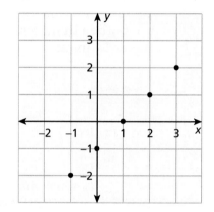

Independent Practice

In Exercises 7–12, copy and complete the table at the right.

Input	Output
m	y
0	?
1	?
2	?
3	?

7. $y = 5 \times m$
8. $y = m + 10$
9. $y = m - 4$
10. $y = m - 1$
11. $y = m \cdot 3$
12. $y = 8 - m$

In Exercises 13–15, write a function that will give the output y in the table from the corresponding input x. Then graph the data.

13.

Input	Output
x	y
0	0
1	3
2	6
3	9

14.

Input	Output
x	y
0	-6
1	-5
2	-4
3	-3

15.

Input	Output
x	y
0	5
1	6
2	7
3	8

In Exercises 16–18, use the graph to make an input-output table.
Then match the graph with the function that represents the data.

a. $y = x$ b. $y = x - 2$ c. $y = x + 2$

16.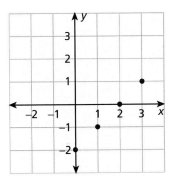

17.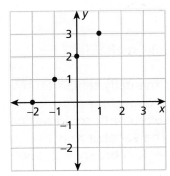

18.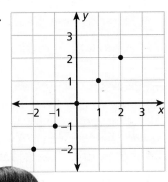

19. *Geometry*   The table below shows
the diameter d and circumference C
for different circles. Find a function
that outputs the circumference using
the diameter as input.

Input	Output
d	C
1	3.14
2	6.28
3	9.42
4	12.56
5	15.70

*Alexia Abernathy invented
the Oops! Proof No-Spill
Feeding Bowl for babies that
is now on the market.*

20. *Inventions*   The cost of producing 1
whistle that you invented is 0.75.
Make a table that shows the cost
of producing 5, 10, 15, 20, 25, and
30 whistles. Then write a function
that you can use to find the cost.

Writing Functions   In Exercises 21–23, copy and complete the
table. Describe the pattern. Write a rule for the function.

21. You are finding the area of a triangle that has a height
of x units and a base of 10 units.

22. You are grading a quiz that has x questions answered
correctly. Each correct answer gets a score of 3 points.

23. You are finding the ages of your two cats: Buttons and
Tiger. Buttons is x-years old. Tiger is 2 years older than
Buttons.

Input	Output
x	?
1	?
2	?
3	?
4	?
5	?
6	?

Probability In Exercises 24–26, use the spinner at the right. Find the probability that the spinner will land on the letter as described.

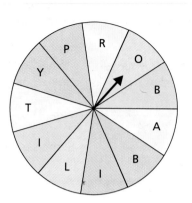

24. A vowel   25. Not a *B*   26. A consonant

In Exercises 27–29, match the event with its probability.

  a. About 1   b. About $\frac{1}{2}$ c. About 0

27. Independence Day falls on July 4.
28. A 1st grader is 6 feet tall.
29. A baby is a girl.

Exploration and Extension

30. *Group Activity* Use a watch with a second hand to find the number of times you can write your first name in 10 seconds, in 20 seconds, and in 30 seconds. Make an input-output table. Graph the data. Find a function to represent the number of times you can write your name in 1 second. Compare your function with others in your group.

Mixed REVIEW

Making Connections Write the decimal as a fraction. **(3.4)**

1. 0.5   2. 0.9   3. 0.41   4. 0.75

Geometry Solve for *x*. **(9.7, 10.2)**

5. 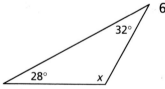   6.   7.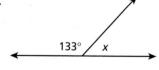

Finding a Pattern Describe the pattern. Then write the next three numbers. **(6.3, 7.3, 11.1)**

8. $\frac{1}{8}, \frac{1}{4}, \frac{3}{8}, \frac{1}{2}, \boxed{?}, \boxed{?}, \boxed{?}$ 9. 5, 2, −1, −4, $\boxed{?}, \boxed{?}, \boxed{?}$

10. *Probability* A bag contains 5 blue marbles, 8 red marbles, 3 green marbles, and 2 yellow marbles. For each color, find the probability of choosing a marble of that color. **(6.7)**

Take this test as you would take a test in class. The answers to the exercises are given in the back of the book.

In Exercises 1–4, write whether you would add or subtract to solve the equation. Then solve and check. **(12.1, 12.2)**

1. $c + 5 = -11$ 2. $p - 12 = 17$ 3. $14 + m = -5$ 4. $z - 7 = -2$

Error Analysis   In Exercises 5–7, describe and correct the error. **(12.1)**

5.
$$12 + x = 21$$
$$\underline{-12 \quad\quad -12}$$
$$x \quad\quad = 9$$

6.
$$x - 17 = -16$$
$$\underline{+ 17 \quad + 16}$$
$$x \quad\quad = 0$$

7.
$$2 = x + 5$$
$$\underline{+ 2 \quad\quad + 2}$$
$$x = 7$$

In Exercises 8–15, solve the equation. Check your solution. **(12.1–12.3)**

8. $x + 14 = -3$ 9. $x - 16 = 25$ 10. $x - 33 = -12$ 11. $12 + x = -4$

12. $\frac{5}{9} + x = \frac{17}{3}$ 13. $x + 5.67 = 9.11$ 14. $x - \frac{1}{3} = \frac{5}{8}$ 15. $x - 12.33 = 19.02$

In Exercises 16 and 17, choose the equation that you would use to answer the question. Then solve the equation and answer the question. **(12.3)**

16. You and 3 friends are buying a chemistry set that costs $39.95. You pay for the set and receive $15.30 in change. How much money did you start with?

   a. $x - 39.95 = 15.30$ b. $x + 15.30 = 39.95$

17. An official tennis ball must have a diameter that is at least $\frac{5}{2}$ inches. The difference between the largest and smallest allowable diameters that it can have is $\frac{1}{8}$ inch. How big can the diameter of the tennis ball be?

   a. $x - \frac{5}{2} = \frac{1}{8}$ b. $x + \frac{1}{8} = \frac{5}{2}$

18. *Geometry*   The area of a triangle with a base of 6 and a height of h is $A = \frac{1}{2} \times 6 \times h = 3 \times h$. Copy and complete the table at the right. Then graph the data.

Input	Output
h	**A**
1	?
2	?
3	?
4	?
5	?
6	?

Materials needed: pencils or pens, paper

Part A *Using a Table*

1. You work at a frozen yogurt store. Today you are offering three flavors of yogurt (vanilla, chocolate, and strawberry) and two different toppings (fudge and caramel). The number of different sundaes, using one flavor and one topping, can be counted with a table, as shown below.

	Vanilla	Chocolate	Strawberry
Fudge	Vanilla Fudge	Chocolate Fudge	Strawberry Fudge
Caramel	Vanilla Caramel	Chocolate Caramel	Strawberry Caramel

Explain how to use the table to count the number of different sundaes that are possible.

2. You decide to add a third topping—bananas. Draw a table that can be used to find the number of sundaes that are possible now.

Part B *Using a Table*

3. You are choosing uniforms for your school's soccer team. You have five choices for shorts (white, blue, green, yellow, and black) and four choices for shirts (red, white, blue, and orange). The number of different color combinations is shown in the table. How many combinations are there?

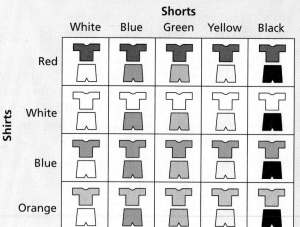

4. How many different color combinations are possible? Explain.

   a. Shorts: 6 color choices, Shirts: 5 color choices

   b. Shorts: 7 color choices, Shirts: 4 color choices

   c. Shorts: 5 color choices, Shirts: 7 color choices

Part C *Making Connections*

5. Your band plays 6 musical instruments (piano, saxophone, trumpet, guitar, drums, and clarinet). Your friend's band plays 4 musical instruments (saxophone, trumpet, guitar, and clarinet). Use the table at the right to find the number of instrument combinations your band and your friend's band could play.

6. How are the numbers of rows and columns in the table related to the number of possible combinations?

7. How many different instrument combinations are possible? Explain your reasoning.

   a. Your band: 5 instruments
      Friend's band: 4 instruments

   b. Your band: 8 instruments
      Friend's band: 3 instruments

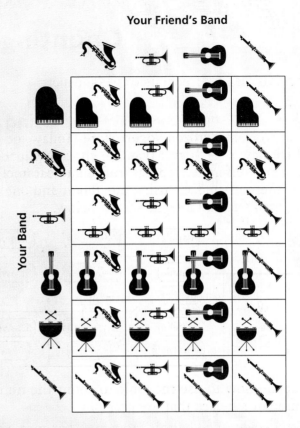

Your Friend's Band

Your Band

On Your Own   *Critical Thinking*

8. *Using a Table* You are selecting a committee that is to have one boy and one girl. For the boys, you can choose from Luis, Ralph, Larry, and Orlando. For the girls, you can choose from Sue, Alma, Carmen, and Flo. Use a table to show how many different committees you can choose.

9. *Connections to Geometry* A rectangle has a width of n units and a length of m units. How many square units are in the rectangle? How does this question relate to the problems in this Lab?

10. *Summarizing Results* You are choosing uniforms for the soccer team. You have n choices for shorts and m choices for shirts. How many different combinations are possible? Explain.

12.5

Counting Techniques

What you should learn:

Goal 1 How to use a tree diagram to count the number of ways an event can happen

Goal 2 How to use the Counting Principle to count the number of ways an event can happen

Why you should learn it:

Knowing how to count the number of ways something can happen can help you figure out your options. An example is figuring out the different sets of pets you can buy.

Goal 1 Using Tree Diagrams

In Lab 12.5, you may have found the number of possible combinations by making a table. Other ways are to make a list or use a tree diagram.

Example 1 *Using a List or a Tree Diagram*

At the school lunch room, you have a choice of a hamburger or a hot dog *and* a choice of peas, corn, or green beans. How many different lunches are possible?

Solution One way to solve this is to make a list.

Hamburger, peas   Hamburger, corn   Hamburger, beans

Hot dog, peas   Hot dog, corn   Hot dog, beans

There are 6 different lunches possible. ∎

Another way to count the number of possible lunches is to use a **tree diagram.**

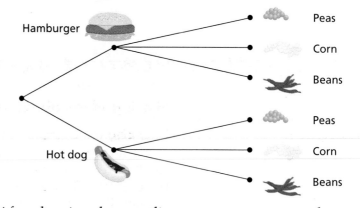

Hamburger   Peas
             Corn
             Beans

Hot dog   Peas
             Corn
             Beans

After drawing the tree diagram, you can count the number of different lunches by counting the number of "branches." For instance, the branch "hamburger and peas" represents one of the lunches.

The Counting Principle

In Example 1, it is easy to use a list or a tree diagram to count the possible lunches. In other cases, the **Counting Principle** can be helpful.

Counting Principle

One item is to be selected from each of two or more sets. The total number of possible combinations is the product of the number of items in each set.

If you applied the Counting Principle to Example 1, you would get the following.

$$\begin{array}{c}\text{2 choices}\\\text{for sandwich}\end{array} \times \begin{array}{c}\text{3 choices}\\\text{for vegetable}\end{array} = \text{6 possible lunches}$$

Real Life
Pets

Example 2 *Counting Principle*

You are buying 3 pets. At the pet store, you can choose among 2 puppies, 3 kittens, and 5 gerbils. You want one of each. How many different sets of pets can you choose?

Solution   You could try listing all the different combinations. But because there are so many, it is easier to use the Counting Principle.

$$\begin{array}{c}2\\\text{puppies}\end{array} \times \begin{array}{c}3\\\text{kittens}\end{array} \times \begin{array}{c}5\\\text{gerbils}\end{array} = \begin{array}{c}\text{30 possible}\\\text{combinations}\end{array} \quad \blacksquare$$

Communicating about MATHEMATICS

Problem Solving
Making a List

▶ **Sharing Ideas about the Lesson**

Extending the Example In Example 2, let $P1$ and $P2$ represent the puppies. Let $K1$, $K2$, and $K3$ represent the kittens, and let $G1$, $G2$, $G3$, $G4$, and $G5$ represent the gerbils. Write a list that represents the possible sets of pets. Then use the Counting Principle to check your answer. Do you prefer making a list or using the Counting Principle? Why?

EXERCISES

Guided Practice

▶ CHECK for Understanding

Think and Discuss

1. You are buying a new bicycle. You have a choice of a BMX® bike, a mountain bike, or a racing bike. Each style comes in green or black. Complete the tree diagram at the right to find how many different bicycles you could choose.

2. Find the number of possible abbreviations that could be made using 2 letters.

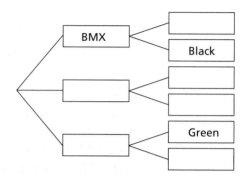

In Exercises 3–5, decide whether you would make a tree diagram or use the Counting Principle to find the number. Explain your choice. Then find the number.

3. The number of possible 5-digit zip codes
4. The number of possible combinations of heads and tails when tossing 3 pennies
5. The number of possible 2-digit numbers on a baseball jersey
6. *It's Up to You* Make up a problem that can be solved using the tree diagram at the right.

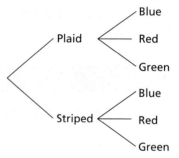

Independent Practice

In Exercises 7–10, make a tree diagram to solve the problem.

7. *Reasoning* You are redecorating your room. You can choose from sky blue, pale green, or lemon yellow paint for the walls, and dark blue, forest green, or light brown carpeting. How many different ways can you redecorate?

8. The first question on a history exam asks you to write about the Pilgrims, Plymouth Rock, or the Mayflower. The second question asks you to write about Walt Whitman or Louisa May Alcott. How many different ways can you choose your two topics?

9. *Community Service* You are selling raffle tickets for a fund-raiser. The tickets are printed with a 3-digit number using only the numbers 1 through 4. How many different tickets can be printed?

10. *Cake Baking* You are baking a birthday cake for your friend. The choices for the cake are vanilla, chocolate, or marble. The choices for the filling are cherry or lemon. The frosting can be pink, white, or green. How many different cakes can you make?

In Exercises 11 and 12, use the Counting Principle to solve.

11. On a map, the numbers 1 through 12 appear across the top and the letters A through J appear down the side. You can locate a city using a number and a letter. How many different location labels are possible?

12. At summer camp, you have a choice of 4 morning activities, 5 afternoon activities, and 3 evening activities. If you are at camp for 60 days, will you ever have to spend two days doing the same three activities? Explain.

13. *English* How many possible words can you make using the prefixes *bi-* and *tri-* and the endings *cycle, annual, color, focal,* and *angular*?

14. *Games* In the game *Clue*®, a murder has been committed. Players must find out who did it, what weapon was used, and in what room. The possible suspects, weapons, and rooms are shown at the right. In how many different ways could the murder have been committed?

Colonel Mustard	Mrs. Peacock
Professor Plum	Miss Scarlet
Mr. Green	Mrs. White
Knife	Rope
Candlestick	Lead Pipe
Revolver	Wrench
Hall	Billiard Room
Kitchen	Lounge
Study	Library
Conservatory	Ballroom
Dining Room	

Integrated Review

Making Connections within Mathematics

Multiply the fractions. Simplify, if possible.

15. $\frac{4}{5} \times \frac{1}{10}$

16. $\frac{1}{6} \times \frac{5}{8}$

17. $\frac{2}{3} \times \frac{5}{9}$

18. $\frac{7}{20} \times \frac{3}{4}$

Exploration and Extension

19. *Building Your Chapter Project* Your Native American pen pal in Arizona writes about the following Hopi game. *In one version of the game Totolospi, 3 "cane dice" are used. A cane die is flat on one side and round on the other. The 2 players start at the circles at opposite ends of the board. They take turns tossing the 3 dice. If 3 round sides land up, the player moves 2 lines. If 3 flat sides land up, the player moves 1 line. If a combination of round and flat sides is thrown, the player loses a turn. The player reaching the opposite circle first wins. How many different ways are there for the cane dice to land?* Write an answer that uses a tree diagram to your pen pal.

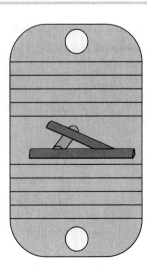

12.6

Additional Probability Concepts

What you should learn:

Goal 1 How to find the probability of two independent events

Goal 2 How to use probability to solve real-life problems

Why you should learn it:

Knowing how to find probabilities can help you play games. An example is finding the probability of winning a game.

Goal 1 Finding Probabilities

Lesson Investigation

■ **Investigating Independent Events**

Group Activity Put 3 blue and 2 red marbles in a cup. Then put 1 blue and 1 red marble in another cup. Without looking, choose one marble from each cup. Record the colors in a table. Replace the marbles. Repeat the experiment 20 times. From your results, estimate the probability that both marbles will be red.

In this investigation, the two events are **independent** because the occurrence of one event doesn't affect the occurrence of the other.

Probability of Independent Events
The probability that two independent events will occur is the product of their probabilities.

> **Study Tip**
>
> Events that are not independent are **dependent.** For instance, the events "The sun is shining," and "You are wearing sunglasses," are dependent.

Example 1 *Finding Probabilities*

In the investigation above, what is the probability that both marbles will be red?

Solution The probability of choosing a red marble from the first cup is $\frac{2}{5}$. The probability of choosing a red marble from the second cup is $\frac{1}{2}$. Because the events are independent, the probability of choosing two red marbles is

$$\frac{2}{5} \cdot \frac{1}{2} = \frac{2 \cdot 1}{5 \cdot 2} = \frac{2}{10}, \text{ or } \frac{1}{5}.$$

The probability of choosing two red marbles is $\frac{1}{5}$. ■

Solving Real-Life Problems

Real Life
Games

Example 2 *Finding Probabilities*

You are playing a game with a number cube and a spinner, as shown at the left. What is the probability that you will get a 5 on the number cube *and* a blue region on the spinner?

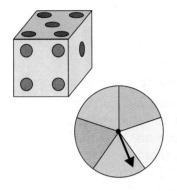

Solution The probability of getting a 5 on the number cube is $\frac{1}{6}$. The probability of getting a blue region on the spinner is $\frac{2}{5}$. Because the events are independent, the probability of getting a 5 and a blue region is

$$\frac{1}{6} \cdot \frac{2}{5} = \frac{1 \cdot 2}{6 \cdot 5} = \frac{2}{30}, \text{ or } \frac{1}{15}.$$

This means that you should get a 5 and a blue region about 1 out of every 15 times you toss the number cube and spin the spinner.

Another way to find the probability in Example 2 is to list all the possible outcomes. From this listing, you can see that 2 of the 30 outcomes have a 5 and a blue region.

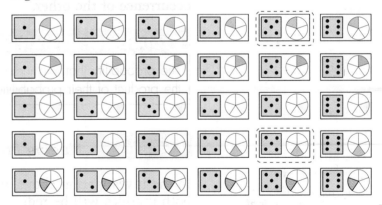

Communicating about MATHEMATICS

▶ **Sharing Ideas about the Lesson**

Partner Activity In Example 2, what is the probability of tossing an even number *and* landing on a red area? Solve the problem in two ways.

Cooperative
Learning

EXERCISES

Guided Practice

Think and Discuss

▶ **CHECK for Understanding**

1. What does it mean for events to be independent? Name two ways to find their probability.

In Exercises 2 and 3, are the events independent? Explain.

2. You like to play video games.
   You like to swim.

3. It is raining outside.
   You are holding an umbrella.

4. *Group Activity: The Guessing Game* Choose a letter from A to C and a number from 1 to 5. Write your choices on a piece of paper. Ask others in your group to guess your combination (for instance, "A3" or "C4"). Record the guesses in a list. Count the number of times it takes to guess the correct combination. Repeat the experiment several times. Record your results in a table. From your results, estimate the probability of guessing the correct combination. Then find the theoretical probability that the correct combination is chosen.

5. Find the probability of landing on green on both spinners shown at the right. Show how you can solve the problem by making a list.

Independent Practice

In Exercises 6–8, are the events independent? Explain your reasoning.

6. You studied for your test 3 nights.
   You will do well on your test.

7. You own a dog.
   You like to roller skate.

8. You will play baseball this year.
   You collect football cards.

9. *Basketball* You and a friend are shooting baskets. Your friend makes an average of 3 out of 5 and you make an average of 2 out of 3. What is the probability that both of you make your next basket?

In 1994, these students were chosen by **Sports Illustrated for Kids** *to help the Orlando Magic basketball team's staff.*

10. You are a contestant on a game show. You have a chance to win a trip to Mississippi or Tennessee. The letters of each state are placed in two separate bags. You choose one letter from each bag. To win, you must choose an "s" from each bag. What is the probability that you will win the trip?

Geometry In Exercises 11 and 12, imagine that the geometric figures at the right are cut out and put in two bags. One figure is randomly selected from each bag.

11. What is the probability that both figures are polygons?

12. What is the probability that both figures are parallelograms?

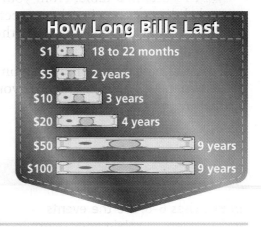

Bag 1   **Bag 2**

Integrated Review

Reading a Graph Use the bar graph.
(Source: Federal Reserve Bank of Los Angeles)

13. How much longer does a $20 bill last than a $5 bill?

14. How much longer does a $100 bill last than a $10 bill?

15. Why do you think that less valuable bills don't last as long as more valuable ones?

Making Connections within Mathematics

How Long Bills Last

$1	18 to 22 months
$5	2 years
$10	3 years
$20	4 years
$50	9 years
$100	9 years

Exploration and Extension

16. **Building Your Chapter Project** Your pen pal from Israel writes the following in a letter. *Dreidel is an Israeli game that is played with four-sided tops. The sides have Hebrew letters that can be assigned numbers as shown. To play, take turns spinning two tops and adding the numbers. The player with the highest score after 10 rounds wins.*

 50 Nun   5 Gimmel   3 Hay   300 Shin

Find the probability of getting a score of 600 in 1 turn. Then explain to your pen pal how you found this probability.

12

Chapter Summary

What did you learn?

Why did you learn it?

Equations, functions, and probability can be used to solve many different types of real-life problems. Here are some examples you studied in this chapter.

How does it fit into the bigger picture of mathematics?

One of the things you learned this year is that mathematics has many different parts. We hope this book has opened windows for you to see several of these parts: number operations, algebra, geometry, statistics, and probability.

We also hope you have learned that there are many connections among the different parts of mathematics. In this chapter you learned that the Counting Principle can be modeled with an area model; that is a connection between probability and geometry.

In your future studies, we suggest that you continue to look for the many connections among the different parts of mathematics. Finding the connections helps open more windows so you can see more and more of the bigger picture of mathematics.

In Exercises 1–8, solve the equation. Then check. **(12.1–12.3)**

1. $m + 3 = 11$

2. $\frac{5}{12} + t = \frac{7}{12}$

3. $\frac{1}{9} = p - \frac{1}{6}$

4. $n - 15 = 22$

5. $16 + x = -34$

6. $-25 = b - 17$

7. $z - 8.9 = 25.15$

8. $4.75 + s = 13.2$

Communicating Math In Exercises 9 and 10, write the equation represented by the sentence. Then solve. **(12.1–12.3)**

9. Fourteen is the sum of a number and 18.

10. The difference of a number and two tenths is 3.

In Exercises 11 and 12, write a rule for the function. Then graph the data. **(12.4)**

11.

Input	Output
x	**y**
−3	0
−2	1
−1	2
0	3
1	4

12.

Input	Output
x	**y**
1	3
2	6
3	9
4	12
5	15

In Exercises 13 and 14, use a tree diagram to solve. **(12.5)**

13. You are planning your schedule for next year. You can choose from band, chorus, or art for your first period class, and math or science for your second period class. How many different first and second period schedules can you have?

14. You see a display in a clothing store that has mannequins wearing all possible combinations of 3 colors of tee shirts and 3 colors of shorts. The tee shirts are red, yellow, and white, and the shorts are blue, black, and tan. How many mannequins are in the display?

15. You play one song from a CD that has 9 songs. Then you play one song from a CD that has 8 songs. How many different combinations of two songs could you have played?

Are the events independent? Explain. **(12.6)**

16. You practice softball every day. You are chosen for the softball team.

17. You have a quiz in math class. The sun is shining.

These Mah-jongg tiles are engraved with Chinese drawings.

18. *Mah-jongg*   Mah-jongg is a Chinese game that uses engraved tiles. There are 4 wind tiles, 3 dragon tiles, and 4 flower tiles. If you choose one from each group, how many different sets of 3 tiles can you choose? Explain.

19. *Tsyanshidzi* is an ancient Chinese game for 2 players that uses 2 piles of stones. Players can either take as many stones as they want from one pile, *or* they can take the same number from each pile. The winner is the one to pick up the last stone. There are 2 stones left in one pile and 1 in the other, and it's your turn. Can you win? Explain.

20. The African game *Wari* uses 24 black and 24 white stones and the playing board shown. To play, stones are removed. At any time, each player can have between 1 and 24 stones on the board. What is the probability that at any time, the same number of black and white stones are on the board?

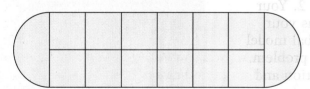

21. *Language*   Copy the puzzle onto grid paper. Then find each word and circle it.

backgammon
bingo
bridge
canasta
charades
checkers
chess
cribbage
darts
dominoes
hearts
jacks
monopoly
pinochle
rummy
solitaire
tic tac toe
tiddlywinks

22. In Exercise 21, the letters that were *not* circled can be used to form a question. Find the question and write a sentence that answers it.

W	H	S	K	N	I	W	Y	L	D	D	I	T
A	Y	T	T	S	E	D	A	R	A	H	C	N
I	M	R	E	S	S	E	O	N	I	M	O	D
Y	M	A	G	E	S	O	U	R	F	M	A	S
C	U	D	A	G	E	J	V	O	M	O	R	T
H	R	P	B	D	H	A	I	A	C	N	T	R
E	E	I	B	I	C	C	G	M	A	O	A	A
C	T	N	I	R	H	K	C	O	N	P	N	E
K	C	O	R	B	C	S	E	P	A	O	T	H
E	Y	C	C	A	O	U	L	E	S	L	A	R
R	N	H	B	I	N	G	O	E	T	Y	D	T
S	O	L	I	T	A	I	R	E	A	H	I	S
Y	E	E	O	T	C	A	T	C	I	T	A	R

In Exercises 1–9, solve the equation. Then check the solution.

1. $p + 9 = 2$

2. $25 + s = 0$

3. $\frac{10}{11} = m + \frac{2}{11}$

4. $x + 20.8 = 30.03$

5. $32 + b = -8$

6. $n - \frac{2}{3} = \frac{4}{5}$

7. $y - 16.35 = 1.68$

8. $-19 = t - 18$

9. $-24 = z - 42$

In Exercises 10–12, use the graph to make an input-output table. Then write a function to represent the data.

10.

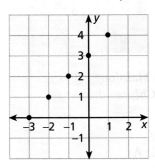

11.

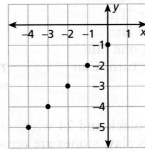

12.

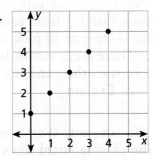

13. *Writing an Equation*   You are playing a card game and lose 55 points in Round 2. Your score is now -15 points. What was your score before Round 2? Write a verbal model using subtraction to represent the problem. Assign labels. Then write an equation and solve.

14. *Tropical Fish*   At the pet store, you buy 1 swordtail and 1 guppy from a tank that contains 16 guppies and 12 swordtails. How many different combinations of fish can be selected to fill your order?

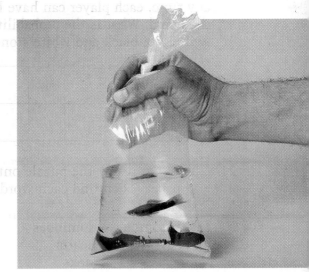

Chess   In the game of chess, each player has 16 playing pieces in a box: 1 king, 1 queen, 2 rooks, 2 bishops, 2 knights, and 8 pawns. You and a friend decide to play. You each choose a piece from your box at random.

15. What is the probability that you both choose rooks?

16. What is the probability that you both choose pawns?

17. What is the probability that you choose a queen and your friend chooses a knight?

1. **Error Analysis** Are both solutions correct? Explain. **(7.3)**

   Solution A: $\frac{3}{4} + \frac{1}{6} = \frac{18}{24} + \frac{4}{24} = \frac{22}{24}$ Solution B: $\frac{3}{4} + \frac{1}{6} = \frac{9}{12} + \frac{2}{12} = \frac{11}{12}$

In Exercises 2–5, solve. Simplify, if possible. **(7.4–7.6)**

2. $6\frac{2}{5} + 1\frac{4}{5}$ 3. $4\frac{1}{8} + 4\frac{5}{16}$ 4. $5\frac{1}{6} - 2\frac{5}{6}$ 5. $8\frac{1}{2} - 3\frac{9}{16}$

Geometry In Exercises 6–9, match the multiplication problem with the area model. Then find the product. **(8.2)**

a.    b. 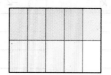   c. 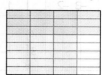   d.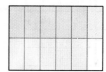

6. $\frac{5}{6} \times \frac{1}{2}$ 7. $\frac{3}{7} \times \frac{1}{3}$ 8. $\frac{4}{5} \times \frac{1}{2}$ 9. $\frac{3}{4} \times \frac{3}{8}$

In Exercises 10 and 11, use the animal tracks below. **(7.6, 8.5)**

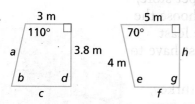

Fox $1\frac{3}{4}$ in.

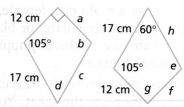

Raccoon $4\frac{1}{2}$ in.

Elk $4\frac{1}{2}$ in.

10. How *many times longer* is the elk track than the fox track?
11. How *much longer* is the raccoon track than the fox track?

Geometry In Exercises 12 and 13, the two figures are congruent. Find the missing sides and angles. **(9.3)**

12.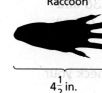

    3 m   110°   a   3.8 m   b   d   c   5 m   70°   h   4 m   e   g   f

13.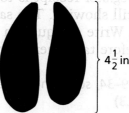

    12 cm   a   105°   b   17 cm   d   c   17 cm   60°   h   105°   e   12 cm   g   f

Use the figure at the right. Classify the triangle using as many of the words as possible: *equilateral, isosceles, scalene, right, acute, obtuse.* **(9.6)**

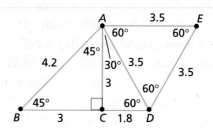

    A   3.5   E   60°   60°   45°   4.2   30°   3.5   3   3.5   60°   45°   B   3   C   1.8   D   60°

14. Triangle ACD 15. Triangle ADE
16. Triangle BAD 17. Triangle BAC

In Exercises 18–23, use a number line to solve. **(11.2, 11.3)**

18. $-6 + 13$

19. $-4 + (-9)$

20. $-11 + 11$

21. $-8 - 7$

22. $4 - (-3)$

23. $-10 - (-3)$

In Exercises 24–26, find the area of the figure. **(10.4, 10.6, 11.6)**

24.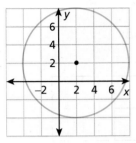

25.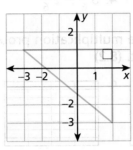

26.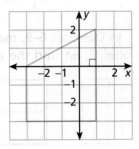

27. You threw a penny into a wishing well. The penny started at 3 feet above ground and landed 8 feet below ground. How many feet did the penny fall? Explain your steps. **(11.3)**

28. The top of a cash register receipt is torn off. The sales tax and the total are still showing. The sales tax is $3.36 and the total is $59.36. Write an equation that you can use to find the amount before tax. Then solve. **(12.1)**

Algebra In Exercises 29–34, solve the equation. Then check your solution. **(12.1, 12.2, 12.3)**

29. $5 + x = 31$

30. $12 = m - 3$

31. $z - 17 = -1$

32. $p - \frac{3}{8} = \frac{1}{2}$

33. $24.52 = t + 9.8$

34. $k - 6.67 = 34.05$

In Exercises 35 and 36, use a tree diagram to solve the problem. **(12.5)**

35. You are buying a Labrador retriever puppy. At the pet store, you can choose a male or a female. You can also choose the color from yellow, chocolate, or black. What is the least number of Labrador retriever puppies the store must have to offer all these choices?

36. You are making a sandwich. You can choose from turkey, roast beef, or ham for the meat. You can also choose from white bread, rye bread, or sourdough bread. How many different sandwich combinations are there?

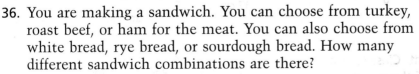

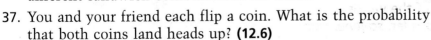

37. You and your friend each flip a coin. What is the probability that both coins land heads up? **(12.6)**

38. *Making Connections* In the Chapter Project for Chapter 1, you wrote a review quiz. Now write a quiz about the top ten most important ideas you learned in math this year.

Student Handbook

Table of Contents

■ Arithmetic and Algebra

$=$	Is equal to
$\neq$	Is not equal to
$>$	Is greater than
$<$	Is less than
$\approx$	Is approximately equal to
ab, $a \cdot b$, or $a(b)$	a times b
a^n	A number a raised to the nth power
$(\ )$, $\{\ \}$	Grouping symbols
5 or $+5$	Positive 5
-5	Negative 5
$\frac{a}{b}$	Ratio of a to b, or $a \div b$

■ Geometry

(a, b)	Ordered pair a, b
$\cong$	Is congruent to
$\triangle ABC$	Triangle ABC
$\overleftrightarrow{AB}$	Line AB
$\overline{AB}$	Segment AB
$\overrightarrow{AB}$	Ray AB
$\angle A$	Angle A
π	Pi (≈ 3.14)
$\perp$	Perpendicular lines or right angle

■ Perimeter and Circumference

Perimeter of a rectangle:
$2 \cdot length + 2 \cdot width$

Perimeter of a square:
$4 \cdot side\ length$

Circumference of a circle:
$\pi \cdot diameter$

■ Area

Area of a rectangle:
$length \cdot width$

Area of a square:
$(side\ length)^2$

Area of a triangle:
$\frac{1}{2} \cdot base \cdot height$

Area of a circle:
$\pi \cdot (radius)^2$

Try This Activity

Regular polygons have all sides the same length and all angles the same size. Can you write a formula for the perimeter of each of these regular polygons?

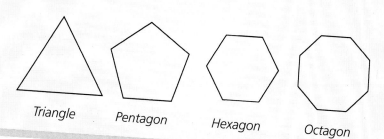

Triangle   Pentagon   Hexagon   Octagon

■ **Length**

10 millimeters (mm) = 1 centimeter
10 centimeters = 1 decimeter (dm)
100 centimeters (cm) = 1 meter (m)
1000 meters = 1 kilometer (km)
100,000 centimeters = 1 kilometer

■ **Area**

100 sq mm = 1 sq cm
100 sq cm = 1 sq dm
100 sq dm = 1 sq m
1,000,000 sq m = 1 sq km

■ **Capacity**

1000 milliliters (mL) = 1 liter (L)
10 deciliters (dL) = 1 liter

■ **Mass**

1000 milligrams (mg) = 1 gram (g)
1000 grams = 1 kilogram (kg)

■ **Rewriting Measurements in Other Units**

In the metric system, the units are related by powers of 10.

Table of Units

Prefix	Power of 10	Length	Capacity	Mass
kilo (k)	1000 units	kilometer	kiloliter*	kilogram
hecto (h)	100 units	hectometer*	hectoliter*	hectogram*
deka (dk)	10 units	dekameter*	dekaliter*	dekagram*
	1 unit	meter	liter	gram
deci (d)	0.1 unit	decimeter*	deciliter*	decigram*
centi (c)	0.01 unit	centimeter	centiliter*	centigram*
milli (m)	0.001 unit	millimeter	milliliter	milligram

*These units are seldom used.

Study Tip

When you rewrite a measurement using a smaller unit, you multiply.

0.24 m = ? cm

In the Table of Units, there are 2 steps from meters to centimeters, so multiply by 10^2, or 100.

0.24 × 100 = 24

0.24 m = 24 cm

Study Tip

When you rewrite a measurement using a larger unit, you divide.

3500 mg = ? kg

In the Table of Units, there are 6 steps from milligrams to kilograms, so divide by 10^6, or 1,000,000.

3500 ÷ 1,000,000 = 0.0035

3500 mg = 0.0035 kg

■ Length

12 inches (in.) = 1 foot (ft)
3 feet = 1 yard (yd)
36 inches = 1 yard
5280 feet = 1 mile (mi)
1760 yards = 1 mile

■ Area

144 sq in. = 1 sq ft
9 sq ft = 1 sq yd
640 acres = 1 square mile

■ Time

60 seconds (sec) = 1 minute (min)
3600 seconds = 1 hour (hr)
60 minutes = 1 hour
24 hours = 1 day
7 days = 1 week

■ Capacity

1 cup (c) = 8 fluid ounces (fl oz)
2 cups = 1 pint (pt)
2 pints = 1 quart (qt)
2 quarts = 1 half-gallon
4 quarts = 1 gallon (gal)

■ Weight

16 ounces (oz) = 1 pound (lb)
2000 pounds = 1 ton

360 days = 1 business year
365 days = 1 year
366 days = 1 leap year
10 years = 1 decade
10 decades = 1 century = 100 years

Try This Activity

The units above are the most common ones, but there are also many unusual ones. Some were common many years ago. Others are common only within a particular trade. How many of the units below do you recognize?

Cubit   Peck   Stone   Carat
Grain   Gill   Fathom   Span
Rod   Furlong   Skein   Bolt

How many other unusual units can you and your friends think of?

Use after Lesson 1.1, page 4

Describe the pattern. Then write the next three numbers.

1. 100, 98, 96, 94, 92, . . .

2. 1, 4, 7, 10, 13, . . .

3. 1, 2, 4, 8, 16, . . .

4. 1, 2, 4, 5, 7, . . .

5. 0, 100, 5, 95, 10, . . .

6. 3, 7, 11, 15, 19, . . .

7. $\frac{1}{2}, \frac{2}{3}, \frac{3}{4}, \frac{4}{5}, \frac{5}{6}, \ldots$

8. $\frac{1}{3}, \frac{2}{5}, \frac{3}{7}, \frac{4}{9}, \frac{5}{11}, \ldots$

Describe the pattern. Then write the next three letters.

9. A, C, E, G, I, . . .

10. A, Y, C, W, E, . . .

11. A, C, F, H, K, . . .

12. Z, Y, W, V, T, . . .

Use after Lesson 1.2, page 8

Make a table. Describe any patterns that you see. Complete the next three rows of the table.

1. Areas of rectangles with dimensions 2-by-2, 2-by-3, 2-by-4, 2-by-5, . . .

2. Perimeters of rectangles with dimensions 1-by-2, 2-by-3, 3-by-4, 4-by-5, . . .

3. Areas of squares with side lengths 1, 2, 3, 4, . . .

4. Areas of rectangles with dimensions 1-by-2, 2-by-3, 3-by-4, 4-by-5, . . .

5. Perimeters of squares with side lengths 1, 2, 3, 4, . . .

Copy and complete the table. Describe any patterns that you see. Find the sum of the numbers in the tenth row by using a pattern.

6.

Row	Addends	Sum
1	2 + 4	?
2	2 + 4 + 6	?
3	2 + 4 + 6 + 8	?
?	?	?
?	?	?

7.

Row	Addends	Sum
1	1 + 3	?
2	1 + 3 + 5	?
3	1 + 3 + 5 + 7	?
?	?	?
?	?	?

Use after Lesson 1.3, page 12

Make a list to find the following.
1. Ways to make $0.35 using nickels, dimes, and quarters
2. Ways to arrange 4 flags in a line if you have a red, a blue, a green, and a yellow flag
3. Orders in which Lisa, Enrico, and Tom can stand in a line
4. Ways to choose 2 flavors of ice cream from 5 possibilities
5. Ways to combine a white, blue, or gray shirt with a red or navy tie

Use after Lesson 1.4, page 17

Use the graph at the right.
1. What might the data represent?
2. What was the approximate number out of 100 in 1992? 1993?
3. In what year was the number out of 100 nearly double another year?
4. What pattern can you see in the graph?
5. What would you expect the number out of 100 to be in 1996?

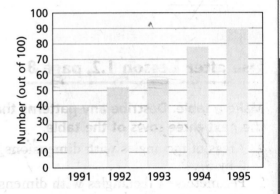

Use after Lesson 1.5, page 21

Use a 5-by-6 grid of dot paper.
1. How many different rectangles with whole-number dimensions can be drawn?
2. List the possible perimeters of the rectangles.
3. How many of the rectangles are squares?

Solve the following.
4. Starting from home, you walk 6 blocks east, turn north and walk 3 blocks, turn west and walk 2 blocks, turn south and walk 4 blocks and arrive at the mall. What is the shortest route home if you don't cut across blocks?
5. Starting from home, you walk 3 blocks north, 7 blocks east, 5 blocks south and 4 blocks west. How far are you from the mall in Exercise 4?

Use after Lesson 1.6, page 28

Use mental math to solve.

1. $7 + j = 9$ **2.** $t - 3 = 5$ **3.** $m + 11 = 54$
4. $21 - p = 12$ **5.** $k \times 4 = 28$ **6.** $7 \times w = 21$
7. $56 \div r = 8$ **8.** $n \div 6 = 9$ **9.** $s \times s = 81$
10. $13 \times g = 39$ **11.** $60 \div b = 5$ **12.** $43 - y = 23$
13. $v + 12 = 62$ **14.** $x - 9 = 15$ **15.** $g \div 2 = 45$

Write an equation for the statement, then solve.

16. The sum of 3 and a number is 12.   **17.** The product of a number and 2 is 24.
18. The product of 5 and a number is 55.   **19.** A number divided by 5 is 4.
20. A number times itself is 64.   **21.** The quotient of a number and 7 is 4.

Use after Lesson 1.7, page 34

Work backward to complete each diagram.

1. $+6$ -3 $\div 4$ $\times 6$ | ? | ? | ? | ? | 30 |

2. $\div 3$ $+4$ $\times 8$ $\div 4$ | ? | ? | ? | ? | 16 |

3. $\times 4$ -9 $\div 11$ $\times 9$ | ? | ? | ? | ? | 45 |

4. $\times 9$ $\div 6$ -5 $+7$ | ? | ? | ? | ? | 14 |

5. $\div 3$ $+19$ -2 $\div 4$ | ? | ? | ? | ? | 6 |

6. $+11$ $\times 3$ $\div 8$ -7 | ? | ? | ? | ? | 2 |

Use after Lesson 1.8, page 38

1. If every person in a club with 8 members exchanges a dozen cookies with each other member, how many cookies change hands?
2. How many red squares are on a 2×2 checkerboard? A 4×4 checkerboard? A 6×6 checkerboard?
3. Use the digits from 0–9. How many combinations can be made using 1 digit? 2 digits? 3 digits? Using this pattern, how many can be made using 10 digits?
4. If a phone tree starts with one person calling 3 people, and each person who was called calls 3 other people, how many people will be called by the time your phone tree has branched three times? How many times will your phone tree need to branch to call everyone in a class with 75 students?

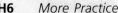

Use after Lesson 1.9, page 42

1. How many multiples of 3 from 1 to 100 are also multiples of 2? Are also multiples of 9?
2. You go to a concert and spend a third of your money on the ticket. You buy a sweatshirt with $\frac{3}{4}$ of what you have left, then spend half of the remaining amount on refreshments. You then have $3.00 left. How much money did you start with? How much did the sweatshirt cost?
3. The number of ants in your ant farm doubles every 10 days. On the 61st day there are 640 ants in the farm. How many ants did you start with? How many will you have on day 81?
4. Three friends went on a fishing trip. On the first day they caught a total of 22 fish. Lloyd caught twice as many as Jock and 3 more than Gary. How many fish did each catch?

Use after Lesson 2.1, page 56

Write the number in expanded notation.

1. 247	**2.** 3095	**3.** 11,974	**4.** 40,908
5. 500,050	**6.** 659,003	**7.** 40,004,400	**8.** 18,080,605

Complete the statement

9. $3,800 = \boxed{?}$ hundreds   10. $3,404,000 = \boxed{?}$ thousands
11. $5400 = \boxed{?}$ tens   12. $4,230,000 = \boxed{?}$ ten thousands

Write the number given by the expanded notation.

13. $5 \times 10,000 + 4 \times 100 + 6 \times 1$ 14. $6 \times 1000 + 2 \times 100 + 5 \times 10$
15. $8 \times 100,000 + 3 \times 1000$ 16. $4 \times 10,000 + 9 \times 1000 + 4 \times 1$

Use after Lesson 2.2, page 60

Solve each problem without using a calculator. Show your work.

1. $325 + 387$	**2.** $432 + 987$	**3.** $923 + 654$
4. $862 - 465$	**5.** $576 - 379$	**6.** $103 - 68$
7. $10,548 + 436$	**8.** $32,756 - 10,958$	**9.** $87,078 - 989$
10. $6439 - 4985$	**11.** $4987 + 10,498$	**12.** $3987 + 98,834$

Use mental math to solve.

13. $96 - t = 42$	**14.** $j + 87 = 99$	**15.** $b - 32 = 37$
16. $4390 + w = 10,000$	**17.** $m - 354 = 220$	**18.** $n + 543 = 1100$

Use after Lesson 2.3, page 68

Draw the indicated model to solve the problem.

1. Set model; 6×4
2. Area model; 7×3
3. Number line model; 3×9
4. Set model; 5×6

For each area, draw two models with different dimensions. Write the multiplication problem each shows.

5. 42 square units
6. 45 square units
7. 50 square units
8. 44 square units
9. 75 square units
10. 63 square units

Write the multiplication problem shown by the number line.

11.
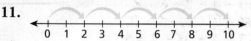

12.
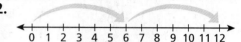

Use mental math to solve.

13. $c \times 3 = 63$
14. $7 \times n = 56$
15. $m \times 8 = 32$
16. $9 \times j = 45$
17. $a \times 4 = 52$
18. $12 \times g = 72$
19. $6 \times b = 54$
20. $y \times 11 = 121$
21. $z \times 5 = 70$

Use after Lesson 2.4, page 74

Draw a set model to solve.

1. $32 \div 4$
2. $20 \div 5$
3. $15 \div 3$
4. $24 \div 8$

Draw a number line model to solve.

5. $12 \div 2$
6. $14 \div 7$
7. $16 \div 8$
8. $27 \div 9$

Draw an area model to solve.

9. $32 \div 8$
10. $46 \div 11$
11. $54 \div 9$
12. $70 \div 8$

Solve and write the quotient in two ways.

13. $35 \div 4$
14. $19 \div 3$
15. $24 \div 9$
16. $31 \div 2$
17. $98 \div 9$
18. $46 \div 5$
19. $77 \div 8$
20. $64 \div 7$
21. $143 \div 6$
22. $398 \div 7$
23. $523 \div 5$
24. $453 \div 9$

Solve the equation using mental math.

25. $t \div 3 = 121$
26. $510 \div m = 102$
27. $y \div 7 = 22$
28. $880 \div z = 22$
29. $440 \div s = 11$
30. $j \div 8 = 20$
31. $999 \div e = 9$
32. $p \div 3 = 33$
33. $x \div 10 = 70$
34. $990 \div y = 30$
35. $z \div 8 = 60$
36. $s \div 4 = 400$

Use after Lesson 2.5, page 79

Evaluate each expression.

1. $4 \times 3 + 7 \times 2$
2. $15 - 2 \times 3 + 1$
3. $6 \times (7 - 5) + 4$
4. $3 - 1 + 4 \times 8$
5. $2 \times 9 + 7 - 3$
6. $50 - (2 + 4) \times 8$
7. $27 + 4 \times (3 + 1)$
8. $12 - 2 \times 6 + 5$
9. $24 \div 4 - 2 + 10$
10. $9 + 3 \times 4 - 2$
11. $34 - 3 + 2 \times 5$
12. $65 - (4 + 6) - 7$
13. $21 \times 2 + 6 \div 3$
14. $30 \div 3 + 12 \times 2$
15. $(52 + 8) \div 6 + 4$
16. $54 \div 3 + 2 - 3$
17. $14 \times 4 - 20 - 8$
18. $(4 + 8 \times 2) \div 4$

Add parentheses to make each equation true.

19. $3 + 10 \times 2 - 8 = 18$
20. $27 - 9 + 4 \times 2 = 1$
21. $3 + 16 - 10 \times 3 = 27$
22. $40 - 4 \times 2 + 6 = 8$
23. $16 - 12 \times 7 + 2 = 36$
24. $60 \div 2 + 8 - 4 = 10$
25. $18 + 6 \div 2 + 6 = 3$
26. $72 \div 4 + 16 \div 2 = 6$

Write the expression that is described. Then evaluate. Use parentheses if necessary.

27. The product of 18 and the difference of 7 and 4.
28. The product of the difference of 12 and 8 and the sum of 5 and 3.
29. The sum of 12 and the product of 5 and 7.
30. The quotient of 210 and the difference of 11 and 5.

Use after Lesson 2.6, page 84

Evaluate the expression in two ways. Show all work.

1. $3(10 + 4)$
2. $5(4 + 12)$
3. $9(7 + 4)$
4. $8(7 + 12)$
5. $12(4 + 10)$
6. $6(11 + 6)$
7. $7(8 + 10)$
8. $14(2 + 3)$
9. $4(12 + 11)$

Use mental math to evaluate.

10. 16×9
11. 7×42
12. 12×93
13. 8×22
14. 53×6
15. 4×64
16. 5×23
17. 42×4
18. 7×61

Use the Distributive Property to rewrite the expression. Then evaluate.

19. $4 \times 3 + 7 \times 3$
20. $8 \times 15 + 8 \times 5$
21. $6 \times 21 + 6 \times 9$
22. $7 \times 14 + 7 \times 16$
23. $27 \times 4 + 13 \times 4$
24. $75 \times 9 + 25 \times 9$
25. $5 \times 12 + 5 \times 10$
26. $12 \times 2 + 9 \times 2$
27. $50 \times 8 + 20 \times 8$
28. $3 \times 10 + 3 \times 5$
29. $14 \times 3 + 16 \times 3$
30. $42 \times 4 + 8 \times 4$

Use after Lesson 2.7, page 90

Write the number in base ten.

1. 342_5 2. 321_5 3. 1011_2
4. 10110_2 5. 402_5 6. 110011_2
7. 235_5 8. 110101_2 9. 1324_5

Write the number in the given base.

10. 473, base 5   11. 97, base 2   12. 46, base 2
13. 79, base 2   14. 254, base 5   15. 125, base 2
16. 389, base 5   17. 983, base 5   18. 512, base 5

Use after Lesson 3.1, page 104

Complete the statement.

1. 45 ones = ? tenths   2. 10 hundredths = ? tenths
3. 45 tenths = ? hundredths   4. 764 hundredths = ? ones
5. 65 ones = ? hundredths   6. 690 tenths = ? ones
7. 45 tenths = ? thousandths   8. 760 thousandths = ? hundredths

Solve the equation using mental math. Then write the answer in words.

9. $0.765 \times m = 76.5$ 10. $8.843 \times j = 0.008843$ 11. $47.5 \times k = 4.75$
12. $0.978 \times w = 978$ 13. $973 \times p = 9.73$ 14. $1.23 \times y = 1230$

Write the number in expanded notation.

15. 57.03   16. 9001.405   17. 307.022
18. 304.32   19. 298.1   20. 7000.07

Use after Lesson 3.2, page 108

Complete the statement.

1. 1 m = 10 ?   2. 1 m = 100 ?   3. 1 m = 1000 ?
4. 1 dkm = ? m   5. 1 hm = ? m   6. 1 km = ? m
7. 7 m = ? mm   8. 740 cm = 7.4 ?   9. ? m = 34 km
10. ? km = 4792 cm   11. 945 ? = 9450 mm   12. 0.54 ? = 54 cm
13. ? mm = 43 km   14. 27.44 m = ? cm   15. ? cm = 92 mm
16. 345 m = ? km   17. 7 mm = 0.007 ?   18. 9.1 ? = 910 cm

Use after Lesson 3.3, page 116

Sketch a number-line model to show the following.

1. 0.3   **2.** 0.5   **3.** 1.4

4. 2.1   **5.** 0.15   **6.** 1.62

Sketch a set model to show the following.

7. 0.4   **8.** 0.8   **9.** 0.2

10. 0.25   **11.** 0.63   **12.** 0.12

Sketch an area model to show the following.

13. 0.2   **14.** 0.35   **15.** 2.72

16. 1.3   **17.** 0.43   **18.** 1.75

Use after Lesson 3.4, page 120

Rewrite as a fraction and a percent.

1. 0.23   **2.** 0.25   **3.** 0.8   **4.** 1.4

5. 0.605   **6.** 4.75   **7.** 1.125   **8.** 9.3

Rewrite as a decimal and a fraction.

9. 30%   **10.** 92%   **11.** 65.3%   **12.** 21.44%

13. 1.0%   **14.** 250%   **15.** 6.8%   **16.** 380.2%

Rewrite as a decimal and a percent.

17. $\frac{33}{100}$ **18.** $\frac{7}{10}$ **19.** $\frac{2}{100}$ **20.** $\frac{231}{1000}$

21. $\frac{851}{100}$ **22.** $\frac{16}{10}$ **23.** $\frac{3}{50}$ **24.** $\frac{31}{25}$

25. $\frac{32}{50}$ **26.** $\frac{20}{25}$ **27.** $\frac{52}{10}$ **28.** $\frac{4}{500}$

Use after Lesson 3.5, page 125

Order the numbers from least to greatest.

1. 1.24, 1.04, 1.2, 1.4, 1.52, 1.71   **2.** 0.23, 0.231, 0.209, 0.229, 0.210, 0.22

3. 2.32, 3.01, 3.90, 2.15, 2.99, 2.89   **4.** 4.01, 4.1, 4.7, 4.25, 4.8, 4.81

5. 0.325, 1.005, 1.5, 3.25, 0.35, 1.53   **6.** 3.14, 3.65, 3.1, 3.7, 3.25, 3.05

7. Name the numbers represented by letters on the number line.

Use after Lesson 3.6, page 130

Round to the given place value.

1. 734 (tens)
2. 963 (hundreds)
3. 546 (tens)
4. 10,481 (thousands)
5. 11,999 (ten thousands)
6. 15,797 (thousands)
7. 101,946 (hundreds)
8. 423,686 (hundred thousands)
9. 436,943 (ten thousands)
10. 3.634 (tenths)
11. 2.934 (ones)
12. 0.7235 (hundredths)
13. 9.99 (tenths)
14. 4.425 (hundredths)
15. 1.2543 (thousandths)
16. 3.38 (ones)
17. 4.9999 (thousandths)
18. 7.091 (tenths)
19. 38.632 (tens)
20. 5.832 (hundredths)
21. 6.929 (tenths)
22. How many digits to the right of the decimal point are needed to round to tenths? Hundredths? Thousandths?

Use after Lesson 3.7, page 136

Fill in the missing value. State whether it is the base or the exponent.

1. $3^{\boxed{?}} = 9$
2. $\boxed{?}^3 = 64$
3. $2^{\boxed{?}} = 64$
4. $\boxed{?}^3 = 125$
5. $3^{\boxed{?}} = 81$
6. $\boxed{?}^2 = 144$

Evaluate the power.

7. 5^2
8. 3^3
9. 2^4
10. 10^3
11. 10^5
12. 7^2
13. $\frac{1}{10^2}$
14. $\frac{1}{10^4}$
15. $\frac{1}{10^6}$

Use a calculator to evaluate the power.

16. 4^5
17. 7^4
18. 2^9

Use after Lesson 3.8, page 140

Find the value of each expression. Use a model if necessary.

1. 30% of 10
2. $\frac{3}{5}$ of 20
3. 0.15 of 100
4. 0.2 of 40
5. 25% of 60
6. $\frac{2}{9}$ of 18
7. $\frac{1}{3}$ of 21
8. 0.75 of 32
9. 80% of 60
10. 70% of 400
11. $\frac{3}{10}$ of 150
12. 0.22 of 200

Choose the expression that is *not* equivalent.

13. $\frac{2}{10}$, 2% , 0.2
14. $\frac{400}{1000}$, 4%, 0.04
15. $\frac{70}{100}$, 70%, 0.07

Use after Lesson 4.1, page 156

Use a vertical form to add.

1. $3.21 + 5.24$
2. $4.43 + 2.35$
3. $0.63 + 5.12$
4. $7.91 + 3.28$
5. $6.34 + 1.48$
6. $2.97 + 9.48$
7. $21.93 + 6.47$
8. $11.54 + 10.09$
9. $15.85 + 7$
10. $43.27 + 10.04$
11. $86.32 + 17.43$
12. $9.87 + 0.31$
13. $32.58 + 1.9$
14. $17.432 + 21.3$
15. $3.9071 + 28.26$
16. $0.008 + 78.4$
17. $19.9 + 0.01$
18. $25.498 + 112.7$

Find the missing digits.

19. $4.\boxed{?}5 + \boxed{?}.62 = 7.4\boxed{?}$
20. $\boxed{?}.54 + 9.\boxed{?}1 = 17.7\boxed{?}$
21. $7.0\boxed{?} + 1.\boxed{?}6 = \boxed{?}.14$
22. $6.\boxed{?}2 + 2.8\boxed{?} = \boxed{?}.4$

Use after Lesson 4.2, page 160

Use a vertical form to subtract.

1. $7.54 - 2.31$
2. $9.68 - 7.46$
3. $14.88 - 9.23$
4. $10.54 - 5.35$
5. $8.05 - 3.61$
6. $4.23 - 0.87$
7. $23.46 - 16.39$
8. $34.54 - 8.72$
9. $43.001 - 19.05$
10. $11.43 - 0.07$
11. $61.04 - 29.27$
12. $5.93 - 1.86$
13. $32.124 - 2.735$
14. $49.5 - 27.23$
15. $31.4 - 8.91$
16. $43.03 - 19.116$
17. $300 - 0.98$
18. $38.1 - 0.54$
19. $29.22 - 9.99$
20. $1.43 - 1.08$
21. $7 - 5.32$
22. $10 - 4.3$
23. $2.17 - 1.19$
24. $3.701 - 2.003$
25. $21.18 - 19$
26. $90.02 - 89.31$
27. $3.22 - 0.065$

Use after Lesson 4.3, page 166

Round each number to the given place value.

1. 3905 (hundreds)
2. 76,756 (thousands)
3. 5398 (tens)
4. 43.325 (ones)
5. 6.734 (hundredths)
6. 3.967 (tenths)

Estimate the sum or difference.

7. $\$7.23 + \$2.65$
8. $\$4.76 + \$9.41$
9. $\$12.40 - \$9.80$
10. $\$8.73 + \$5.21$
11. $\$19.32 - \$7.86$
12. $\$12.90 - \$11.60$
13. $1234 + 3342$
14. $102{,}833 + 411{,}834$
15. $4.32 + 5.51$
16. $12.411 - 8.7$
17. $5{,}793 - 3{,}112$
18. $903 - 239$
19. $16.25 - 12.75$
20. $805 - 650$
21. $7.82 + 3.74$

Use after Lesson 4.4, page 172

Find the product.

1. 1.3×4
2. 9.74×0.6
3. 3×4.33
4. 6.44×3.9
5. 121×4.2
6. 42×2.8
7. 32.1×0.23
8. 5.32×1.2
9. 0.8×0.4
10. 0.3×0.12
11. 3.87×42
12. 0.34×62.7
13. 77.1×0.01
14. 0.04×0.95
15. 0.07×0.04
16. 1.25×0.4
17. 4×6.12
18. 8.12×2.1
19. 61.2×1.5
20. 0.9×3.6
21. 0.16×0.3
22. 0.01×0.02
23. 6.14×21
24. 4.12×0.04

Write a multiplication problem and solve it to answer the question.

25. What is 70% of 452?
26. What is $\frac{9}{10}$ of 84?
27. What is 0.5 of 65?
28. What is 14% of 90?
29. What is $\frac{32}{100}$ of 56?
30. What is 0.35 of 180?
31. What is 6% of 25?
32. What is $\frac{3}{10}$ of 210?
33. What is 0.76 of 322?
34. What is 120% of 44?
35. What is $\frac{17}{1000}$ of 800?
36. What is 0.09 of 404?
37. What is 22% of 72?
38. What is $\frac{74}{100}$ of 38?

Use after Lesson 4.5, page 177

Use a vertical form to solve.

1. $3.87 \div 3$
2. $19.26 \div 6$
3. $10.7 \div 5$
4. $24.8 \div 2$
5. $174.3 \div 3$
6. $170.1 \div 7$
7. $50.4 \div 4$
8. $162.9 \div 9$
9. $18.8 \div 8$
10. $60.9 \div 3$
11. $78.54 \div 7$
12. $3.3 \div 6$
13. $15.7 \div 25$
14. $3.2 \div 50$
15. $0.02 \div 4$
16. $2.7 \div 30$
17. $10.1 \div 250$
18. $2.65 \div 5$
19. $2.45 \div 70$
20. $42.64 \div 52$
21. $76.16 \div 68$
22. $1.1 \div 20$
23. $8.2 \div 40$
24. $6.24 \div 20$
25. $4.55 \div 5$
26. $12 \div 60$
27. $3.2 \div 16$
28. $5.2 \div 2$
29. $14.04 \div 9$
30. $24.3 \div 6$
31. $16.25 \div 5$
32. $9.35 \div 17$
33. $74.4 \div 12$
34. $9.6 \div 3$
35. $7.5 \div 6$
36. $97.68 \div 8$
37. $86.4 \div 72$
38. $31.8 \div 70$
39. $6.97 \div 17$
40. $19.5 \div 3$
41. $64 \div 20$
42. $14.84 \div 7$
43. $1.92 \div 6$
44. $1.36 \div 8$
45. $58.68 \div 9$

Use after Lesson 4.6, page 182

Write the number as a power of 10.

1. 1000
2. 100,000
3. 10,000,000,000
4. 10,000
5. 1,000,000,000,000
6. 100,000,000

Write the expression in decimal form.

7. 10^8
8. 10^2
9. 10^{11}
10. 4×10^6
11. 6.7×10^4
12. 32.3×10^5

Solve the problem.

13. $932 \div 10$
14. 450×1000
15. $60,000 \div 10^3$
16. 43.32×10^4
17. $77,800 \div 100$
18. 1.9×10^8
19. $150,000 \div 10^3$
20. 3.1×10^5
21. $12,000 \div 10^2$
22. 0.003×10^4
23. $1900 \div 100$
24. 27×1000
25. $4200 \div 10^3$
26. 650×10^4
27. $9.83 \div 10^2$

Solve the equation using mental math.

28. $3.727 \times t = 3727$
29. $m \times 1000 = 660,000$
30. $k \div 100 = 0.739$
31. $3200 \div j = 3.2$
32. $w \times 10,000 = 43.71$
33. $712,000 \div a = 7.12$

Use after Lesson 4.7, page 188

Write the smallest power of 10 that you would multiply by to make the number a whole number.

1. 3.44
2. 7.233
3. 18.900
4. 0.023
5. 325.1055
6. 0.433281

Divide.

7. $17.94 \div 2.6$
8. $15.75 \div 2.5$
9. $34.02 \div 6.3$
10. $23.1 \div 5.25$
11. $153.3 \div 9.125$
12. $25.35 \div 7.8$
13. $125.84 \div 5.5$
14. $38.764 \div 2.2$
15. $148.19 \div 10.15$
16. $0.13692 \div 0.021$
17. $0.1368 \div 0.009$
18. $86.472 \div 7.2$
19. $0.04675 \div 0.055$
20. $0.9054 \div 0.9$
21. $2.652 \div 8$
22. $0.0031 \div 0.62$
23. $65.34 \div 6.05$
24. $160.16 \div 6.4$

For each rectangle, find the length.

25. Area: 18.75 sq in., width: 6 in.
26. Area: 38.08 sq ft, width: 4.76 ft
27. Area: 31.2 sq cm, width: 6.5 cm
28. Area: 65.625 sq in., width: 6.25 in.
29. Area: 79.92 sq m, width: 3.6 m
30. Area: 1.875 sq mm, width: 0.75 mm

Use after Lesson 4.8, page 192

Find the number.

1. 45% of 140   **2.** 72% of 200   **3.** 20% of 160

4. 15% of 166   **5.** 65% of 190   **6.** 75% of 125

Find the sale price.

7. 10% off $23.00   **8.** 13% off $30.00   **9.** 30% off $140.00

10. 8% off $50.00   **11.** 12% off $90.00   **12.** 18% off $42.50

13. 25% off $27.80   **14.** 20% off $49.95   **15.** 35% off $55.60

16. 15% off $68.80   **17.** 40% off $165.75   **18.** 30% off $135.80

Use after Lesson 5.1, page 206

Make a line plot of the data. Find the mode and the range of the data.

1. Scores on a 10 point quiz:

    6, 8, 4, 5, 5, 6, 3, 8, 5, 7, 4, 9, 5, 3, 7, 6, 4, 8, 8, 5

2. Ages that teachers in a certain school retired:

    65, 61, 53, 47, 52, 54, 52, 56, 57, 48, 61, 64, 55, 59, 58, 62

3. Ages of people getting married for the first time:

    22, 25, 24, 23, 26, 23, 26, 25, 21, 25, 26, 22, 24, 23, 21, 25, 23, 26, 27, 24

4. Numbers of sunny days in a 3 month period in different cities:

    76, 74, 89, 75, 76, 84, 85, 86, 84, 78, 80, 75, 81, 84, 77, 75, 79, 82, 84

5. Numbers of students attending class each day:

    34, 36, 31, 32, 31, 37, 37, 18, 31, 38, 32, 38, 34, 31, 38, 37, 33, 31, 33, 38, 31

Use after Lesson 5.2, page 212

Organize each set of data with a stem-and-leaf plot. Remember to include a key.

1. 45, 36, 33, 57, 44, 51, 54, 33, 45, 46, 51, 50, 56, 38, 42, 38, 40,
59, 42, 39, 42, 54, 46, 40, 33

2. 7, 23, 54, 34, 54, 23, 38, 17, 27, 16, 52, 43, 29, 6, 32, 27, 26, 33,
39, 15, 47, 46, 32, 19, 28

3. 45, 41, 45, 13, 10, 2, 70, 76, 65, 22, 26, 82, 95, 33, 39, 86,
87, 58, 24, 22, 17, 14, 35, 89, 85, 35, 39, 53, 84, 97, 55, 89,
14, 89, 76

4. 76, 48, 19, 49, 72, 79, 78, 73, 58, 72, 78, 55, 66, 61, 76, 42, 63,
39, 52, 59, 79, 43, 76, 70, 76, 74, 49, 78, 75, 77, 70, 72, 63, 69,
55, 78, 79, 75, 78, 58, 79, 67, 47, 44, 70, 81, 74

5. 30, 30, 30, 30, 29, 29, 27, 28, 31, 33, 16, 20, 26, 32, 21, 21, 21,
21, 21, 18, 27, 27, 27, 26, 26, 27, 22, 23, 24, 23, 24, 24, 22, 22

Use after Lesson 5.3, page 218

Find the mean of the numbers.

1. 24, 23, 28
2. 10, 11, 30
3. 27, 30, 39
4. 6, 7, 7, 12
5. 13, 6, 5, 20
6. 35, 67, 42, 68
7. 21, 25, 23, 19
8. 26, 32, 33, 19
9. 11, 20, 17, 18
10. 7, 2, 7, 32, 7
11. 26, 31, 33, 28, 28
12. 19, 12, 16, 14, 18
13. 8.4, 6.5, 7.6, 7.9
14. 22.15, 19.8, 21.7, 20.35
15. 9.35, 7.87, 8.8, 6.7
16. 9.5, 18, 11.2, 10.9
17. 20.5, 18.3, 13, 15.2
18. 13.5, 14.9, 12.9, 14.7

Use Guess, Check, and Revise to find the missing number so the data has the given mean.

19. Mean: 43; data: 39, 41, 45, [?]
20. Mean: 19; data: 17, 21, 22, [?]
21. Mean: 65; data: 58, 66, 64, [?]
22. Mean: 37; data: 39, 39, 35, [?]

Use after Lesson 5.4, page 222

Find the mean, median and mode of the data. Round to hundredths if necessary. Which, if any, represents the data best? Why?

1. 138, 109, 127, 147, 135, 107, 138, 130, 133, 124, 98, 140, 138, 135
2. 3, 1, 3, 6, 5, 3, 2, 1, 2, 7, 2, 3, 3, 6, 2, 3, 2, 1, 3, 4, 2, 6
3. 88, 88, 78, 83, 77, 193, 88, 79, 78, 77, 79, 80, 80
4. 9836, 9051, 9931, 9723, 9282, 6931, 9375, 9588, 9216
5. 7.0, 7.5, 7.2, 6.7, 7.8, 9.0, 7.4, 8.3, 7.5, 7.8, 8.2, 7.1, 7.9, 7.6
6. 5.4, 5.6, 5.5, 5.7, 5.7, 5.6, 5.5, 5.7, 5.7, 5.8, 5.7, 5.1, 3.5, 5.1, 5.8
7. 27, 29, 30, 34, 28, 22, 31, 38, 43, 32, 36, 34, 49, 58, 64

Use after Lesson 5.5, page 229

Draw a bar graph of the data. Use an appropriate scale.

1. 3, 2, 3, 6, 5, 3
2. $2.25, $3.75, $4.50, $4.95, $3.50, $2.75
3. 21, 42, 57, 50, 35, 19
4. 144, 362, 280, 577, 525, 330, 206

Estimate the number represented by each bar in the graph. Fill in any gaps in the scale.

5.

6.
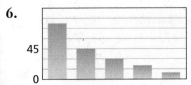

7.
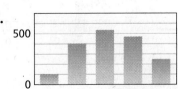

Use after Lesson 5.6, page 234

Make a line graph of the given data.

1. Numbers of rocks in your collection: 1990: 25, 1991: 30, 1992: 40, 1993: 50, 1994: 55, 1995: 60
2. Leon's weekly allowance: 1990: $3.00, 1991: $4.25, 1992: $3.50, 1993: $3.00, 1994: $4.50, 1995: $5.00

Find the missing numbers on both scales. Estimate the values for each year.

3.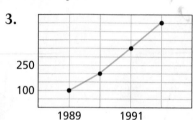

4.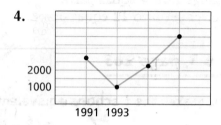

Use after Lesson 5.7, page 240

Draw pictographs for the following data.

1. Cars, 25; bus, 15; plane, 10; train, 5
2. Tulip, 40; petunia, 35; rose, 45; lily, 15

Match the description of the data with the graph that would best represent it.

a. line graph   b. line plot   c. bar graph   d. stem-and-leaf plot

3. Numbers of miles traveled each week by a football team
4. Numbers of "donut holes" sold each week for a year
5. Numbers of students choosing each of the colors red, yellow, blue, green, orange, and purple as their favorite
6. The heights of the students in your math class
7. Make up data for one of the descriptions in Exercises 3–6 and graph them.

Use after Lesson 6.1, page 254

What fraction is shown by the model?

1. 2. 3.

Draw an area model for each fraction.

4. $\dfrac{3}{10}$ 5. $\dfrac{5}{9}$ 6. $\dfrac{9}{13}$

7. $\dfrac{13}{7}$ 8. $1\dfrac{5}{8}$ 9. $1\dfrac{6}{11}$

Use after Lesson 6.2, page 260

Write your answer as a fraction or mixed number.

1. Divide 4 cans of soda into 5 equal parts.
2. Divide 3 pizzas into 8 equal parts.
3. Divide 5 candy bars into 7 equal parts.
4. Divide 6 bags of marbles into 8 equal parts.
5. Divide 8 cups of milk into 3 equal parts.
6. Divide 12 oranges into 8 equal parts.
7. Divide 7 trays of fudge into 4 equal parts.
8. Divide 15 tablets of paper into 12 equal parts.

Use after Lesson 6.3, page 265

Write the number that makes the fractions equivalent.

1. $\dfrac{4}{5} = \dfrac{\boxed{?}}{15}$

2. $\dfrac{6}{7} = \dfrac{\boxed{?}}{42}$

3. $\dfrac{3}{4} = \dfrac{15}{\boxed{?}}$

4. $\dfrac{24}{30} = \dfrac{4}{\boxed{?}}$

5. $\dfrac{\boxed{?}}{8} = \dfrac{45}{72}$

6. $\dfrac{\boxed{?}}{36} = \dfrac{3}{12}$

7. $\dfrac{48}{\boxed{?}} = \dfrac{6}{9}$

8. $\dfrac{5}{11} = \dfrac{25}{\boxed{?}}$

Write three equivalent fractions.

9. $\dfrac{3}{5}$

10. $\dfrac{4}{7}$

11. $\dfrac{2}{9}$

12. $\dfrac{12}{24}$

13. $\dfrac{1}{13}$

14. $\dfrac{18}{63}$

Use after Lesson 6.4, page 272

Simplify the fraction.

1. $\dfrac{10}{15}$

2. $\dfrac{24}{42}$

3. $\dfrac{64}{72}$

4. $\dfrac{26}{54}$

5. $\dfrac{32}{76}$

6. $\dfrac{30}{75}$

7. $\dfrac{25}{15}$

8. $\dfrac{18}{12}$

9. $\dfrac{27}{18}$

Solve the proportion.

10. $\dfrac{18}{45} = \dfrac{6}{\boxed{?}}$

11. $\dfrac{\boxed{?}}{11} = \dfrac{12}{33}$

12. $\dfrac{\boxed{?}}{2} = \dfrac{45}{10}$

13. $\dfrac{24}{56} = \dfrac{\boxed{?}}{112}$

14. $\dfrac{16}{\boxed{?}} = \dfrac{32}{10}$

15. $\dfrac{20}{55} = \dfrac{\boxed{?}}{11}$

Order the fractions from least to greatest.

1. $\frac{3}{5}, \frac{3}{2}, \frac{3}{8}, \frac{3}{4}, \frac{3}{7}$

2. $\frac{5}{10}, \frac{5}{7}, \frac{5}{11}, \frac{5}{19}, \frac{5}{13}$

3. $\frac{5}{6}, \frac{2}{3}, \frac{7}{12}, \frac{2}{5}, \frac{9}{15}$

4. $\frac{17}{15}, \frac{4}{2}, \frac{5}{3}, \frac{8}{6}, \frac{9}{10}$

5. $\frac{6}{5}, \frac{4}{3}, \frac{2}{5}, \frac{4}{7}, \frac{11}{8}$

6. $\frac{15}{4}, \frac{12}{8}, \frac{9}{2}, \frac{27}{8}, \frac{16}{4}$

7. $\frac{4}{7}, \frac{10}{6}, \frac{5}{2}, \frac{12}{21}, \frac{11}{7}$

8. $\frac{7}{11}, \frac{7}{13}, \frac{7}{7}, \frac{7}{20}, \frac{7}{18}$

9. $\frac{6}{15}, \frac{2}{10}, \frac{4}{6}, \frac{5}{2}, \frac{1}{2}$

Find a fraction that is between the two fractions.

10. $\frac{2}{5}, \frac{3}{5}$

11. $\frac{5}{7}, \frac{6}{7}$

12. $\frac{3}{13}, \frac{4}{13}$

13. $\frac{5}{8}, \frac{3}{4}$

14. $\frac{2}{3}, \frac{5}{6}$

15. $\frac{5}{9}, \frac{11}{18}$

Rewrite the improper fraction as a mixed number.

1. $\frac{21}{10}$

2. $\frac{13}{4}$

3. $\frac{16}{9}$

4. $\frac{27}{7}$

5. $\frac{16}{5}$

6. $\frac{35}{8}$

7. $\frac{19}{3}$

8. $\frac{17}{6}$

9. $\frac{51}{12}$

Rewrite the mixed number as an improper fraction.

10. $1\frac{2}{7}$

11. $1\frac{7}{15}$

12. $2\frac{3}{5}$

13. $3\frac{1}{8}$

14. $2\frac{9}{20}$

15. $1\frac{7}{30}$

16. $4\frac{2}{9}$

17. $9\frac{1}{2}$

18. $3\frac{5}{6}$

You have a bag containing 3 blue, 6 yellow, 9 green, 4 red, and 2 orange marbles. You pick one marble without looking. Find each probability.

1. You pick an orange marble.
2. You pick a red marble.
3. You pick a purple marble.
4. You pick a yellow or an orange marble.
5. You pick a green or a red marble.
6. You don't pick a yellow marble.

You pick a number at random from a hat that contains the numbers 1 through 10. Find the probability.

7. You pick the number 5.
8. You pick a number greater than 7.
9. You pick an even number.
10. You pick a number between 2 and 8.
11. You pick a multiple of 3.
12. You pick a number less than 9.

Use after Lesson 7.1, page 302

Write each measurement in feet and inches.

1. 39″

2. 54″

3. 98″

4. $1\frac{1}{2}$ feet

5. $\frac{1}{2}$ yard

6. $2\frac{1}{3}$ feet

7. $13\frac{1}{3}$ yards

8. $12\frac{1}{6}$ feet

9. $2\frac{1}{4}$ yards

Complete the statement.

10. 12 inches = $\boxed{?}$ feet

11. 2 feet = $\boxed{?}$ inches

12. 1 yard = $\boxed{?}$ inches

13. 9 feet = $\boxed{?}$ yards

14. $\boxed{?}$ yard = 12 inches

15. 4 yards = $\boxed{?}$ feet

16. 30 inches = $\boxed{?}$ feet

17. 2 yards = 72 $\boxed{?}$

18. $3\frac{1}{2}$ $\boxed{?}$ = 42 inches

Write each of the following in inches.

19. $2\frac{2}{3}$ feet

20. $3\frac{1}{2}$ yards

21. $4\frac{1}{4}$ feet

22. $1\frac{2}{9}$ yards

23. $2\frac{5}{6}$ feet

24. $7\frac{5}{12}$ yards

25. $20\frac{1}{4}$ yards

26. $92\frac{3}{4}$ feet

27. $15\frac{5}{6}$ yards

Use after Lesson 7.2, page 306

Find the least common multiple of the numbers.

1. 2, 5

2. 3, 8

3. 4, 6

4. 3, 7

5. 6, 9

6. 12, 18

7. 4, 12

8. 10, 8

9. 9, 12

10. 2, 3, 5

11. 4, 6, 8

12. 2, 7, 14

Rewrite the fractions using the least common denominator.

13. $\frac{1}{2}, \frac{2}{3}$

14. $\frac{1}{5}, \frac{1}{8}$

15. $\frac{1}{12}, \frac{1}{8}$

16. $\frac{1}{9}, \frac{1}{6}$

17. $\frac{3}{4}, \frac{1}{6}$

18. $\frac{2}{5}, \frac{2}{7}$

19. $\frac{5}{12}, \frac{1}{4}$

20. $\frac{9}{11}, \frac{1}{2}$

21. $\frac{3}{8}, \frac{1}{3}$

22. $\frac{9}{4}, \frac{1}{4}$

23. $\frac{5}{7}, \frac{1}{5}$

24. $\frac{4}{15}, \frac{2}{5}$

Which fraction is not equivalent?

25. $\frac{2}{7}, \frac{8}{35}, \frac{6}{21}$

26. $\frac{10}{25}, \frac{3}{5}, \frac{8}{20}$

27. $\frac{49}{56}, \frac{14}{16}, \frac{5}{8}$

28. $\frac{4}{8}, \frac{25}{40}, \frac{10}{16}$

29. $\frac{21}{24}, \frac{35}{40}, \frac{26}{32}$

30. $\frac{11}{34}, \frac{13}{39}, \frac{14}{42}$

Use after Lesson 7.3, page 314

Add the fractions. Simplify, if possible.

1. $\frac{5}{8} + \frac{1}{8}$

2. $\frac{1}{5} + \frac{3}{5}$

3. $\frac{3}{4} + \frac{3}{4}$

4. $\frac{7}{9} + \frac{5}{9}$

5. $\frac{3}{10} + \frac{7}{10}$

6. $\frac{8}{15} + \frac{4}{15}$

7. $\frac{5}{6} + \frac{5}{12}$

8. $\frac{3}{8} + \frac{1}{4}$

9. $\frac{2}{3} + \frac{13}{18}$

10. $\frac{2}{5} + \frac{3}{4}$

11. $\frac{1}{2} + \frac{5}{7}$

12. $\frac{3}{8} + \frac{1}{12}$

Subtract the fractions. Simplify, if possible.

13. $\frac{5}{7} - \frac{2}{7}$

14. $\frac{5}{9} - \frac{1}{9}$

15. $\frac{15}{19} - \frac{7}{19}$

16. $\frac{3}{4} - \frac{1}{2}$

17. $\frac{17}{24} - \frac{5}{24}$

18. $\frac{7}{12} - \frac{5}{12}$

19. $\frac{1}{3} - \frac{2}{9}$

20. $\frac{17}{20} - \frac{3}{10}$

21. $\frac{7}{8} - \frac{2}{3}$

22. $\frac{9}{10} - \frac{4}{15}$

23. $\frac{1}{2} - \frac{4}{9}$

24. $\frac{7}{12} - \frac{7}{18}$

Use after Lesson 7.4, page 320

Add the mixed numbers. Simplify, if possible.

1. $2\frac{2}{9} + 5\frac{5}{9}$

2. $7\frac{3}{11} + 4\frac{6}{11}$

3. $3\frac{4}{7} + 1\frac{6}{7}$

4. $6\frac{7}{12} + 5\frac{5}{12}$

5. $2\frac{3}{5} + 1\frac{4}{5}$

6. $4\frac{9}{13} + \frac{7}{13}$

7. $7\frac{1}{4} + 2\frac{3}{8}$

8. $12\frac{1}{2} + 5\frac{3}{8}$

9. $2\frac{4}{15} + 3\frac{7}{12}$

10. $1\frac{18}{27} + 7\frac{7}{9}$

11. $6\frac{7}{8} + 6\frac{5}{12}$

12. $9\frac{1}{32} + 3\frac{3}{4}$

Subtract the mixed numbers. Simplify, if possible.

13. $4\frac{9}{17} - 1\frac{5}{17}$

14. $8\frac{9}{10} - 3\frac{3}{10}$

15. $2\frac{7}{11} - 1\frac{4}{11}$

16. $6\frac{5}{7} - \frac{3}{7}$

17. $13\frac{7}{12} - 2\frac{1}{6}$

18. $10\frac{3}{5} - 4\frac{1}{10}$

19. $14\frac{5}{9} - 11\frac{1}{3}$

20. $5\frac{17}{26} - \frac{7}{13}$

21. $4\frac{1}{2} - 1\frac{11}{23}$

22. $7\frac{1}{2} - 3\frac{2}{9}$

23. $3\frac{9}{10} - \frac{3}{8}$

24. $11\frac{5}{6} - 5\frac{3}{4}$

Change each improper fraction to a mixed number, and each mixed number to an improper fraction.

25. $\frac{17}{5}$

26. $\frac{47}{9}$

27. $6\frac{5}{12}$

28. $20\frac{1}{8}$

Use after Lesson 7.5, page 328

Complete the statement using regrouping.

1. $6 = 5\frac{?}{10}$
2. $11 = 10\frac{?}{12}$
3. $7 = 6\frac{?}{5}$
4. $3\frac{1}{13} = 2\frac{?}{13}$
5. $1\frac{5}{8} = \frac{?}{8}$
6. $15\frac{5}{21} = 14\frac{?}{21}$

Complete the statement using >, <, or =.

7. $4\frac{1}{4}\ \boxed{?}\ 3\frac{4}{4}$
8. $2\frac{5}{17}\ \boxed{?}\ 1\frac{20}{17}$
9. $1\frac{1}{9}\ \boxed{?}\ \frac{11}{9}$
10. $5\frac{23}{20}\ \boxed{?}\ 6\frac{3}{20}$
11. $6\frac{19}{18}\ \boxed{?}\ 7\frac{5}{18}$
12. $10\frac{9}{11}\ \boxed{?}\ 9\frac{19}{11}$

Subtract. Simplify, if possible.

13. $15 - 3\frac{1}{5}$
14. $4 - \frac{7}{9}$
15. $8 - 7\frac{3}{4}$
16. $5\frac{2}{7} - 1\frac{4}{7}$
17. $11\frac{7}{12} - 10\frac{11}{12}$
18. $21\frac{1}{6} - 15\frac{5}{6}$
19. $12\frac{4}{21} - 9\frac{8}{21}$
20. $30 - 6\frac{2}{15}$
21. $17\frac{1}{8} - 6\frac{5}{8}$
22. $2\frac{1}{4} - \frac{3}{4}$
23. $15\frac{1}{11} - 2\frac{9}{11}$
24. $3\frac{5}{32} - 1\frac{27}{32}$
25. $14\frac{4}{15} - 7\frac{11}{15}$
26. $6\frac{2}{9} - 5\frac{8}{9}$
27. $16 - 3\frac{11}{40}$

Use after Lesson 7.6, page 334

Complete the statement using regrouping.

1. $6\frac{1}{3} = 5\frac{?}{15}$
2. $4\frac{2}{4} = 3\frac{3}{?}$
3. $2\frac{1}{?} = 1\frac{8}{7}$
4. $3\frac{?}{8} = 2\frac{22}{16}$
5. $7\frac{2}{5} = 6\frac{?}{25}$
6. $10\frac{1}{2} = 9\frac{?}{24}$

Label each problem "n" if it needs renaming, "g" if it needs regrouping, or "b" if it needs both. Then subtract and simplify.

7. $4\frac{4}{9} - 1\frac{1}{18}$
8. $13\frac{4}{11} - 5\frac{6}{11}$
9. $8\frac{3}{14} - 2\frac{1}{6}$
10. $9\frac{1}{4} - 3\frac{1}{3}$
11. $11\frac{3}{5} - \frac{5}{12}$
12. $16\frac{7}{13} - 15\frac{11}{13}$
13. $7\frac{1}{8} - 4\frac{3}{8}$
14. $20\frac{1}{5} - 10\frac{3}{7}$
15. $3\frac{2}{7} - \frac{4}{9}$
16. $19\frac{7}{16} - 5\frac{1}{4}$
17. $12 - \frac{5}{17}$
18. $13\frac{1}{2} - \frac{11}{2}$
19. $1\frac{1}{7} - \frac{1}{3}$
20. $6\frac{7}{15} - 2\frac{13}{15}$
21. $4\frac{1}{5} - 2\frac{3}{5}$
22. $14\frac{7}{9} - 2\frac{11}{21}$
23. $5\frac{2}{11} - 3\frac{1}{5}$
24. $16\frac{3}{10} - \frac{7}{10}$

Use after Lesson 7.7, page 338

Rainfall amounts for 6 months were recorded in your city. The results were: January: $\frac{3}{4}''$, February: $1\frac{3}{4}''$, March: $2''$, April: $2\frac{3}{5}''$, May: $4\frac{1}{2}''$, June: $3\frac{7}{8}''$.

1. How much more rain fell in the month with the most rainfall than in the month with the least rainfall?
2. What was the total rainfall in the six month period?
3. During the first 5 months, the amount increased each month. Write and solve subtraction problems to find:
   a. How much more rain fell in February than in January.
   b. How much more rain fell in March than in February.
   c. How much more rain fell in April than in March.
   d. How much more rain fell in May than in April.

Use after Lesson 8.1, page 352

Find the product. Simplify, if possible.

1. $9 \times \frac{2}{3}$ 2. $\frac{3}{5} \times 35$ 3. $4 \times \frac{1}{8}$

4. $\frac{4}{9} \times 12$ 5. $15 \times \frac{2}{7}$ 6. $\frac{5}{11} \times 6$

7. $5 \times \frac{7}{15}$ 8. $\frac{11}{12} \times 8$ 9. $7 \times \frac{3}{10}$

10. $\frac{5}{18} \times 4$ 11. $10 \times \frac{7}{25}$ 12. $\frac{2}{17} \times 17$

13. $16 \times \frac{5}{8}$ 14. $\frac{5}{12} \times 20$ 15. $21 \times \frac{4}{7}$

16. $\frac{49}{100} \times 5$ 17. $3 \times \frac{7}{12}$ 18. $\frac{13}{25} \times 5$

Use after Lesson 8.2, page 358

Find the product. Simplify, if possible.

1. $\frac{1}{2} \times \frac{3}{8}$ 2. $\frac{5}{6} \times \frac{3}{4}$ 3. $\frac{1}{5} \times \frac{1}{3}$

4. $\frac{4}{9} \times \frac{1}{6}$ 5. $\frac{9}{10} \times \frac{3}{10}$ 6. $\frac{2}{7} \times \frac{1}{2} \times \frac{3}{4}$

7. $\frac{1}{3} \times \frac{3}{14}$ 8. $\frac{3}{7} \times \frac{1}{2} \times \frac{2}{3}$ 9. $\frac{5}{8} \times \frac{4}{5}$

10. $\frac{1}{4} \times \frac{11}{12}$ 11. $\frac{10}{11} \times \frac{17}{100}$ 12. $\frac{2}{9} \times \frac{1}{10}$

13. $\frac{2}{3} \times \frac{7}{8}$ 14. $\frac{2}{3} \times \frac{4}{5} \times \frac{1}{6}$ 15. $\frac{2}{17} \times \frac{1}{3}$

16. $\frac{4}{5} \times \frac{5}{7}$ 17. $\frac{10}{21} \times \frac{2}{5}$ 18. $\frac{5}{6} \times \frac{1}{6} \times \frac{1}{2}$

Use after Lesson 8.3, page 366

Write the answer in hours, then write it in hours and minutes.

1. What is $\frac{3}{4}$ of 5 hours?

2. What is $3\frac{1}{3}$ of 6 hours?

3. What is $1\frac{2}{3}$ of 8 hours?

4. What is $\frac{3}{8}$ of $4\frac{2}{3}$ hours?

Multiply. Simplify, if possible.

5. $\frac{1}{2} \times 2\frac{3}{5}$

6. $1\frac{2}{9} \times \frac{5}{6}$

7. $4 \times 7\frac{1}{2}$

8. $2\frac{1}{8} \times 1\frac{4}{9}$

9. $6\frac{3}{7} \times \frac{1}{8}$

10. $3\frac{1}{4} \times \frac{3}{10}$

11. $8\frac{1}{5} \times 10$

12. $9\frac{1}{2} \times \frac{1}{3}$

13. $2\frac{3}{8} \times \frac{2}{3}$

14. $\frac{7}{11} \times 4\frac{3}{4}$

15. $5\frac{3}{4} \times \frac{3}{4}$

16. $11 \times 1\frac{1}{3}$

Find the area of the rectangle.

17. 6 in. by $2\frac{1}{8}$ in.

18. $4\frac{1}{2}$ ft by $1\frac{1}{6}$ ft

19. $2\frac{1}{2}$ yd by $3\frac{1}{4}$ yd

20. $1\frac{3}{4}$ mi by $\frac{3}{10}$ mi

Use after Lesson 8.4, page 372

Complete the statement.

1. $\frac{16}{5} \div \boxed{?} = \frac{16}{2}$

2. $\frac{4}{5} \div \frac{2}{5} = \boxed{?}$

3. $\boxed{?} \div \frac{12}{8} = \frac{21}{12}$

4. $\boxed{?} \div \frac{3}{7} = \frac{21}{3}$

5. $\frac{14}{6} \div \boxed{?} = \frac{14}{4}$

6. $\boxed{?} \div \frac{7}{10} = \frac{18}{7}$

Find the quotient. Simplify, if possible.

7. $3\frac{4}{9} \div 2\frac{1}{9}$

8. $\frac{6}{8} \div \frac{1}{8}$

9. $\frac{4}{5} \div 1\frac{1}{5}$

10. $6\frac{2}{7} \div \frac{5}{7}$

11. $\frac{9}{10} \div 2\frac{1}{10}$

12. $3 \div \frac{1}{2}$

13. $1\frac{2}{3} \div \frac{2}{3}$

14. $4\frac{5}{9} \div 2\frac{2}{9}$

15. $10\frac{4}{7} \div 5\frac{2}{7}$

16. $2\frac{3}{4} \div \frac{3}{8}$

17. $\frac{8}{11} \div 1\frac{1}{11}$

18. $2\frac{1}{2} \div \frac{5}{12}$

Solve using mental math.

19. $\frac{14}{9} \div m = 7$

20. $b \div \frac{2}{3} = 6$

21. $d \div \frac{7}{10} = \frac{8}{7}$

22. $p \div \frac{12}{5} = \frac{1}{2}$

23. $\frac{14}{3} \div x = 13$

24. $4\frac{4}{5} \div s = 4$

Use after Lesson 8.5, page 377

Find the reciprocal of the number.

1. $\frac{3}{7}$

2. $\frac{11}{12}$

3. $\frac{15}{31}$

4. $\frac{9}{71}$

5. 4

6. $\frac{1}{6}$

7. 163

8. $\frac{1}{11}$

9. $\frac{2}{5}$

10. $\frac{24}{179}$

11. $\frac{5}{9}$

12. $\frac{5}{98}$

Find the quotient. Simplify, if possible.

13. $\frac{1}{8} \div \frac{1}{4}$

14. $\frac{3}{5} \div \frac{2}{7}$

15. $\frac{9}{10} \div \frac{1}{2}$

16. $\frac{2}{9} \div \frac{5}{7}$

17. $\frac{3}{8} \div 4$

18. $\frac{7}{8} \div \frac{2}{3}$

19. $\frac{2}{5} \div \frac{1}{2}$

20. $\frac{3}{4} \div \frac{5}{8}$

21. $\frac{1}{4} \div \frac{5}{6}$

22. $9 \div \frac{1}{3}$

23. $\frac{1}{2} \div \frac{14}{21}$

24. $\frac{1}{5} \div \frac{1}{15}$

25. $\frac{9}{14} \div \frac{3}{7}$

26. $\frac{1}{8} \div \frac{1}{6}$

27. $\frac{2}{5} \div \frac{4}{5}$

28. $\frac{12}{13} \div 2$

29. $\frac{3}{8} \div \frac{9}{10}$

30. $\frac{5}{7} \div \frac{3}{4}$

Use after Lesson 8.6, page 382

Find the quotient. Simplify, if possible.

1. $1\frac{4}{7} \div 2\frac{2}{3}$

2. $3\frac{1}{2} \div 5\frac{4}{5}$

3. $2\frac{6}{9} \div 4$

4. $5\frac{1}{2} \div 2\frac{1}{3}$

5. $1\frac{2}{5} \div \frac{3}{4}$

6. $2\frac{6}{7} \div \frac{1}{7}$

7. $9 \div 4\frac{1}{4}$

8. $2\frac{5}{9} \div 2$

9. $8 \div 1\frac{1}{3}$

10. $1\frac{2}{9} \div 3$

11. $\frac{7}{10} \div 1\frac{3}{7}$

12. $\frac{4}{5} \div 1\frac{1}{5}$

13. $\frac{1}{9} \div 2\frac{1}{3}$

14. $2\frac{3}{8} \div 5$

15. $8\frac{1}{2} \div \frac{3}{2}$

16. How many $5\frac{1}{4}''$ pieces can you cut from a board that is 42″ long? From a board that is 63″ long?

17. How many $1\frac{1}{2}''$ slices can you cut from a nutbread that is 6″ long? From a nutbread that is 9″ long?

18. You are making tablecloths for picnic tables by cutting a $32\frac{1}{2}$ foot strip of cloth into $6\frac{1}{8}$ foot pieces. How many tables can you cover completely?

19. How many times will you have to fill a $\frac{2}{3}$ cup measure with milk to make a recipe that calls for $5\frac{1}{3}$ cups of milk?

MORE PRACTICE

Use after Lesson 8.7, page 388

The base and height of a right triangle are given. Find the area.

1. Base: 4 in.

   Height: $2\frac{1}{8}$ in.

2. Base: $3\frac{1}{6}$ cm

   Height: 2 cm

3. Base: $7\frac{2}{5}$ m

   Height: $\frac{2}{5}$ m

4. Base: $5\frac{1}{2}$ ft

   Height: $7\frac{1}{2}$ ft

5. Base: $\frac{1}{3}$ mi

   Height: $8\frac{1}{3}$ mi

6. Base: $2\frac{1}{6}$ yards

   Height: 6 yards

7. Base: 4 in.

   Height: $2\frac{1}{5}$ in.

8. Base: $2\frac{1}{5}$ km

   Height: $\frac{1}{5}$ km

9. Base: $6\frac{1}{3}$ ft

   Height: 4 ft

The figure is made of right triangles. Find the area of the figure.

10.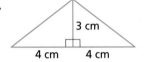

11.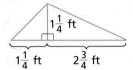

12.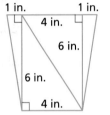

Use after Lesson 9.1, page 400

Sketch the described figure on grid paper by connecting the points. Name the figure and estimate its perimeter.

1. Start at *A*. Move left 2 and down 1 to *B*. Move right 3 and down 1 to *C*. Move up 2 and left 2 back to *A*.
2. Start at *P*. Move right 2 to *Q*. Move down 2 to *R*. Move up one and left 2 to *S*. Move right one to *T*. Move up 1 and left 1 back to *P*.
3. Start at *D*. Move up 2 and right 3 to *E*. Move right 1 and up 5 to *F*. Move left 4 and down 3 to *G*. Move up 3 and left 4 to *H*. Move down 5 and right 2 to *I*. Move left 1 and down 1 to *J*. Move down 1 and right 3 back to *D*.
4. Start at *K*. Move up 2 and right 2 to *L*. Move up 1 and right 3 to *M*. Move down 3 and right 1 to *N*. Move down 3 and left 2 to *O*. Move left 4 and up 3 back to *K*.
5. Start at *W*. Move left 1 and down 3 to *X*. Move up 10 and right 6 to *Y*. Move left 8 and down 4 to *Z*. Move right 3 and down 3 back to *W*.

Use after Lesson 9.2, page 406

Write the name of each angle. State whether it is acute, right, or obtuse. Then use a protractor to measure the angle.

1.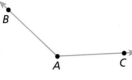

2.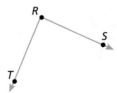

3.

4.

5.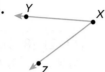

6.

Use after Lesson 9.3, page 412

Use the figure at the right. All right triangles in the figure have angles of 30° and 60°.

1. Name all congruent polygons.
2. Name all similar (but not congruent) polygons.
3. Fill in the missing measures *a*, *b*, *c*, and *d*.

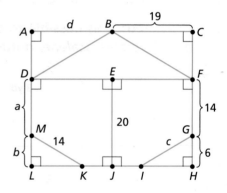

Use after Lesson 9.4, page 418

Decide if each figure has line symmetry. If so, trace the figure and sketch the line or lines of symmetry.

1.

2.

3.

4.

5.

6.

Use after Lesson 9.5, page 426

Plot the points in a coordinate plane. Connect the points to form a polygon. Name the polygon.

1. $A(4, 9)$, $B(7, 9)$, $C(8, 6)$, $D(5, 3)$, $E(2, 7)$
2. $F(3, 9)$, $G(6, 12)$, $H(6, 8)$, $I(10, 5)$, $J(5, 2)$, $K(5, 6)$, $L(2, 7)$
3. $M(0, 1)$, $N(2, 2)$, $O(2, 5)$, $P(6, 5)$, $Q(6, 2)$, $R(2, 0)$

Plot both sets of points in a coordinate plane. Connect the points to form triangles. If the second triangle is a slide of the first triangle, describe the slide.

4. Triangle 1: $(1, 4)$, $(3, 8)$, $(5, 4)$; Triangle 2: $(8, 11)$, $(6, 7)$, $(10, 7)$
5. Triangle 1: $(8, 7)$, $(5, 4)$, $(2, 7)$; Triangle 2: $(11, 2)$, $(8, 5)$, $(14, 5)$
6. Triangle 1: $(8, 1)$, $(6, 3)$, $(9, 6)$; Triangle 2: $(5, 9)$, $(5, 5)$, $(1, 6)$

Use after Lesson 9.6, page 430

Use as many words as possible to describe the triangle:
equilateral, isosceles, scalene, obtuse, right, or *acute.*

1.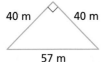
40 m, 40 m, 57 m

2.
3 yd, 3 yd, 3 yd

3.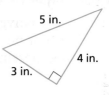
5 in., 4 in., 3 in.

4.
7 ft, 2 ft, 6 ft

5.
31 mm, 19 mm, 19 mm

6.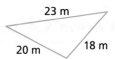
23 m, 20 m, 18 m

Use after Lesson 9.7, page 436

Decide whether a triangle could have the given angle measures.

1. $45°$, $66°$, $69°$
2. $52°$, $43°$, $87°$
3. $37°$, $15°$, $128°$
4. $108°$, $10°$, $12°$
5. $112°$, $57°$, $10°$
6. $8°$, $168°$, $4°$

Two angles of a triangle are given. Find the missing angle measure.

7. $62°$, $10°$, $\boxed{?}$
8. $22°$, $49°$, $\boxed{?}$
9. $145°$, $20°$, $\boxed{?}$
10. $19°$, $77°$, $\boxed{?}$
11. $31°$, $92°$, $\boxed{?}$
12. $50°$, $120°$, $\boxed{?}$

Use after Lesson 10.1, page 452

Use the figure at the right. Describe each pair of lines
as parallel, perpendicular, or intersecting.

1. $\overleftrightarrow{AB}$ and $\overleftrightarrow{BE}$
2. $\overleftrightarrow{CF}$ and $\overleftrightarrow{DE}$
3. $\overleftrightarrow{AD}$ and $\overleftrightarrow{BC}$
4. $\overleftrightarrow{AB}$ and $\overleftrightarrow{CF}$
5. $\overleftrightarrow{CF}$ and $\overleftrightarrow{AD}$
6. $\overleftrightarrow{AC}$ and $\overleftrightarrow{DF}$
7. $\overleftrightarrow{BE}$ and $\overleftrightarrow{AD}$
8. $\overleftrightarrow{DF}$ and $\overleftrightarrow{BE}$

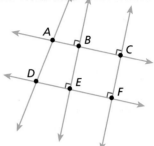

Use after Lesson 10.2, page 456

Find the measure of the angle that is complementary to the
given angle. Then use a protractor to draw each of the angles.

1. $43°$
2. $12°$
3. $79°$
4. $66°$
5. $9°$
6. $38°$

Find the measure of the angle that is supplementary to the
given angle. Then use a protractor to draw each of the angles.

7. $58°$
8. $117°$
9. $5°$
10. $170°$
11. $83°$
12. $31°$

Use after Lesson 10.3, page 464

One angle measure of a parallelogram is given. Determine the
measures of the other 3 angles.

1. $105°$
2. $36°$
3. $47°$
4. $71°$
5. $150°$
6. $95°$

Name the figure in as many ways as you can using the words
polygon, quadrilateral, parallelogram, rectangle, and *square.*

7.

8.

9.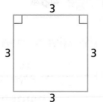

10.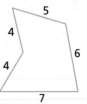

11.

12.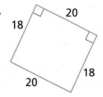

13.

14.

Use after Lesson 10.4, page 470

You are given the base and height of a triangle. Find the area.

1. Base: 15 cm
Height: 6 cm

2. Base: 4 m
Height: 9 m

3. Base: 24 mm
Height: 30 mm

4. Base: 7 in.
Height: 14 in.

5. Base: 30 ft
Height: 21 ft

6. Base: 7 yd
Height: 9 yd

Find the value of x.

7.

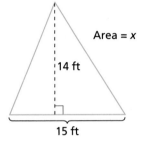

Area = x

14 ft

15 ft

8.

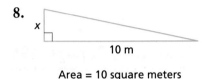

x

10 m

Area = 10 square meters

Use after Lesson 10.5, page 478

Find the circumference of a circle with the given diameter.

1. Diameter is 13 m.

2. Diameter is 8 yd.

3. Diameter is 7 in.

4. Diameter is 21 cm.

5. Diameter is 12 mi.

6. Diameter is 16 ft.

7. Diameter is 40 in.

8. Diameter is 66 mm.

9. Diameter is 38 cm.

10. Diameter is 90 mi.

11. Diameter is 28 ft.

12. Diameter is 10 m.

Find the diameter of a circle with the given circumference.

13. Circumference is 157 mm.

14. Circumference is 288.88 ft.

15. Circumference is 125.6 m.

16. Circumference is 28.26 yd.

Use after Lesson 10.6, page 484

Find the area of a circle with the given measurement.

1. Radius is 13 ft.

2. Diameter is 20 cm.

3. Radius is 15 mm.

4. Diameter is 5 mi.

5. Radius is 8 m.

6. Diameter is 10 ft.

7. Radius is 1 km.

8. Diameter is 100 yd.

9. Radius is 7 cm.

10. Diameter is 80 in.

11. Radius is 35 ft.

12. Diameter is 64 mi.

Find the radius of a circle with the given measurement.

13. Diameter is 12 in.

14. Diameter is 8 m.

15. Diameter is 108 cm.

16. Diameter is 24 ft.

Use after Lesson 10.7, page 488

Seventy-two people were asked to name their favorite color; 22 said blue, 16 said green, 11 said purple, 10 said yellow, and 8 said orange.

1. How many people named other colors?
2. What fraction of the people surveyed named each color or "other"?
3. If you drew a circle graph, how many degrees should each section have?

Fifty people were asked what they drink with dinner; $\frac{3}{10}$ said juice, $\frac{2}{5}$ said milk, $\frac{1}{5}$ said soda, and $\frac{1}{10}$ said water.

4. How many people named other beverages?
5. How many people named each kind of drink?
6. If you drew a circle graph, how many degrees should each section have?

Use after Lesson 10.8, page 492

The figure below represents a gameboard. Each grid mark is 1 foot. You toss a beanbag onto the gameboard. Find the probability that it lands on:

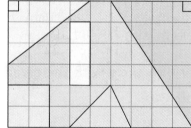

1. The large right triangle
2. The small right triangle
3. The square
4. The acute triangle
5. The small rectangle

Use after Lesson 11.1, page 506

Write the opposite of each number.

1. 12 2. −9 3. 0 4. −177 5. 34

Complete the statement with > or < .

6. 6 (?) −4   7. −12 (?) 5   8. 3 (?) −9   9. 8 (?) −2   10. −7 (?) 11

Graph the integers on a number line. Describe the pattern. Then list the next two integers of the pattern.

11. 15, 10, 5, 0, −5, [?], [?]
12. −2, 2, 6, 10, 14, [?], [?]
13. 10, 7, 4, 1, −2, [?], [?]
14. −8, −6, −4, −2, 0, [?], [?]
15. 10, −10, 8, −8, 6, −6, [?], [?]
16. 1, −2, 3, −4, 5, [?], [?]

Use after Lesson 11.2, page 514

Add the integers.

1. $4 + (-9)$
2. $8 + (-3)$
3. $-5 + 12$
4. $-6 + 4$
5. $-11 + (-3)$
6. $2 + (-15)$
7. $-8 + (-7)$
8. $-16 + 10$
9. $-9 + (-8)$
10. $5 + (-11)$
11. $-2 + 2$
12. $17 + (-2)$
13. $-8 + (-8)$
14. $-10 + 19$
15. $-12 + (-4)$

You are playing a card game where you can either gain or lose points. Write an addition problem to express each of the following. Solve the problem.

16. You gain 6 points and then lose 10 points.
17. You gain 12 points and then lose 5 points.
18. You lose 3 points and then lose 7 points.
19. You lose 4 points and then lose 9 points.

Use after Lesson 11.3, page 520

Subtract the integers.

1. $3 - 7$
2. $5 - 12$
3. $-4 - 8$
4. $2 - (-5)$
5. $-6 - (-3)$
6. $13 - (-8)$
7. $-7 - (-14)$
8. $-12 - (-12)$
9. $9 - 11$
10. $15 - (-12)$
11. $0 - 10$
12. $-7 - (-5)$
13. $-9 - 9$
14. $16 - 22$
15. $20 - (-5)$
16. $-6 - (-6)$
17. $-5 - 0$
18. $8 - (-3)$
19. $10 - (-8)$
20. $-8 - (-2)$
21. $3 - (-8)$

Use after Lesson 11.4, page 528

Plot the points represented by the ordered pairs. Connect the sides of the polygon. Then name the type of polygon.

1. $A(0, 1)$, $B(2, 2)$, $C(-1, 2)$, $D(-2, -1)$, $E(3, -4)$
2. $F(1, -2)$, $G(-1, -4)$, $H(-3, 2)$, $I(-1, 4)$, $J(2, 4)$, $K(3, 2)$, $L(0, 0)$

Plot each set of points. Form polygons by connecting the points. If the second polygon is a slide of the first polygon, describe the slide.

3. Polygon 1: $(0, 0)$, $(-1, -2)$, $(1, -3)$, $(3, -2)$
   Polygon 2: $(0, -1)$, $(3, -2)$, $(3, 0)$, $(1, 1)$
4. Polygon 1: $(2, 4)$, $(2, 0)$, $(-1, 2)$, $(0, 2)$
   Polygon 2: $(3, 7)$, $(3, 3)$, $(0, 5)$, $(1, 5)$

Use after Lesson 11.5, page 534

Complete the table. Write the points as ordered pairs, then graph them in a coordinate plane. Describe any patterns that you see.

1.

x	−3	−2	−1	0	1	2	3
x + 5							

2.

x	−3	−2	−1	0	1	2	3
4 − x							

3.

x	−3	−2	−1	0	1	2	3
0 − x							

4.

x	−3	−2	−1	0	1	2	3
3 + x							

5.

x	−3	−2	−1	0	1	2	3
x − 2							

6.

x	−3	−2	−1	0	1	2	3
x − 1							

7.

x	−3	−2	−1	0	1	2	3
6 + x							

8.

x	−3	−2	−1	0	1	2	3
x − 4							

Use after Lesson 11.6, page 538

Plot the ordered pairs and connect them to form a polygon. Name the polygon. Find the area.

1. $(5, 7), (6, 3), (2, 3)$
3. $(0, −1), (3, −1), (−3, 3)$
5. $(−1, 1), (3, 1), (−1, −3), (3, −3)$
7. $(0, 4), (0, 3), (−5, 3), (−5, 4)$

2. $(−5, −3), (−2, −3), (−2, −7), (−5, −7)$
4. $(2, 1), (2, 3), (−1, 3), (−1, 1)$
6. $(−7, 0), (−4, 6), (−1, 0)$
8. $(0, 0), (3, 0), (3, −3), (0, −3)$

Find the area of the figure.

9.

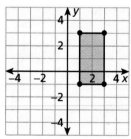

10.

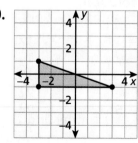

11.

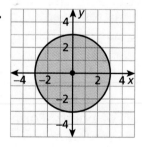

Use after Lesson 12.1, page 552

Solve the equation. Then check your solution.

1. $x + 4 = 11$
2. $x + 3 = -8$
3. $5 + x = 2$
4. $7 + x = 3$
5. $x + 4 = -9$
6. $-3 + x = 1$
7. $-12 + x = 5$
8. $6 + x = -10$
9. $x + 4 = 3$
10. $x + 3 = -4$
11. $-7 + x = -1$
12. $x + 5 = 12$
13. $9 + x = 0$
14. $x + 2 = 15$
15. $6 + x = -8$
16. $-4 + x = 0$
17. $x + 3 = -13$
18. $8 + x = -4$
19. $x + 2 = -8$
20. $-5 + x = 4$
21. $7 + x = -10$

Write the equation represented by the sentence. Then solve the equation.

22. The sum of a number and 7 is 5.
23. The sum of a number and 1 is -10.
24. The sum of 15 and a number is 7.
25. The sum of 12 and a number is 19.
26. The sum of a number and 21 is 25.
27. The sum of -13 and a number is -10.
28. The sum of -5 and a number is 12.
29. The sum of -8 and a number is -10.
30. The sum of a number and 10 is -2.
31. The sum of a number and 1 is -9.
32. The sum of 16 and a number is 10.
33. The sum of a number and 12 is 23.

Use after Lesson 12.2, page 558

Decide whether the solution is correct. If not, find the correct solution.

1. $p - 7 = 15$
   $p = 22$
2. $4 = d - 3$
   $d = -7$
3. $m - 6 = 12$
   $m = 6$
4. $6 = x - 1$
   $x = 7$
5. $y - 4 = -2$
   $y = 6$
6. $z + 14 = -2$
   $z = -16$

Solve the equation. Then check your solution.

7. $x - 12 = 2$
8. $x - 3 = -11$
9. $x - 5 = -1$
10. $x - 20 = 3$
11. $x - 17 = 14$
12. $x - 8 = 7$
13. $x - 13 = -19$
14. $10 = x - 4$
15. $x - 9 = 11$
16. $x - 1 = -5$
17. $x - 7 = -12$
18. $-8 = x - 17$
19. $16 = x - 5$
20. $x - 4 = -9$
21. $x - 7 = -3$
22. $x - 5 = 23$
23. $12 = x - 5$
24. $-3 = x - 2$
25. $15 = x - 4$
26. $-4 = x - 3$
27. $x - 5 = -11$
28. $18 = x - 6$
29. $20 = x - 1$
30. $x - 8 = 21$
31. $x - 7 = -10$
32. $x - 3 = -2$
33. $-2 = x - 10$
34. $x - 5 = -3$
35. $-4 = x - 1$
36. $-4 = x - 6$
37. $x - 6 = -2$
38. $x - 11 = -10$
39. $x - 15 = 30$

Use after Lesson 12.3, page 562

Solve the equation. Then check your solution.

1. $\frac{3}{10} + x = \frac{7}{10}$

2. $x + 0.92 = 2.48$

3. $x + \frac{1}{4} = \frac{7}{8}$

4. $x - 1.22 = 8.17$

5. $\frac{5}{6} + x = 2\frac{1}{3}$

6. $5.67 + x = 7.74$

7. $\frac{2}{9} + x = 1\frac{1}{6}$

8. $x - 4.85 = 6.25$

9. $x - \frac{5}{12} = \frac{11}{12}$

10. $x - 12.77 = 5.32$

11. $x - \frac{4}{5} = \frac{1}{2}$

12. $x + 3.74 = 8.28$

13. $x - 1\frac{1}{2} = \frac{3}{4}$

14. $9.74 + x = 12.12$

15. $\frac{4}{7} + x = \frac{5}{7}$

16. $x - 1.45 = 3.34$

17. $x + \frac{2}{3} = 6\frac{1}{2}$

18. $1.82 + x = 2.19$

19. $x + \frac{2}{3} = \frac{5}{6}$

20. $1.63 + x = 3.14$

21. $\frac{1}{5} + x = \frac{7}{10}$

22. $x + 1.15 = 3.28$

23. $x + \frac{1}{9} = \frac{2}{3}$

24. $x + 0.81 = 3.56$

25. $1.33 + x = 2.56$

26. $x + \frac{1}{6} = \frac{3}{12}$

27. $2.07 + x = 8.69$

28. $0.21 + x = 9.33$

29. $\frac{3}{4} + x = \frac{15}{16}$

30. $x + \frac{7}{8} = \frac{23}{24}$

Use after Lesson 12.4, page 567

Make an input-output table for the function. Use input values of 0, 1, 2, 3, 4, 5, and 6.

1. $y = x - 12$

2. $y = x + 7$

3. $y = x + 10$

4. $y = 14 + x$

5. $y = x + 33$

6. $y = x - 3$

7. $y = x - 1$

8. $y = 4 + x$

9. $y = x - 5$

10. $y = 10 + x$

11. $y = x - 6$

12. $y = x + 11$

13. $y = x - 9$

14. $y = x + 21$

15. $y = 12 + x$

Write a function that will give the output y in the table from the corresponding input x. Then graph the data.

16.

Input x	Output y
0	2
1	3
2	4
3	5

17.

Input x	Output y
0	6
1	7
2	8
3	9

18.

Input x	Output y
0	-4
1	-3
2	-2
3	-1

MORE PRACTICE

Use after Lesson 12.5, page 576

Make a tree diagram or use the Counting Principle to solve the problem.

1. When buying sneakers, you can choose low- or high-tops; black or white; and use black, white, red or blue laces. How many different styles of sneakers can you buy?

2. The telephone company gives you a choice of dial or touch tone phones; wall, desk, or cordless models; and colors of black, white, beige, brown, or blue. How many different phones do they offer?

3. On a picnic, you can have a hotdog, a hamburger, or cold cuts. You can pick from cole slaw, potato salad or chips, and one of 6 different brands of soda. How many meals do you have to choose from? How many if someone brings a tossed salad and iced tea?

4. Your little sister has in her closet 5 pairs of pants, 7 shirts, and 2 pairs of shoes. How many different outfits can she put together?

5. For an English literature class you need to read one book from each of 3 lists. The lists include 10 classics, 8 adventures, and 6 poetry collections. In how many ways can you complete your assignment?

Use after Lesson 12.6, page 580

State whether the events are dependent or independent.

1. You like to go camping. Your favorite color is red.

2. You are on the hockey team. You skate well.

3. You like cake. You have green socks.

4. You ran 10 miles. You are out of breath.

Find the probability.

5. There are 3 red and 4 purple marbles in one cup and 2 red and 5 purple marbles in a second cup. Without looking, you choose 1 marble from each cup. What is the probability they are both purple?

6. You roll 2 number cubes. What is the probability that both number cubes show an even number?

7. Refer to question #2, Lesson 12.5, above. What is the probability that randomly choosing, you will pick a white phone? The probability that you will pick a beige wall phone? The probability that you will pick a black, dial, desk phone?

acute angle (406) An angle whose measure is between 0° and 90°.

acute triangle (431) A triangle with three acute angles.

add (60) To find the sum of two or more numbers.

algebra (28) A branch of mathematics in which letters or variables are used to represent some numbers.

angle (406) A figure formed by two rays that begin at the same point. The rays are the *sides* of the angle, and the point is the *vertex* of the angle.

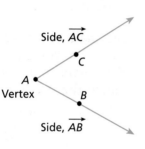

Side, $\overrightarrow{AC}$
C
A Vertex
B
Side, $\overrightarrow{AB}$

area (8) A measure of how much surface is covered by a figure. Area is measured in *square* units.

area model (68) A model used to display the product or quotient of two numbers.

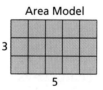

Area Model
3
5

area model (114) A model used to show fractional parts of a whole. A unit square represents the number one.

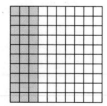

average (218) The sum of numbers in a list divided by the number of numbers in the list.

balance point of a triangle (541) The point at which a model of a triangle will balance on a pencil point. It is the intersection of the lines drawn from each vertex to the midpoint of the opposite side.

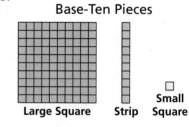

Balance Point

bar graph (17) A graph that organizes a collection of data by using bars.

base of a power (136) A number that is used as the factor in repeated multiplication. For example, in the expression 2^3, 2 is the base.

base of a triangle *See* **triangle.**

base-ten pieces (60) Counting pieces used to represent place values of base-ten numbers.

Base-Ten Pieces

Large Square   Strip   Small Square

base ten (56) A system for writing numbers which groups by ten.

center of a circle (476) The point inside a circle that is the same distance from all points on the circle.

check (34) The process of showing that a solution is correct.

circle (476) A closed curve in a plane for which every point is the same distance from a given point called the *center*.

circle graph (488) A graph that displays fractional parts of a data collection as parts of a circular region. The whole circle represents the entire collection.

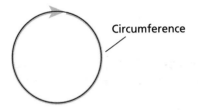

circumference (476) The distance around a circle.

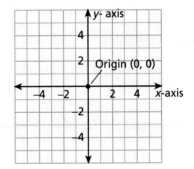

Circumference

common denominator (306) The same denominator used in two or more fractions. For example, $\frac{1}{4}$ and $\frac{3}{4}$ have a common denominator of 4.

common factor (271) A number that is a factor of two or more numbers. For example, 5 is a common factor of 10 and 15.

common multiple (307) A number that is a multiple of two or more numbers. For example, 24 is a common multiple of 3 and 4 because it is a multiple of 3 and a multiple of 4.

Commutative Property of Addition (326) If a and b are any numbers, then changing the order in which they are added will not change the sum; that is $a + b = b + a$. For example, $3 + 4 = 4 + 3$.

comparing fractions (278) Determining which of two fractions is greater.

complementary angles (456) Two angles whose measures have a sum of 90°.

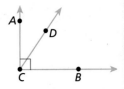

composite number (13) A whole number that has three or more factors.

congruent figures (412) Figures that have the same size and shape.

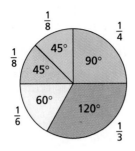

Same size
Same shape

coordinate geometry (538) A branch of geometry that studies figures in a coordinate plane.

coordinate plane (426) A plane that contains a horizontal number line called the *x*-axis, and a vertical number line called the *y*-axis.

coordinates (426) The two numbers of an ordered pair that locate a point in a coordinate plane.

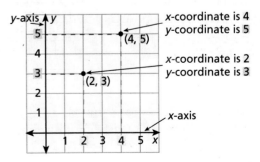

x-coordinate is 4
y-coordinate is 5

x-coordinate is 2
y-coordinate is 3

Counting Principle (577) A way of calculating the possible combinations of one item from each of two or more sets. The number of combinations is the product of the number of items in each set. For example, the number of combinations of one of 6 cards with one of 4 marbles is 6 × 4 or 24.

cube (135) A rectangular prism whose six faces are congruent squares.

cube (136) A power with an exponent of 3. For example, 6^3.

customary system (108) A system of measurement based on the inch, foot, and yard.

cylinder (487) A solid figure with congruent circular bases that lie in parallel planes.

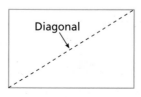

data (5) A collection of numbers or facts.

decimal point (156) A symbol that establishes place value.

denominator (254) The number below the line in a fraction. It tells into how many pieces the whole has been divided. For example, the denominator of $\frac{2}{3}$ is 3.

dependent events (580) Events for which the outcome of one event will change the probability of the outcomes of other events.

diagonal (388) A segment that connects two vertices of a polygon and is not a side.

diameter (476) The distance across a circle through its center.

dimensions (8) The measure of the size of an object. For example, the dimensions of a rectangle are its length and width.

discount (192) The amount by which a regular price is reduced.

Distributive Property (84) If a, b, and c are any numbers, then $a \times (b + c) = a \times b + a \times c$. For example, $3 \times (4 + 5) = 3 \times 4 + 3 \times 5$.

divide (74) To find a quotient of two numbers.

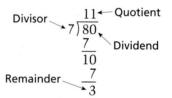

dividend (74) *See* **divide.**

divides evenly (74) Division with a whole-number quotient, or zero remainder.

divisor (74) *See* **divide.**

equation (28) A mathematical sentence with an equal sign "=" in it.

equilateral triangle (430) A triangle with three congruent sides.

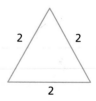

equivalent fractions (265) Fractions that represent the same number. For example, $\frac{1}{2} = \frac{25}{50}$.

GLOSSARY

evaluate (79) To find the value of an expression after all variables are replaced by numbers.

expanded notation (56) A number written as the sum of each digit times a power of 10. For example, $374 = (3 \times 100) + (7 \times 10) + (4 \times 1)$.

experimental probability (288) A probability that is based on the frequency of outcomes that have occurred after performing an experiment.

exponent (136) The number of times a base is used as a factor. For example, in the expression 2^3, 3 is the exponent.

expression (79) A collection of numbers or variables that can be linked by addition, subtraction, multiplication, and division symbols.

factor (136) A natural number that divides another natural number evenly. For example, 1, 2, 3, 4, 6, and 12 are all factors of 12.

fair game (495) A game in which every player has an equal probability of winning.

flip (416) An operation that moves a figure about a line so that its new position is its mirror image on the opposite side of the line.

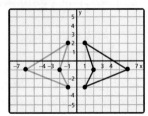

frequency table (204) A table that organizes data by displaying the number of items or events that occur in an interval.

front-end estimation (167) An estimating strategy that uses the leading digits of given numbers.

function (567) A rule that tells how to perform one or more operations on a number called the *input* to produce a result called the *output*.

geometric probability (492) To find the probability of an event occurring based on area.

grouping symbols (79) Parentheses or brackets that group parts of an expression.

height of triangle (388) *See* **triangle.**

heptagon (401) A 7-sided polygon.

Heptagon
(7 sides)

hexagon (401) A 6-sided polygon.

Hexagon
(6 sides)

improper fraction (284) A fraction that is greater than or equal to 1. For example, $\frac{4}{3}$ and $\frac{8}{8}$ are improper fractions.

independent events (580) Events for which the outcome of one event will not change the possible outcomes of other events.

inflation (234) The amount that a price increases from year to year.

input (567) A number on which a function operates.

input-output table (567) A table showing input and output values for a function.

integers (506) The set of whole numbers and their opposites.

intersecting lines (450) Lines that meet at a point.

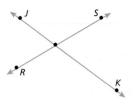

isosceles triangle (430) A triangle with *at least* two congruent sides.

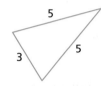

key (212) An explanation of the symbols used in a graph or stem-and-leaf plot.

least common denominator (307) The least common multiple of the denominators of two or more fractions. For example, the least common denominator of $\frac{1}{2}$ and $\frac{2}{3}$ is 6.

least common multiple (307) The smallest common multiple of two or more numbers. For example, 6 is the least common multiple of 2 and 3.

length (8) The measurement of how long an object is.

line (400) A straight path extending without end in two directions.

line graph (234) A graph that uses line segments to connect data points. It can show how data changes over time.

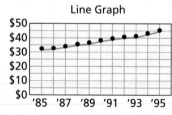

line of symmetry (418) A line that divides a figure into two parts, each of which is the mirror image of the other.

line plot (206) A diagram that uses a number line to show frequency of data.

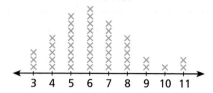

line segment (400) A part of a line consisting of two endpoints and all the points between them.

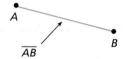

line symmetry (418) The property of a figure that indicates it can be flipped about a line and land exactly on itself.

mean (218) The average of a set of numbers.

median (222) The middle number (or the average of the two middle numbers) of a set of numbers when the numbers are listed in order.

metric system (108) An international base-ten measuring system.

midpoint (539) The point on a line segment that is halfway between the two endpoints.

mixed number (254) The sum of a whole number and a fraction. For example, $6\frac{3}{5}$ is a mixed number.

mode (223) The number (or numbers) in a set of data that appears most often.

multiple of a number (307) The product of the number and any whole number. For example, 3, 6, 9, and 12 are multiples of 3.

multiply (68) To find the product of two or more numbers.

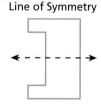

Line of Symmetry

negative integer (506) Any integer less than 0.

negative sign (506) The symbol "−" used to represent negative numbers.

number-line model (68) A diagram used to display the product or quotient of two numbers.

Number Line Model of 5 × 3 or 3 × 5

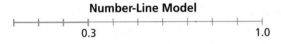

number-line model (116) A model used to show fractional parts of a whole.

Number-Line Model

numerator (254) The number above the line in a fraction. It represents the number of equal portions out of the whole.

numerical expression (79) A collection of numbers linked by mathematical operations.

obtuse angle (406) An angle whose measure is greater than 90° and less than 180°.

obtuse triangle (431) A triangle that has one obtuse angle.

octagon (401) An 8-sided polygon.

Octagon (8 sides)

opposites (506) Numbers on a number line that are the same distance from zero, but in opposite directions. For example, 4 and −4 are opposites.

order of operations (79) A procedure for evaluating expressions that have more than one operation. The steps are as follows.

1) First do operations within grouping symbols.
2) Then evaluate powers.
3) Then multiply and divide from left to right.
4) Finally add and subtract from left to right.

ordered pair (426) A pair of numbers that locates a point in a coordinate plane.

ordering (125) Arranging numbers from least to greatest or greatest to least.

origin (526) The point, (0, 0) on the coordinate plane which is the intersection of the x-axis and y-axis.

outcome (288) The result of an experiment. For example, heads is an outcome of tossing a coin.

output (567) The number that is produced by a function rule using an input number.

parallel lines (450) Lines in the same plane that never meet.

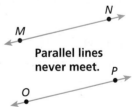

Parallel lines never meet.

parallelogram (21) A quadrilateral whose opposite sides are parallel.

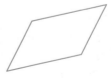

Pascal's triangle (6) A number arrangement.

```
                1
Row 1 ──────→  1   1
Row 2 ──────→ 1   2   1
Row 3 ────→  1   3   3   1
Row 4 ──→ 1   4   6   4   1
        1   5  10  10   5   1
      1   6  15  20  15   6   1
    1   7  21  35  35  21   7   1
```

pentagon (401) A 5-sided polygon.

Pentagon (5 sides)

percent (121) The value of a ratio that compares a number to 100. *Percent* means "per hundred".

perimeter (8) The distance around a polygon. Perimeter is measured in units.

perpendicular lines (451) Two lines that meet at a 90°, or right angle.

pi (π) (483) The number that represents the ratio of the circumference of a circle to its diameter, approximately 3.14.

pictograph (240) A graph that uses pictures or symbols to represent data.

place-value system (56) A number system in which the value of a symbol depends upon its position in relation to the other symbols. For example, the value of 5 in the numbers 5, 50, and 0.5 is different for each number.

plane (424) A flat surface that extends in all directions without ending.

point (400) A position in space represented by a dot.

polygon (401) A closed figure in a plane made up of line segments that meet only at their endpoints.

positive integer (506) Any integer greater than 0.

power (136) An expression such as 4^2 that has a base (4) and an exponent (2).

powers of 10 (136) The numbers 10^1, 10^2, 10^3, 10^4, ... They can also be written as 10, 100, 1000, 10,000, ...

prime factorization (24) A number written as the product of prime factors. For example, 20 is $2 \times 2 \times 5$.

prime number (13) A number that has exactly two factors, itself and 1.

probability of an event (288) A measure of the likelihood that the event will happen.

product (68) The result obtained by multiplying two or more numbers.

proportion (273) An equation stating that two ratios are equal.

protractor (407) A device used to measure angles.

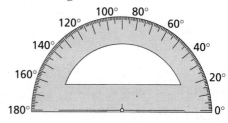

pyramid (11) A solid figure that has a polygonal base and triangular sides that share a common vertex.

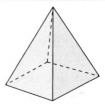

GLOSSARY

quadrant (528) One of four regions in a coordinate plane formed by the coordinate axes.

quadrilateral (21) A 4-sided polygon.

Quadrilateral
(4 sides)

quotient (74) *See* **divide.**

radius of a circle (484) A segment that has one endpoint at the center of a circle and the other endpoint on the circle; also the length of this segment.

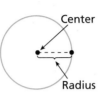

Center

Radius

random outcomes (291) Outcomes of an experiment that are all equally likely.

range (207) The difference between the greatest number and the least number in a set of data.

ratio (261) A comparison of two numbers by division.

ray (406) Part of a line that has one endpoint and extends in one direction without ending.

P

Q

reciprocals (377) Two numbers whose product is one. For example, $\frac{4}{3}$ is the reciprocal of $\frac{3}{4}$.

rectangle (8) A parallelogram that has four right angles.

regroup (61) To rewrite a form of a number as an equivalent form. For example, $3\frac{2}{3}$ can be rewritten as $2\frac{5}{3}$.

remainder (74) *See* **divide.**

rename (333) To rewrite numbers in another form. For example, $3\frac{1}{3}$ can be renamed as $3\frac{2}{6}$

replace (34) To substitute a number for a variable.

right angle (388) An angle that measures 90°.

Exactly 90°

right triangle (388) A triangle that has a right angle.

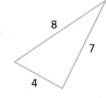

round a number (130) To replace a number with another one of approximately the same value that is easier to use. For example, 387 rounded to the nearest ten is 390; 387 rounded to the nearest hundred is 400.

scale (230) The numbers on the axes of a graph.

scale drawing (266) A drawing whose measurements are proportional to the actual dimensions.

scalene triangle (430) A triangle that has three sides of different lengths.

8

7

4

set model (68) A model used to display the product or quotient of two numbers.

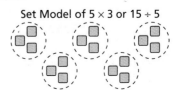

Set Model of 5 × 3 or 15 ÷ 5

set model (116) A model used to show fractional parts of a whole.

Set Model

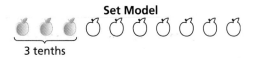

3 tenths

side of an angle (406) One ray of an angle.

similar figures (412) Figures that have the same shape, but not necessarily the same size.

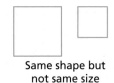

Same shape but
not same size

simplest form of a fraction (272) A fraction is in simplest form if the only common factor of the numerator and denominator is 1.

simplify (272) To rewrite a fraction so that it is in simplest form.

slide (427) To move a figure without turning or flipping.

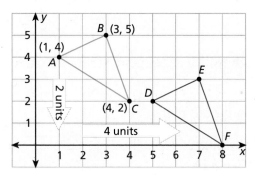

solve a proportion (273) To find a missing number in a proportion. For example, if $\frac{2}{3} = \frac{x}{9}$, then the solution is $x = 6$.

solve an equation (28) To find the value of the variable that makes an equation true.

sphere (11) A figure in space for which every point is the same distance from a given point called its center.

spreadsheet (227) A software program used for organizing and analyzing data.

square (401) A rectangle with four sides of the same length.

square of a number (136) A number multiplied by itself. For example, 4^2 or 16.

statistics (244) The branch of mathematics that deals with collecting, organizing, and analyzing data.

stem-and-leaf plot (212) A method of organizing data in increasing or decreasing order.

subtract (60) To find the difference of two numbers.

supplementary angles (456) Two angles whose measures have a sum of 180°.

surface area (487) The sum of the areas of all the faces of a three-dimensional figure.

tally sheet (204) A table used to list the numbers of times different outcomes occur.

tessellation (424) Repeating congruent figures that cover a surface without overlapping or leaving holes.

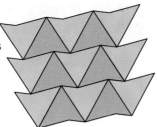

theoretical probability (288) A probability that is based on the frequency of outcomes that *should* occur.

tiling (424) A tessellation.

time line (83) A graph on a number line of the dates of several occurrences.

tree diagram (24) A diagram that shows the prime factorization of a number.

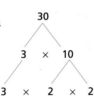

tree diagram (576) A diagram that shows total possible outcomes of an experiment.

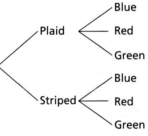

triangle (401) A 3-sided polygon.

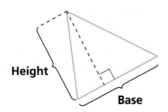

Height

Base

turn (404) An operation that turns a figure a given angle (clockwise or counterclockwise) about a point (a rotation).

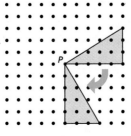

twin primes (14) Prime numbers that are two units apart such as 3 and 5 or 5 and 7.

unit (104) A standard of measurement.

variable (85) A letter that can be replaced by any number.

variable expression (85) An expression that contains at least one variable.

Venn Diagram (464) A diagram using shapes to show relationships among sets of objects or numbers.

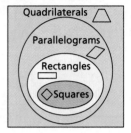

verbal model (554) A way to model a problem to better understand it.

vertex of an angle (406) The initial point of both rays of an angle.

vertical form (156) A form for adding, subtracting, multiplying, or dividing numbers in which place values are aligned vertically. For example, $\begin{array}{r} 2.20 \\ +0.87 \\ \hline 3.07 \end{array}$

width (8) Measurement across an object.

x-axis (426) The horizontal axis in a coordinate plane.

x-coordinate (426) The first number of an ordered pair.

y-axis (426) The vertical axis in a coordinate plane.

y-coordinate (426) The second number of an ordered pair.

zero pair (512) A group containing a positive and a negative number counter that represents a sum of zero.

CHAPTER I

■ **I.1 Communicating about Mathematics, p. 5**

For 4-digit numbers greater than 1111, the product is a 5-digit number whose middle 3 digits are all 9. The first digit of the product is one less than the digit in the 4-digit number. The last digit is the difference of 9 and the first digit of the product.

■ **I.1 Exercises, pp. 6–7**

1. Each number increases by 8. **2.** 56, 64, 72 **3.** No; yes; only 104 is divisible by 8. **4.** Answers will vary; possible response: numbers on lockers. **5.** Each number is two more than the previous number; 9, 11, 13 **7.** Each number is 3 times the previous number; 405, 1215, 3645 **9.** Each denominator is twice the previous one; $\frac{1}{32}, \frac{1}{64}, \frac{1}{128}$ **11.** Starting at A, list every third letter; M, P, S **13.** Starting at Z, and working backward, list every other letter; R, P, N
15.

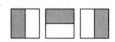

17. 8, 16, 32, 64, 128; the sum of each row is twice the sum of the previous row. **19.a.** 15, 18, 21, 24, 27, 30, 33, which connects the points 5, 8, 1, 4, 7, 0, 3; the design keeps being retraced.
b.

Multiples of 4

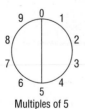

Multiples of 5

Multiples of 6

Multiples of 7

Multiples of 8

c. The designs for multiples of 4 and 6 are the same; the designs for multiples of 3 and 7 are the same. **d.** 43: repeats the patterns of multiples of 3 or 7 to form a ten-pointed star; 65: repeats the pattern of multiples of 5 to form a straight line between 0 and 5; last digit determines the design. **21.** 284 **23.** 6014 **25.** 8390 **27.** 79,500 **29.** 382

■ **I.2 Communicating about Mathematics, p. 9**

No

Field	Perimeter (Feet)	Field	Area (Sq Ft)
Football Field	990	Football Field	58,500
Soccer Field	900	Soccer Field	45,000
Pool	488	Softball Field	14,400
Softball Field	480	Pool	13,120
Basketball Court	288	Basketball Court	4700

■ **I.2 Exercises, pp. 10–11**

1. 3 by 2 and 4 by 1. **2.** 4 by 3, 6 by 2, 12 by 1 **3.** Multiply the length by the width, or count the unit squares. **4.** area, perimeter

5. a

7.

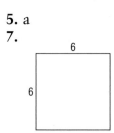

$P = 24$ units, $A = 36$ sq units

9.

9
7

$P = 32$ units, $A = 63$ sq units

11.

Figure	Perimeter	Area
a.	6	2
b.	10	4
c.	14	6
d.	18	8
e.	22	10
f.	26	12

Perimeter increases by 4; area increases by 2.

13. never **15.a.** Sneakers **b.** 45–64 **17.** c
19. a

■ *1.3 Communicating about Mathematics, p. 13*

64; $2 \times 2 \times 2 \times 2 \times 2 \times 2$

■ *1.3 Exercises, pp. 14–15*

1. 2 **2.** A prime number can't be written as the product of whole numbers other than 1 and itself; 2, 7, and 11; a composite number can be written as the product of whole numbers other than 1 and itself; 10, 15, and 16. **3.** *Hot Fudge*–chocolate, vanilla, strawberry; *Pineapple*–chocolate, vanilla, strawberry; *Cherry*–chocolate, vanilla, strawberry. **4.** *Chocolate Yogurt*–Hot fudge and pineapple, Hot fudge and cherry, Pineapple and cherry; *Vanilla Yogurt*–Hot fudge and pineapple, Hot fudge and cherry, Pineapple and cherry; *Strawberry Yogurt*–Hot fudge and pineapple, Hot fudge and cherry, Pineapple and cherry **5.** Even; 2 + 4; 6 + 8 **7.** Odd; 2 + 1; 4 + 3 **9.** 48 and 84 **11.** 18 **13.** 684 **15.** 24; 1359, 1395, 1539, 1593, 1935, 1953; 3159, 3195, 3519, 3591, 3915, 3951; 5139, 5193, 5319, 5391, 5913, 5931; 9135, 9153, 9315, 9351, 9513, 9531 **17.** 5 **19.** 8 **21.** 6

■ *1.3 Mixed Review, p. 16*

1. 7×9 **3.** 4×9 **5.** 8×7 **7.** 5×15 **9.** Yes **11.** Yes **13.** 8 **15.** 1 **17.** No; too long; 5 meters is about 15 feet. **19.** Yes; possible; 5 kilometers is about 3 miles.

■ *1.4 Communicating about Mathematics, p. 18*

A. Answers will vary, but could include the following: gas is cheaper; greater distances to drive. **B.** Approximately $2000–$2196 **C.** Mountain, Northeast, Pacific, and South Atlantic; Eastern South Central and Western South Central

■ *1.4 Exercises, pp. 19–20*

1. One possibility is percent of involvement in sports **2.** One possibility is population density **3.** About 44 **4.** About 56 **5.** Scanning checkouts; pharmacy **9.** 100 **11.** 100 **13.** 2000 **15.** 1000

■ *1.5 Communicating about Mathematics, p. 22*

53 sq in.; area of three shelves: 55.0 sq in. $\times$ 3 = 165 sq in.; area of both sides: 71.5 sq in. $\times$ 2 = 143 sq in.; area of back:

143 sq in.; the total is 451 sq in. The board is 504 sq in. and the box uses 451 sq in.

■ **1.5 Exercises, pp. 23–24**

1. 6

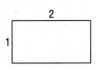

2. 10

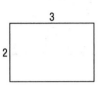

3. 14

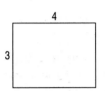

4. 18

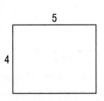

5. The perimeter of each rectangle increases by 4; 22. **7.** 4 **9.** 8

11.

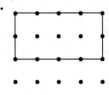

13.

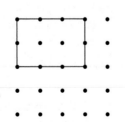

15. Yes

17. Yoko; 3 blocks **19.** West 4 blocks

21.

23.

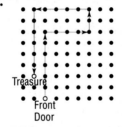

■ **Mid-Chapter Self-Test, p. 25**

1. b **2.** a **3.** c **4.** Bread and oranges **5.** Bread–1993; Eggs–1989; Ice Cream–1989; Oranges–1991 **6.** 32 **7.** Tell problems **8.** Similar; even though numbers are different, men and women ranked factors in the same order.

9.

■ **Lab 1.6, On Your Own, p. 27**

3.A. 340; multiplication; to find the total number of cards, multiply number of cards by number of boxes. **B.** 13; division; to find the number on each shelf, divide number of cars by number of shelves.

4.

	Multiplication Sentence	Division Sentence
Problem A	$85 \times 4 = 340$	$340 \div 4 = 85$
Problem B	$3 \times 13 = 39$	$39 \div 3 = 13$

■ 1.6 Communicating about Mathematics, p. 29

The first one, because the "$\times$" is too much like the letter "x".

■ 1.6 Exercises, pp. 30–31

1. equation **2.** solution **3.** Answers will vary but could include f for food. **4.** Total hours = Number of cans $\times$ Hours for each can. **5.** $x = 336 \times 3\frac{1}{2}$; $x = 1176$ **6.** $m = 10$ **7.** 7 **9.** 7 **11.** 23 **13.** 6 **15.** 3 **17.** 32 **19.** $6 + x = 21$; $x = 15$ **21.** $5 \cdot x = 40$; $x = 8$ **23.** 8, 6, 4, 2; d decreases by 2 **25.** 5, 6, 7, 8; d increases by 1 **27.** $12 \cdot x = 288$; $x = 24$ **29.** $61.5 - 59 = x$; $x = 2.5$ **31.** $36 \cdot 2 = x$; $x = 72$ **33.** 60 **35.** $8\frac{1}{2}$ **37.** $3\frac{1}{2}$

■ 1.6 Mixed Review, p. 32

1. 53.8 **3.** 21.6 **5.** 54.73 **7.** 25.05 **9.** 8 in. **11.** Answers will vary. **13.** 0.75 **15.** 1.0

■ 1.7 Communicating about Mathematics, p. 35

9; use inverse operations: $5 \times 3 = 15$; $15 - 7 = 8$; $8 \div 2 = 4$; $4 + 5 = 9$.

■ 1.7 Exercises, pp. 36–37

1. Use inverse operations: $15 + 5 = 20$; $20 - 8 = 12$; $12 + 8 = 20$. **2.** What number added to 78 equals 93? 15; $78 + 15 = 93$ **3.** What number subtracted from 54 = 48? 6; $54 - 6 = 48$. **4.** What number multiplied by 3 equals 39? 13; $13 \times 3 = 39$.

5. 42 divided by what number equals 6? 7; $42 \div 7 = 6$. **6.** To check a solution, replace the variable with your answer. Check for Ex. 1; $15 + 5 = 20$; $20 - 8 = 12$; $12 + 8 = 20$; $20 - 8 + 8 - 5 = 15$. **7.** 32, 4, 0, 0 **9.** 27, 35, 7, 21 **11.** What number added to 5 equals 24? 19 **13.** 32 subtracted from what number equals 51? 83 **15.** What number added to 55 equals 66? 11 **17.** What number multiplied by 8 equals 48? 6 **19.** What number divided by 8 equals 14? 112 **21.** What number multiplied by 63 equals 189? 3 **23.** $18 + x = 27$; 9 **25.** $7 \cdot x = 105$; 15 **27.** 6 m **29.** 2; 3 **31.** < **33.** < **35.** <

■ 1.8 Communicating about Mathematics, p. 39

No, more than 4 times as much. Doubling the number of people increases number of pairs to 120, increasing cost to $270.

■ 1.8 Exercises, pp. 40–41

1. Solve a Simpler Problem. **2.** Draw a Diagram **3.** Make a List. **4.** Begin by finding out how many sit-ups you would do on the third day. **5.** Begin by finding out how many rings would be exchanged by 3 people. **7.** 36
9.

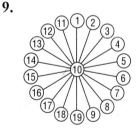

11. About 200 miles **13.** About 400 miles

■ 1.9 Communicating about Mathematics, p. 43

Answers will vary, but could include the following: you can work backward, multiplying by the inverse of the fraction remaining. For example, $2 \times 2 = 4$; $4 \times \frac{3}{2}$ $= 6$; $6 \times \frac{4}{3} = 8$; $8 \times \frac{5}{4} = 10$; $10 \times \frac{6}{5} = 12$.

■ 1.9 Exercises, pp. 44–45

1.–4. Answers will vary.
5.

6	1	8
7	5	3
2	9	4

7. 7 minutes; draw a diagram to find out number of lines needed. **9.** 1984–5 days; 1985–5 days; 1986–5 days; 1987–$4\frac{1}{2}$ days; 1988–5 days; 1989–$5\frac{1}{2}$ days; 1990–$4\frac{1}{2}$ days **11.** 16

■ Chapter Review, pp. 47–48

1. Each fraction decreases by $\frac{1}{8}$; $\frac{4}{8}, \frac{3}{8}, \frac{2}{8}$
3. Starting at A, list the letters in the following positions: 1, 2, 4, 7, 11,...; K, P, V
5. The perimeter increases by 4 each time and the area is the square of the length of the side of the figure.

Perimeter	Area
4	1
8	4
12	9
16	16
20	25
24	36

7. $\$25 - x = \$9$; $x = \$16$
9.

11. 1989 **13.** None **15.** 35; Key: maple–m, oak–o, beech–b, hickory–h, birch–bi, poplar–p, aspen–a; mob, moh, mobi, mop, moa, mbh, mbbi, mbp, mba, mhbi, mhp, mha, mbip, mbia, mpa, obh, obbi, obp, oba, ohbi, ohp, oha, obia, obip, opa, bhbi, bhp, bha, bbip, bbia, bpa, hbip, hbia, hpa, bipa **17.** $4.50 **19.** $60.
21.

CHAPTER 2

■ Lab 2.1, On Your Own, p. 55

8. No; they would use the symbol for 100. **9.** No, they would have written symbols for larger numbers first.
10.

11. Answers will vary, but could include using a bar with tally marks above and below it to represent a number less than 1.

■ 2.1 Communicating about Mathematics, p. 57

A. One hundred fifty-seven **B.** Two thousand forty-eight **C.** Ten thousand nine hundred four **D.** One million two hundred forty thousand fifty-two

■ 2.1 Exercises, pp 58–59

1. No, it is grouped by 5's and 10's. **2.** No; the position of the symbols does not matter, also there is no symbol for 0. **3.** CCCLXII **4.** One hundred two thousand six hundred eighty-one

5. False; the Egyptian system is a base-ten system with no symbol for zero. **6.** True; 1 meter = 100 cm and 1 cm = 10 mm. **7.** 640 **9.** 44,040 **11.** 52 **13.** 325 **15.** d **17.** c **19.** 865 **21.** 386 **23.** Nova Scotia—ones, New Brunswick—tens, Manitoba—ten thousands, Saskatchewan—ten thousands, British Columbia—tens, Quebec—hundred thousands **25.** Yes; they are grouped by 10's. **27.** 10,759 **29.** = **31.** <

■ **2.2 Communicating about Mathematics, p. 61**

A. 229 **B.** 501 **C.** 425; answers may vary; one possibility: C was easiest. Round 99 up to 100, subtract, then add 1 back to the answer.

■ **2.2 Exercises, pp. 62–63**

1. $25 + 18 = 43$ **2.** $23 - 18 = 5$ **3.** $22 - 17 = 5$ **4.** One possibility: regrouping, $37 + 49$; not, $25 + 13$ **5.** One possibility: regrouping, $37 - 29$; not, $32 - 22$. **7.** $33 + 18 = 51$ **9.** 197 **11.** 311 **13.** 782 **15.** 7323

17.

$$\begin{array}{r} \boxed{1}\,9\,4 \\ +\,3\,3\,\boxed{9} \\ \hline 5\,3\,3 \end{array}$$

19.

$$\begin{array}{r} 5\,\boxed{2}\,5\,\boxed{4} \\ +\boxed{1}\,7\,\boxed{6}\,2 \\ \hline 7\,0\,1\,6 \end{array}$$

21. 40 **23.** 99 **25.** 798 **27.** 49, 35 **29.** 25, 16 **31.** True; total from Entertainment, Drawing, and Home Education = $410 + 325 + 243 = $978 < $1022 for Word Processing. **33.** 2 **35.** 3 **37.** 3

■ **Lab 2.2, On Your Own, p. 65**

8. $80 + 40 = 120$, so 146 is unreasonable. The friend reversed the digits of 36 and then added 83 and 63. **9.** The sum should fall between 110 and 120. **10.a.** One possibility: 6, 10, 14, 20, 50 **b.** Not possible; sum will be an odd number. **c.** One possibility: 11, 12, 13, 14, 50 **d.** Only possibility: 1, 2, 3, 4, 90. **11.a.** Not possible; sum will be under 100. **b.** One possibility: 10, 13, 19, 25, 33 **c.** Not possible; the sum will be greater than 100.

■ **2.2 Mixed Review, p. 66**

1. 4200 **3.** 500 **5.** 66 **7.** 8 **9.** 4, 8, 12, 16, 20, 24, 28, 32, 36, 40, 44, 48 **11.** 2, 3, 5, 7, 11, 13, 17, 19, 23, 29, 31, 37, 41, 43, 47 **13.** Grams **15.** Milligrams **17.** Milligrams
19. One possibility:

■ **2.3 Communicating about Mathematics, p. 69**

A. 736 tiles **B.** 2944 tiles; you need 4 times as many. You can fit four 3-in. square tiles onto one 6-in. square tile.

■ **2.3 Exercises, pp. 70–71**

1. 9×7 **2.** 4×11 **3.** 77 sq units **4.** Approximately 87,500 sq miles **5.** $2 \times 2 = 4$ **7.** $6 \times 8 = 48$ **9.** $4 \times 6 = 24$ **11.** 48 **13.** 52
15.

17.

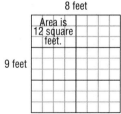

19. 11 **21.** 4 **23.** Even; $2 \times 4 = 8$ and $6 \times 10 = 60$ **25.** Even; $3 \times 2 = 6$ and $15 \times 12 = 180$ **27.** 44, 88, 176; n doubles **29.** Yes

Area is 12 square feet.
8 feet
9 feet

31. 15 **33.** 64 **35.** 17

■ Lab 2.4, On Your Own, p. 73

3.

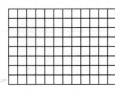

Area is 96 square units.

4. Sample response: A software company ships 8 boxes of computer games to your store. If the total number of games is 96, how many games are in each box? 12

5. Sample responses: Six of your friends have brought you 9 roses each. How many roses did you receive? You made a batch of 54 cookies for your party. If you expect 9 people to come, how many cookies can each person have?

6. Answers will vary but may include: draw groups of 5 until you get to 30. You'll have 2 left over.

■ 2.4 Communicating about Mathematics, p. 75

A. Butter; $\frac{3}{4}$ cup **B.** Peanuts; $1\frac{3}{4}$ cup

C. Sugar; $1\frac{1}{4}$ cup

■ 2.4 Exercises, pp. 76–77

1. Dividend is 27; divisor is 4.

2.

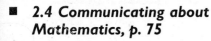

3. 6 R3, or $6\frac{3}{4}$ **4.** c; 4 R1, $4\frac{1}{3}$ **5.** a; 2 R1, $2\frac{1}{6}$

6. b; 3 R1, or $3\frac{1}{6}$ **7.** $52 \div 4$; 13 **9.** $9\frac{3}{4}$ or 9 R3

11. $14\frac{1}{3}$, or 14 R1 **13.** $23\frac{4}{5}$ or 23 R4

15. $61\frac{1}{4}$ or 61 R1 **17.** $8 \div 4$ or $8 \div 2$

19. $2\frac{4}{5}$, or 2 R4;

21. $3\frac{3}{4}$, or 3 R6;

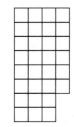

23. The friend read $720 \div 45$ as 45 divided by 720, not as 720 divided by 45; 16. **25.** $2\frac{1}{2}$ **27.** 9 units

■ Mid-Chapter Self-Test, p. 78

1. 780 **2.** 41,035 **3.** 6209 **4.** 2,080,060 **5.** Four thousand fifty-four **6.** Thirty thousand eight hundred seventy **7.** Six hundred fifty-two thousand one **8.** $41 - 29 = 12$ **9.** $35 + 28 = 63$

10.

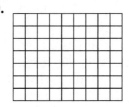

Area is 63 square units.

11.

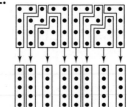

12.

13. 20 **14.** 36 **15.** 85 **16.** 7 **17.** 4 **18.** 50
19. 200–300 **20.** 50–150 **21.** 400–500

2.5 Communicating about Mathematics, p. 80

A. 33; does not change the value: $(32 - 5) + 6 = 33$; changes the value: $32 - (5 + 6) = 21$ **B.** 2; does not change the value: $32 - (5 \times 6) = 2$; changes the value: $(32 - 5) \times 6 = 162$

2.5 Exercises, pp. 81–82

1. b **2.** d **3.** a **4.** c **5.** $5 \times (9 - 3) + 12 \div 6 = 32$ **6. a.** $\div\, 8, -21,$ or $\times \frac{1}{8}$ **b.** $+\, 11, \times \frac{14}{3},$ or $\div \frac{3}{14}$ **c.** $-12, \div\, 7,$ or $\times \frac{1}{7}$ **d.** $+\, 3, \times \frac{5}{2},$ or $\div \frac{2}{5}$ **e.** $\times\, 9, +\, 40,$ or $\div \frac{1}{9}$ **f.** $\div\, 3, -30,$ or $\times \frac{1}{3}$ **7.** 21 **9.** 8 **11.** 4 **13.** 18 **15.** 16 **17.** 144 **19.** 100 **21.** 0 **23.** $4 + 8 \times 4 = 36$ **25.** 7, 5, 9 **27.** 9, 4, 2 **29.** $+, \times, -$ **31.** $\times, +, \div$ **33.** $400 - (2 \times 43 + 2 \times 2 \times 40)$ **35.** 296 **37.** Mays and Rose

2.5 Mixed Review, p. 83

1. Perimeter: 34 in.; area: 66 sq in. **3.** Perimeter: 28 ft; area: 49 sq ft **5.** 110; add 1 to 119 and 1 to 229, then subtract. **7.** 70; subtract 40 from 110 **9.** 25; divide 125 by 5; or find the missing factor **11.** 50; divide 500 by 10 **13.** 70 **15.** 1110 **17.** 2000 **19.** Each increases by 8; 27, 35, 43

2.6 Communicating about Mathematics, p. 85

A. $3 \times (3 + 5) = 3 \times 3 + 3 \times 5$; $24 = 24$ **B.** $2 \times (2 + 4) = 2 \times 2 + 2 \times 4$; $12 = 12$. The model or models on each side of the equal sign show the same value.

2.6 Exercises, pp. 86–87

1. Without an established order of operations, the Distributive Property is not valid; $5 \times 6 + 5 \times 5 = 30 + 5 \times 5 = 35 \times 5 = 175$; instead of $5(6 + 5) = 5 \times 6 + 5 \times$ $5 = 30 + 25 = 55$ **2.** $5(6 + 5) = 5 \times 6 + 5 \times 5 = 30 + 25 = 55$ **3.** $7(10) + 7(8) = 70 + 56 = 126$; or $7(18) = 126$. Preferences will vary. **4.** $4 \times (4 + 2) = 4 \times 4 + 4 \times 2$; $24 = 24$; the model or models on each side of the equal sign show the same value. **5.** $3(4) + 3(7)$, or $3(11)$; 33 **7.** $6(8) + 6(1)$, or $6(9)$; 54 **9.** $4(25) + 4(5)$, or $4(30)$; 120 **11.** $2(15) + 2(50)$, or $2(65)$; 130 **13.** c; 36; answers are the same. **15.** d; 56; answers are the same. **17.** $5(4 + 1) = 5 \times 4 + 5 \times 1$ **19.** 144 **21.** 371 **23.** Explanations will vary; $n = 4$ **25.** Explanations will vary; $y = 4$ **27.** Write 72 as $70 + 2$. Then the area is $60(70 + 2) = 60(70) + 60(2) = 4200 + 120 = 4320$. **29.** \$645. **31.** Begin with 1, each number is the product of 2 and the preceding number; 16, 32, 64 **33.** 620 **35.** 17 R1 or $17\frac{1}{5}$

Lab 2.7, On Your Own, p. 89

10. When you get to 5, you trade for the next bigger piece. **11.** 444_5; 124 pieces **12.** It was written and computed in base ten. **13. a.** No, there are only 4 nickels and 4 pennies. **b.** Yes, trade 5 nickels for 1 quarter.

2.7 Communicating about Mathematics, p. 91

A. 111_2

B. 11111_2

C. 10001_2

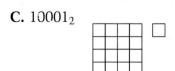

2.7 Exercises, pp. 92–93

1. a **2.** 302_5 **3.** 123_5 **4.** 19 **5.** 0, 1, 2, 3, 4, and 5

6.

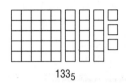

$4^2 = 16 \quad 4^1 = 4 \quad 4^0 = 1$

7. Base-five digits only go up to 4.

9. 133_5

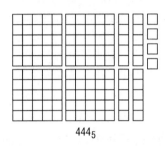

133_5

11. 444_5

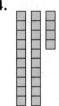

444_5

13. 78 **15.** 232 **17.** 624 **19.** 300_5 **21.** 1034_5 **23.** 2220_5 **25.** a **27.** c **29.** 10 **31.** 26 **33.** 31 **35.** 10111_2 **37.** 111011_2 **39.** 111110_2 **41.** 53 **43.** d **45.** f **47.** b

Chapter Review, pp. 95–96

1. Ninety-seven; $(9 \times 10) + (7 \times 1)$ **3.** Thirty-five thousand seven hundred ninety; $(3 \times 10,000) + (5 \times 1000) + (7 \times 100) + (9 \times 10)$ **5.** 405 **7.** 536 **9.** 22 R8; $22\frac{4}{9}$ **11.** 27 **13.** 81 **15.** $3 \times 9 = 27$ **17.** $2 \times 11 = 22$ **19.** 25, 20, 15; each number is 5 less than the last; 10, 5 **21.** 120, 231, 342; each number increases by 111; 453, 564 **23.** 120 **25.** 45 **27.** $80(100 + 50)$ is the same as 80×150, and $15 \times 8 \times 100$. **29.** 545,500; 3,370,000 **31.** 10 m **33.** mouse **35.** pixel

CHAPTER 3

Lab 3.1, On Your Own, p. 103

11.

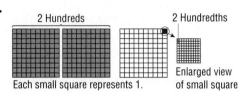

3 tens

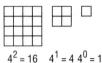 3 tenths

12.

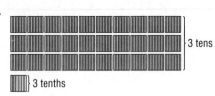

2 Hundreds   2 Hundredths

Each small square represents 1.   Enlarged view of small square

13. 110; 1.1

14.

3.1 Communicating about Mathematics, p. 105

A. \$200.00; move the decimal point 2 places to the right. **B.** \$0.40; move the decimal point 1 place to the left. **C.** \$30.00; move the decimal point 1 place to the right. **D.** \$6.00; decimal point is in the correct place.

3.1 Exercises, pp. 106–107

1. c **2.** b **3.** a **4.** Sample answer: 7000.007 **5.** \$6.78 **6.** 79¢, \$0.79

7. 1.12 ones, 11.2 tenths, 112 hundredths

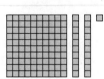

9. 1.21 ones, 12.1 tenths, 121 hundredths

11. 0.58 or 58 hundredths **13.** ones
15. tenths **17.** 12.52 **19.** 500.03
21. $(2 \times 10) + (3 \times 1) + (9 \times 0.1) +$
$(3 \times 0.01) + (6 \times 0.001)$ **23.** True; 10
tenths equals 1 one and $10 \times 10 = 100$,
so 100 tenths = 10 ones **25.** True; 10
hundredths equals 1 tenth **27.** $0.12
29. $5.00 **31.** 35,400 mg **33.** $<$ **35.** $<$

■ 3.2 Communicating about Mathematics, p. 109

A. 2.5 m **B.** 25 cm **C.** 4 km **D.** 2 cm

■ 3.2 Exercises, pp. 110–111

1. No, units don't change by multiples of
10. **2.** cm **3.** mm **4.** cm **5.** m **6.** Answers
will vary but could include: eraser, 5.5
cm; pencil lead, 1 mm; and pen 1.5 dm.
7. 10 **8.** 10 **9.** b **11.** d **13.** 1000 **15.** 0.25
17. mm **19.** mm **21.** m **23.** 2.2 cm × 5 cm;
14.4 cm **25.** 5.7 dm **27.** 2.8 hm **29.** 4 mm
31. $<$ **33.** $>$ **35.** $>$
37.

Dinosaur	Length in meters
Ornitholestes	1.8
Ankylosaurus	4.8
Stegosaurus	6.0
Torosaurus	9.0
Tyrannosaurus Rex	12.0
Brachiosaurus	24.0

39. 6 **41.** 15 **43.** 12 **45.** 11

■ 3.2 Mixed Review, p. 112

1. One thousand four hundred thirty-two
3. Nine and fifty-five hundredths
5. $(2 \times 1000) + (1 \times 100) + (6 \times 10) +$
(7×1) **7.** $(2 \times 10,000) + (4 \times 100) +$
(5×10) **9.** $(3 \times 100,000) + (6 \times 1000) +$
$(5 \times 100) + (2 \times 10)$ **11.** 14 **13.** 3 **15.** 10

17.

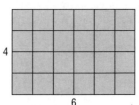

19.

■ Lab 3.3, On Your Own, p. 115

6.a. 46.7 **b.** 0.467 **c.** 46.7 **7.** Move the
decimal point one place to the right. For
example: 3 tenths = 30 hundredths. **8.**
Move the decimal point one place to the
left. For example: 30 hundredths = 3
tenths.

■ 3.3 Communicating about Mathematics, p. 117

A.

B.

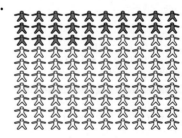

■ 3.3 Exercises, pp. 118–119

1. 0.6 **2.** 0.27 **3.** 0.4 **4.** Answers will vary.
5.

7.

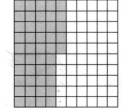

9. It is a set model with 100 circles

11.

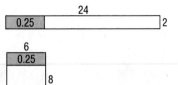

13.

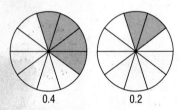

15. 1.0, 0.8, 0.6; numbers decrease by 2 tenths; 0.4, 0.2

17. GREAT JOB

■ **3.4 Communicating about Mathematics, p. 121**

A. 5% **B.** 50% **C.** 72%

■ **3.4 Exercises, pp. 122–123**

1. 0.56 **2.** $\frac{56}{100}$ **3.** 56% **4.** Sixty-seven percent **5.** Fifteen hundredths **6.** Forty-five hundredths **7.** 0.50, 50%, $\frac{5}{10}$ **8.** 0.1, 10% $\frac{1}{10}$ **9.** 0.65, $\frac{65}{100}$, 65% **11.** $\frac{55}{100}$ **13.** $\frac{45}{100}$ **15.** $\frac{35}{100}$ **17.** True **19.** True **21.** 24% **23.** 85% **25.** $\frac{35}{100}$, 35% **27.** $\frac{82}{100}$, 82% **29.** 20% **31.** $0.10 **33.** 100 **35.** $749.00

■ **Mid-Chapter Self-Test, p. 124**

1.

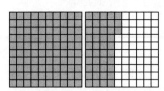

2.

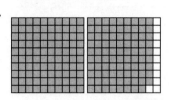

3.

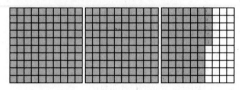

4. hundredths **5.** thousandths **6.** 1000
7. 560 **8.** hm **9.** 0.0123
10.

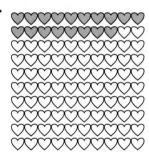

11.

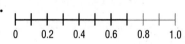

12.

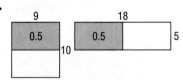

13. 0.6, $\frac{6}{10}$, 60% **14.** 0.29, $\frac{29}{100}$, 29%
15. 0.74, $\frac{74}{100}$, 74%

SELECTED ANSWERS

16.

Event	Distance	
	Men	**Women**
High Jump	2.45 m	2.09 m
Long Jump	8.95 m	7.52 m
Discus	74.10 m	76.80 m

17. Discus **18.** Music—about 40%, Dance—about 23%, Creative Writing—about 15%

■ 3.5 Communicating about Mathematics, p. 126

1. 24.3 cm **2.** 23.5 cm **3.** 22.9 cm **4.** 22.0 cm **5.** 21.7 cm **6.** 22.3 cm; 21.7 cm, 22.0 cm, 22.3 cm, 22.9 cm, 23.5 cm, 24.3 cm

■ 3.5 Exercises, pp. 127–128

1. D–0.2, E–0.8, C–1.1, A–1.6, B–2.1
2. 0.68, 0.69, 0.70

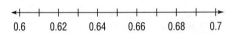

3. Answers will vary. **4.** 0.04, 0.4, 0.45, 0.5, 0.54 **5.** 0.02, 0.2, 0.25, 0.5, 2.5 **7.** 6.08, 6.12, 6.18, 6.8, 6.82 **9.** No; 0.026, 0.06, 0.126, 0.2, 0.26 **11.** No; 1.107, 1.69, 1.709, 1.76, 1.9 **13.** > **15.** < **17.** = **19.** = **21.** C, A, B, E, D **23.** C **25.** B and C **27.** 0.3 **29.** 0.2, 0.23, 0.3 **31.** Virginia: 3.5, Georgia: 4.0, Missouri: 4.225, Arkansas: 4.5, and Kansas: 4.9 **33.** one tenth **35.** four and twenty-six hundredths **37.** sixty-one thousandths **39.** thirteen and twenty-two thousandths **41.** Decreases by 0.3; 0.9, 0.6, 0.3 **43.** Decreases by 0.02; 0.06, 0.04, 0.02

■ 3.5 Mixed Review, p. 129

1. composite **3.** composite **5.** 7 R3 or $7\frac{1}{2}$
7. 24 R1 or $24\frac{1}{5}$ **9.** 12 **11.** 3 **13.** 8 **15.** 13 **17.** 1.5 **19.** 100.01

■ 3.6 Communicating about Mathematics, p. 131

A. 0.2 **B.** 0.4 **C.** 0.3 **D.** 0.7 **E.** 0.6 **F.** 0.9

■ 3.6 Exercises, pp. 132–133

1. Answers will vary.
2. 0.24 is closer to 0.2 than it is to 0.3.

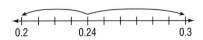

3. 4.524 **4.** 4.52 **5.** 4.5 **6.** 5 **7.** No; by rounding to the nearest hundredth first, your friend made the number seem larger than it is.
9. 6.263 is closer to 6.3.

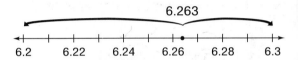

11. 270 **13.** 412,000 **15.** 21 **17.** True **19.** False; 5.4 **21.** 2000 **23.** 110 **25.** $25.00 **27.** $1210.00 **29.** 6.5; acid **31.** 6.2; acid **33.** 13.09, 13.89, 14.02, 14.27 **35.** 0.002, 0.012, 0.02, 0.2

■ Lab 3.7, On Your Own, p. 135

15. 100 **16.** 1000 **17.** Large strip **18.** 100 **19.** 0.001 **20.** 1000; each layer contains 10 × 10 cubes, and there are 10 layers.

■ 3.7 Communicating about Mathematics, p. 137

Explanation of steps should demonstrate a knowledge of proper order of operations: do operations within grouping symbols, evaluate powers, multiply and divide from left to right, finally add and subtract from left to right. **A.** 125 **B.** 29 **C.** 83

3.7 Exercises, pp. 138–139

1. 22 **2.** 6 **3.** 22^6 **4.** 100; 1000; 10,000; 100,000; 1,000,000 **5.** $(2 \times 10) + (9 \times 1) + (2 \times \frac{1}{10}) + (3 \times \frac{1}{10^2})$ **6.** False; 9 **7.** 2 **9.** 3 **11.** 9 **13.** 2 **15.** 625 **17.** 729 **19.** $\frac{1}{1,000,000}$ **21.** 12,167 **23.** 14,641 **25.** $(7 \times 10) + (5 \times 1)$ **27.** $(1 \times 10^3) + (3 \times 10)$ **29.** 49; 50 **31.** 2197; 2200 **33.** 8 cm **35.** 10 mm **37.** 10^2 **39.** 27 **41.** 14 **43.** 84 **45.** 8; 576 **47.** 14; 3087

3.8 Communicating about Mathematics, p. 141

A. 0.50, $\frac{5}{10}$, 50% **B.** 0.3, $\frac{3}{10}$, 30% **C.** 0.2, $\frac{20}{100}$, 20%

3.8 Exercises, pp. 142–143

1. 24 strawberries

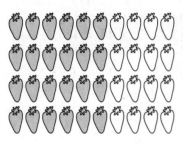

2. 500 **3.** 0.40, 40%, $\frac{4}{10}$ **4.** 0.25, 25%, $\frac{1}{4}$ **5.** $\frac{35}{100}$, $\frac{7}{20}$, 35% **7.** 0.6, $\frac{6}{10}$, 60%
9. $9.00

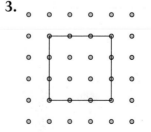

11. 200

13. A–20, B–15, C–10, D–5

A A A A	B B B	C C	D
A A A A	B B B	C C	D
A A A A	B B B	C C	D
A A A A	B B B	C C	D
A A A A	B B B	C C	D

15. Yes, 55% of 200 is 110. **17.** 41.5; the third number in each row and column is the difference of previous numbers.

Chapter Review, pp. 145–146

1. 1000 **3.** 0.10 **5.** $(7 \times 10) + (5 \times 1) + (2 \times 0.1) + (4 \times 0.01)$ **7.** $(5 \times 100) + (4 \times 10) + (1 \times 1) + (9 \times 0.1) + (9 \times 0.01)$
9. mm **11.** cm **13.** $\frac{25}{100}$, 25%; $\frac{5}{10}$, 50%; $\frac{75}{100}$, 75%; answers will vary. **15.** $\frac{67}{100}$
17. $\frac{897}{1000}$ **19.** 10.5, 10.8, 11.0, 11.0, 11.1
21. $\frac{4}{10}$ **23.** 64 **25.** 1000
27. 50

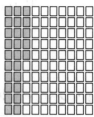

29. 0.28 **31.** $5 bills–2.1 million, $10 bills–1.9 million, $20 bills–4.0 million **33.** 34, 36, 26, 35; taka

Cumulative Review, pp. 148–149

1.

Figure	Perimeter	Area
1	4	1
2	6	2
3	8	3
4	10	4
5	12	5
6	14	6

3.

5. 26 **7.** 325 **9.** 11 **11.** 240 **13.** 3 **15.** 52, 45, 15, 19 **17.** 815 **19.** 57.5 **21.** small squares **23.** 15 **25.** 1 **27.** 66; $3 \times 12 + 3 \times 10$ or 3×22 **29.** 45; $3 \times 13 + 3 \times 2$ or 3×15
31.

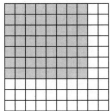

33. False; 30% is $\frac{30}{100}$ **35.** True; 70% is $\frac{70}{100} = \frac{7}{10}$ **37.** 25 **39.** ttt, tth, tht, htt, thh, hth, hht, hhh **41.** 0.54, 0.59, 0.70, 0.73, 0.66 **43.** 0.50, 0.60, 0.70, 0.70, 0.70

CHAPTER 4

■ *Lab 4.1, On Your Own, p. 155*
10.a. 4.09

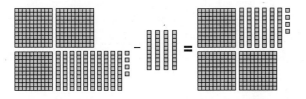

b. 3.04

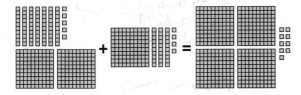

c. 3.64

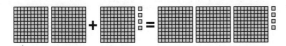

d. 2.4

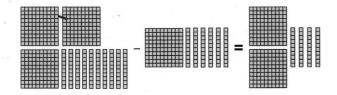

11. c; place value alignment **12.** a; place value alignment

■ *4.1 Communicating about Mathematics, p. 157*

A. Pasta and green salad **B.** Pasta, onion soup, and milk **C.** Steak, fruit salad, and tea; choices add up to amounts.

■ *4.1 Exercises, pp. 158–159*
1. 4.83

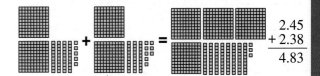
$$\begin{array}{r} 2.45 \\ + 2.38 \\ \hline 4.83 \end{array}$$

2. Decimal points are not aligned; 1.6 + 0.4 = 2.0 **3.** Answers will vary.
5. 1.63

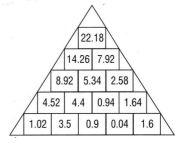
$$\begin{array}{r} 1.14 \\ + 0.49 \\ \hline 1.63 \end{array}$$

7. 9.36 **9.** 16.75 **11.** 6.07 + 3.84 = 9.91 **13.** 32. + 4.3 = 36.3 **15.** 31 **17.** 18.94 m **19.** 122.312, 123.423, 124.534; sums increase by 1.111; 31.345 + 94.3 = 125.645; 32.456 + 94.3 = 126.756
21.

```
            22.18
        14.26   7.92
      8.92   5.34   2.58
   4.52   4.4   0.94   1.64
 1.02   3.5   0.9   0.04   1.6
```

23. 267.06; Silver **25.** 3.1 **27.** 8.01 **29.** 17

4.2 Communicating about Mathematics, p. 161

A. $6.47 change; $13.54, $13.55, $13.65, $13.75, $14.00, $15.00, $20.00 **B.** $8.82 change; $21.19, $21.20, $21.25, $21.50, $21.75, $22.00, $23.00, $24.00, $25.00, $30.00

4.2 Exercises, pp. 162–163

1. $2.45 - 2.38 = 0.07$ **2.** No; line up the decimal points. **3.** Yes **4.** No; $7.20 - 1.05$ **5.** $1.01 - 0.34 = 0.67$ **7.** b; 1.19 **9.** 2.69% **11.** 0.43 **13.** 2.542 **15.** 4.348 **17.** 1.194 **19.** 10.992 **21.** 7.683 **23.** 2.7 lb per person **25.** Yes **27.** 5.01

4.2 Mixed Review, p. 164

1. Denominator increases by 3; $\frac{1}{12}$, $\frac{1}{15}$, $\frac{1}{18}$ **3.** $469 + 135 = 604$ **5.** $89 \times 2 = 178$ **7.** Three thousand two hundred twelve **9.** 170

4.3 Communicating about Mathematics, p. 167

Estimates will vary, but should be between the following:
Week 1: $11.00–$12.00,
Week 2: $11.00–$12.00,
Week 3: $11.00–$11.50,
Week 4: $13.00–$14.00

4.3 Exercises, pp. 168–169

1. Rounding and front-end estimation; answers will vary. **2.** Add or subtract the digits in the column at the far left, adjust by estimating sum or difference of remaining digits, and total sum or difference. **3.a.** $9 + 12 = 21$; $0.75 + 0.54$ is about 1; $21 + 1 = 22$ **b.** $8 - 2 = 6$; $0.62 - 0.18$ is about 0.5; $6 + 0.5 = 6.5$

4. 4 **5.** 9 **7.** 20,000 **9.** 2.6 **11.** R: 1300; FE: 1250 **13.** R: $12.00; FE: $12.00 **15.** R: 24,000; FE: 23,600 **17.** ≈ 9 units **19.** ≈ 5 units **21.** 3 **23.** 6.3 units

Lab 4.4, On Your Own, p. 171

4.a. 0.07 **b.** 0.24 **c.** 0.18 **d.** 0.81 **e.** 0.84 **f.** 1.04 **g.** 1.08 **h.** 0.22 **5.a.** Always; examples will vary **b.** Sometimes; examples will vary. **6.** Never

4.4 Communicating about Mathematics, p. 173

A. $0.75; $25.70 **B.** $0.06; $1.56 **C.** $7.00; $146.90 **D.** $95.40; $1685.40

4.4 Exercises, pp. 174–175

1. 3 **2.** 5 **3.** 6 **4.** 22 **5.** 176 **7.** d; it's about half of 0.235. **9.** a; it's close to 5×2. **11.** 189.503 **13.** 11.844 **15.** 3 **17.** 4.4 **19.** 0.7225 sq km **21.** 12.6225 **23.** 6.62625 **25.** 9.931285 **27.** 10.16 cm **29.** 1.016 cm **31.** $0.3 \times 6 = ?$; 1.8 **33.** $0.48 \times 6.75 = ?$; 3.24 **35.** $585.60 **37.** 10% **39.** 80%

Mid-Chapter Self-Test, p. 176

1. 9.23 **2.** $4.43 **3.** 3.95 **4.** 9.18 **5.** 11.62 **6.** $24.27 **7.–9.** Estimation procedures will vary. **7.** Between $11.00–$12.00 **8.** Between 26,000–27,000 **9.** Between $29.00–$30.00 **10.** 3.5 **11.** 4.56 **12.** 35.90 **13.** 3.06 **14.** 0.54 **15.** 0.05 **16.** 12.57 units **17.** 33.6 units **18.** 36.48 sq units **19.** $0.80 \times 75 = ?$; 60 **20.** $0.50 \times 37 = ?$; 18.5 **21.** $0.35 \times 46 = ?$; 16.1 **22.** Ice cream; by rounding to the nearest dollar, you spent $7.00 and have $2.00 left for dessert. **23.** Lasagna, garden salad, soda, and pie; or spaghetti, Caesar salad, tea, and pie; explanations will vary. **24.** $11.67

■ 4.5 Communicating about Mathematics, p. 178

A. 2.45

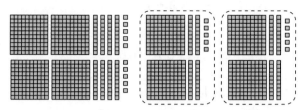

B. 0.9

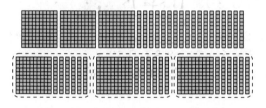

■ 4.5 Exercises, pp. 179–181

1. $4.56 \div 4 = 1.14$

2. 1.6

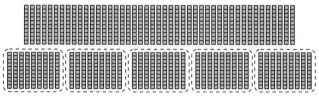

3. Explanations will vary.

4. About 3; 2.7

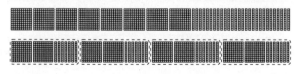

5. About 3; 3.25

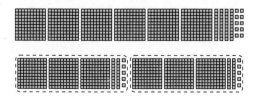

6. About 2; 1.75

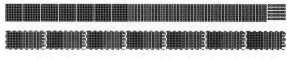

7. $3.9 \div 3 = 1.3$

9. About 2; 2.2

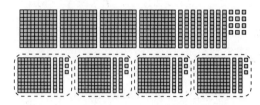

11. About 1; 1.23

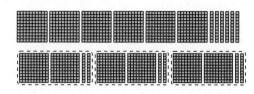

13. 1.65 **15.** 16.7 **17.** $1.6 \div 0.8 = 2$, or $1.6 \div 2 = 0.8$ **19.** 9 **21.** 10 **23.** The 8 should be placed above the 6; correct answer is 8.03. **25.** always **27.** $1.23 **29.** $1.70 **31.** 9.48 in. $\times$ 9.48 in. **33.** 77 **35.** 0.03 **37.** 4 **39.** 64

■ 4.5 Mixed Review, p. 181

1. 18 **3.** 10 **5.** $27 - (9 - 4) + 2 = 24$ **7.** $12 \div (6 + 6) \times 7 = 7$ **9.** 9.4, 9.45, 9.5, 9.54 **11.** 3 **13.** 5

15.

■ 4.6 Communicating about Mathematics, p. 183

A. 100 **B.** 1000 **C.** 10 **D.** 10 **E.** 1000 **F.** 100

■ *4.6 Exercises, pp. 184–185*

1. To multiply, move the decimal point right one place for each zero in the power of 10; to divide, move the decimal point left one place for each zero in the power of 10; examples will vary. **2.** Multiplying makes a number greater so decimal point moves right. **3.** 4.2 **4.** 0.056 **5.** 1.7 **6.** 8300 **7.** 9000 **9.** 0.007 **11.** 23.7 **13.** 1200 **15.** 0.126 **17.** 18,000 **19.** 250 **21.** 40 **23.** 0.039 **25.** 1000 **27.** 987.6 **29.** > **31.** = **33.** 200,000,000,000,000,000,000; 20 **35.** 100 **37.** cm

■ *Lab 4.7, On Your Own, p. 187*

7. $12 \div 6$; 2 **8.** $120 \div 6$; 20 **9.** $1.2 \div 6$; 0.2 **10.** $120 \div 6$; 20 **11.** $1200 \div 6$; 200 **12.** $1200 \div 6$; 200 **13.** d; explanations will vary but should include looking at the value of the dividend. **a.** 0.4 **b.** 4 **c.** 40 **d.** 400 **14.a.** 0.4 **b.** 0.04 **c.** 0.004 **d.** 0.0004

■ *4.7 Communicating about Mathematics, p. 189*

$100 \div 0.00165 = 60,606$ bills; $60,606 \times \$1 = \$60,606$; $60,606 \times \$5 = \$303,030$; $60,606 \times \$10 = \$606,060$; $60,606 \times \$20 = \$1,212,120$

■ *4.7 Exercises, pp. 190–191*

1. Change "quotient" to "divisor" because you don't know the quotient before you divide. **2.** Change "two" to "three" or change "1000" to "100" because moving a decimal point two places right is the same as multiplying by 100. **3.** 22 **4.** 2.2 **5.** 220 **6.** 0.22 **7.** 10 **9.** 10^2; 100 **11.** 13 **13.** 15.7 **15.** 11 **17.** 1570 **19.** 2000 **21.** 219 **23.** 2.5 km **25.** 0.65; 0.065 **27.** 100; 1000 **29.** $1.34 per meter **31.** Carrot 14 lb, Onion 10.1 lb, Radish 34.42 lb, Zucchini 58.5 lb

■ *4.8 Communicating about Mathematics, p. 193*

7% or 14 people; the top five activities accounted for 93%, leaving 7% for other.

■ *4.8 Exercises, pp. 194–195*

1. b **2.** c **3.** a **4.** 84 **5.** 30 **6.** Answers will vary. **7.** 24 **9.** 36 **11.** $15.00; $22.50 **13.** $1.60; $6.40 **15.** 5,000,000 **17.** 500,000 **19.** 54 **21.** 33 **23.** 852,390 **25.** 820,380 **27.** All except b are $\frac{6}{100}$ **29.** All except b are $\frac{45}{1000}$

■ *Chapter Review, pp. 197–198*

1. 8.795 **3.** 15.88 **5.** $0.55 **7.** $6.54 **9.** 0.12 **11.** No; not enough time, the tasks round to $10 + 30 + 40 = 80$ minutes. **13.** 0.28 **15.** 12.474 **17.** 55.822 **19.** 36.125 **21.** 100 **23.** 5.5 m **25.** False **27.** 42 **29.**

Across: **4.** 8.49 **6.** 2.201 **8.** 34.06 **10.** 1700 **12.** 22.26 **13.** 25.215 **14.** 8.05; Down: **1.** 54.439 **2.** 3.03 **3.** 1.205 **5.** 5.148 **7.** 420 **9.** 200 **11.** 6.69

CHAPTER 5

■ *Lab 5.1, On Your Own, p. 205*

13.–15. Answers will vary.

■ 5.1 Communicating about Mathematics, p. 208

Answers will vary but could include: weights of 30 dogs.

■ 5.1 Exercises, pp. 209–210

1. c **2.** a **3.** b **4.** Answers will vary.
5.

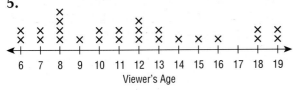

Viewer's Age

6. 13; 8
7. 7; 5; 11; 6

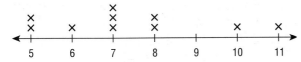

9. 16; 11; 17; 6

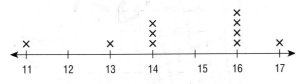

11.

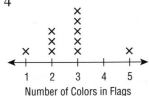

Braille Letters

13. Answers will vary but could include: the range of the data is 4, the smallest number of dots is 1, and the largest number of dots is 5. **15.** Answers will vary.
17. 4

Number of Colors in Flags

■ 5.1 Mixed Review, p. 211

1. $5 + x = 27$; $x = 22$ **3.** $(3 \times 1000) + (2 \times 100) + (5 \times 1)$ **5.** $(8 \times 1) + (2 \times \frac{1}{10}) + (5 \times \frac{1}{100})$ **7.** 4.4 m **9.** 1.25 m **11.** $\frac{54}{100}$
13. $\frac{87}{100}$

■ 5.2 Communicating about Mathematics, p. 213

21, 31, 39, 44, 45, 48, 48, 49, 49 50, 52, 54, 56, 56, 56, 56, 57, 60, 60, 63; questions will vary.

■ 5.2 Exercises, pp. 214–215

1. Draw a vertical line. The tens digits form the stem and are placed on the left, in order from least to greatest. The ones digits form the leaves and are placed on the right side of the vertical line, in order from least to greatest.

2.
```
0 | 1 2 5
1 | 0 1 4 6 8
2 | 1 2 6 7 9
3 | 3 3 5 9
```
Key: 3 | 9 = 39

1, 2, 5, 10, 11, 14, 16, 18, 21, 22, 26, 27, 29, 33, 33, 35, 39 **3.** 7.1, 7.2, 7.7, 8.2, 8.5, 8.6, 8.8, 8.9, 9.0, 9.3, 9.4, 9.4, 9.8
5. b **7.** 1, 2, 3, 5
9.
```
0 | 2 3 5 9
1 | 0 5 6 7
2 | 3 4
3 | 0 1 1 4 8 9
4 | 2
5 | 6 9 9
```
Key: 5 | 9 = 59
11.
```
5 | 4
6 | 1 3 3 3 4 5 5 7 8 8 9 9 9 9
7 | 0 0 1 2 2 3 4 4 4 4 4 5 5 6 6 7 7 7 9 9
8 | 0 0 0 1 1 3 3 4 4 6 7 8 8 9
9 | 4
```
Key: 8 | 9 = 89
December Record High Temperatures
13. 74°F **15.** 3, 21, 25, 5 **17.** 5.5, 2.75, 5, 1.3

Lab 5.3, On Your Own, p. 217

6.a. 11 **b.** 11.5 **c.** 11 **7.a.** Answers will vary, one possibility: 8, 12 **b.** Answers will vary, one possibility: 9, 11 **c.** Not possible. **8.a.** 11 **b.** 14 **c.** 17 **d.** Number increases by 3.

5.3 Communicating about Mathematics, p. 219

Answers will vary but could include: tops of the higher bars could be moved to shorter bars to make all same height.

5.3 Exercises, pp. 220–221

1. 7 **2.** 8, 2, 5 **3.** 33 **4.** 41 **5.** 114 **7.** The average of 11 and 7 is 9. **9.** 60 **11.** 104 **13.** 74 **15.** 262 **17.** 435 **19.** 27 **21.** Estimates will vary; average is 39. **23.** 12 ÷ 4 or 12 ÷ 3 **25.** 15 ÷ 3 or 15 ÷ 5 **27.** 40

5.4 Communicating about Mathematics, p. 224

Answers will vary but could include: mode, because it appears most often. Mean: $8.50, median: $6.50, mode: $6.00; answers will vary but could include mode because it appears most often.

5.4 Exercises, pp. 225–226

1. 55.79; 50; 70 **2.** True **3.** False; data has no mode. **4.** False; median is mean of two middle numbers or 6.5 **5.** 46.50; 45 **7.** 12; 12 **9.** b **11.** 142.57; 143; 111 **13.** 40.96; 41; 41 **15.** 14, 12, 12; answers will vary but could include: the age of the bus driver inflates the mean or "average" age. **17.** About 160

Mid-Chapter Self-Test, p. 228

1. a **2.** c **3.** b
4.

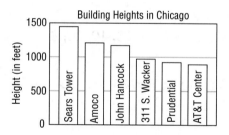

Super Bowls Won

5. Answers will vary but could include: the most common number of wins is 1 and the range of the data is 4. **6.** 1

7.
```
0 | 1 3 4 4 4 5 7 9
1 | 0 0 2 3 6 7 7 7 7 8 9 9
2 | 1 2 4 5 9
3 | 2 5 6
4 | 5
   Key: 3 | 6 = 36
```

8. 49ers **9.** Giants; they won by only 1 point. **10.** 44 **11.** 28 **12.** 74 **13.** 30, 31, 40; answers will vary.

5.5 Communicating about Mathematics, p. 230

Comparisons will vary.

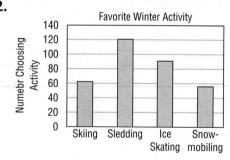

5.5 Exercises, pp. 231–233

1. Answers will vary.
2.

Favorite Winter Activity

3. Answers will vary. **4.** c **5.** False
7. Answers will vary but should include:
no title, or bars are different widths. **9.** a
11. b
13.

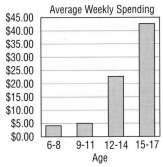

15.

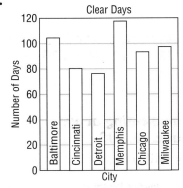

17. 9 **19.** 25 **21.** 9 **23.** 10; 10; 8

■ **5.5 Mixed Review, p. 233**

1. 12 **3.** 18 **5.** 34.5 **7.** 3.8 **9.** 2 **11.** 27
13. 14.32 **15.** 8.77 **17.** False; 0.048
19. True

■ **5.6 Communicating about
Mathematics, p. 235**

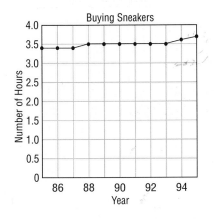

Year	Hours
1985	$32.37 \div 9.54 \approx 3.4$
1986	$32.65 \div 9.73 \approx 3.4$
1987	$34.10 \div 9.91 \approx 3.4$
1988	$35.58 \div 10.19 \approx 3.5$
1989	$35.56 \div 10.48 \approx 3.5$
1990	$38.26 \div 10.83 \approx 3.5$
1991	$39.68 \div 11.18 \approx 3.5$
1992	$40.66 \div 11.46 \approx 3.5$
1993	$41.22 \div 11.76 \approx 3.5$
1994	$43.16 \div 12.05 \approx 3.6$
1995	$45.32 \div 12.34 \approx 3.7$

Conclusions will vary but could include:
data show small increases every 3–5
years.

■ **5.6 Exercises, pp. 236–237**

1. Answers will vary but could include:
changes over time. **2.** Answers will vary
but could include: grid lines not evenly
spaced. **3.** Answers will vary but could
include: numbers don't start at zero. **4.**
1982–1984 **5.** Answers will vary but
could include numbers in the range of
60–70 million. **7.** Answers will vary but
should include numbers in a range of
20–40. **9.** No definite trend.
11. Answers will vary.

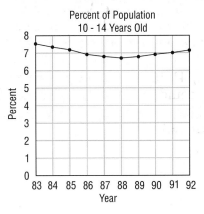

13. Answers will vary but could include numbers in a range of 30–40. **15.** 1, 3, 5, 7; numbers increase by 2. **17.** 2, 3, 5, 8; numbers increase by 1, 2, 3,… .

■ **Lab 5.7, On Your Own, p. 239**

8. Answers will vary but could include: total doesn't add to 40 or increments on scale uneven.

9.

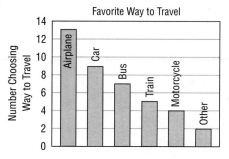

10. The airplane bar is about 3 times the size of the motorcycle bar.

■ **5.7 Communicating about Mathematics, p. 241**

Answers will vary.

■ **5.7 Exercises, pp. 242–243**

1. Yes; unequal flower sizes **2.** No **3.** Yes; no key **4.–6.** Descriptions will vary. **4.** Bar **5.** Line plot **6.** Line graph **7.** d **9.** a **11.** c

13.

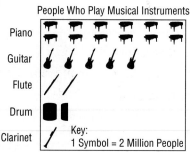

15.

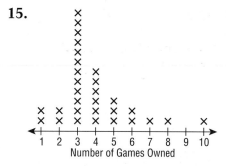

A stem-and-leaf plot, in this case, has only 2 stems and is not suitable.

17. 4 | 1 4 5
         5 | 3 6
         6 | 5 8
         7 | 4 9
         8 | 3 6 7
         Key: 7 | 9 = 79

19. Between 1.5 and 2

■ **Chapter Review, pp. 245–246**

1. a. 5 **b.** 5

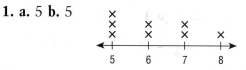

3. 43 **5.** 45

7.

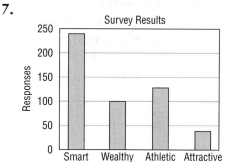

9.

Sports Equipment Bought in One Day

Hockey Sticks
Bowling Shoes
Soccer Balls
Skateboards
Basketballs

11.–13. Answers will vary. **15.** 8; H **17.** 18; R **19.** 15; O **21.** 11; K **23.** 15; O **25.** 13; M **27.** 19; S; Sherlock Holmes

CHAPTER 6

■ Lab 6.1, On Your Own, p. 253

7. $\frac{1}{4}$ **8.** $\frac{3}{4}$ **9.** $\frac{6}{8}$ **10.** $\frac{2}{6}$ **11.** $\frac{1}{4}$ **12.** $\frac{3}{5}$ **13.** $\frac{20}{30}$
14. $\frac{13}{30}$

15.

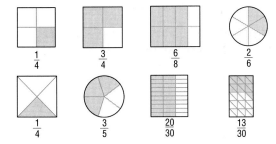

$\frac{1}{4}$ $\qquad$ $\frac{3}{4}$ $\qquad$ $\frac{6}{8}$ $\qquad$ $\frac{2}{6}$

$\frac{1}{4}$ $\qquad$ $\frac{3}{5}$ $\qquad$ $\frac{20}{30}$ $\qquad$ $\frac{13}{30}$

■ 6.1 Communicating about Mathematics, p. 255

Equal to $\frac{1}{2}$: D; equal to 1: B; close to 0: A, H; close to $\frac{1}{2}$: E, F; close to 1: C, G

■ 6.1 Exercises, pp. 256–257

1. No, all parts not same size. **2.** numerator; denominator **3.** mixed number **4.** 12 **5.** c **6.** a **7.** b **8.** Answers will vary but could include: sharing snacks with friends. **9.** Yes; $\frac{2}{3}$ **11.** Yes; $\frac{4}{8}$ **13.** Yes; $\frac{2}{10}$
15.

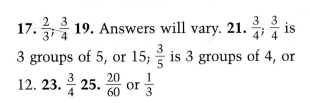

17. $\frac{2}{3}$; $\frac{3}{4}$ **19.** Answers will vary. **21.** $\frac{3}{4}$; $\frac{3}{4}$ is 3 groups of 5, or 15; $\frac{3}{5}$ is 3 groups of 4, or 12. **23.** $\frac{3}{4}$ **25.** $\frac{20}{60}$ or $\frac{1}{3}$

■ Lab 6.2, On Your Own, p. 259

7. $\frac{7}{12}$; $\frac{5}{12}$ **8.** $\frac{7}{10}$; $\frac{3}{10}$ **9.** $\frac{9}{16}$; $\frac{7}{16}$ **10.** $\frac{5}{14}$; $\frac{9}{14}$

11. One possible model:

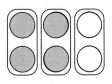

12. One possible model:

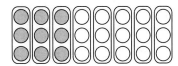

13. One possible model:

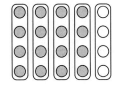

14. One possible model:

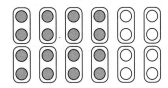

15. 24

■ 6.2 Communicating about Mathematics, p. 261

All are the ratio $\frac{9}{14}$; value of ratios not affected by units.

■ 6.2 Exercises, pp. 262–263

1. Cut each pizza into five pieces. Each person gets four pieces; $\frac{4}{5}$ **2.** $\frac{3}{2}$
3. $1\frac{1}{2}$, or $\frac{3}{2}$

4. Make sure the numbers to be compared have the same units of measure. Use them as the numerator and denominator of a fraction.

5. 24

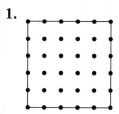

7. $\frac{3}{8}$ **9.** $\frac{1}{2}$ dollar **11.** $1\frac{1}{3}$, or $\frac{4}{3}$ pies **13.** Answers will vary. **15.** Answers will vary. **17.** $\frac{12}{24}$, or $\frac{1}{2}$ **19.** $\frac{8}{8}$, or 1 **21.** $\frac{63}{72}$ **23.** $6\frac{4}{5}$, or 6 R4 **25.** 9.7 **27.** 12.3 **29.** The numerator increases by 1; $\frac{4}{5}$, $\frac{5}{5}$, $\frac{6}{5}$

■ 6.2 Mixed Review, p. 264

1.

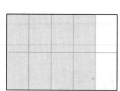

3. 12.8 **5.** $\frac{4}{8}$, or $\frac{1}{2}$ **7.** $\frac{9}{15}$, or $\frac{3}{5}$ **9.** 0.2 **11.** 0.72

■ 6.3 Communicating about Mathematics, p. 266

They are equivalent.

■ 6.3 Exercises, pp. 267–268

1. $\frac{3}{5}$, or $\frac{12}{20}$

2.

3. $\frac{1}{3}$ and $\frac{3}{6}$; no. **4.** Yes; $\frac{1 \times 2}{6 \times 2} = \frac{2}{12}$ **5.** No; numerator and denominator not multi-

plied by the same number **6.** Yes; $\frac{5 \times 3}{8 \times 3} = \frac{15}{24}$ **7.** b; $\frac{6}{18}$ **9.** d; $\frac{2}{3}$ **11.** 10 **13.** 9 **15.–18.** Multiply each fraction by other names for 1, such as $\frac{2}{2}$, $\frac{3}{3}$, etc. **15.** One possible set: $\frac{14}{16}$, $\frac{21}{24}$, $\frac{28}{32}$ **17.** One possible set: $\frac{5}{6}$, $\frac{10}{12}$, $\frac{20}{24}$ **19.** False; 6 **21.** True

23.

Dollars	1	2	5	8	10
Quarters	4	8	20	32	40
Dimes	10	20	50	80	100

$\frac{\text{Quarters}}{\text{Dimes}}$: $\frac{4}{10}$, $\frac{8}{20}$, $\frac{20}{50}$, $\frac{32}{80}$, $\frac{40}{100}$; the ratios are equivalent.

25. $\frac{35}{63}$; $\frac{5}{9}$; the ratios are equivalent **27.** 0.62, $\frac{62}{100}$ **29.** 0.1, $\frac{1}{10}$ **31.** 0.07

■ Mid-Chapter Self-Test, p. 269

1. $\frac{5}{8}$; a **2.** $\frac{7}{8}$; d **3.** $\frac{1}{8}$; b **4.** $\frac{4}{8}$; c

5.

6.

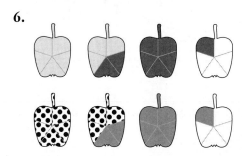

7. $\frac{6}{10}$ **8.** $\frac{3}{5}$ **9.** $\frac{9}{15}$ **10.** They are all equivalent; $\frac{3 \cdot 2}{5 \cdot 2} = \frac{6}{10}$; $\frac{3 \cdot 3}{5 \cdot 3} = \frac{9}{15}$ **11.** False; 28 **12.** False; 3 **13.** True **14.** $\frac{5}{28}$ **15.** $\frac{5}{7}$ **16.** $\frac{2}{6}$ **17.** 8 ft

4.

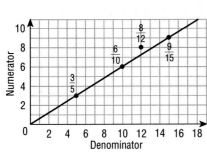

$\frac{3}{5}$, $\frac{6}{10}$, and $\frac{9}{15}$ are equivalent because they are in the same line.

5.

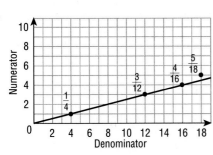

$\frac{1}{4}$, $\frac{3}{12}$, and $\frac{4}{16}$ are equivalent because they are in the same line.

6.

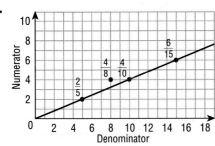

$\frac{2}{5}$, $\frac{4}{10}$, and $\frac{6}{15}$ are equivalent because they are in the same line.

7.

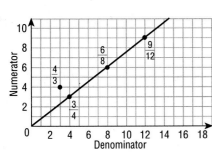

$\frac{3}{4}$, $\frac{6}{8}$, and $\frac{9}{12}$ are equivalent because they are in the same line.

8.

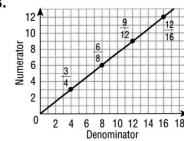

$\frac{6}{8} = \frac{3 \cdot 2}{4 \cdot 2}$, $\frac{9}{12} = \frac{3 \cdot 3}{4 \cdot 3}$, $\frac{12}{16} = \frac{3 \cdot 4}{4 \cdot 4}$; $\frac{3}{4}$ is the simplest form.

9.

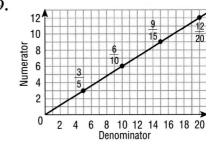

$\frac{6}{10} = \frac{3 \cdot 2}{5 \cdot 2}$; $\frac{9}{15} = \frac{3 \cdot 3}{5 \cdot 3}$; $\frac{12}{20} = \frac{3 \cdot 4}{5 \cdot 4}$; $\frac{3}{5}$ is the simplest form

10.

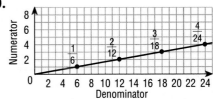

$\frac{2}{12} = \frac{1 \cdot 2}{6 \cdot 2}$; $\frac{3}{18} = \frac{1 \cdot 3}{6 \cdot 3}$; $\frac{4}{24} = \frac{1 \cdot 4}{6 \cdot 4}$; $\frac{1}{6}$ is the simplest form

11. It is the first one on the left.

■ *6.4 Communicating about Mathematics, p. 273*

No; pace is not the same; $\frac{2}{3}$ is not equivalent to $\frac{28}{40}$.

■ 6.4 Exercises, pp. 274–275

1. c 2. a 3. b 4. d 5. $\frac{9}{21}$, $\frac{3}{7}$ and $\frac{6}{14}$; $\frac{3}{7}$

6. $\frac{6}{18}$; $\frac{1}{3}$

7. 12

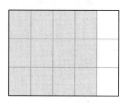

8. Answers will vary. 9. $\frac{4}{16}$; $\frac{1}{4}$ 11. $\frac{3}{8}$ 13. $\frac{1}{2}$

15. 1 17. 7 19. $\frac{5}{8}$ 21. False; there are no common factors. 23. 30 25. 8 27. 12 29. $\frac{?}{7} = \frac{8}{28}$; 2 ft 31. True; explanations will vary. 33. < 35. > 37. = 39. > 41. =

■ Lab 6.5, On Your Own, p. 277

7. $\frac{1}{2}$ is greater.

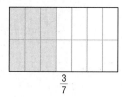

$\frac{3}{7}$

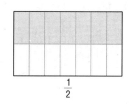

$\frac{1}{2}$

8. $\frac{5}{8}$ is greater.

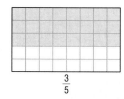

$\frac{3}{5}$

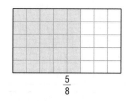

$\frac{5}{8}$

9.–12.

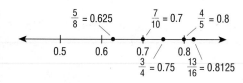

$\frac{5}{8} = 0.625$ $\frac{7}{10} = 0.7$ $\frac{4}{5} = 0.8$

0.5 0.6 0.7 0.8

$\frac{3}{4} = 0.75$ $\frac{13}{16} = 0.8125$

9. $\frac{7}{10}$ 10. $\frac{4}{5}$ 11. $\frac{4}{5}$ 12. $\frac{13}{16}$

■ 6.5 Communicating about Mathematics, p. 279

$\frac{2}{3}$ and $\frac{3}{4}$; $\frac{2}{3}$ is smaller; $\frac{2}{3}$ of $48 is $32.

■ 6.5 Exercises, pp. 280–282

1. Model, write as decimals, and rewrite as equivalent fractions; preferences will vary. 2. $\frac{1}{4}$ and $\frac{2}{5}$; $\frac{2}{5}$ is greater.

3. From the diagram $\frac{1}{5} > \frac{1}{6}$; $\frac{4}{5} > \frac{4}{6}$ because the fractions have the same numerator and fifths are greater than sixths.

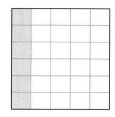 

4. $\frac{4}{9}$ is less than half, and $\frac{5}{9}$ is more than half; therefore $\frac{5}{9}$ is greater than $\frac{4}{9}$. 5. $\frac{1}{3}$ is less than half, and $\frac{3}{4}$ is more than half; therefore $\frac{3}{4}$ is greater than $\frac{1}{3}$. 6. $\frac{3}{7}$ is less than half, and $\frac{2}{3}$ is more than half; therefore $\frac{2}{3}$ is greater than $\frac{3}{7}$. 7. $\frac{1}{3}$ and $\frac{2}{4}$; $\frac{2}{4}$

9. $\frac{2}{4}$ equals $\frac{1}{2}$, and $\frac{3}{4}$ is more than half; so $\frac{3}{4}$ is greater than $\frac{2}{4}$. 11. $\frac{3}{8}$ is less than half, and $\frac{4}{6}$ is more than half; so $\frac{4}{6}$ is greater than $\frac{3}{8}$.

13. $\frac{3}{10}$, $\frac{2}{5}$, $\frac{5}{10}$, $\frac{4}{5}$

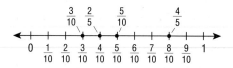

$\frac{3}{10}$ $\frac{2}{5}$ $\frac{5}{10}$ $\frac{4}{5}$

0 $\frac{1}{10}$ $\frac{2}{10}$ $\frac{3}{10}$ $\frac{4}{10}$ $\frac{5}{10}$ $\frac{6}{10}$ $\frac{7}{10}$ $\frac{8}{10}$ $\frac{9}{10}$ 1

15. $\frac{1}{10}, \frac{1}{2}, \frac{6}{10}, \frac{4}{5}$

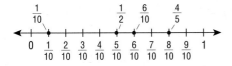

17. > **19.** > **21.** $\frac{8}{9}$ **23.** $\frac{1}{2}$ **25.** One possibility: $\frac{1}{2}$ **27.** $\frac{7}{8}$ is greater than $\frac{7}{9}$, $\frac{7}{10}$, or $\frac{7}{11}$ **29.** $\frac{4}{6}$ **31.** $\frac{7}{12}$
33. 6 chose science, 8 chose English, 4 chose computer science, and 6 chose math.

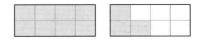

35. English. **37.** $\frac{12}{18}$; $\frac{2}{3}$ **39.** $\frac{21}{28}$; $\frac{3}{4}$

■ **6.5 Mixed Review, p. 282**

1. 3 **3.** 7 **5.** 11.09 **7.** $\frac{48}{100}$, $\frac{12}{25}$ **9.** $\frac{32}{100}$, $\frac{8}{25}$
11. 2.02, 2.12, 2.19, 2.2, 2.3 **13.** 0.009, 0.05, 0.09, 0.19, 0.6

■ **6.6 Communicating about Mathematics, p. 285**

A. Answers will vary but could include: use the half-cup measure 5 times. **B.** Answers will vary but could include: use the half-cup measure twice and the quarter-cup measure once. **C.** Answers will vary but could include: use the half-cup measure once and the quarter-cup measure once.

■ **6.6 Exercises, pp. 286–287**

1. It is equal to or larger than one; a proper fraction is less than one. **2.** $3\frac{1}{2}$; there are 3 wholes and $\frac{1}{2}$ of another whole. **3.** $\frac{7}{2}$
4. Model it first, divide the whole into fourths, then add up the fourths; $\frac{9}{4}$.

5. $5\frac{2}{3}$ **6.** $\frac{19}{4}$ **7.** always **9.** sometimes
11. $2\frac{4}{6}$, $\frac{16}{6}$ **13.** a **15.** b
17. $1\frac{3}{8}$

19. $4\frac{5}{6}$

21. $\frac{7}{4}$

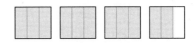

23. $\frac{11}{3}$

25. $\frac{59}{2}$; it means 59 half dollars. **27.** 4.34
29. 4.284 **31.** 51.8

■ **6.7 Communicating about Mathematics, p. 289**

Answers will vary.

1. $\frac{5}{10}$ **2.** $\frac{3}{10}$ **3.** $\frac{4}{10}$ **4.–6.** Examples will vary. **4.** c **5.** a **6.** b **7.–8.** Answers will vary. **9.** $\frac{2}{6}$ **11.** $\frac{4}{12}$ **13.** b **15.** c **17.** Answers will vary. **19.** $\frac{13}{100}$ **21.** $\frac{3}{4}$ **23.** $<$

■ **Chapter Review, pp. 293–294**

1. $\frac{2}{4}, \frac{4}{9}, \frac{9}{16}; \frac{4}{9}, \frac{2}{4}, \frac{9}{16}$ **3.** Answers will vary but could include: $\frac{12}{14}, \frac{18}{21}, \frac{24}{28}$ **5.** Answers will vary but could include: $\frac{3}{4}, \frac{6}{8}, \frac{12}{16}$ **7.** $\frac{6}{9}$, or $\frac{2}{3}$ **9.** $\frac{24}{64}$, or $\frac{3}{8}$ **11.** 20 **13.** 42 **15.** 52 **17.** c **19.** d **21.** 0 **23.** $\frac{1}{2}$ **25.** $\frac{1}{2}$; explanations will vary **27.** Australia **29.** Answers will vary but could include $\frac{4}{10}$ or 0.40.

■ **Cumulative Review–Chapters 1–6, pp. 296–297**

1. 12 **3.** 5 **5.** 3 **7.** 3 **9.** 16 **11.** 27 **13.** 1.39 **15.** $\frac{16}{24}$ **17.** 70 **19.** 48 **21.** 14 **23.** 0.01, 0.011, 0.02, 0.1, 0.11 **25.** $\frac{1}{2}, \frac{4}{7}, \frac{2}{3}, \frac{4}{5}$ **27.** 1600 **29.** 15 **31.** 7.85 **33.** 2.44 **35.** Mean, median, and mode are all 14. **37.** Answers will vary. **39.** 70 lb **41.**

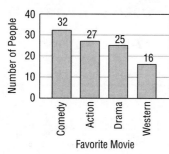

43. Drama **45.** 1991 **47.** 12

CHAPTER 7

■ **7.1 Communicating about Mathematics, p. 303**

Answers will vary.

■ **7.1 Exercises, pp. 304–305**

1. $1\frac{1}{8}''$, $\frac{9}{8}''$ **2.** $1\frac{2}{8}''$ or $\frac{10}{8}$ **3.** $\frac{1}{8}, \frac{2}{8}, \frac{3}{8}, \frac{4}{8}, \frac{5}{8}, \frac{6}{8}, \frac{7}{8}, \frac{8}{8}$; number increases by $\frac{1}{8}$ each time. **4.** $8\frac{1}{8}'' \times 10\frac{2}{8}''$; about 37 in. **5.a.** 2 **b.** 30 **6.** Five feet three and one-half inches; $63\frac{1}{2}''$ **7.** $2\frac{5}{8}$; c **9.** $4\frac{1}{2}$; e **11.** $1\frac{1}{8}$; a **13.** $2\frac{2}{8}$ or $2\frac{1}{4}''$ **15.** Answers will vary. **17.** Answers will vary. **19.** 5 **21.** 9 **23.** 3 **25.** 5 feet 11 inches **27.** $5'7\frac{3}{4}''$ **29.** About 12 ft **31.** Answers will vary but could include: first, change 40 yards into 1440 inches and divide by 72. The number of tire rotations is 20.

■ **7.2 Communicating about Mathematics, p. 307**

$\frac{9}{24}$; $\frac{20}{24}$; $\frac{14}{24}$; $\frac{3 \cdot 3}{8 \cdot 3} = \frac{9}{24}$, $\frac{5 \cdot 4}{6 \cdot 4} = \frac{20}{24}$, $\frac{7 \cdot 2}{12 \cdot 2} = \frac{14}{24}$; the least common multiple of these three fractions is 24. Rewriting helps you order these fractions because you can see the difference in size by looking at the numerator.

■ **7.2 Exercises, pp. 308–309**

1. c; it shows 3 out of 12 parts or $\frac{1}{4}$. **2.** True, $3 \times 10 = 30$, $5 \times 6 = 30$, $3 \times 15 = 45$, and $5 \times 9 = 45$. **3.** False; the least common multiple of 3 and 5 is 15. **4.** True; the least common multiple of 3 and 5 is 15. **5.** False; there may be a common multiple of two numbers that is smaller than their product. **6.** $\frac{2}{5}$; answers will vary but could include: you can use a common denominator. **7.** 5, 10, 15, 20, 25, 30, 35, **40**, 45, 50; 8, 16, 24, 32, **40**, 48, 56, 64, 72, 80; the least common multiple is 40. **9.** 5, 10, 15, 20, 25, **30**, 35, 40, 45, 50; 6, 12, 18, 24, **30**, 36, 42, 48, 54, 60; the least common multiple is 30.

11.

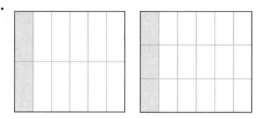

13.

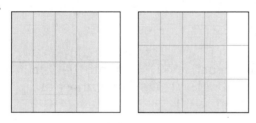

15. 12; $\frac{4}{12}$, $\frac{11}{12}$ **17.** 30; $\frac{5}{30}$, $\frac{21}{30}$ **19.** $\frac{1}{12} = \frac{2}{24}$, $\frac{1}{6} = \frac{4}{24}$, $\frac{3}{8} = \frac{9}{24}$, $\frac{5}{12} = \frac{10}{24}$, $\frac{2}{3} = \frac{16}{24}$, $\frac{5}{6} = \frac{20}{24}$, $\frac{7}{8} = \frac{21}{24}$, $\frac{11}{12} = \frac{22}{24}$; Well Done **21.** $\frac{3}{8}$ is not equivalent; LCD = 216; $\frac{6}{18} = \frac{6 \cdot 12}{8 \cdot 12} = \frac{72}{216}$; $\frac{3}{8} = \frac{3 \cdot 27}{8 \cdot 27} = \frac{81}{216}$; $\frac{9}{27} = \frac{9 \cdot 8}{27 \cdot 8} = \frac{72}{216}$.

23. $\frac{8}{34}$ **25.** Distance: $\frac{5}{8} = \frac{5 \cdot 3}{8 \cdot 3} = \frac{15}{24}$, $\frac{7}{12} = \frac{7 \cdot 2}{12 \cdot 2} = \frac{14}{24}$; you walked farther. Time: $\frac{3}{5} = \frac{3 \cdot 3}{5 \cdot 3} = \frac{9}{15}$, $\frac{2}{3} = \frac{2 \cdot 5}{3 \cdot 5} = \frac{10}{15}$; your friend walked longer. Speed: Since you walked farther in less time, you walked faster.

27. $\frac{45}{100}$ **29.** $\frac{8}{100}$

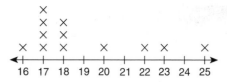

■ **7.2 Mixed Review, p. 310**
1. > **3.** = **5.** 7.85 **7.** 16.48 **9.** 100 **11.** 32

13. Mode is 17; answers will vary.

■ **Lab 7.3, On Your Own, p. 313**

11. $\frac{5}{6}$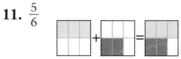

12. $\frac{6}{5}$ or $1\frac{1}{5}$

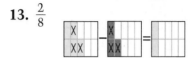

13. $\frac{2}{8}$

14. $\frac{2}{5}$

15. $\frac{3}{4}$

16. $\frac{13}{15}$

17. $\frac{3}{10}$

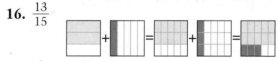

18. $\frac{5}{12}$

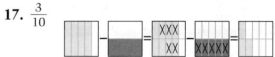

19. Yes; $\frac{2}{4} + \frac{3}{4} = \frac{5}{4}$ or $1\frac{1}{4}$.

20. Denominator could be 20; $\frac{3}{4} + \frac{2}{5} = \frac{15}{20} + \frac{8}{20} = \frac{23}{20}$ or $1\frac{3}{20}$

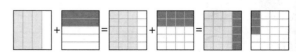

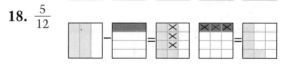

SELECTED ANSWERS

■ 7.3 Communicating about Mathematics, p. 315

5; $\frac{1}{8}$, $\frac{3}{4}$, and $\frac{5}{8}$; $\frac{1}{8}$, $\frac{1}{2}$, and $\frac{7}{8}$; $\frac{1}{4}$, $\frac{3}{8}$, and $\frac{7}{8}$; $\frac{1}{4}$, $\frac{1}{2}$, and $\frac{3}{4}$; $\frac{3}{8}$, $\frac{1}{2}$, and $\frac{5}{8}$

■ 7.3 Exercises, pp. 316–317

1. always; $\frac{3}{5} - \frac{1}{5} = \frac{2}{5}$; $\frac{4}{6} - \frac{2}{6} = \frac{2}{6}$ **2.** sometimes; $\frac{1}{7} + \frac{2}{7} + \frac{3}{7} = \frac{6}{7}$; $\frac{1}{4} + \frac{2}{4} + \frac{3}{4} = 1\frac{1}{2}$ **3.** sometimes; LCD of $\frac{1}{5}$ and $\frac{1}{3}$ is 15; LCD of $\frac{1}{6}$ and $\frac{1}{8}$ is 24. **4.** When adding or subtracting with common denominators, add or subtract their numerator and keep the same denominator; when adding or subtracting with unlike denominators, rewrite with a common denominator, then add or subtract. Explanations will vary. **5.a.** You forgot to rewrite using a common denominator. $\frac{2}{3} + \frac{4}{5} = \frac{10}{15} + \frac{12}{15} = \frac{22}{15}$ or $1\frac{7}{15}$. **b.** Keep the same denominator. $\frac{2}{3} + \frac{1}{6} = \frac{4}{6} + \frac{1}{6} = \frac{5}{6}$

6. $\frac{1}{5} + \frac{3}{5} = \frac{4}{5}$ **7.** $\frac{3}{4} - \frac{1}{2} = \frac{1}{4}$ **8.** Answers will vary.

9. $\frac{3}{4}$

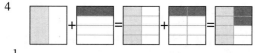

11. $\frac{1}{6}$

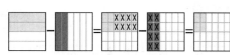

13. $\frac{4}{10}$ or $\frac{2}{5}$ **15.** $1\frac{3}{8}$ **17.** $\frac{9}{18}$ or $\frac{1}{2}$ **19.** $1\frac{6}{10}$ or $1\frac{3}{5}$ **21.** $2\frac{1}{12}$ yd **23.** $\frac{4}{7}$ **25.** $\frac{6}{3} - \frac{4}{3}$ **27.** $\frac{3}{8}$ **29.** No; $\frac{3}{4}$ **31.** No; $\frac{1}{2}$ **33.** 12.82 **35.** 8.54 **37.** 0.13

■ Lab 7.4, On Your Own, p. 319

12. $2\frac{5}{6}$

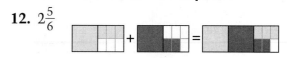

13. 1

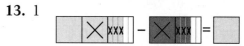

14. $2\frac{3}{4}$

15. $1\frac{3}{10}$

16. About 13; $\frac{2}{3}$ is over half and $\frac{1}{6}$ is nearly 0, so add 9 + 4. **17.** About 9; $\frac{4}{5}$ is over half and $\frac{1}{4}$ is under half, so add 6 + 3. **18.** About $3\frac{1}{2}$; $\frac{2}{3}$ is nearly $\frac{3}{4}$ so $7\frac{3}{4} - 4\frac{1}{4} = 3\frac{1}{2}$ **19.** About 1; $\frac{7}{8}$ and $\frac{5}{6}$ are almost equal to 1, so subtract 3 − 2. **20.** 1.4; it's similar because when subtracting fractions, you "line up" the whole numbers and the fractions.

■ 7.4 Communicating about Mathematics, p. 321

$4\frac{1}{2}$ in.

■ 7.4 Exercises, pp. 322–324

1. Answers may vary but could include: to find the sum, draw a $5\frac{5}{8}$ inch line segment, place end of ruler at end of original line segment and continue the line another $3\frac{1}{4}$ in. Measure total length; $8\frac{7}{8}$ in. To find the difference, mark $3\frac{1}{4}$ in. on the $5\frac{5}{8}$ in. line segment and measure from your mark to the end; $2\frac{3}{8}$ in. **2.** Add fractions, add whole numbers, simplify mixed number. **3.** Rewrite with a common denominator, subtract, and simplify mixed number.

4. $1\frac{1}{3} + 1\frac{3}{5} = 1\frac{5}{15} + 1\frac{9}{15} = 2\frac{14}{15}$

5. $2\frac{4}{5} - 1\frac{1}{5} = 1\frac{3}{5}$

7. c **9.** a **11.** $6\frac{8}{9} - 2\frac{4}{9} = 4\frac{4}{9}$ **13.** $3\frac{6}{8} + 1\frac{1}{2} =$ $5\frac{1}{4}$ **15.** $3\frac{4}{8}$ or $3\frac{1}{2}$ **17.** $11\frac{2}{10}$ or $11\frac{1}{5}$ **19.** $4\frac{1}{15}$ **21.** $9\frac{19}{24}$ **23.** $7\frac{3}{4} - 2\frac{2}{4}$; answer already in simplest form. **25.** 6 **27.** $1\frac{2}{8}$ or $1\frac{1}{4}$ **29.** $\frac{1}{5}$ **31.** $1\frac{6}{8}$ or $1\frac{3}{4}$; $1\frac{5}{8}$; $1\frac{4}{8}$ or $1\frac{1}{2}$; number decreases by $\frac{1}{8}$ **33.** $8\frac{1}{5}$; $8\frac{2}{5}$; $8\frac{3}{5}$; number increases by $\frac{1}{5}$ **35.** $2\frac{1}{5}$ and $3\frac{3}{5}$ **37.** $5\frac{1}{6}$ feet **39.** b **41.** c

▪ *7.4 Mixed Review, p. 324*

1. One possibility: a rectangle divided into 10 equal parts. **3.** 56 **5.** 325 **7.** $\frac{1}{9}$ **9.** 5 **11.** $\frac{14}{5}$ **13.** $\frac{47}{12}$

▪ *Mid-Chapter Self-Test, p. 325*

1. $2\frac{1}{8}$ in.; $\frac{17}{8}$ in. **2.** $2\frac{4}{8}$ or $2\frac{1}{2}$ in.; $\frac{20}{8}$ in. **3.** 76 in. **4.** No **5.** Yes **6.** No **7.** Yes **8.** e **9.** c **10.** d **11.** a **12.** f **13.** b **14.** 1 **15.** $\frac{4}{15}$ **16.** $\frac{7}{18}$ **17.** $\frac{11}{12}$ **18.** 1 **19.** $\frac{3}{8}$ **20.** 6 **21.** $7\frac{3}{6}$ or $7\frac{1}{2}$ **22.** $4\frac{6}{10}$ or $4\frac{3}{5}$ **23.** Less than half; $\frac{1}{5} + \frac{1}{4} = \frac{4}{20} + \frac{5}{20} = \frac{9}{20}$

▪ *Lab 7.5, On Your Own, p. 327*

7. a, $\frac{1}{2}$ **8.** d, $\frac{1}{5}$ **9.** a, $\frac{2}{3}$ **10.** b, $\frac{1}{2}$ **11.** c, $\frac{1}{4}$ **12.** Rewrite the whole number as a mixed number or improper fraction, then subtract.

▪ *7.5 Communicating about Mathematics, p. 329*

$1.75 more, $1\frac{75}{100}$

▪ *7.5 Exercises, pp. 330–331*

1. b **2.** c **3.** a **4.** $4\frac{100}{100} - 1\frac{35}{100} = 3\frac{65}{100}$; 5.00 − 1.35 = 3.65; preferences will vary. **5.** $2\frac{3}{4}$ sq yd **6.** $1\frac{1}{2}$ sq yd **7.** 8 **9.** 5 **11.** = **13.** < **15.** $14\frac{2}{3}$ yd **17.** $2\frac{5}{12}$ **19.** $1\frac{4}{5}$ **21.** $1\frac{8}{9}$ **23.** $2\frac{3}{5}$ **25.** $2\frac{1}{3}$ hours **27.** $1\frac{2}{5}$ **29.** $1\frac{3}{5}$ **31.** Yes; $5\frac{3}{8} - 2\frac{5}{8} = 2\frac{6}{8} > 2\frac{5}{8}$ **33.** music **35.** Answers will vary.

▪ *Lab 7.6, On Your Own, p. 333*

8. d; $3\frac{2}{3} - \frac{1}{3} = 3\frac{1}{3}$ **9.** a; $3\frac{3}{4} - 2\frac{2}{3} = 3\frac{9}{12} - 2\frac{8}{12} = 1\frac{1}{12}$ **10.** c; $3\frac{2}{3} - 2\frac{3}{4} = 3\frac{8}{12} - 2\frac{9}{12} = \frac{11}{12}$ **11.** b; $3\frac{1}{3} - 2\frac{2}{3} = 2\frac{4}{3} - 2\frac{2}{3} = \frac{2}{3}$

▪ *7.6 Communicating about Mathematics, p. 335*

$\frac{3}{8}$ and $\frac{11}{16}$, $\frac{7}{16}$ and $\frac{3}{4}$, $\frac{1}{2}$ and $\frac{13}{16}$, $\frac{9}{16}$ and $\frac{7}{8}$, $\frac{5}{8}$ and $\frac{15}{16}$, $\frac{11}{16}$ and 1, $\frac{3}{4}$ and $1\frac{1}{16}$, $\frac{13}{16}$ and $1\frac{1}{8}$, $\frac{7}{8}$ and $1\frac{3}{16}$, $\frac{15}{16}$ and $1\frac{1}{4}$; explanations will vary.

▪ *7.6 Exercises, pp. 336–337*

1. Rename; $\frac{2}{3}$ and $\frac{1}{4}$ have different denominators; $2\frac{5}{12}$ **2.** Regroup; $\frac{1}{8}$ is smaller than $\frac{5}{8}$; $\frac{1}{2}$ **3.** Rename; $\frac{7}{12}$ and $\frac{1}{3}$ have different denominators; $1\frac{1}{4}$ **4.** Answers will vary. **5.** d, b, c, a **7.** c **9.** a **11.** $2\frac{19}{24}$ **13.** $2\frac{13}{24}$ **15.** $11\frac{7}{15}$ **17.** $4\frac{5}{6}$ **19.** $1\frac{87}{100}$ **21.** $4\frac{3}{4}$ in. **23.** $1\frac{1}{4}$ in. **25.** $\frac{5}{6}$ hour

27.

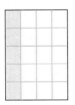

$\frac{1}{4}$ $\frac{2}{3}$	$\frac{4}{6}$ $1\frac{2}{3}$	$\frac{17}{9}$	$1\frac{8}{9}$ $\frac{1}{2}$	$\frac{1}{6}$	$\frac{2}{12}$ $\frac{3}{5}$
$\frac{2}{8}$ $\frac{4}{5}$	$\frac{8}{10}$ $\frac{5}{3}$ $\frac{6}{3}$	$\frac{3}{3}$	1	$\frac{2}{4}$ $\frac{4}{12}$	$\frac{6}{10}$ $\frac{1}{3}$ $\frac{3}{8}$
$\frac{5}{6}$ $\frac{10}{12}$	$\frac{1}{5}$ $\frac{2}{10}$	2 $\frac{3}{2}$	$\frac{1}{8}$ $\frac{1}{7}$	$\frac{2}{16}$ $\frac{2}{14}$ $\frac{5}{8}$	$\frac{6}{16}$ $\frac{10}{16}$
$2\frac{6}{6}$ 3	$\frac{3}{7}$	$\frac{6}{14}$ $1\frac{1}{2}$ $4\frac{3}{3}$	$\frac{3}{4}$ 5	$\frac{6}{8}$ $\frac{12}{24}$	$\frac{2}{6}$ $\frac{1}{3}$ $\frac{1}{2}$

■ 7.7 Communicating about Mathematics, p. 339

A. $9,859,230; 82 gold bars $\times$ 22.25 = 1824.5 lb; 1824.5 $\times$ $5400 = $9,852,300. 15 silver bars $\times$ 5.5 = 82.5 lb; 82.5 $\times$ $84 = $6930. $9,852,300 + 6930 = $9,859,230. **B.** $9,859,230 $\div$ 3 = $3,286,410 per person.

■ 7.7 Exercises, pp. 340–341

1. e **2.** c **3.** d **4.** f **5.** a **6.** b
7. Remaining teams;

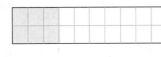

8. $\frac{1}{20}$; subtract $\frac{3}{10}$ from $\frac{14}{40}$. **9.** 1, it represents the whole amount of tickets **11.** $72\frac{3}{4}$ **13.** $60\frac{2}{5}$ in.; sixty and two fifths inches. **15.** 5'1", 5'8" **17.** Quarter horse; quarter horse can run $\frac{1}{4}$ mile in 20 seconds; thoroughbred can run $\frac{1}{4}$ mile in about 22 seconds. **19.** 120 **21.** 56 **23.** 5 **25.** 2

■ Chapter Review, pp. 343–344

1. 1 ft 3 in. **3.** 3 ft 2 in. **5.** $\frac{15}{36}$ **7.** $\frac{7}{8}$ **9.** $\frac{13}{30}$ **11.** $2\frac{3}{10}$ **13.** $5\frac{5}{12}$ **15.** = **17.** = **19.** $2\frac{3}{8}$ **21.** The sum is 1. All uses of water are listed in the table. **23.** $\frac{29}{100}$ **25.** $\frac{5}{12}$; $\frac{7}{12}$; $\frac{1}{6}$ more trees with white blossoms. **27.** $3\frac{7}{12}$ **29.** $1\frac{19}{24}$ **31.** $3\frac{7}{12}$ **33.** $2\frac{17}{24}$ **35.** $1\frac{9}{20}$ **37.** $4\frac{5}{7}$

CHAPTER 8

■ Lab 8.1, On Your Own, p. 351

5. $\frac{2}{3} + \frac{2}{3} + \frac{2}{3} + \frac{2}{3} = \frac{8}{3}$ or $2\frac{2}{3}$

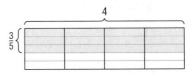

$\frac{8}{3} = 2\frac{2}{3}$

6. $\frac{2}{5} + \frac{2}{5} + \frac{2}{5} = \frac{6}{5}$ or $1\frac{1}{5}$

7.a. $\frac{3}{5} + \frac{3}{5} + \frac{3}{5} + \frac{3}{5} = \frac{12}{5}$ or $2\frac{2}{5}$ **b.** $\frac{4}{5} + \frac{4}{5} + \frac{4}{5} = \frac{12}{5}$ or $2\frac{2}{5}$; answers are the same, fractions are different.

8. $\frac{12}{5}$ or $2\frac{2}{5}$; explanations will vary.

9. Multiply 3×4 and put the product over 7.

■ 8.1 Communicating about Mathematics, p. 353

$\frac{6}{4}, \frac{9}{4}, \frac{12}{4}, \frac{15}{4}$; numerator increases by 3; $\frac{18}{4}, \frac{21}{4}, \frac{24}{4}$.

1. $2 \times \frac{5}{6}$; $\frac{10}{6}$, or $1\frac{2}{3}$ **2.** The denominator was also multiplied by the whole number. $\frac{2}{3} \times 6 = \frac{12}{3}$, or 4. **3.** $3\frac{3}{4}$ **4.** Yes; changing the order doesn't change the answer. **5.** 8 **7.** $4 \times \frac{2}{3} = \frac{8}{3}$ or $2\frac{2}{3}$ **9.** $\frac{2}{3}$ **11.** $1\frac{1}{3}$ **13.** $2\frac{2}{11}$ **15.** 6 **17.** 4 **19.** Answers will vary. **21.** Answers will vary. **23.** *J* **25.** *H* **27.** Coho Salmon: 24 in. Rainbow Trout: 14 in. **29.** $2 \times 7.5 = 15$ **31.** $\frac{35}{10} \times 20 = 70$

■ *Lab 8.2, On Your Own, p. 357*

7. 20 equal parts; 4×5 is 20 equal parts. **8.** Multiply both numerators together to get a new numerator; multiply both denominators together to get a new denominator.

■ *8.2 Communicating about Mathematics, p. 359*

Descriptions will vary but could include: you ate $\frac{2}{6}$ or $\frac{1}{3}$ of the pizza. Each $\frac{1}{3}$ pizza has $\frac{1}{4}$ cup of cheese. Therefore you ate $\frac{1}{4}$ cup of cheese.

■ *8.2 Exercises, pp. 360–361*

1. $\frac{3}{8}$ lb **2.** $\frac{5}{21}$ **3.** $\frac{9}{20}$ **4.** $\frac{1}{3} \times \frac{1}{2} = \frac{1}{6}$ **5.** 7 **6.** You forgot to multiply the denominator; $\frac{8}{9} \times \frac{2}{9} = \frac{16}{81}$. **7.** d; $\frac{5}{12}$ **9.** a; $\frac{3}{8}$ **11.** $\frac{8}{25}$ **13.** $\frac{15}{28}$ **15.** $\frac{9}{25}$ **17.** $\frac{2}{27}$ **19.** 3 **21.** 7 **23.** $\frac{1}{2}$ **25.** True; $\frac{1}{3} + \frac{1}{3} = \frac{2}{3}$ and $\frac{1}{3} \times \frac{1}{3} = \frac{1}{9}$; $\frac{2}{3} > \frac{1}{9}$ **27.** $\frac{1}{12}$ foot **29.** $\frac{1}{3}$ foot **31.** $\frac{2}{3} \times 2 = \frac{4}{3}$, or $1\frac{1}{3}$

■ *8.2 Mixed Review, p. 362*

1.a. $1\frac{1}{4}$ in.; $\frac{5}{4}$ in. **b.** $1\frac{3}{4}$ in.; $\frac{7}{4}$ in. **c.** $2\frac{3}{8}$ in.; $\frac{19}{8}$ in. **d.** $3\frac{1}{8}$ in.; $\frac{25}{8}$ in. **e.** $3\frac{1}{2}$ in.; $\frac{7}{2}$ in. **f.** $3\frac{7}{8}$ in.; $\frac{31}{8}$ in. **g.** $4\frac{5}{8}$ in.; $\frac{37}{8}$ in. **h.** $4\frac{7}{8}$ in.; $\frac{39}{8}$ in. **3.** 53.63 **5.** 50 **7.** 5 **9.** 48 **11.** $\frac{5}{6}$ **13.** $\frac{1}{8}$

■ *Lab 8.3, On Your Own, p. 365*

8.a. $1\frac{3}{4} \times 2\frac{2}{3}$; $4\frac{2}{3}$ **b.** $1\frac{1}{2} \times 2\frac{2}{3}$; 4 **9.** First change each mixed number into an improper fraction; then multiply the numerators together to get a new numerator and multiply the denominators together to get a new denominator.

■ *8.3 Communicating about Mathematics, p. 367*

A. Chun ran $3\frac{3}{8}$ mile; $1\frac{1}{8}$ mile farther than Pam and $\frac{7}{8}$ mile farther than Josh or Dionne. **B.** Charles ran $2\frac{1}{2}$ mile; $\frac{1}{4}$ mile more than Pam and the same distance as Josh and Dionne.

■ *8.3 Exercises, pp. 368–369*

1. Did not change to improper fractions first; $2\frac{2}{3} \times 3\frac{4}{5} = \frac{8}{3} \times \frac{19}{5} = \frac{152}{15}$ or $10\frac{2}{5}$. **2.** Did not change to improper fractions first; $4 \times 3\frac{3}{4} = 4 \times \frac{15}{4} = 15$. **3.** $2\frac{1}{2} \times 3\frac{1}{3} = 8\frac{1}{3}$ **4.** $2\frac{1}{7} \times 2\frac{1}{3} = \frac{15}{7} \times \frac{7}{3} = \frac{105}{21} = 5$; rewrite as improper fractions, multiply, and simplify. **5.** $2\frac{2}{3}$ hour; 2 hours 40 min **6.** $1\frac{3}{4}$ hour; 1 hour 45 min **7.** $\frac{5}{2} \times \frac{5}{2} = \frac{25}{4}$, or $6\frac{1}{4}$ **9.** $6\frac{3}{4}$ **11.** $\frac{6}{7}$ **13.** 16 **15.** $6\frac{3}{16}$ **17.** $2\frac{11}{27}$ sq yd **19.** $1\frac{1}{2}$ sq mi **21.** $\frac{21}{2}$ or $10\frac{1}{2}$, $\frac{28}{2}$ or 14, $\frac{35}{2}$ or $17\frac{1}{2}$; number increases by $3\frac{1}{2}$; $3\frac{1}{2} \times 6 = 21$; $3\frac{1}{2} \times 7 = 24\frac{1}{2}$

23. $1\frac{1}{2}$, or $2\frac{3}{4}$, 4; number increases by $1\frac{1}{4}$; $4\frac{1}{5} \times 1\frac{1}{4} = 5\frac{1}{4}$; $5\frac{1}{5} \times 1\frac{1}{4} = 6\frac{1}{2}$ **25.** $112\frac{14}{15}$ **27.** $2\frac{2}{3}$; $\frac{8}{3}$ **29.** 3.12; $5\frac{2}{10} \times \frac{6}{10} = \frac{52}{10} \times \frac{6}{10} = \frac{312}{100}$; $3.12 = \frac{312}{100}$ **31.** 16.8; $10\frac{1}{2} \times 1\frac{6}{10} = \frac{21}{2} \times \frac{16}{10} = \frac{168}{10}$, or $\frac{84}{5}$; $16.8 = \frac{168}{10}$

■ Lab 8.4, On Your Own, p. 371

9. 5 **10.** 6 **11.** $3\frac{3}{8}$ **12.** Answers and explanations will vary but could include: divide the numerators to get an answer.

■ 8.4 Communicating about Mathematics, p. 373

10; $7\frac{1}{2} \div \frac{3}{4} = \frac{15}{2} \div \frac{3}{4} = \frac{30}{4} \div \frac{3}{4} = 10$.

■ 8.4 Exercises, pp. 374–375

1. $2\frac{2}{3} \div \frac{2}{3}$ **2.** $1\frac{1}{6} \div \frac{5}{6}$ **3.** $\frac{3}{5}$ **4.** $\frac{15}{9}$, or $1\frac{2}{3}$ **5.** Answers will vary. **7.** $1\frac{3}{4} \div \frac{1}{2}$ **9.** $\frac{1}{7}$ **11.** $6\frac{1}{3}$ **13.** 32 **15.** $4\frac{7}{8}$ **17.** Less than 1; explanations will vary. **19.** $\frac{11}{6}$, or $1\frac{5}{6}$ **21.** $\frac{3}{4}$ **23.** 5 and $\frac{2}{5}$ of another. **25.** $3.52

■ Mid-Chapter Self-Test, p. 376

1. $\frac{3}{4}$ **2.** $2\frac{6}{7}$ **3.** $\frac{5}{18}$ **4.** $\frac{1}{8}$ **5.** $4\frac{4}{21}$ **6.** $1\frac{1}{5}$ **7.** 18 **8.** $8\frac{2}{3}$ **9.** 3 **10.** 12 **11.** 2 **12.** 9 **13.** $\frac{6}{7}$ **14.** 1 **15.** $1\frac{4}{5}$ sq yd **16.** $\frac{7}{20}$ sq mi **17.** 30 sq ft **18.** 2 **19.** $\frac{1}{6}$ **20.** $\frac{4}{3}$, or $1\frac{1}{3}$ **21.** 3 **22.** 8; 18; 16; 6 **23.** 6 times

■ 8.5 Communicating about Mathematics, p. 378

The area would be 35 sq in. making it 21 sq in. larger than the gold mosaic, and $2\frac{1}{2}$ times larger.

■ 8.5 Exercises, pp. 379–381

1. $\frac{5}{7}$ **2.** 9 **3.** Did not multiply by the reciprocal of the second fraction; $\frac{7}{8} \div \frac{5}{6} = \frac{7}{8} \times \frac{6}{5} = \frac{21}{20}$ or $1\frac{1}{20}$. **4.** Did not multiply by the reciprocal of the second fraction; $\frac{5}{9} \div \frac{3}{5} = \frac{5}{9} \times \frac{5}{3} = \frac{25}{27}$. **5.** 1 mile longer. **6.** $1\frac{2}{3}$ times longer. **7.** $\frac{5}{4}$ **9.** $\frac{6}{11}$ **11.** $2\frac{2}{8}''$ and $\frac{5}{8}''$; $3\frac{3}{5}$ **13.** 126 pieces **15.** $\frac{14}{8}, \frac{21}{8}, \frac{28}{8}$; the numerators increase by 7. **17.** $\frac{1}{4}, \frac{1}{3}, \frac{1}{2}$; denominators decrease by 1. **19.** $2\frac{1}{4}$ **21.** $1\frac{1}{3}$ **23.** $1\frac{11}{15}$ **25.** $4\frac{1}{2}$ **27.** $2\frac{1}{4}$ inches wider. **29.** $5\frac{1}{9}$ times wider. **31.** $\frac{1}{2}$ **33.** $\frac{5}{24}$

■ 8.5 Mixed Review, p. 381

1. 6, 18, 3, 12 **3.** 15.3 **5.** 7.4 **7.** 0.68 **9.** 3 **11.** 39 **13.** 70 **15.** Answers will vary but could include: rewrite the fractions with common denominators and check that the numerator of the fraction you wrote is between the others.

■ 8.6 Communicating about Mathematics, p. 383

$1\frac{5}{6}$ ft; average length did not change; average length of the first five is the same as the average length of the next two.

■ 8.6 Exercises, pp. 384–385

1. Rewrite as improper fraction, rewrite as a product using the reciprocal, multiply. **2.** Rewrite as improper fraction, rewrite as a product using the reciprocal, multiply, simplify. **3.** $5 \div 3\frac{3}{4} = 5 \div \frac{15}{4} = \frac{20}{4} \div \frac{15}{4} = \frac{20}{15}$ or $1\frac{1}{3}$; $5 \div \frac{15}{4} = 5 \times \frac{4}{15} = \frac{20}{15}$, or $1\frac{1}{3}$; preferences will vary. **4.** $\frac{1}{8}$; each student gets $\frac{1}{8}$ of a cake. **5.** Yes; finding the reciprocal of the first fraction gives an incorrect answer; examples will vary. **7.** $\frac{9}{10}$ cup

9. $2\frac{1}{4}$
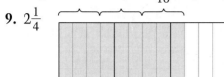

11. d **13.** b **15.** $5\frac{1}{3}$ **17.** $\frac{16}{19}$ **19.** $\frac{19}{20}$ **21.** $1\frac{3}{4}$ **23.** Sometimes **25.** About $10\frac{1}{2}$ min **27.** 2 times more **29.** $\frac{2}{10}$; $\frac{2}{10} \neq \frac{11}{2}$ **31.** 12.5; $12.5 \neq \frac{5}{4}$ **33.** $\frac{1}{16}$ of 2; $\frac{1}{16}$ of $2 \neq \frac{1}{3}$

■ Lab 8.7, On Your Own, p. 387

6. $\frac{1}{2}(6 + \frac{2}{3}) = 3 + \frac{2}{6} = 3\frac{1}{3}$; $\frac{1}{2} \times \frac{20}{3} = \frac{20}{6} = 3\frac{2}{6}$ or $3\frac{1}{3}$ **7.** $\frac{1}{3}(6 + \frac{3}{5}) = 2 + \frac{1}{5}$; $\frac{1}{3} \times \frac{33}{5} = \frac{33}{15} = 2\frac{3}{15}$ or $2\frac{1}{5}$ **8.** $\frac{2}{3}(4 + \frac{1}{4}) = \frac{8}{3} + \frac{2}{12} = \frac{16}{6} + \frac{1}{6} = \frac{17}{6} = 2\frac{5}{6}$; $\frac{2}{3} \times \frac{17}{4} = \frac{34}{12} = 2\frac{10}{12}$ or $2\frac{5}{6}$ **9.** $\frac{2}{5}(5 + \frac{1}{5}) = 2 + \frac{2}{25}$; $\frac{2}{5} \times \frac{26}{5} = \frac{52}{25}$ or $2\frac{2}{25}$ **10.** Didn't change to improper fraction or use the Distributive Property correctly. First change mixed numbers to improper fractions, then solve; or distribute $2\frac{1}{3}$.

■ 8.7 Communicating about Mathematics, p. 389

Answers will vary but could include: first recognize that $\frac{1}{2} \times 2 = 1$, then $1 \times 1\frac{2}{10} = 1\frac{2}{10}$, etc.

1. c **2.** a **3.** b **4.** Yes; it has a right angle. **5.** No right angle. **6.** No right angle. **7.** Answers will vary.
9.
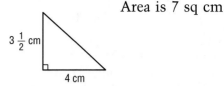
Area is 7 sq cm

11. Pattern descriptions will vary but could include: numerator of areas increases by consecutive odd numbers or sides increase by 0.5 units; $\frac{1}{8}$; $\frac{4}{8}$, or $\frac{1}{2}$; $\frac{9}{8}$, or $1\frac{1}{8}$; $\frac{16}{8}$, or 2.

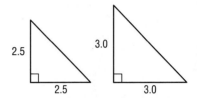

13. 60 **15.** 8 in. **17.** 0.6 m **19.** 30 sq in. **21.**

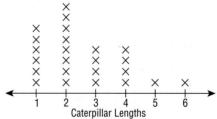

Caterpillar Lengths

■ Chapter Review, pp. 393–394

1. d **3.** c **5.** $2\frac{5}{8}$ **7.** $\frac{1}{8}$ **9.** $1\frac{1}{2}$ **11.** $2\frac{2}{5}$ **13.** $1\frac{5}{9}$ **15.** $1\frac{1}{3}$ **17.–21.** Answers will vary. **23.** $\frac{3}{7}$ sq mi **25.** $10\frac{1}{2}$ sq km **27.** Approximately 8370 sq mi **29.** 2,020,000 visitors **31.** $12\frac{3}{5}$ sq cm **33.** $28\frac{4}{5}$ sq cm **35.** $19\frac{4}{5}$ sq cm

CHAPTER 9

■ **9.1 Communicating about Mathematics, p. 401**

Designs and shapes will vary.

■ **9.1 Exercises, pp. 402–404**

1. No, it has a curved side. **2.** Yes, pentagon. **3.** Yes, hexagon. **4.a.** Start at *A*, move up 2 to *B*, right 6 to *C*, down 2 to *D*, left 6 to *A*. **b.** Start at *R*, move left 3, up 2 to *S*, right 4, up 2 to *T*, right 3, down 3 to *U*, left 4, down 1 to *R*. **5.** About 12 units. **7.–9.** Sketches will vary. **11.** about 9 units

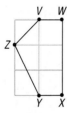

13. Start at *M*, move right 1, down 2 to *Q*, right 3 to *P*, left 1, up 3 to *O*, left 2 to *N*, down 1, left 1 to *M*. **15.** 6 sq units **17.** 10 sq units **19.**

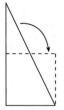

21. 13 **23.** Perimeter = 18.5 m; Area = 21 sq m

■ **Lab 9.2, On Your Own, p. 405**

10. 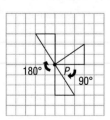   **11.**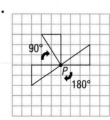

12. Yes; 90° + 180° = 180° + 90°

■ **9.2 Communicating about Mathematics, p. 407**

Angles and answers will vary.

■ **9.2 Exercises, pp. 408–409**

1. $\angle QPR$, $\angle RPQ$, or $\angle P$ **2.** $\overleftrightarrow{PQ}$ and $\overrightarrow{PR}$ **3.** *P* **4.** Answers will vary. **5.** Triangles will vary. **6.** Approximately 48° **7.** b **9.** c **11.** 125° **13.** 60° **15.** 175° **17.** 15° **19.** 360; there are 360° in a full circle. **21. a.** Obtuse, so they sum to 180°. **b.** Right, so they sum to 180°. **23.** Fold your paper from top to bottom; fold again from left to right so the first fold lines match. The corner where the folds meet makes a right angle that you can use for measuring; obtuse. **25.** About 120°, obtuse. **27.** d **29.** a

■ **9.2 Mixed Review, p. 410**

1. $\frac{3}{4}$ **3.** $\frac{37}{100}$ **5.** 54 **7.** 300 **9.** 7600 **11.** 32, 29 **13.** 7, 7 **15.** No

■ **9.3 Communicating about Mathematics, p. 413**

Answers will vary.

■ **9.3 Exercises, pp. 414–415**

1. c **2.** d **3.** b **4.** a **5.** Answers will vary. **6.** No, side measures are different; yes, same shape. **7.** Answers will vary. **9.** a and d **11.** $a = 90°$, $b = 6.8$, $c = 90°$, $d = 4$. **13.** No, to change the angle measures, you need to change the length of 2 of the sides. **15.** Designs will vary. **17.** True **19.** False, 0.003 **21.** False, 7 **23.** True

■ Lab 9.4, On Your Own, p. 417

11. c **12.** b **13.** a **14.** d **15.** a and c; the line splits the figure symmetrically.

■ 9.4 Communicating about Mathematics, p. 419

Answers will vary but should include: no more than 4 lines of symmetry are possible for a square.

■ 9.4 Exercises, pp. 420–421

1.–3. Answers will vary.
4. 1 line of symmetry.

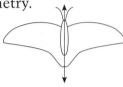

5. Answers will vary.
6. **7.** No

9. Yes

11. Yes, 2 **13.** No **15.** No, flipping about the line doesn't give an exact match.
17. No; flipping about the line doesn't give an exact match.
19. One possible figure:

21. 3
23. **25.**

27. **29.**

31. 154

■ 9.4 Mixed Review, p. 422

1. 5 **3.** $\frac{1}{2}, \frac{4}{7}, \frac{5}{6}, \frac{5}{7}$ **5.** $2\frac{1}{4}$ **7.** 3 **9.** Quadrilateral; 2 right angles ($\angle N$, $\angle O$), 1 acute angle ($\angle P$), 1 obtuse angle ($\angle M$)

■ Mid-Chapter Self-Test, p. 423

1. Move right 4 up 1 to B, left 2 up 3 to C, left 2 down 4 to A; $\overleftrightarrow{AB}$ is between 4 and 5 units. **2.** Move right 4 up 3 to B, left 3 up 3 to C, left 2 down 1 to D, right 1 down 5 to A; $\overleftrightarrow{AB}$ is between 4 and 6 units. **3.** Move right 1 down 1 to B, right 2 to C, right 2 up 2 to D, left 5 up 2 to E, down 3 to A; $\overleftrightarrow{AB}$ is between 1 and 2 units. **4.** Right, 90° **5.** Acute, 60° **6.** Obtuse, 120° **7.** Neither, different size and shape. **8.** Similar, same shape different size. **9.** Congruent and similar, same size and shape. **10.** 1 **11.** 1 **12.** 2
13.

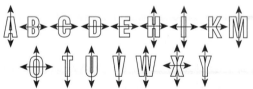

14.a. quadrilateral **b.** quadrilateral **c.** acute isosceles triangle **d.** right scalene triangle **e.** acute isosceles triangle **f.** square, rectangle, quadrilateral **g.** right scalene triangle **h.** right isosceles triangle

■ Lab 9.5, On Your Own, p. 424

8.a. Yes **b.** No **c.** No

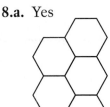

■ 9.5 Communicating about Mathematics, p. 427

Yes, move A up 1 and over 4 to cover C.

■ 9.5 Exercises pp. 428–429

1. Coordinate plane **2.** *y*-axis **3.** (4, 3)
4. *x*-coordinate; it shows position on the *x*-axis **5.** Answers will vary.
6. rectangle, quadrilateral

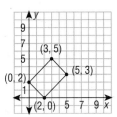

7. *R* **9.** *S*
11. Δ*ABC* slides to Δ*JKL*; Δ*DEF* slides to Δ*GHI*

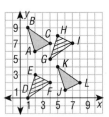

13. Yes, it has same side lengths and angle measures. **15.** Up 5, right 2 **17.** Down 1, right 2
19.

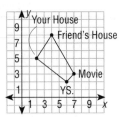

21. The triangle rotates 90° clockwise.

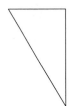

■ 9.6 Communicating about Mathematics, p. 431

A. No; no; explanations will vary. **B.** They are acute.

■ 9.6 Exercises, pp. 432–433

1. Right, isosceles **2.** Obtuse, scalene **3.** Acute, equilateral, isosceles **4.–6.** Answers will vary. **7.** 4.2 cm, 4.2 cm, 2.2 cm; isosceles **9.** 1.4 cm, 3.5 cm, 4 cm; scalene **11.** Obtuse; 120°, 25°, 35° **13.** Obtuse, scalene **15.** Right, scalene **17.–19.** Sketches will vary. **21.** No **23.** Yes

25. Never
27. 2 right triangles, or 1 acute and 1 obtuse

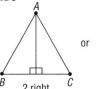

29. 3 **31.** 5 **33.** 3

■ Lab 9.7, On Your Own, p. 435

7.a. 70° **b.** 75° **c.** 50° **8.** Yes, make similar but change side lengths. **9.a.** 70° **b.** 100°

■ 9.7 Communicating about Mathematics, p. 437

Δ1: $\overline{BC}$, $\overline{AC}$, $\overline{AB}$; $\angle A$, $\angle B$, $\angle C$; Δ2: $\overline{BC}$, $\overline{AC}$, $\overline{AB}$; $\angle A$, $\angle B$, $\angle C$; Δ3: $\overline{BC}$, $\overline{AC}$, $\overline{AB}$; $\angle A$, $\angle B$, $\angle C$; Δ4: $\overline{AC}$, $\overline{BC}$, $\overline{AB}$; $\angle B$, $\angle A$, $\angle C$; Δ5: $\overline{AC}$, $\overline{BC}$, $\overline{AB}$; $\angle B$, $\angle A$, $\angle C$. The shortest side is opposite the smallest angle, and longest side is opposite largest angle.

1. c **2.** a **3.** b **4.** d **5.** Angle measures will vary; third angle measures 180° minus the sum of 90° and the other acute angle. **6.** 102° **7.** Yes, sum is 180°. **9.** Yes, sum is 180°. **11.** $\angle A$ is 80°, $\angle B$ is 60°, $\angle C$ is 40°; sum is 180° **13.** 60° **15.** 30° **17.** 90° **19.** 367

■ Chapter Review, pp. 441–442

1. Sketches will vary but should have 3 sides **3.** Sketches will vary but should have 7 sides. **5.** $\angle D = 50°$, acute; $\angle E = 115°$ obtuse; $\angle F = 90°$, right; $\angle G = 105°$, obtuse

7. One possibility: **9.** One possibility:

   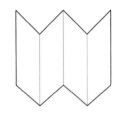

11.   **13.** No

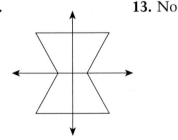

15.

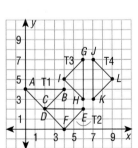

Triangles 1 and 2 are slides of each other; triangles 3 and 4 are flips of each other; all are turns of each other.

17. Sketches will vary but must have an obtuse angle and different side lengths. **19.** 1, 7, 9, and 14 are obtuse scalene triangles; 2, 3, 5, 6, 11, and 12 are quadrilaterals; 4 is acute equilateral triangle; 8 is a hexagon; 10 and 13 are right scalene triangles **21.** All are 60°; all angles of an equilateral triangle are the same.

■ Cumulative Review for Chapters 7–9, pp. 444–445

1.a. $1\frac{1}{8}$ in., $\frac{9}{8}$ in. **b.** $1\frac{3}{4}$ in., $\frac{7}{4}$ in. **c.** $2\frac{1}{4}$ in., $\frac{9}{4}$ in. **d.** $2\frac{5}{8}$ in., $\frac{21}{8}$ in. **e.** $3\frac{1}{2}$ in., $\frac{7}{2}$ in. **f.** $4\frac{7}{8}$ in., $\frac{39}{8}$ in. **3.** $6\frac{1}{2}$ **5.** $2\frac{1}{6}$ **7.** $3\frac{1}{2}$ **9.** $4\frac{2}{3}$ **11.** $3\frac{1}{4}$ units **13.** $1\frac{1}{2}$ units **15.** $\frac{9}{14}$ sq units **17.** $1\frac{1}{2} \div 6 = \frac{1}{4}$ **19.** $3\frac{1}{6} \times \frac{6}{7} = 2\frac{5}{7}$ **21.** Pentagon; $\angle A$, 55°, acute; $\angle B$, 135°, obtuse; $\angle C$, 120°, obtuse; $\angle D$, 90°, right; $\angle E$, 140°, obtuse **23.** a and b

25. One possibility: **27.** One possibility:

   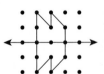

29.

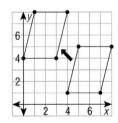

31. Sketches will vary but must include two equal sides and three acute angles

33. Acute angle; $\frac{1}{5}$ mile

CHAPTER 10

■ *Lab 10.1, On Your Own, p. 451*

11. a.

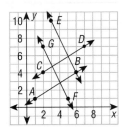

b. Parallel: $\overleftrightarrow{CD}$ and $\overleftrightarrow{AB}$, $\overleftrightarrow{FG}$ and $\overleftrightarrow{BE}$. Perpendicular: $\overleftrightarrow{CD}$ and $\overleftrightarrow{FG}$, $\overleftrightarrow{CD}$ and $\overleftrightarrow{BE}$, $\overleftrightarrow{AB}$ and $\overleftrightarrow{FG}$, $\overleftrightarrow{AB}$ and $\overleftrightarrow{BE}$. Parallel lines don't intersect; perpendicular lines intersect at a right angle. **c.–d.** Answers will vary.

■ *10.1 Communicating about Mathematics, p. 453*

Answers will vary but should include the fact that the distance between two parallel lines is the same at all points.

■ *10.1 Exercises, pp. 454–455*

1. b **2.** c **3.** a and b **4.** True; definition of perpendicular lines **5.** False; lines can intersect at any angle. **6.** Answers will vary. **7.** Parallel; they stay the same distance apart. **9.** Parallel; they stay the same distance apart. **11.** $\overleftrightarrow{EF}$ and $\overleftrightarrow{GH}$ **13.** $\overleftrightarrow{CD}$ is perpendicular to $\overleftrightarrow{EF}$ and $\overleftrightarrow{GH}$. **15.** Sometimes; can intersect at any angle. **17.** $\overleftrightarrow{CD}$ **19.** $\overleftrightarrow{GH}$ and $\overleftrightarrow{EF}$ **21.** West 6th St. **23.** They do not intersect at right angles. **25.** Obtuse, 120°

■ *10.2 Communicating about Mathematics, p. 457*

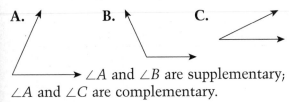

$\angle A$ and $\angle B$ are supplementary; $\angle A$ and $\angle C$ are complementary.

■ *10.2 Exercises, pp. 458–459*

1. perpendicular **2.** complementary **3.** 55° **4.** 35° **5.** Answers will vary but could include: $\angle DFA$ and $\angle AFC$, $\angle DFE$ and $\angle EFC$, $\angle AFC$ and $\angle CFB$, $\angle CFB$ and $\angle BFD$, and $\angle BFD$ and $\angle DFA$. **6.** Answers will vary. **7.** $\angle 1$ and $\angle 3$ are supplementary and $\angle 1$ is 125°; $\angle 3$ and $\angle 4$ are supplementary and $\angle 3$ is 55°; both $\angle 1$ and $\angle 4$ measure 125°. **9.** 25° **11.** 88° **13.** 35° **15.** 20°

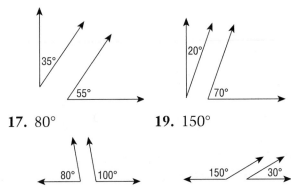

17. 80° **19.** 150°

21. False; examples will vary. **23.** $\angle 2$ and $\angle 3$ are the two acute angles in a right triangle and $\angle 2$ is 60°, so $\angle 3$ is 30°. **25.** Complementary **27.** 84° **29.** 124°

■ *10.2 Mixed Review, p. 460*

1. $\frac{2}{5}$ **3.** $\frac{3}{10}$ **5.** 0.38; 38% **7.** 0.55; 55% **9.** 6.8 **11.** 3.33
13.

```
0 | 8 8 9
1 | 3 4
2 | 2 2 5 7
Key: 2 | 7 = 27
```

■ *Lab 10.3, On Your Own, p. 463*

7. Each adds a triangle

8. Perimeter increases by one with each added triangle.

Number of Triangles	Perimeter (P)
1	3
2	4
3	5
4	6
5	7
6	8
7	9
8	10
9	11
10	12
11	13
12	14

9. No; $P = n + 2$
10. 22

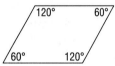

■ **10.3. Communicating about Mathematics, p. 465**

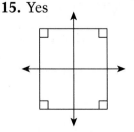

Since opposite angles have the same measure, two angles are 60° and the other two have a sum of $360 - (2 \times 60) = 240$. Therefore, each of the other angles measures 120°.

■ **10.3 Exercises, pp. 466–467**

1. a, b, c, d **2.** c **3.** c, d **4.** a, c, d **5. a.** C **b.** AB, ABC, BCD, C **c.** AB, ABC, C **d.** AB, ABC, $ABCD$, BC, BCD, C, CD **6.** No, no; all four sides have the same length no matter how you move them. **7.** Green **9.** Yellow **11.** True **13.** False; not all quadrilaterals have parallel sides.
15. Yes   **17.** Yes

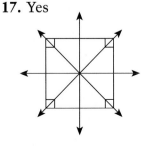

19. Rectangle; $x = 3$, $y = 8$, $z = 90°$ **21.** Neither; $x = 4$, $y = 4$, $z = 65°$ **23.** Square, rectangle, parallelogram, quadrilateral **25.** 18 sq units **27.** $4\frac{1}{2}$ sq units

■ **Lab 10.4, On Your Own, p. 469**
7. a. 22.5 sq units **b.** 20 sq units **c.** 20 sq units **8.** Area $= \frac{1}{2} \times$ base $\times$ height

■ **10.4 Communicating about Mathematics, p. 471**

3.2 ft and 2 ft; $\frac{1}{2} \cdot 3.2 \cdot 10 = 16$ sq ft and $\frac{1}{2} \cdot 2 \cdot 10 = 10$ sq ft

■ **10.4 Exercises, pp. 472–474**
1. 24 sq units **2.** 12 sq units **3.** 9 sq units **4.** Your friend used a non-perpendicular side as the height. **5.** Any triangle with a base and a height whose product is 36. **6.** 4 sq in. **7.** 18 sq m **9.** 26 sq in. **11.** 5 cm, 3 cm; $7\frac{1}{2}$ sq cm **13.** 72 sq units **15.** 48 sq units **17.** 2 mi **19.** About 110,400 sq mi **21.** Sometimes
23.

Congruent Figures	Name
A and R	Right triangle
B and L	Parallelogram
C and Q	Pentagon
D and T	Rectangle
E and O	Quadrilateral
F and P	Equilateral triangle
G and N	Quadrilateral
H and V	Rectangle
I and U	Quadrilateral
J and S	Square
K and M	Hexagon

10.5 Mixed Review, p. 474

1. Answers will vary. 3. Answers will vary. 5. 60 7. 40 9. 36 11. 22

Mid-Chapter Self-Test, p. 475

1. $\overleftrightarrow{GH}$ 2. $\overleftrightarrow{AB}$ 3. $\angle 2$ 4. $\angle 7$ 5. $\overleftrightarrow{EF}$ or $\overleftrightarrow{AB}$ 6. $\angle 4$ 7. Rectangle, parallelogram, and quadrilateral. 8. Parallelogram and quadrilateral 9. Square, rectangle, parallelogram, and quadrilateral 10. Quadrilateral 11. 9 sq units 12. 21 sq units 13. Find area of each triangle and add them, or treat as one triangle with a base of 10 and height of 6. 14. False, quadrilaterals do not always have parallel sides. 15. True, squares have four right angles and parallel sides. 16. Ivory 17. 4 18. 56.25 sq in.

Lab 10.5, On Your Own, p. 476

6. Multiply diameter by 3.14. 7.a. 6.28 in. b. 9.42 ft c. 12.56 cm d. 15.70 m

10.5 Communicating about Mathematics, p. 479

Divide circumference by 3.14; A. 4.46 ft B. 2.87 m

10.5 Exercises, pp. 480–481

1. b; the distance across a circle through the center 2. c; the point inside a circle that is the same distance from all points on the circle 3. a; the distance around a circle 4. 14.13 ft 5. 7.01 in. 7. 21.98 units 9. 18.84 units 11. 50.24 in. 13. 4.71 ft 15. 62.8 in. 17. $P = 24.8$ cm; $A = 38.44$ sq cm 19. 210 21. $\frac{6}{8}, \frac{3}{4}$ 23. $\frac{3}{9}, \frac{1}{3}$

Lab 10.6, On Your Own, p. 483

6. Multiply the radius by itself, then by π (3.14). 7.a. 3.14 sq units b. 6.24 sq units c. 9.40 sq units d. 12.56 sq units

10.6 Communicating about Mathematics, p. 485

340.06 sq in.; area of mat = area of rectangle − area of circle

10.6 Exercises, pp. 486–487

1. e 2. c 3. b 4. a 5. d 6.a. 153.86 sq in. b. 452.16 sq in. 7. 78.5 sq in. 9. 113.04 sq cm 11. 175.96 sq cm 13. > 15. > 17. 10,236.4 mi 19. 7850 sq mi; no, the area increases to 31,400 sq mi, more than double. 21. Twice as popular.

10.7 Communicating about Mathematics, p. 489

Answers will vary.

10.7 Exercises, pp. 490–491

1. $\frac{1}{12}$ of 360° is 30°, not 40°. 2. Fractions do not total 1; $\frac{2}{15}$ of 360° = 48°. 3. Find fraction for each part, find degree of each part, use circle graph paper to draw each part, add up the fractions and angle measures; or, find fraction for each part, find degree of each part, add up the fractions and angle measures, use circle graph paper to draw each part. 4. 35% + 57% + 8% = 100%; $\frac{35}{100} + \frac{57}{100} + \frac{8}{100} = \frac{100}{100}$ or 1. 5. Casual Wear; $\frac{35}{100} \cdot 360° \approx 126°$. 6. Casual Wear is about $4\frac{1}{2}$ times Sports/Fitness 7. $a = 135°$ $b = 120°$ $c = 45°$ $d = \frac{1}{6}$

9.

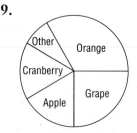

Orange, 120°;
Grape, 90°;
Apple, 60°;
Cranberry, 60°;
Other, 30°

11.

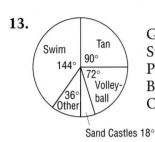

Mystery, 135°;
Autobiography, 120°;
Science Fiction, 60°;
Humor, 45°

13.

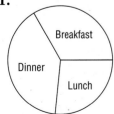

Sand Castles 18°

Get a tan, 5;
Swim, 8;
Play volleyball, 4;
Build a sand castle, 1;
Other, 2

15. 3 **17.** 2 **19.** 20

■ 10.8 Communicating about Mathematics, p. 493

$\frac{23}{36}$; zones 1, 2, and 3 contain 115 squares

■ 10.8 Exercises, pp. 494–495

1. $\frac{9}{100}$ **2.** $\frac{1}{10}$ **3.** $\frac{1}{25}$ **4.** Answers will vary.
5. $\frac{1}{2}$ **6.** $\frac{1}{2}$ **7.** $\frac{9}{25}$ **9.** $\frac{125}{157}$ **11.** $\frac{157}{1400}$ **13.** $\frac{1}{7}$ **15.** $\frac{1}{6}$
17. $\frac{1}{2}, \frac{2}{3}, \frac{7}{6}$ **19.** $\frac{3}{16}, \frac{1}{4}, \frac{3}{8}$ **21.** $\frac{4}{9}, \frac{2}{3}, \frac{5}{6}$

■ Chapter Review, pp. 497–498

1. intersecting **3.** supplementary **5.a.** ab
b. ab, abcd, bc, cd **c.** ab, abcd, cd **d.** ab,
abc, abcd, bc, bcd, c, cd **7.** 4 sq in.
9. $C = 12.56$ km, $A = 12.56$ sq km
11.

Breakfast, 120°;
Lunch, 96°;
Dinner, 144°

13. Answers will vary but should
include: measure several points. **15.** $\frac{6}{10}$
17. S **19.** O **21.** P **23.** O **25.** Y **27.** Q **29.** I

CHAPTER 11

■ Lab 11.1, On Your Own, p. 505

12.
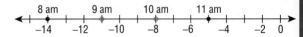
7 9 11 13 15 17 19 21

Numbers are consecutive odd integers;
pattern moves right.

13. ←‖+●+●+●+●+●+●+●+●+●+●+‖→
−11 −10 −9 −8 −7 −6 −5 −4 −3 −2 −1 0 1 2 3

Numbers are decreasing odd integers; to
the left of the first eight numbers.
14. One possibility: subtract a larger
number from a smaller number.

■ 11.1 Communicating about Mathematics, p. 508

```
      8 am      9 am      10 am     11 am
←+●+++++◆+++++●+++++++◆++++++++++→
  −14    −12    −10   −8    −6    −4    −2    0
```

Answers will vary but could include: dividing the number line into equal parts
gives you −11°C at 9 A.M. and −8°C at
10 A.M.

■ 11.1 Exercises, pp. 509–511

1. −4, −3, −2, −1, 0, 1, 2, 3, 4 **2.** D **3.** C
4. E **5.** B **6.** A **7.** 0 **8.** −5, −4, −3 **9.** −4; 8
11. ←‖+●+++●++++‖+++●++●→
−5 −4 −3 −2 −1 0 1 2 3

Numbers increase by 2; 5, 7
13. > **15.** < **17.** > **19.** −4, −3, 1, 3, 6 **21.**
−6, −5, −3, −1, 0 **23.** b **25.** a **27.** −5 **29.**
9 **31.** −1 **33.** 6 **35.** −80°F; negative eighty
degrees Fahrenheit; it is 10 degrees
cooler. **37.** $\frac{3}{4}, \frac{5}{8}, \frac{2}{4}, \frac{2}{8}$ **39.** $\frac{8}{4}, \frac{7}{4}, \frac{3}{2}, \frac{11}{8}$

■ 11.1 Mixed Review, p. 511

1. 1.15 **3.** 0.036 **5.** $\frac{4}{15}$ **7.** $\frac{3}{8}$ **9.** True; $\frac{5}{6} =$
$\frac{5 \cdot 3}{6 \cdot 3} = \frac{15}{18}$ **11.** True; $\frac{1}{3} = \frac{1 \cdot 15}{3 \cdot 15} = \frac{15}{45}$ **13.** $\frac{9}{8}$
15. $\frac{12}{7}$

5. $-5 + (-2) = -7$ 6. $-3 + (-9) = -12$ 7. $-4 + 3 = -1$ 8. $5 + (-5) = 0$ 9. c; 1 10. a; -1 11. b; 0 12.–14. Examples will vary. 12. Never 13. Always 14. Sometimes

■ **11.2 Communicating about Mathematics, p. 515**

Yes you get the same results.

■ **11.2 Exercises, pp. 516–517**

1. You should have moved 5 to the right of -2; $-2 + 5 = 3$. 2. You should have moved 3 to the left of -4; $-4 + (-3) = -7$. 3. $3 + (-5) = -2$ 4. 10 5. -1 6. 4 7. -7 8. If the positive integer is farther from 0 than the negative integer, the sum is positive; if the negative integer is farther from 0, the sum is negative; if both integers are the same distance from 0, the sum is zero. 9. $3 + 3 = 6$ 11. $-2 + (-7) = -9$ 13. a 15. d 17. 14 19. -1 21. -14 23. 7

25.

$4 + (-5) + 2 = 1$

27.a. \$22. b. \$11. 29. 4 yd gain 31. $\frac{5}{6}$ 33. $\frac{2}{3}$ 35. $5\frac{1}{12}$ 37. $2\frac{3}{4}$

■ **Lab 11.3, On Your Own, p. 519**

6. 2 7. -2 8. -1 9. 1 10. -1 11. 11 12. -11 13. 1 14.a. Positive, 7 b. Zero, 0 c. Negative, -2 d. Positive, 2 15. Add zero pairs when there aren't enough red or black counters for you to take away; examples will vary; one possibility: $7 - 8$ and $-6 - (-2)$.

■ **11.3 Communicating about Mathematics, p. 522**

A. $6 - 2 = 4$ B. $0 - (-5) = 5$

■ **11.3 Exercises, pp. 523–524**

1. Left 2. Left 3. Right 4. Right 5. No, operations don't depend on starting point. 6. Problems will vary; -35. 7. c 9. d 11. -10 13. 11 15. 5 17. 6 ft 19. 8 seconds 21. 11 23. 1, 2, 3, 4; the number being subtracted decreases by 1 and the answer increases by 1. 25. $-8, -7, -6, -5$; the number being subtracted decreases by 1 and the answer increases by 1. 27. b; $20{,}300 - (-300)$ is about $20{,}600$. 29. A 31. E 33. B

■ **Lab 11.4, On Your Own, p. 527**

10.a. $A(6, 0)$, $B(5, -1)$, $C(4, -1)$, $D(3, -2)$, $E(4, -3)$, $F(3, -3)$, $G(1, -3)$, $H(1, -2)$, $I(-4, -3)$, $J(-6, -2)$, $K(-7, -1)$, $L(-6, -1)$, $M(-5, 2)$, $N(-3, 3)$, $O(-1, 3)$, $P(2, 2)$, $Q(1, 4)$, $R(2, 5)$, $S(3, 3)$, $T(3, 6)$, $U(4, 5)$, $V(4, 3)$, $W(5, 2)$ b. Rabbit c. Right 7, up 1 d. One possibility: left 7, down 7.

■ **11.4 Communicating about Mathematics, p. 529**

In (a) x-coordinates increased 5 and y-coordinates decreased 2. In (b) the sign of the x-coordinates changed and the y-coordinates stayed the same.

■ **11.4 Exercises, pp. 530–531**

1. The negative scales on the x- and y-axis are reversed; statements will vary but could include: draw two intersecting perpendicular lines. Label the horizontal line "x" and the vertical line "y". Numbers should increase from left to right and from bottom to top. 2. $A(-4, 4)$, $B(4, 3)$, $C(0, 0)$, $D(-3, 1)$, $E(-2, -4)$, $F(3, -1)$; C is called the Origin. 3. From $(0, 0)$ move left 3, up 4. 4. From $(0, 0)$ move right 2, up 7. 5. From $(0, 0)$ move left 4, down 6. 6. From $(0, 0)$ move down 8.

7. Parallelogram

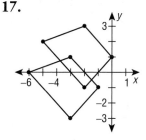

9. Quadrant 1 **11.** Quadrant 4 **13.** Fish

15. **17.**

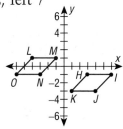

Quadrilateral

19. Slide up 2, left 7

21. Triangles will vary; sign of x-coordinate changes, sign of y-coordinate doesn't change. **23.** #4, about 15 miles **25.** Left 1, down 5 **27.** 10 square units **29.** 10 square units

■ **11.4 Mixed Review, p. 532**

1. $3\frac{3}{5}$ **3.** $1\frac{13}{24}$ **5.** $\frac{3}{9}$ **7.** $\frac{5}{9}$ **9.** $\frac{1}{3}$ **11.** $\frac{1}{15}$

■ **Mid-Chapter Self-Test, p. 533**

1. b **2.** d **3.** c **4.** a **5.** < **6.** > **7.** < **8.** > **9.** 2 **10.** -4 **11.** -10 **12.** -6 **13.** -5 **14.** -11 **15.** 11 **16.** 12 **17.** $(-4, 3)$, $(-2, 1)$, $(-2, -4)$, $(-4, -2)$; after $(2, 2)$, $(4, 0)$, $(4, -5)$, $(2, -3)$ **18.** $(-3, 5)$, $(2, 3)$, $(2, 0)$; after $(-3, -5)$, $(2, -3)$, $(2, 0)$ **19.** $(2, -3)$, $(4, -1)$, $(5, -1)$, $(5, -5)$, $(4, -5)$; after $(-2, -3)$, $(-4, -1)$, $(-5, -1)$, $(-5, -5)$, $(-4, -5)$ **20.** Answers will vary. **21.** $20.

■ **11.5 Communicating about Mathematics, p. 535**

$(-3, -5)$, $(-2, -4)$, $(-1, -3)$, $(0, -2)$, $(1, -1)$, $(2, 0)$, $(3, 1)$;

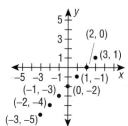

the points lie in a line.

■ **11.5 Exercises, pp. 536–537**

1. d, c, b, and a
2. $(-2, 1)$, $(-1, 2)$, $(0, 3)$, $(1, 4)$, $(2, 5)$

x	-2	-1	0	1	2
$x + 3$	1	2	3	4	5

3. The x- and y-coordinates are the same and the points lie in a line. **4.** a, d; because they continue the line and x- and y-coordinates are the same.

5.

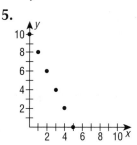

x	Days late	0	1	2	3	4	5
y	Score	10	8	6	4	2	0

x-coordinates increase by 1, y-coordinates decrease by 2, and the points lie in a line.

7.

x	-3	-2	-1	0	1	2	3
$6 - x$	9	8	7	6	5	4	3

x-coordinates increase and y-coordinates decrease.

9.

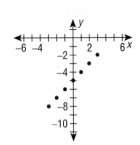

x	−3	−2	−1	0	1	2	3
−5 + x	−8	−7	−6	−5	−4	−3	−2

x- and y-coordinates increase by 1 and points lie in a line.

11.–13.

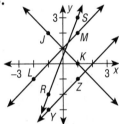

11. b **13.** a **15.** 78.5 sq ft **17.** 4.5 sq yd

■ 11.6 Communicating about Mathematics, p. 539

Sketches will vary; yes.

■ 11.6 Exercises, pp. 540–541

1. f **2.** e **3.** a **4.** b **5.** d **6.** c **7.** 12 sq units
9. 10 sq units
11. 12 sq units

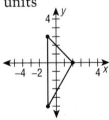

13. (0, 1), (0, 0); no **15.** b; explanations will vary. **17.** a; explanations will vary. **19.** 24 sq units; 96 sq mi

■ Chapter Review, pp. 543–544

1. −7, −6, −2, 2, 7 **3.** −9, −8, −5, −3, −2 **5.** −1 **7.** −15 **9.** 6 **11.** −11 **13.** Butterfly
15.

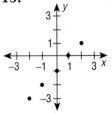

x	−2	−1	0	1	2
x − 1	−3	−2	−1	0	1

The points lie in a line.
17. Midpoints are (1, 3), (3, 1), (−1, −1), (−3, 1); parallelogram.

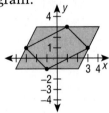

19. Midpoints are (2, 0), (0, −3), (−2, 0); triangle.

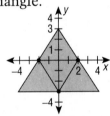

21. Approximately 64,000 sq mi **23.** Winter; range is 54°. **25.** −6, 9, −13, −9, −2; whale **27.** −2, −9, −13, 5; seal

CHAPTER 12

■ Lab 12.1, On Your Own, p. 551

7. 4

8. 10

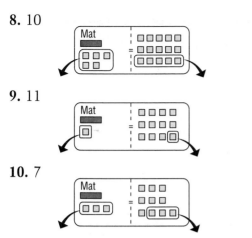

9. 11

10. 7

11. b; the same operation has to be done to *both* sides of the equation.

■ *12.1 Communicating about Mathematics, p. 554*

A. 7 **B.** −10 **C.** 11 **D.** −21 **E.** −7 **F.** −7. Always subtract the number that is on the same side as the variable.

■ *12.1 Exercises, pp. 555–556*

1. Write the original equation, subtract 2 from both sides to isolate the variable; solution is $x = 7$. **2.** Write the original equation, subtract 1 from both sides to isolate the variable; solution is $m = -2$. **3.** Write the original equation, subtract 3 from both sides to isolate the variable; solution is $t = -3$. **4.** Write the original equation, subtract the same number from both sides to isolate the variable and then check your solution. **5.** −1 **6.** 3 **7.** −8 **8.** $x + 5 = -10$; −15 **9.** Yes **11.** Yes **13.** −5 **15.** 8 **17.** 0 **19.** −14 **21.** 10 **23.** −24 **25.** $n + 2 = -10$; −12 **27.** $5 + n = 18$; 13 **29.** $2 + (-3) = -1$ **31.** −4 **33.** a; explanations will vary. **35.** 0 **37.** −10 **39.** 12 **41.** −3

■ *12.1 Mixed Review, p. 557*

1. 3 **3.** 3.3 **5.** $\frac{3}{4}$ **7.** −7, 1, −3, −4 **9.–11.** Answers will vary.

■ *12.2 Communicating about Mathematics, p. 559*

A. 7 **B.** −4 **C.** 11 **D.** −21 **E.** −7 **F.** 7. Answers will vary but should focus on adding or subtracting to isolate the variable.

■ *12.2 Exercises, pp. 560–561*

1. Add 3 to both sides to isolate the variable; $t = 17$ **2.** Subtract 5 from both sides to isolate the variable; $u = -38$ **3.** Add 12 to both sides to isolate the variable; $s = -2$ **4.** Original temperature − Change = New temperature. **5.** Original temperature = x; Change = 5; New temperature $= -8$; $x - 5 = -8$ **6.** $x = -3$; the temperature at 5 P.M. was −3°F. **7–9.** Answers will vary. **11.** Yes **13.** No **15.** 26 **17.** 65 **19.** 4 **21.** −3 **23.** Reading on Tuesday = x, Change = 2, Reading on Wednesday = 27; $x - 2 = 27$; $x = 29$. **25.** 31.45 **27.** $1\frac{1}{4}$

■ *12.3 Communicating about Mathematics, p. 563*

A. You subtracted different numbers, you should have subtracted 4.6 from both sides; $x = 3.2$. **B.** You subtracted 5.6, you should have added 5.6 to both sides; $n = 14.4$.

■ *12.3 Exercises, pp. 564–565*

1. Subtract $\frac{1}{6}$ from both sides. **2.** Subtract 7.6 from both sides. **3.** Add 9.4 to both sides. **4.** $x - \frac{1}{2} = \frac{2}{3}$; $1\frac{1}{6}$ **5.** $1\frac{3}{8}$ **6.** $\frac{1}{10}$ **7.** 15.7 **8.** Total cost = 24.91, List price = 23.50, Sales tax = t; $24.91 = 23.50 + t$; $1.41 **9.** d **11.** a **13.** $x - \frac{1}{3} = \frac{1}{4}$; $x = \frac{1}{4} + \frac{1}{3}$; $x = \frac{7}{12}$ **15.** $11.4 + z = 23.1$; $z = 23.1 - 11.4$; $z = 11.7$ **17.** $\frac{6}{8}$, or $\frac{3}{4}$ **19.** 6.05 **21.** 40.00 **23.** 10.25, 15.25, 20.25; t increases by 5; 25.25, 30.25 **25.** a or d; each shows a true equation of the verbal model. **27.** $\frac{1}{4}$; $\frac{1}{4} \neq$ 0.4 **29.** $\frac{10}{6}$; $\frac{10}{6} \neq 1.25$

■ **12.4 Communicating about Mathematics, p. 569**

Input	L	1	2	3	4	5	6
Output	P	4	6	8	10	12	14

The tables are the same.

■ **12.4 Exercises, pp. 570–572**

1.

Input	Output
x	y
9	1
8	0
7	−1
6	−2
5	−3

2.

Month	Number m	Temp °C T
Jan.	1	4
Feb.	2	8
March	3	12
April	4	16
May	5	20
June	6	24

3.

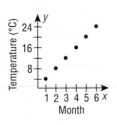

4. No, this function would make temperatures in December higher than those in July. **5.** $e = 12 \times c$

6.

Input	Output
x	y
−1	−2
0	−1
1	0
2	1
3	2

$y = x - 1$

7.

Input	Output
m	y
0	0
1	5
2	10
3	15

9.

Input	Output
m	y
0	−4
1	−3
2	−2
3	−1

11.

Input	Output
m	y
0	0
1	3
2	6
3	9

13. $y = 3 \cdot x$ **15.** $y = x + 5$

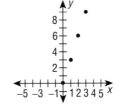   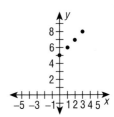

17. c

Input	Output
x	y
−2	0
−1	1
0	2
1	3

19. $C = d \cdot 3.14$

21.

Input	Output
x	**A**
1	5
2	10
3	15
4	20
5	25
6	30

As input (x) increases by 1, output (A) increases by 5; $A = \frac{1}{2} \cdot 10 \cdot x$, or $A = 5 \cdot x$.

23.

Input	Output
x	**T**
1	3
2	4
3	5
4	6
5	7
6	8

As input (x) increases by 1, output (T) increases by 1; $T = x + 2$.

25. $\frac{9}{11}$ **27.** a **29.** b

■ **12.4 Mixed Review, p. 572**

1. $\frac{1}{2}$ **3.** $\frac{41}{100}$ **5.** 120° **7.** 47° **9.** Number decreases by 3; −7, −10, −13

■ **Mid-Chapter Self-Test, p. 573**

1. Subtract; −16 **2.** Add; 29 **3.** Subtract; −19 **4.** Add; 5 **5.** You subtracted 12 instead of adding; $x = 33$ **6.** You added different numbers to each side of the equation; $x = 1$ **7.** You added 2 instead of subtracting 5 from each side; $x = -7$ **8.** −17 **9.** 41 **10.** 21 **11.** −16 **12.** $5\frac{1}{9}$ **13.** 3.44 **14.** $\frac{23}{24}$ **15.** 31.35 **16.** a; $55.25 **17.** a; $2\frac{5}{8}$ inches

18.

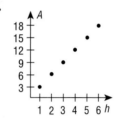

Input	Output
h	**y**
1	3
2	6
3	9
4	12
5	15
6	18

■ **Lab 12.5, On Your Own, p. 575**

8. 16

	Sue	Alma	Carmen	Flo
Luis	Sue, Luis	Alma, Luis	Carmen, Luis	Flo, Luis
Ralph	Sue, Ralph	Alma, Ralph	Carmen, Ralph	Flo, Ralph
Larry	Sue, Larry	Alma, Larry	Carmen, Larry	Flo, Larry
Orlando	Sue, Orlando	Alma, Orlando	Carmen, Orlando	Flo, Orlando

9. $n \times m$; same as possible combinations of n and m. **10.** $n \times m$; multiply n shorts by m shirts to get possible combinations.

■ 12.5 Communicating about Mathematics, p. 577

P1K1G1, P1K1G2, P1K1G3, P1K1G4, P1K1G5, P1K2G1, P1K2G2, P1K2G3, P1K2G4, P1K2G5, P1K3G1, P1K3G2, P1K3G3, P1K3G4, P1K3G5, P2K1G1, P2K1G2, P2K1G3, P2K1G4, P2K1G5, P2K2G1, P2K2G2, P2K2G3, P2K2G4, P2K2G5, P2K3G1, P2K3G2, P2K3G3, P2K3G4, P2K3G5

$2 \times 3 \times 5$ checks that there are 30 sets of pets. Preferences will vary, but the Counting Principle is faster.

■ 12.5 Exercises, pp. 578–579

1. 6

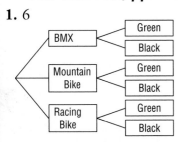

2. 676 **3.–5.** Explanations will vary. **3.** 100,000 **4.** 8 **5.** 90 **6.** Answers will vary. **7.** 9

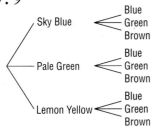

9. 64

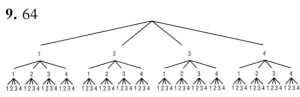

11. 120 **13.** 10 **15.** $\frac{2}{25}$ **17.** $\frac{10}{27}$

■ 12.6 Communicating about Mathematics, p. 581

Solve by taking the product of their two independent probabilities, or list all possible outcomes; the probability is $\frac{1}{10}$.

■ 12.6 Exercises, pp. 582–583

1. Occurrence of one event isn't related to the other event; you can find the probability by using the product of their probabilities or by making a list. **2.** Yes; playing video games isn't related to liking to swim. **3.** No; the fact that it is raining is related to the use of an umbrella. **4.** Answers will vary but the theoretical probability is $\frac{1}{15}$. **5.** GB, GG$_1$, GG$_2$, GR, GY, RB, RG$_1$, RG$_2$, RR, RY, YB, YG$_1$, YG$_2$, YR, YY, BB, BG$_1$, BG$_2$, BR, BY; you will land on green on both spinners 1 out of every 10 spins, or $\frac{1}{10}$. **7.** Yes; owning a dog isn't related to liking to roller skate. **9.** $\frac{2}{5}$ **11.** $\frac{5}{8}$ **13.** Two years **15.** They are used more.

■ Chapter Review, pp 585–586

1. 8 **3.** $\frac{5}{18}$ **5.** -50 **7.** 34.05 **9.** $14 = x + 18$; -4
11. $y = x + 3$

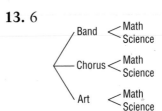

13. 6

15. 72 **17.** Yes, explanations will vary. **19.** No; you have four options: take one stone from the pile of one or 2 or from both piles; take 2 stones from the pile of 2. No matter which option is chosen, you cannot win.

21.

W	H	S	K	N	I	W	Y	L	D	D	I	T
A	Y	T	T	S	E	D	A	R	A	H	C	N
I	M	R	E	S	S	E	O	N	I	M	O	D
Y	M	A	G	E	S	O	U	R	F	M	A	S
C	U	D	A	G	E	J	V	O	M	O	R	T
H	R	P	B	D	H	A	I	A	C	N	T	R
E	E	I	B	I	C	C	G	M	A	O	A	A
C	T	N	I	R	H	K	C	O	N	P	N	E
K	C	O	R	B	C	S	E	P	A	O	T	H
E	Y	C	C	A	O	U	L	E	S	L	A	R
R	N	H	B	I	N	G	O	E	T	Y	D	T
S	O	L	I	T	A	I	R	E	A	H	I	S
Y	E	E	O	T	C	A	T	C	I	T	A	R

1. Yes, solutions do not require using *least* common denominator; $\frac{22}{24} = \frac{11}{12}$ **3.** $8\frac{7}{16}$ **5.** $4\frac{15}{16}$ **7.** a, $\frac{1}{7}$ **9.** c, $\frac{9}{32}$ **11.** $2\frac{3}{4}$ in. **13.a.** 12 cm **b.** 105° **c.** 17 cm **d.** 60° **e.** 105° **f.** 12 cm **g.** 90° **h.** 17 cm **15.** Equilateral, isosceles, acute **17.** Right, isosceles **19.** −13 **21.** −15 **23.** −7 **25.** 10 sq units **27.** 11 ft; explanations will vary. **29.** 26 **31.** 16 **33.** 14.72 **35.** 6

37. $\frac{1}{4}$

Appreciation to the staff at Larson Texts, Inc:
who assisted with proofreading the manuscript and
preparing and proofreading the art package.

*Appreciation to the following art/photo
production staff:*
Art: Joan Williams
Photographs: Martha Friedman, Susan Doheny
Cover design: Linda Fishborne.
Cover photos: inset: Frank Cezus/FPG International.
Frank Cezus/FPG International.

ILLUSTRATION CREDITS

Patrice Rossi: 17, 25, 59, 117, 119, 124, 157, 176, 193,
285, 291, 297, 305, 336, 375, 439, 455, 474, 533, 583.

PHOTOGRAPHY CREDITS

Table of Contents   vii: Roger Ressmeyer/Starlight. **ix:**
1t, Tony Stone Images; 1b, Ken O'Donoghue ©D.C.
Heath; ct, Richard Steedman/Stock Market; cb, Steve
Winter © D.C. Heath; r, Ken O'Donoghue © D.C.
Heath;, **x:** Jonathon Nourok/PhotoEdit. **xi;** t, Victor
Masayesva Jr.; b, Ken O'Donoghue © D.C. Heath. **xii:**
David Young-Wolff/Tony Stone Images. **xiii:** t, Stephen
Johnson/Tony Stone Images; b, Ken O'Donoghue © D.C.
Heath. **xiv:** t, AP/Wide World Photos; b, Ken
O'Donoghue © D.C. Heath. **xv:** t, Ken O'Donoghue ©
D.C. Heath; b, Nikolay Zurek/FPG. **xvi:** t, Steve Winter
© D.C. Heath; b, Will Ryan/Stock Market. **xvii:** Rex
Rystedt. **xix:** t, Joseph Nettis; b, Ken O'Donoghue © D.C.
Heath. **xx:** t, Hugh Sitton/Tony Stone Images; b, Ken
O'Donoghue © D.C. Heath. **xxi:** Albert P. Fuchs. **xxii:**
Wolfgang Kaehler. **xxiii:** t, Victor Masayesva Jr.; b, Ken
O'Donoghue © D.C. Heath. **xxv:** l, Jim Yuskavitch; c,
C.R. Rathe/FPG; r, Cosmo Condina/Tony Stone Images.

CHAPTER 1 1: Peter Brenner. **2:** Richard
Hutchings/PhotoEdit. **3:** Peter Brenner. **7:** Franklin Jay
Viola. **9:** David Young-Wolff/PhotoEdit. **11:** Jim Allor.
12: Kent Barker. **14:** Patti Murray/Animals Animals. **15:**
Lee Snider/Image Works. **16:** Victor Ramos © D.C.
Heath. **17:** Robert E. Daemmrich/Tony Stone Images. **19:**
t, Karen Leeds/Stock Market. **19:** b, Ken O'Donoghue ©
D.C. Heath. **20:** Lawrence Migdale/Tony Stone Images.
23: Lewis Kemper/Tony Stone Images. **25:** Anne
Heimann/Stock Market. **26:** t, Robert W. Ginn/The
Picture Cube. **26:** b, Kathy Tarantola/The Picture Cube.
27 : Johnson Studio. **29:** Ken O'Donoghue © D.C. Heath.
30: Roy Morsch/The Stock Market. **31:** Mark
Gamba/The Stock Market. **32:** Mike Gullet/Midwest
Photo Agency. **35:** Tom McCarthy/PhotoEdit. **37:** Robert
E. Daemmrich/The Image Works. **39:** Thomas
Braise/The Stock Market. **40:** Ken O'Donoghue © D.C.
Heath. **43:** Toni Angermayer/Photo Researchers, Inc. **44:**
Gayna Hoffman. **47:** Ken O'Donoghue © D.C. Heath. **48:**
Jim Marvy. **49:** Ken O' Donoghue.

CHAPTER 2 50-51: Stephen Johnson/Tony Stone
Images. **52:** Bettmann Archive. **53:** l, Rob Crandall/The
Image Works. **53:** r, Mug Shots/The Stock Market. **57:**
Ken O'Donoghue © D.C. Heath. **59:** Alan
Oddie/PhotoEdit. **63:** C.R. Rathe/FPG. **66:** Culver
Pictures, Inc. **69:** Miro Vintoniv/Stock Boston. **71:** R.
Sidney/The Image Works. **73:** Stephen Johnson/Tony

Stone Images. **75:** Ken O' Donoghue © D.C. Heath. **76:**
Ken O' Donoghue © D.C. Heath. **77:** David Young-
Wolff/PhotoEdit. **82:** Scott K. Brown, courtesy of Busch
Gardens Williamsburg. **83:** Ken O'Donoghue © D. C.
Heath. **85:** David Young-Wolff/Tony Stone Images. **87:**
Scott Dietisch/Tony Stone Images. **89:** Ken O'Donoghue
© D.C. Heath. **91:** Erich Lessing/Art Resource, NY. **93:**
Zefa Germany/Stock Market. **95:** Tony Stone Images. **96:**
Paula Lerner. **97:** Jeremy Wolff.

CHAPTER 3 98-99: Tim Gibson/Envision. **100:** Bob
Collins/The Image Works. **101:** Henryk T. Kaiser/The
Picture Cube. **105:** Sue Streeter/Tony Stone Images. **108:**
Ken O'Donoghue © D.C. Heath. **111:** Robert W.
Ginn/Envision. **112:** Susan Doheny © D.C. Heath. **117:**
Roger and Donna Aitkenhead/Animals Animals. **119:** Ken
O'Donoghue © D.C. Heath. **124:** Steve Joester/FPG. **126:**
David Madison. **131:** UPI/Bettmann. **136:** Tony
Freeman/PhotoEdit. **138:** Gerald L. Kooyman/Animals
Animals. **140:** Bob Daemmrich/Stock Boston. **141:** Bob
Daemmrich/Stock Boston. **142:** Ken O'Donoghue © D.C.
Heath. **146:** t, Library of Congress. **146:** b, Ken
O'Donoghue © D.C. Heath. **147:** Wide World Photo. **149:**
Ken O'Donoghue © D.C. Heath.

CHAPTER 4 150-51: Susan Lapides. **152:** Richard
Hutchings/PhotoEdit. **152:** Mark Ritchards/PhotoEdit.
153: t, Geoffrey Clifford/The Stock Market. **153:** b, Bob
Daemmrich/The Image Works. **157:** Felicia
Martinez/PhotoEdit. **159:** Hughes Martin/HPI. **166:**
Stephen Frisch/Stock Boston. **168:** Ken O'Donoghue ©
D.C. Heath. **169:** John M. Roberts/The Stock Market.
173: Chris Roger/The Stock Market. **175:** Ken
O'Donoghue © D.C. Heath. **180:** Ken O'Donoghue © D.C.
Heath. **182:** Photri. **184:** Michael Fogden, Oxford
Scientific Films/Animals Animals. **185:** Photri. **189:**
Nikolay Zurek/FPG. **190:** Photo Researchers, Inc. **191:**
Roy Morsch/The Stock Market. **193:** Bob
Daemmrich/Stock Boston. **195:** Ken O'Donoghue © D.C.
Heath. **198:** David Papazian.

CHAPTER 5 200-01: David Young-Wolff/Tony Stone
Images. **202:** tl, John Owens © DC Heath. **202:** tr, Richard
Haynes © DC Heath. **202:** cl, John Owens © DC Heath.
202: bl, John Owens © DC Heath. **202:** br, Sarah Putnam
© DC Heath. **203:** l, Richard Haynes © DC Heath. **203:**
cr, Sarah Putnam © DC Heath. **203:** r, Sarah Putnam ©
DC Heath. **203:** cl, Sarah Putnam © DC Heath. **204:**
Steven Needham/Envision. **206:** Will Ryan/Stock Market.
207: Miro Vintoniv/Stock Boston. **208:** Jim Yuskavitch.
209: Ken O'Donoghue © D.C. Heath. **211:** Steve Winter ©
D.C. Heath. **213:** North Wind Pictures Archive. **214:**
Mark Lawrence/Stock Market. **221:** Jeffrey Lowe/Onyx.
223: Tony Freeman/PhotoEdit. **225:** t, Frans
Lanting/Minden Pictures. **225:** b, Eric Roth/The Picture
Cube. **226:** Ken O'Donoghue © D.C. Heath. **229:** C.
Allan Morgan. **231:** David Madison. **232:** Richard
Steedman/Stock Market. **234:** Terry Wild Studio. **238:**
Tony Stone Images. **240:** Addison Geary/Stock Boston.
243: Phil Schofield. **245:** David Madison. **247:** Mike
Clemmer.

CHAPTER 6 248-49: Scott Francis/Esto. **250:** Sonya
Jacobs/Stock Market. **251:** insert, Dennis
MacDonald/Photo Edit. **251:** Bill Gallery/Stock Boston.
257: Richard Kolar/Animals Animals. **261:** Hal Gage/The

Picture Cube. **263:** Donald Dietz/Stock Boston. **264:** The Bettmann Archive. **266:** Nick Koudis/The Stock Market. **279:** Richard Hutchings/Photo Researchers, Inc. **281:** Digital Semiconductor. **285:** John & Diane Harper/New England Stock Photo. **287:** Rex Rystedt. **291:** Valorie Hodgson/Photo/Nats, Inc. **293:** Ken O'Donoghue © D.C. Heath. **295:** Felicia Martinez/PhotoEdit. **297:** Robert & Eunice Pearcy/Animals Animals.

CHAPTER 7 298-99: Reinstein/The Image Works. **300:** David Jennings/The Image Works. **301:** insert, Sarah Putnam/The Picture Cube; Mark Burnett/Stock Boston. **304:** Ken O'Donoghue © D.C. Heath. **305:** Barbara Alper/Stock Boston. **309:** t, Aaron Haust/Stock Boston. **309:** b, Rob Crandall/The Image Works. **310:** Steve Winter © D.C. Heath. **317:** Roland J. Silva/Picture Cube. **321:** Erich Lessing/Art Resource, NY. **323:** David Madison/Duomo. **324:** Phyllis Picardi/The Picture Cube. **325:** t, Ken O'Donoghue © D.C. Heath. **325:** b, David Young Wolff/PhotoEdit. **330:** David Young-Wolff/PhotoEdit. **331:** Ken O'Donoghue © D.C. Heath. **335:** l, Anthony Salamone © D.C. Heath; r, Ken O'Donoghue © D.C. Heath. **337:** Mary Kate Denny/PhotoEdit. **339:** Mark Greenberg/Envision. **340:** Lawrence Migdale/Stock Boston. **341:** Sari Levin. **344:** Larry Lefever/Grant Heilman.

CHAPTER 8 346-47: David Madison. **348:** Bob Daemmrich/Tony Stone Images. **349:** John & Diane Harper/New England Stock Photo. **353:** Joseph Nettis/Stock Boston. **355:** t, Breck P. Kent; b, Ken O'Donoghue © D.C. Heath. **359:** John Lel/Stock Boston. **361:** Frans Lanting/Minden Pictures. **362:** Michael Holford #EG 453 DF. **367:** Jose Carrillo/PhotoEdit. **369:** Caryn Levy. **373:** Robert W. Ginn/PhotoEdit. **376:** Matthew Klein/Photo Researchers, Inc. **378:** Ken O'Donoghue © D.C. Heath. **378:** Ken O'Donoghue © D.C. Heath. **379:** Michael Dunn/Stock Market. **380:** Patti Murray/Animals Animals. **381:** Ken O'Donoghue © D.C. Heath. **383:** Clay Myers/The Wildlife Collection. **384:** Richard Hutchings for "Zillions" Magazine. **385:** Ken O'Donoghue © D.C. Heath. **391:** Roy M./Stock Market. **394:** tl, Charles Gurche/The Wildlife Collection. **394:** r, Gabriel Jecan/Tony Stone Images. **394:** tc, Michael Osmond/The Wildlife Collection. **394:** bc, Tom Till/The Wildlife Collection. **394:** lb, Robert Franz/The Wildlife Collection.

CHAPTER 9 396-97: Ken O'Donoghue © D.C. Heath. **398:** Ken O'Donoghue © D.C. Heath. **399:** Ken O'Donoghue © D.C. Heath. **401:** Robert Frerck/Tony Stone Images. **403:** Ken O'Donoghue © D.C. Heath. **407:** Michael Howell/Envision. **409:** Scott Camazine/Photo Researchers. **410:** Amy Sweeney for Beverly Times. **413:** Joseph Nettis/Tony Stone Images. **419:** Courtesy of CBS. **420:** Patti Murray/Animals Animals. **421:** Richard During/Tony Stone Images. **422:** NASA. **426:** Mitch Kezar/Tony Stone Images. **431:** Lance Nelson/The Stock Market. **433:** Christopher Springmann. **438:** Hugh Sitton/Tony Stone Images. **439:** Chris Mihulka/Stock Market. **445:** Fleishman Hillard.

CHAPTER 10 446-47: Derek Hudson/Sygma. **448:** Robert W. Ginn/PhotoEdit. **449:** t, David Burnett-Contact/The Stock Market. **449:** b, Jonathan Nourok/PhotoEdit. **452:** Glasheen Graphics/The Picture Cube. **457:** Jan Halaska/Photo Researchers, Inc. **460:** NASA. **471:** Daniel Forster. **473:** James P. Rowan/Tony Stone Images. **475:** Piet Mondrian, Diamond Painting in Red, Yellow and Blue, Gift of Herbert and Nannette Rothschild, © 1995 Board of Trustees, National Gallery

of Art, Washington. **476:** Alinari/Art Resource, NY. **479:** Andrea Pistolesi. **481:** Albert P. Fuchs. **485:** Lassen International. **486:** Joseph Nettis/Photo Researchers, Inc. **491:** t, Ken O'Donoghue © D.C. Heath. **491:** b, Cathlyn Nelloan/Tony Stone Images. **493:** David Frazier/Photo Researchers, Inc. **495:** Lawrence Migdale/Tony Stone Images. **498:** Ken O'Donoghue © D.C. Heath.

Chapter 11 500-01: Wolfgang Kaehler. **501:** Istituto Geografico DeAgostini. **502:** Wolfgang Kaehler. **502:** rt, Wolfgang Kaehler. **502:** rb, Wolfgang Kaehler. **503:** Frans Lanting/Minden Pictures. **508:** t, Wolfgang Kaehler. **508:** b, Frans Lanting/Minden Pictures. **510:** George F. Mobley/National Geographic Image Collection. **511:** Susan Doheny © D.C. Heath. **515:** Tony Freeman/PhotoEdit. **517:** t, Andrew Sacks/Tony Stone Images. **517:** b, Frans Lanting/Minden Pictures. **521:** Wolfgang Kaehler. **524:** Wolfgang Kaehler. **529:** Roger Ressmeyer/Starlight. **531:** Lawrence Migdale/Stock Boston. **537:** Laslo Studio/Stock Market. **544:** Wolfgang Kaehler.

CHAPTER 12 546-47: Victor Masayesva Jr. **548:** Dean Conger/National Geographic Society. **549:** t, Perogpt A./Explorer/Photo Researchers. **549:** b, Cameramann International, LTD. **554:** Mark Richards/PhotoEdit. **556:** American Bowling Congress. **557:** Smithsonian Institution, Photo #87-17827. **559:** Paul Mozell/Stock Boston. **560:** Lee Snider/The Image Works. **561:** Cosmo Condina/Tony Stone Images. **561:** Ken O'Donoghue © D.C. Heath. **563:** Photo Researchers, Inc. **564:** Ken O'Donogue © D.C. Heath. **565:** J. Sohm/The Image Works. **568:** Ken O'Donoghue © D.C. Heath. **571:** John Zich. **573:** Ken O'Donoghue © D.C. Heath. **574:** David Young-Wolffe/PhotoEdit. **576:** Mary Kate Denny/PhotoEdit. **577:** Jean-Michel Labat/Jacana. **579:** Ken O'Donoghue © D.C. Heath. **582:** Tom DiPace. **583:** Jonathan Nourok/PhotoEdit. **585:** b, John Eastcott/Eva Momatiuk/The Image Works. **585:** t, Ken O'Donoghue © D.C. Heath. **586:** Ken O'Donoghue © D. C. Heath. **587:** Ken O'Donoghue © D.C. Heath. **589:** Ken O'Donoghue © D. C. Heath.

INDEX

INDEX

INDEX